D1222071

CRIME AND THE MIND

WALTER BROMBERG, M.D.

Crime and the Mind

A PSYCHIATRIC ANALYSIS OF
CRIME AND PUNISHMENT

The Macmillan Company, New York
Collier-Macmillan Limited, London

COPYRIGHT © WALTER BROMBERG, M.D., 1965 / ALL RIGHTS RESERVED. NO PART OF THIS BOOK MAY BE REPRODUCED OR UTILIZED IN ANY FORM OR BY ANY MEANS, ELECTRONIC OR MECHANICAL, INCLUDING PHOTOCOPYING, RECORDING OR BY ANY INFORMATION STORAGE AND RETRIEVAL SYSTEM, WITHOUT PERMISSION IN WRITING FROM THE PUBLISHER. / FIRST PRINTING / LIBRARY OF CONGRESS CATALOG CARD NUMBER: 65–20199 / THE MACMILLAN COMPANY, NEW YORK, COLLIER-MACMILLAN CANADA, LTD., TORONTO, ONTARIO / DESIGNED BY RONALD FARBER / PRINTED IN THE UNITED STATES OF AMERICA

TO ESTHER

Contents

CONTENTS

Preface

Books about crime and criminals are perennials in the forests of the printed word. Like trees and plants, they provide bitter fruits that repel, flowers that decorate, thorny twigs that prick, exotic blossoms that excite, shrubs that obscure, ground cover that deceives, branches that flaunt dramatically, leafy bowers that shade. Similarly, books on crime serve many psychologic purposes: There are crime mysteries, crime stories, accounts of trials, explications of detective science, theories of causation, sociologic analyses, and psychiatric studies ad infinitum. Reflection will indicate that we all derive psychologic satisfaction from crime in the world, however much we decry it. Crime stories constitute the foliage of our collective unconscious, the tendrils of our inner guilt concerning crime. We try to understand crime with the aid of novelists, psychologists, sociologists, penologists, and statisticians. Many amateurs are engaged in the search for an understanding of crime; several scientific disciplines are enlisted in the serious business of analyzing criminal action. Among these is psychiatry.

This work is in the tradition of understanding criminal behavior through analyzing criminals. It is clinical in orientation and, as far as possible, realistic in substance. The findings, ideas, suggestions, and conclusions expressed herein were developed from contact with criminal offenders encountered in juvenile, adolescent, and adult courts, and in correctional institutions of many types. These were male and female offenders examined for municipal, county, federal, and military courts, for prosecuting and defending attorneys, for probation and parole officers, anxious parents and relatives, physicians and school authorities. The experience collated covered a period of more than thirty years in many parts of this country. The base line of these studies, some intensive and some necessarily cursory, was that of clinical psychiatry, leavened by the dynamic of psychoanalysis, infiltrated by a respect for the law, and liberally mixed with an appreciation of cultural and subcultural trends, sociological investigations, and historical currents. Apart from a half-dozen notable exceptions, where the names are significant, the names of offenders have been altered. Every case reported has been examined by the author, with the exception of two brief cases quoted from the literature. Hence, this work is in a sense a personal view of crime, with an overview of the pertinent literature. The responsibility for the emphasis in the material presented and for the conclusions and observations set down are solely those of the author.

It must be freely stated, although wide ranges of the literature on criminology had been combed, that much has been neglected, in particular the Italian, French, German, Scandinavian, and British literature. The hiatus so formed was partly due to the wish to accent the American scene and the peculiarities of American crime, and partly because of the relative difficulty of finding meaningful material in the foreign literature which is applicable to cases encountered in the courts of this country.

The present work is an enlargement and revision of *Crime and the Mind, An Outline of Psychiatric Criminology,* published by J. B. Lippincott Company, 1948. The present work is an attempt to substantiate the field of psychiatric criminology as differentiated from its sister fields, forensic medicine, legal psychiatry, and medico-legal practice. It does not circumvent medico-legal problems, but lies closest to that subdiscipline etched out by Dr. Ben Karpman under the name "criminal psychodynamics." The term "psychiatric criminology" includes all these areas of interest, adding an interest in psychotherapy of criminals, a perception of social dynamics in reaction to crime, and the dynamics of the criminal in reaction to his society. Further, extension into the area of punishment and its effect on society and the individual offender brings this work closer to the sociology of crime. Psychotherapy in and through legal punishment may yet prove to be psychiatry's contribution to the control of human behavior. For punishment as an ethical value, accepted as a presupposition of social life beyond which no one may probe, is so fixed within the human condition as to arouse relatively little anxiety and hence stimulate relatively little scrutiny.

The acknowledgments of the author are legion. Associates and colleagues by the score have offered ideas, emphases, viewpoints, or objections, which have been considered, digested, rejected, or adopted. To enumerate all these persons would be an infinite task—only a few will be mentioned. Prominent among them are: Dr. Ben Karpman, of St. Elizabeths Hospital, Washington, D.C., and Dr. Paul Schilder, of Bellevue Psychiatric Hospital, New York, both of whom inspired the author during his early professional years by their pioneer therapy with offenders; the Judges of the Court of General Sessions, New York, beginning with Judge Cornelius Collins and extending to other distinguished jurists; and Irving W. Halpern, Chief Probation Officer of the same court, who generously gave permission to use cases examined during the author's activity with the Psychiatric Clinic of that court from 1932 to 1941. It was during this period that the author was associated with Drs. Karl Bowman, Jack Frosch, Sylvan Keiser, Charles B. Thompson, John D. Impastato, John Cassity, psychiatrists, and Dr. Solomon Machover, psychologist; some of the dynamic interpretations of felony offenders examined at the Court and the prison ward of

Bellevue Psychiatric Hospital were developed in company with these men.

For material derived at a later period from this court (now Supreme Court, Criminal Division, County of New York) the author is indebted to Elmer Reeves, current Chief Probation Officer; Miss Ella Reeves, Executive Secretary to the Department; and Dr. Emanuel Messinger, present Director of the Psychiatric Clinic of the Court. Dr. Messinger's close cooperation in the area of drug addiction and his permission to use his unpublished observations on addiction were of inestimable help. The author is further indebted to Michael Honig, Chief Clerk of the Psychiatric Clinic, for aid in locating clinic records and to Dr. Arthur Zitrin, current Director of Bellevue Psychiatric Hospital, for permission to use recent psychiatric records of criminals studied.

At a subsequent period of criminologic experience the author was aided by his associates at the United States Naval Prison, Portsmouth, New Hampshire, especially by Dr. Fabian L. Rouke, psychologist, in group therapy experimentation, and Dr. Terry C. Rodgers in analysis of the drug incidence among naval prisoners. Particularly does the author wish to thank the commanding officer, Colonel J. A. Rossell, USMC (Ret.), for his support of the psychiatric approach to prisoners in a military installation, and the Bureau of Medicine and Surgery, United States Navy, for permision to use materials gathered during the World War II years.

The collation and analysis of material from western areas were aided immeasurably by many officials in California, among them the Director of the Department of Mental Hygiene, State of California, Dr. Walter Rapaport, and his successor, Dr. Daniel Blain. Dr. William Keating, Superintendent of the Medical Correctional Facility at Vacaville, California, was helpful in reviewing material and prisoners in his institution, as was the Superintendent of the Atascadero State Hospital, Atascadero, California, Dr. R. S. Rood, and his successor, Dr. D. L. Sandriter. Dr. John Mitchell, Superintendent of DeWitt State Hospital, and Dr. Freeman Adams, Superintendent of the Stockton State Hospital, were equally helpful in permitting use of case material. Valuable assistance in the interpretation of spontaneous art productions by various offenders was given by Professor Tarmo Pasto and Peter Runkel of the Ars Gratia Hominis project, National Institute of Mental Health, No. 1278–1, based at Sacramento State College.

At the Department of the Youth Authority, Youth and Adult Corrections Agencies, Sacramento, California, Dr. Mark L. Gerstle, Chief Psychiatrist, and B. F. Sherman, Chief Clerk, were of considerable aid in studying records, as was Dr. Edward Hodgson, Director of the Reception Unit of the California Youth Authority at Perkins, California, and his staff. Richard Nicholson, Probation Officer of the Federal Court,

District of Northern California, was extremely helpful in examining court records.

Personnel in the courts of several northern California counties— district attorneys, public defenders, and clerks—generously secured records for the author, who wishes to single out particularly Robert Cole, Chief Public Defender, now judge in the courts of Sacramento County; Oscar Kistle, District Attorney of that county; and Warren E. Thornton, Chief Probation Officer of Sacramento County.

In the legal ramifications of this work the author has received help from many sources: from Law Professor Henry Wiehofen of the University of New Mexico, Law Professor Hubert W. Smith of the University of Texas, the Law Librarian of the Westchester County Court Library, and the New York Bar Association Library, New York City. The tedium of research of pertinent law and criminologic literature was shared by my research assistant, Mr. Stephen Schapiro, of New York. Mr. Milton Rector, Director of the National Committee of Crime and Correction of New York, furnished leads in the sociological literature and made the Committee's library available. Many conversations with the late Joseph Levine, who was my attorney and life-long friend, were especially helpful in analyzing the intricate problems of ethics and legal punishment; he discussed the manuscript critically, providing much food for thought concerning crime and society. My son, Mark B. Bromberg, provided pertinent material from the Greek tragedies. Finally, my research secretary, Mrs. Marilynn Frandsen, of Sacramento, performed a valuable service in extricating the minutiae of records from the California Courts and in typing a complex manuscript. I wish to thank Peter Ritner, Executive Editor of the Macmillan Company, for his encouragement, Miss Judith Clark, Associate Editor, and Mrs. Ruth Bellamy for their painstaking editorial assistance.

Grateful acknowledgment is made to all these persons. In addition, I wish to mention the examined and treated offenders themselves; they gave much that was revealing, even in the face of their anguish, and they have the author's grateful appreciation.

WALTER BROMBERG, M.D.

MOUNT KISCO, NEW YORK
January, 1965

"To dance to flutes, to dance to lutes
　　Is delicate and rare:
But it is not sweet with nimble feet
　　To dance upon the air!"

OSCAR WILDE

CHAPTER I

Crime and Punishment: The Eternal Equation

THE SCOPE OF INQUIRY / CRIME, PUNISHMENT,
AND EMOTIONS / THE ETHICS OF
PUNISHMENT / "WHY CRIME?" / CRIME,
PUNISHMENT, AND THE INNER LIFE /
REFERENCES

THE SCOPE OF INQUIRY

This volume is dedicated to a modern analysis of crime and punishment. Some types of crime have not changed with the centuries. Others have evolved out of the exigencies of a complex modern
civilization. Similarly, methods of punishment have also been modified
in response to changing attitudes and modes of government. The focus
of a large part of this work is on those who have perpetrated crimes;
the focus of the remainder is on the meaning of crime and punishment
to society. The hope in the first instance is that close study of criminals
may illuminate the inner world of the potential, as well as actual,
offender. The hope in the latter instance is that a lifetime of study of
the criminal and of crime may provide a realistic basis for discussion
of punishment and prevention.

Potential wrongdoers constitute a larger section of the population
than heretofore. Where those cursed with poverty, poor heredity,
physical and mental degeneration, and low social ideals were automatically suspect in years gone by, no clear distinction now exists in
the potential or actual criminal population. Where to be law-abiding
meant to eschew the "bad" and espouse the "good," now, although the
moral choices remain as clear, the psychological circumstances that
accompany the choice and the sociological pressures that subtly
influence it have increased enormously.

No longer is it correct to invoke the designation "criminal type" or
"psychopathic criminal" to categorize all criminals, or to search for
obvious physical, psychic, or moral "defects" that stigmatize criminals.
Although repeaters in crime, recidivists, gangsters, professional thieves,
racketeers, check forgers, swindlers, counterfeiters, confidence men,

and drug peddlers do exist, no one is "predestined to the penitentiary by his brain." [1]

Moreover, social and political conditions have changed so definitively during the past half century that a score of new crimes have arisen, while old ones have not been materially reduced. There are numerous infractions of laws and ordinances that were relatively unheard of a half century ago: income-tax evasion, bribery in professional sporting events, pornographic motion pictures, adolescent murder, car thefts, car stripping, violations of food-and-drug acts, racketeering, unlawful union picketing, fraudulent packaging, and so on. Moral values have not changed; but social pressures of urbanization, increased governmental regulations, "the compelling ethic of success, status striving," [2] and the democratization of financial power in many hands have widened the spectrum of crime. These social forces have swollen the "criminal element."

Traditionally, attempts to understand crime have utilized two approaches: scrutiny of the inner (mental and moral) world of the criminal offender and examination of the external (social) world in which he lives. The psychologic and psychiatric disciplines studied instincts and impulses in the individual offender, and sociologists analyzed the social and cultural forces that nurtured and shaped these impulses.

The conclusions drawn from these approaches have been both banal and unexpected. For example, such conscious psychologic attitudes as cunning, deceit, lust, violence, rage, avarice, duplicity, hatred, revenge, sadism, and raw brutality have been encountered among offenders. However, more thoroughgoing analyses of the criminal mind have revealed a wide variety of unconscious motivations. These include counterparts of infantile hates, reactions to early deprivation, early (oral) destructive strivings, aggressive defenses of passive longings, outcroppings of immature sexual desires, reactions to deep inferiority feelings, and magical omnipotence fantasies. In social spheres criminologists encountered the influence of economic disadvantage, slum living, racial discrimination, gang identification, the contradictions of opulence and poverty, business booms and recessions, loose credit structure and humdrum lives, pettiness and high adventure, the seductive influence of alcoholism, the glamour of vice, and the example of frontier lawlessness.

From this vast amount of investigation a truism has been extracted to which almost everyone conversant with crime adheres: no single "cause" can be ascribed to crime, "multiple causation" being a more likely and probable theory.

In this quest for a "causal" answer to one of man's perpetual plagues little has been said of crime's companion—punishment. There are few words in modern language so eternally wed, that so naturally and inevitably complement each other, as "crime" and "punishment." The idea "crime" rarely comes to mind that the idea "punishment" does not immediately follow. No statutory crime is described without a corresponding statement as to its proper penalty; no social action is prohibited without an implied or expressed punishment. The law upholds the sequence of crime and punishment, the ethical sense of all sane persons demands it, religion holds this equation as a fundamental tenet, civilized life and social intercourse rest upon this principle, coexistence in today's world requires its scrupulous observance. Every child and adult is aware of the consequence of wrongdoing. Punishment as a reality is built into the structure of law, social mores, and the conscience of man. The duality of wrongdoing and punishment is as indivisible and eternal in human affairs as is the succession of day and night.

On a practical as well as a scientific level we note less concern with punishment than with crime. This unequal concern does not entirely accord with our inner attitudes, because punishment is hardly a stranger to our daily thoughts. All of us are deeply involved with punishment, morally and psychologically, in varying degrees. As an example, let us point to the tremendous part crime plays in literature, television presentations, the theatre, the daily press, and casual conversation. But if crime provides a never-ending source of entertainment for the reading, viewing public, and an area of eternal emotional involvement, punishment is no less an intriguing subject.

CRIME, PUNISHMENT, AND EMOTIONS

Murder cases make gripping stories: they embody dramatic appeal for most of the population; they stir the emotions, hold interest, and contribute excitement to the presentation. The appeal that a case of homicide holds for the viewer or reader is actually a reflection of the fantasies and impulses within his own mind. The presentation, under the guise of offering the viewer or reader a tense human drama, actually stirs his repressed aggressive impulses. Thus, stories of shootings, poisonings, knifings, or strangulations easily outweigh presentations of other crimes in motion pictures, television, books, and other entertainment media because impulses to shoot, stab, poison, or choke are nascent in the public. On the other hand, stories of burglaries, swindling, bigamy, or check forgery carry little appeal; hence, they are seldom offered. Instead, sex crimes, extortion, and robbery, which stimulate deeply repressed impulses in the viewer, are exhibited. In a word, the more repressed the impulse, that is, the stronger the taboo offended by the crime, the greater the interest displayed by author and public. Consider in this connection the perfect crime—the artfully planned, organized robbery whose perpetrators are never caught. The gang bank-robbery, with its artistic camouflage of raw aggressive emotions, is as satisfying a combination of veiled aggression and induced befuddlement of authority as entertainment can provide. Here the interest is intense, the viewer's gratification complete.

When, in contradistinction, we consider public reaction to *punishment* for crime, as portrayed in books, plays, or movies, we find that an equal degree of fascination is present but that the emotional investment in punishment generally goes unnoticed. It is true that mild punishment arouses our sympathy or approbation; severe punishment arouses our antagonism or disquiet; brutal punishment horrifies many, excites few, gratifies others. Nevertheless, the dramatic values of punishment are absorbed and obscured within the taboo violated. Punishment is so indigenous to human thinking that it needs no statement; taboo and punishment exist as a single psychic unit. In fact, society places greatest psychologic reliance on the actuality of punishment: a crime that goes unpunished produces anxiety in victim and culprit alike, and strong resentment among the public. A crime that is adequately punished produces a sense of righteousness in society and, to a varying degree, in the criminal himself. No one in society welcomes a crime, yet everyone is highly satisfied with its punishment, whether through private or legal channels.

Examined more closely, the punishment motive is relished in a negative way; in a play or story the criminal who blocks, or escapes from, punishment creates much spectator interest and emotion. For this reason, stories of prison escapes are charged with high dramatic intensity. The courage required to contemplate rebellion against society's laws arouses admiration in the viewer until the inevitability of redoubled punishment after capture reinvokes reality. The fugitive will be caught, the reader or viewer will not be caught; hence his psychological identification with the criminal and crime will be avenged. Contrary to the case of aggression or cunning in crime stories, punishment is rarely relished by viewers or readers after the first pang of masochistic pleasure (or exquisite pain) through identification is experienced. We have no need to repress our interest in punishment; we are therefore calm in the atmosphere of retribution.

THE ETHICS OF PUNISHMENT

From this brief summary of human reaction to both members of the crime = punishment equation can be deduced the ethical values of crime and punishment that were seemingly established for human beings from man's first appearance on this planet. Everyone knows that crime is "bad" and punishment is "good"; one is called an "anti-social," the other a "social," activity. The one receives the condemnation of society, the other its approval. In the eyes of the world, punishment represents the obvious need to redress criminal behavior. An evil by a wrongdoer when neutralized by an evil by society (as imprisonment) attains the dignity of correct action.

But how does the offender regard this universally accepted creed? For the prisoner awaiting trial or sentence, or for the inmate of a penal institution, punishment is not so readily apprehended as "right." If one examines many types of offenders soon after apprehension, it becomes clear that the criminal entertains an inner sense of "rightness" concerning the criminal act. This psychological defense is observed in the instant before the commission of an offense, that is, when the planned offense is not yet *really* a crime! Dostoyevsky, in describing Raskolnikov's cogitations on the murder he is planning, makes this point with characteristic penetration:

. . . in his [the murderer's] own case there could not be such a morbid reaction, that his reason and will would remain unimpaired at the time of carrying out his design, for the simple reason that his design was "not a crime. . . ." [3]

When the "design" has reached the level of a "crime" after apprehension by the police, this sense of rightness increases, as witness the feelings of outrage and smoldering resentment frequently encountered among the accused in court proceedings. It is only after appeals by attorneys using the hidden persuasion of the "lesser plea," or by family members or clergymen, that the miscreant alters his surface attitude of rightness in the direction of society's values: he grudgingly admits he "might have" committed the alleged crime! A subtle change in reality perception occurs: ego boundaries expand, social realities loom larger, but at the cost of considerable psychic "work" within the ego.

This intrapsychic transformation of values is, in fact, one hoped-for effect of punishment. Gradually, prisoners serving sentences come to adopt the "as if" principle that society is and was "right" in punishing them for the crime for which they were apprehended. In many cases the inmate's acquiescence is merely nominal, as indicated by the large number of recidivists who leave prison and re-engage in crime soon or ultimately. Yet in the deeper recesses of the inmate's mind he knows that society could not operate without the proscriptions and punishments built into laws and statutes. His inner struggle is with the acceptance of punishment at the cost of his own conviction that he was "right." Knowing society's values, he still struggles in the inner core of his personality to protect values congenial to himself.

When an offender has "paid his debt to society"—a phrase which, oddly, comes easily to the lips of convicted criminals—he has virtually bribed society into believing that he wholeheartedly endorses the validity of punishment. By sooner or later accepting punishment as "right," the prisoner develops a degree of social identification—hence, "integrity." He is then said to be on the road to rehabilitation.

Leopold, the remaining member of the Leopold-Loeb duo who committed the sensational murder of the Frank boy in Chicago in the 1920's, observed this subtle shift in values within himself as a result of punishment. In his memoirs, published after long years in prison, he wrote:

In 1934, I was thirty years old . . . and I had been in prison ten of those thirty years. . . . The first years in prison had, of necessity, been devoted largely to just keeping my head above water . . . there now seemed to be a little surplus left over from the struggle just to live. . . . It seemed a good time for self-examination. . . . The central fact of my psychology was remorse. . . . I don't know just when . . . that feeling came into being. Certainly it had not existed when first I came to prison. . . . But somehow between then and now remorse had not only entered my mental life: it dominated it.[4]

The criminal at this stage has by an act of "rehabilitation" announced his rejection of previously held values. The law-abiding citizen is in a different position since he has already *paid* allegiance to that social value called "punishment." (This use of the word "paid" is significant in that the citizen also has psychologically agreed to accept punishment for his *psychic* crimes.)

The psychologic relation between punishment and crime is extremely intricate. To understand crime requires a perception of its meaning, effect, and social significance to society and the individual. Within the total panorama of crime, punishment is an indigenous, pervasive, almost instinctive aspect of the former, part of the very warp and woof of social thought. As one scholar phrased it:

If there is any opinion to which the man of uncultivated morals is attached, it is the belief in the necessary connexion of punishment and guilt.[5]

Conversely, to analyze the genesis and implications of punishment without studying crime would be an empty endeavor. The problem is that whereas materials for the study of crime are readily available— from criminal offenders themselves, before conviction and while imprisoned, probationers and parolees, delinquent groups, criminal statistics—punishment effects are virtually hidden except when reconstructed by investigators. Among prisoners, reactions to punishment are difficult to study because of man's tendency to shunt pain from consciousness or to deny its influence. A study of society's reaction to punishment is equally difficult. Although demands for retribution following some heinous crime or crime wave are angrily voiced by press, pulpit, and indignant individuals, an objective view of punishment for these crimes is difficult to elicit. Reactions within articulate society to punishment of criminals (excepting the continuing debate on capital punishment) are generally muted.

The presupposition has existed since man's early days that punishment for wrongdoing is essential and ineluctable. The chief question for the scientific investigator has not been "Why punishment?" but "Why crime?" The genesis of crime has therefore held the center of attention in the science of human misbehavior.

"WHY CRIME?"

To start with, who shall be entrusted with the analysis of this phenomenon? Lawyers, judges, sociologists, anthropologists, psychiatrists and psychologists, law enforcement agents, and the man in the street—all have experiences and opinions concerning the genesis of crime. In the sense of scientific investigation, however, sociologists and psychiatrists have predominately pre-empted the task of investigating and advancing theories of crime causation.

The earliest thinkers about crime were mainly philosophers, jurists, and religionists. As naturalistic views of human behavior replaced supernatural explanations, theoretical analyses of criminal behavior passed into the hands of physicians, psychiatrists, and psychologists. In recent years, sociologists and penologists, stressing the importance of the group process and cultural interaction, have come to feel that criminal behavior is essentially a "learning process" arising from group conflicts and subculture mores.[6] Individual differences in people—whether hereditary, biological, psychological, or emotional (psychiatric) in nature—held to account for crime by psychological scientists, were largely discounted by sociologists. To the sociologist, crime is social in essence, more normal than deviated, more learned than instinctive. Crime represents a struggle for power by a government within a government, a conflict to the death of differing standards and values based on cultural diversity. One proof advanced to support this contention is the common experience that penal "treatment" fails to reform many criminals, since on their return to civil status "their life orientation remains unchanged."[7] In the area of crimes against property that Sutherland[8] investigated under the general term "white-collar criminals," personality differences were held not to constitute an adequate explanation for the great degree of crime that is perpetrated against business organizations and individuals in this country. Where psychiatric and psychologic scientists speak of unrepressed libidinal and aggressive drives or lack of superego control, sociologists write of "differential association," wherein persons engaging in criminal behavior learn such behavior from groups of "differential" social organizations. Finally, these writers state:

The psychiatric approach . . . has great prestige at the present time, but it will probably run its course and disappear from current thought after a short period. . . .[9]

To minimize interminable dispute, let us agree that so vast a sector of life as crime represents cannot be subsumed under one theory. For if embezzlement, forgery, extortion reflect opportunistic practices in today's world—a world dedicated to the values of financial success so dear to the American public—crimes of murder, rape, arson, assault bear only a shadowy relation to values surrounding our commercialized civilization. One general theory will not explain both income-tax evasion and homicide. Perhaps, as Cressey suggests, "it is desirable to supplement general theories about specific units within the broad area of crime."[10] Two legal scholars writing on criminal law comment in this vein: "To know the causes of crime we need a complete etiology of human behavior."[11]

Beyond this, workers in the field who search for a "general theory of crime" become involved in that obsessive trait common to all social scientists, one which the author, in another connection, has termed the "explanation-need."[12] This obsessive tendency, present in all thinking persons, aims toward final explanations of human actions, seeking thereby to satisfy the need to extinguish anxiety about the unknown. Since the need to understand crime and criminals in every society has always been an imperative one, the pressure of theory-development has been great indeed.

In recent years there has been an increasing interest in stressing the social versus the psychological genesis of crime. If one may choose Sutherland and Cressey as spokesmen for the sociological school, "behavior systems" are more significant in explaining crime than study of "isolated crime," and "there is no assurance that deviations [psychological] found among criminals would not always be found among the general population."[13] Thus, although sociologists recognize that personality problems exist among offenders, they clearly insist that the "explanation of criminal behavior . . . must be found in social interaction."[14]

In any case, the increasing emphasis on crime studies from a cultural point of view makes necessary some defense of the psychiatrist who essays to study individual crime intensively. Since human beings are the agents of criminality, social values are only significant as they pass through individuals on their way to behavioral or symbolic expression. More important, when the issue of punishment is encountered, we deal with individuals and with individual pain. Each incarcerated person, each offender subject to a fine or placed on probation, feels the pain of his sentence as an intense *individual experience.* The entire personality of the offender—his cultural influences, unconscious conflicts, defenses, personality traits, habitual responses, conscious and subliminal motivations, fantasies, wishes, conative drives, rationalizations, displacements, projections, and psychic scotomata—is involved in his crime and his punishment. This is rationale enough for a science of psychiatric criminology.

CRIME, PUNISHMENT, AND THE INNER LIFE

Since crime, punishment, and the inner life form the area of our investigation, an attitude of objectivity and empathy is necessary. Both *objectivity* and *empathy* demand the softening or removal of distrust, of revulsion, anger, and hatred for criminal offenders. The instinctive feeling of vengeance, an inborn predilection for punishing or correcting the injurious behavior of others, needs to be controlled or dismissed. The objective investigator must hold back that tide of righteousness in the presence of wrongdoing that rises partly from his own unconscious sense of guilt and partly from his sense of justice.

What this means is a reversal of the usual posture of crime appraisal: We need to view a criminal act as a matter of self-assertion springing spontaneously from the wrongdoer's impulses and inner needs. He cannot yet see his act as "criminal." It is an event without a name, even after it has been called a "crime," assigned a punishment, and he himself has become an object of opprobrium. It is, in short, in that state of "acting" not yet denoted as a crime that one must search for a psychologically realistic picture of criminal behavior.

The worker in this jungle of tangled emotions necessarily maintains a loyalty to society because lifelong identifications and a sense of duty to the group he serves as psychiatrist, sociologist, or penal officer color his attitudes toward law and subtly modify his sought-for objectivity toward criminals. Thus a natural distortion develops: the wrongdoer is studied with the equipment of an expert, but through the eyes of a social being.

REFERENCES

1. MUNSTERBERG, HUGO, *On the Witness Stand: Essays on Psychology and Crime* (Doubleday & Company, Inc., New York, 1923), p. 245.

2. NISBET, ROBERT A., "The Study of Social Problems," in *Contemporary Social Problems*, R. K. Merton and Robert A. Nisbet, eds. (Harcourt, Brace & World, Inc., New York, 1961), p. 16.

3. DOSTOYEVSKY, FYODOR, *Crime and Punishment* (The Modern Library, Inc., New York, 1950), p. 72.

4. LEOPOLD, NATHAN F., *Life Plus 99 Years* (Doubleday & Company, Inc., New York, 1958), p. 239.

5. BRADLEY, F. H., *Ethical Studies*, 2nd ed. (Oxford University Press, London, 1927), p. 26.

6. SUTHERLAND, E. H., and CRESSEY, D. R., *Principles of Criminology* (J. B. Lippincott Company, Philadelphia, 1960–1961), p. 74.

7. VOLD, GEORGE B., *Theoretical Criminology* (Oxford University Press, Inc., New York, 1958), chap. 7, p. 109.

8. SUTHERLAND and CRESSEY, *op. cit.*, p. 323.

9. *Ibid.*, p. 56.

10. CRESSEY, DONALD R., "Crime," in *Contemporary Social Problems, ibid.*, p. 66.

11. MICHAEL, JEROME, and WECHSLER, HERBERT, *Criminal Law and Its Administration* (Foundation Press, Chicago, 1940), p. 13.

12. BROMBERG, WALTER, *The Nature of Psychotherapy* (Grune & Stratton, New York, 1961), p. 9.

13. SUTHERLAND and CRESSEY, *op. cit.*, pp. 128, 135.

14. VOLD, *op. cit.*, p. 10.

CHAPTER II

Gallows, Guillotine, and the Gibbet

THE ORIGIN OF PRELEGAL PUNISHMENTS /
PUNISHMENT AND THE PRIMITIVE /
PUNISHMENTS IN ANTIQUITY / THE MOSAIC
LAW / THE GRAECO-ROMAN CODES /
BEGINNINGS OF ENGLISH CRIMINAL LAW /
WITCHCRAFT—PUNISHMENT FOR SIN / THE
ENLIGHTENMENT / THE EVOLUTION OF
PENOLOGY / REVOLUTION IN PUNISHMENT /
REFERENCES

Crime and punishment are coeval in the history of the world and it is difficult to say which had priority. When Eve in her naïveté ate of the forbidden fruit in the Garden of Eden, God immediately decreed everlasting sanctions against Adam and his descendants:

In the sweat of thy face shalt thou eat bread, till thou return unto the ground. . . .[1]

Adam and Eve's fate symbolized recognition of the existence of crime and punishment as the lot of man. Banishment as a punishment has already been established when Cain in his envy slays Abel, for the Lord says to Cain:

. . . the voice of thy brother's blood crieth unto me from the ground . . . and now art thou cursed from the earth. . . .[2]

There was no question as to the judgment, no weighing of facts, no analysis of intent or motivation—there was only the certainty of penalty. Primitive and early man, ruled by taboos, oracles, and the imprecations and pronouncements of gods, apparently had little doubt that punishment by the gods was swift, sure, inescapable. The Babylonians imputed strong emotions to their gods, as representative of the forces of nature:

On the coming of the dawn
There rose dark clouds on the horizon of heaven;
Within them Adad [Storm-god] thundered his thunder;
Naba and the Wind-god marched in front; . . .
The Pestilence-god let loose his demons,
Ninip advances, furious with rage. . . .[3]

As with the Egyptian gods, the Babylonian gods represented truth and law, but there was also good reason to fear punishment from on high. The second Creation Tablet speaks of Tiamat (the sea, or watery chaos, or dragon of Creation) in terms of violent anger:

He saith, Tiamat, our mother, has turned against us with hatred;
With all her force she furiously rages;
All the gods have turned to her. . . .
Unnu Khubur, who planned all things,
Hath made, in addition, invincible weapons; she has spawned monster serpents,
Sharp of tooth, merciless of fang.[4]

It can easily be imagined, as the gods threatened ancient man, shaking the earth with their anger, hurling forked thunderbolts from the heavens, that the idea of punishment was unmistakably imprinted on the plan of human life. Let us examine further into the grounds for this interpretation of the inner feelings and fears of early man. We may begin by scrutinizing the taboo, forerunner of legal proscriptions.

THE ORIGIN OF PRELEGAL PUNISHMENTS

There is general agreement among anthropologists that the custom of taboos appears to extend back to extremely primitive times. Taboos among primitives in contemporary times have been studied in great detail, as have the taboos current in the ancient world.[5] Taboos (the word was contributed by Codrington from his studies of Polynesian culture) [6] relate to ideas, practices, or institutions that when trespassed entail danger to the individual clan or tribe. Many objects were and are taboo, such varied things as plants, animals, parts of animals, rulers or kings. The chief function of the taboo, characterized by Murphy [7] as "a creation of fear," involved techniques and rituals designed to "ward off mysterious, dangerous power from doing him [primitive man] harm. . . ." This "power" or "force," which early man attributed to nature and the gods, constituted both a life-giving aid and a danger. This supernatural force, which Codrington encountered among the Melanesians under the word *mana* (analogous to *manitou* among the Algonquin Indians and identifiable among other groups), is considered to be the psychic basis of primordial religion.[8]

It is quite plausible that the power of *mana,* invested in the super-natural, was at some time in the history of early man imputed to human beings. Frazer has noted that in primitive societies, men were found who appeared to control the course of nature:

Such men were accordingly adored and treated as gods. . . . The divine person is a source of danger as well as of blessing. His sacred organism . . . is charged with powerful magical or spiritual force which may discharge itself with fatal effect. . . .[9]

But the gods themselves were vulnerable: they were deified, de-throned, and killed; like men, they lived and died. Similarly, the totemistic figures who were obeyed were also deified and then de-stroyed.

Regarding the relation between the totem and tribal rules of conduct, including proscriptions and punishment, considerable speculation has arisen. Freud, who developed a detailed theory of the development of group solidarity in the Primal Horde, postulated that their cohesion originated from their common wish to kill the Primal father (the Totem). The horde killed the Totem before he could punish them for wishing to do it.[10] The sons of the Totem (the tribesmen) were held together ambivalently by their hostility to the father and their need of his love and protection.[11] Although the material on which Freud based his theories of Totem is now discredited by anthropolgists—that is, his insistence on the patriarchal society—the implication of his thinking (that crime and punishment were always aspects of man's nature) appears to be sound. Phillip Reiff, the philosopher, states it thus:

Society *begins* with a crime. Man *begins* as a killer, Freud argued. Yet not merely a killer, but a *remorseful* killer. And the primal crime is the crime to end all crimes.[12]

Modern anthropologists agree [13] that a psychological explanation of totemism is hopelessly inadequate and unconvincing. Some totems, for example, have no relation to punishment, but most *taboos,* whether related to a totem or not (either of the present day or ancient times), impose sanctions or are involved with rules of conduct. It is equally true that *mana,* the power inherent in nature and, by implication, in the gods ruling nature, punishes man for breaking taboos. Whether the totemistic figure directed the penalty or the god or oracle decreed the sanction, or it was prompted by man's conscience, the taboo with its attendant penalties serves as a highly condensed statement of the crime = punishment equation as it has been known throughout human history.

PUNISHMENT AND THE PRIMITIVE

Scholars are agreed that primitive law, although unwritten, was scrupulously observed, for the very existence of the group, their dependence on the beneficence of the gods for their food, good weather, success in war, and deliverance from pestilence, was sensitive to infractions of taboos. Offenses against tribal taboos, unless punished, might bring down the vengeance of supernatural beings upon the entire clan or tribe. Hence, the elimination of the miscreant who violated a taboo became the duty of the whole tribe: he may have been beaten to death, exiled, cast into the wilderness to die (and, which was worse, to brave the wrath of the gods alone), or maimed. The brutality of the punishment bore little relation to the offender's intent; his crime may have been accidental or committed without malice. Cleansing the tribe of contact with the wrongdoer became the essence of primitive "law."

Examination of taboos in primitive cultures and ancient legal codes indicates how deeply religion and ritual influenced the growth of modern criminal law. Divine sanction underlay the need and rationale of punishment for sin and crime. This situation led the British legal expert Sir Henry Maine to remark: "There is no system of recorded law, literally from China to Peru, which when it first emerges into notice is not seen to entangle with religious ritual and observances." [14]

If the primitive cultures studied by anthropologists within the past half century can serve as analogues of the culture of early man, the entanglement of religion in criminal law can easily be recognized, and the intermingling of secular with god-given laws also becomes clear.

Hoebel, who studied the legal machinery of the Plains Indians, showed how infractions of tribal fetishes (taboos), as well as offenses against the person (murder, theft), were dealt with in a secular way, notwithstanding the fact that basically a crime was a sin against the tribe.[15] Among the Cheyenne Indians, Hoebel found certain basic principles in their "law" that were rooted in the tribal religion. For example, he set down as legal postulates such religious attitudes held by these tribes as these:

1. Man is subordinate to supernatural forces and spirit beings which are benevolent in nature.
2. The killing of a Cheyenne by a fellow Cheyenne pollutes the tribal fetishes and also the murderer.
3. The murderer must be separated temporarily from the social body. . . .

Thus, homicide was not only a "sin," but also a crime against the group. The transition from sin to crime is mirrored in the Cheyenne society's effort to purify itself. It "brought homicide under public law." [16] While the offender was exiled for his social crime, purification rites (the Renewal of the Medicine Arrows) [17] satisfied religious requirements. Among the Comanches, a tribe with less formalized systems of social control which also felt that "the great spirits (Sun and Earth)" exercised power of legal judgment,[18] punishment was meted out for such crimes as wife-stealing and homicide through a complicated system of bargaining. If the matter could not be adjudicated between the parties involved (using horses or blankets as restitution for the crime), the "brothers" of the tribe were called in to powwow; if justice was not then forthcoming, personal revenge followed. Hence some crimes, such as murder, were considered in-group problems— "essentially a wrong and vaguely a crime"—punishable by permitting one of the victim's kinsmen to kill the murderer.[19]

Earlier theories of the religious origin of ancient law, first enunciated by Maine,[20] have been re-examined in the light of the Plains Indians' experiences.[21] Here Hoebel agrees that the life of man

is subordinate to the will of spirit beings and life must be made to harmonize with their dictates . . . in the legal realm . . . the element postulates of the supernatural also appear as jural postulates. . . .[22]

But this investigation further concluded that although the spirits were omniscient, *man* directed the punishment: he beat, killed, or choked the criminal, or the latter was lynched or sent into the wilderness to die.[23] These findings led Hoebel to remark that the "simple idea that law originates in religion is overly naïve." [24] There have been other recent criticisms of the doctrine of the religious origin of law, principally by Diamond.[25] Examining the ancient legal codes, he concluded that there was little evidence to support the religious origin of law theory.

On the other hand, the intrusion of religious ideas into early or primitive law seems not to be doubted when criminal punishment is closely observed. Paul Reiwald, the Swiss lawyer who subjected the entire criminal law to psychoanalytic scrutiny, makes the point that the judge, father, and God are equated psychologically in the social psyche, and hence in the law. Reiwald points out that

. . . in the course of evolution a psychological similarity developed . . . between the conceptions of God, the King, and the Judge, who all derive their dynamic force from early experiences of the father . . . a kind of *union of personalities* which was cemented by the unconscious.[26]

The appeal to the supernatural remains as a vestige of this bond in present-day court practices. In the matter of testimony, we, as did our ancestors, invoke the aid of God: a witness testifies to the truth of his or her statement by adding "so help me God" to the oath. Convicted prisoners are condemned to death with the prayer uttered by the court "May God have mercy on your soul." The court speaks of the laws of "God and man" in giving its instructions to the jury; we suggest to the prisoner the soul-saving value of meditation and penitence and so on. "The whole system of law," write Llewellyn and Hoebel,[27] "still holds a mystic flavor in the public mind." God's punishment for sin and man's crime are still equated in the mind of man.

PUNISHMENTS IN ANTIQUITY

The criminal law of ancient man as reconstructed from the earliest codes of recorded history furnishes a suggestive, although incomplete, picture of early punishment. Such a reconstruction, however, does not amount to historical fact. As one scholar has pointed out,

the growth of institutions is much too complicated, even if we confine our attention to one society, to be represented as a simple series in order of time. . . .[28]

Customarily, the Code of Hammurabi (Babylon, 2250 B.C.) is cited as the first of these ancient compilations. The Assyrian Code (*circa* 2000 B.C.) and the Hittite Code, laws of an early people who "straddled the back of Asia Minor," and, lastly, the so-called Mosaic law are also significant in tracing the evolution of criminal law. At a later period, the Twelve Tables of Rome, the Draconian Code, the Germanic Salic law, and others have been used to reconstruct a picture of criminal practices. In the ancient codes punishments were often drastic, albeit not so severe as the generally cited *lex talionis* (the "eye for an eye" doctrine) might imply. Hammurabi, "the exalted prince, the worshiper of the gods," [29] decreed many punishments of surprising mildness. It is true that his code clearly upheld death for such crimes as bearing false witness,[30] theft of temple property, or associating with known criminals,[31] but it was not always so explicit as to the eventuality:

If the wife of a man be taken in lying with another man, they shall bind them and throw them into the water. If the husband of the woman would save his wife, or if the king would save his male servant . . . (he may).[32]

Then, as now, sexual crime, murder, and assault were socially troublesome offenses. In the Code of Hammurabi, the laws relating to incest were quite severe:

If a man lie in the bosom of his mother after [the death of] his father, they shall burn both of them.[33]

Malpractice was dealt with summarily:

If a physician operate on a man for a severe wound with a bronze lancet and cause the man's death; or open an abscess [in the eye] of a man with a bronze lancet and destroy the man's eye, they shall cut off his fingers.[34]

In other ancient codes it is worthy of note that in many instances, compensation in money sufficed as punishment for criminal as well as civil misdeeds. In the Hittite Code mutilation was reserved for slaves, sexual misdeeds, or offenses against the dignity of the king.[35] Even murder did not necessarily call for death:

If anyone slays in anger a man or woman, he must hand over the latter and must give four persons . . . then he discharges his liability.

The four persons "given" were apparently slaves.

Among the Hittites compensation and restitution were ordered for assault, black magic, theft, and some homicides:

If anyone breaks a freeman's arms or leg, he pays him twenty shekels of silver and he [the plaintiff] lets him go home.

If anyone kills a man or woman in a quarrel, he buries him and gives four persons, men or women, and he [the victim's heir] lets him go home.[36]

Apparently, restitution for crime was a constant feature of Hittite justice. Gurney reports an instance of a mild penalty for homicide, based on the fact that the law of private vengeance operated in that civilization:

If anyone kills a Hittite merchant he pays 1½ pounds of silver and he [the heir] lets him go home.[37]

In contradistinction to the Mosaic law of the Hebrews, mainly set forth in the Pentateuch (the first five books of the Old Testament), which deals in depth with criminal offenses, the Hittite Code considered murder as extrajudicial.

There is a discernible difference in approach between the older codes and the Hebrew codes concerning types of crime with respect to varieties of punishment. The Mosaic law mirrors a more settled civilization; its prohibitions are imbued with a stronger sense of right-

eousness, in which crime and sin are more closely related. Further, the
ecclesiastical courts of the Hebrews (the Sanhedrin) assumed the
burden of judgment and sentencing previously enjoyed by earlier
kings.

THE MOSAIC LAW

In the Old Testament, punishment is set down as the direct com-
mandment of the Lord. The general tone is severe; at times the details
of punishment are precise, at times ambiguous. For example:

He that sacrificeth unto any god save unto the Lord only, he shall be utterly
destroyed.[38]

Bring forth him that hath cursed without the camp; and let all that heard
him lay their hands upon his head, and let all the congregation stone him.[39]

Breach for breach, eye for eye, tooth for tooth; as he hath caused a blemish
in a man so shall it be done to him again. . . .[40]

Such punishments as burning (Gen. 38:24), amputation of the hand
(Deut. 25:12), flogging (Deut. 25:2-3), stoning (Deut. 22:21) are
detailed for infraction of "divers laws" transmitted by the Lord to
Moses for his people's guidance. On the other hand, the notion of
restitution softened some severe penalties:

And if men strive together and one smite the other with a stone, or with his
fist, and he die not . . . if he rise again, and walk abroad upon his staff,
then shall he that smote him be quit: only he shall pay for the loss of his
time. . . .[41]

In the case of the Mosaic law, the extensive Talmudic commentaries
provide opportunity for a thorough scrutiny of punishment and
crime in biblical days. These tractates, written in the early centuries
of the Christian Era, deal with the theory and practice of civil and
criminal law as well as the spiritual side of the ancient Jewish
theocracy. Here ambiguities of the Old Testament are resolved, cases
are cited, and the meaning of the Mosaic law expounded in minutest
detail. As Kastein has pointed out, the Ten Commandments re-
semble the Code of Hammurabi, while "now and again the wording
is reminiscent of the Egyptian Book of the Dead (1500 B.C.)." However, Kastein notes the essentially Jewish character of the Mosaic law:

Whereas, in the Egyptian Book of the Dead, the soul of the deceased pleads
before the god Osiris, "I have done no murder," the Decalogue makes moral
conduct a duty," Thou Shalt do no murder." [42]

One significant aspect of legal institutions among the ancient Hebrews was the supreme council and tribunal of the Jews, the Sanhedrin, to which major criminal offenders were delivered. These ecclesiastical courts (the Great and the Lesser Sanhedrin) deliberated on many legal issues, including criminal guilt, punishments or fines, appeals, and so on. The Sanhedrin interpreted the blunt and often generalized statements of the Pentateuch in terms of specific cases. The Talmud is replete with detailed case-law. The following excerpt from a case of assault illustrates both the spirit of the punishment administered and the close reasoning surrounding the words of the Mosaic law:

If one throws a stone into the public road and kills a person, he is banished. R. Eliezer b. Jacob said, Should the stone have left his hand at the time when the person put his head forth and was struck by it, the thrower is free of guilt. If he threw the stone inside his private premises and killed a person, he is banished in the case where the injured party had the right to enter there; otherwise he is not banished.[43]

This precision in differentiating degrees of guilt, well illustrated in the Talmudic tractates, indicates that although the prescribed punishments were severe their application was often modified. The same exceptions to the rigidity of punishment (the ancient Hebrews adhered closely to the biblical text) may be seen in the Roman law of the Twelve Tables. In one section, death was prescribed for homicide, but

if the weapon sped from his hand rather than was thrown by him (the assailant) . . . then a ram was substituted (for death).[44]

Nevertheless, it may well be posited that the underlying tone of finality and authority that has contributed a characteristic flavor to legal punishment in the Western world, flowed from the Mosaic law into the Judaeo-Christian system of ethical values. As Hartland put it,

The Mosaic Law in more respects than one has set the tune to which Christian Europe has danced.[45]

In any event, as is indicated in the following Talmudic excerpt, the explication of punishment carried a religious overtone, a sense of transliteration of divine commands:

This was the method of stoning: "The judgment having been delivered, the prisoner is taken out to be stoned. The place of stoning was outside the Court; as it is said, "Bring forth him that hath cursed without the camp" (Lev. 24:14). If one of the judges said, "I have something to plead in favor of the prisoner," the rider hurried away and stopped (the execution). Even if the prisoner said, "I have something to plead on my behalf," he is taken back to the Court four or five times, provided there is some substance in his words. Should they find in his favour, he is set free; otherwise he goes forth to be stoned. When he was four cubits away from the place of stoning, they removed his garments. In the case of a man, they leave a covering in front; in the case of a woman, both before and behind. This is the opinion of R. Judah; but the Rabbis declare that a man, but not a woman, is stoned naked. . . . the place of stoning was a height equal to that of two men. One of the witnesses pushed him by the loins, and should he turn himself over on his face, the witness reverses the position. If he die through the fall, the law has been carried out; but if not, the second witness takes the stone and hurls it upon his heart. If he die from it, the law has been carried out; otherwise his stoning must be done by Israelites generally, as it is said, "The hand of the witnesses shall be first upon him to put him to death, and afterward the hand of all the people" (Deut. 17:7).[46]

It has been apparent that the various legal codes of the ancient world dealt with crimes other than murder, assault, and sexual offenses. Problems of libel and slander, theft, usury, false witness and perjury, arson, malicious mischief, injury to an animal, fraud were all described in detail in the codes mentioned.

THE GRAECO-ROMAN CODES

Greek law also, in its relation to crime and punishment, linked the assumed wishes of the deities to mortal law. It was a common belief throughout Greece, writes one historian, that "the King had in ancient times received his laws directly from Zeus." [47] About 621 B.C., Draco, the Athenian legislator, preserved these divine commandments in a code that stood relatively unchanged for centuries. Although punishments remained severe—death and exile for capital crimes—the elements of a true jurisprudence appeared in the Draconian decrees. Draco insisted that the motives of the slayer be taken into account; his laws of homicide graded penalties according to degrees of guilt. Yet even Draco's codification met with criticism later. Solon, the lawgiver, modified the inevitable death penalty, complaining that "those that stole a cabbage or an apple had to suffer even as villains that committed sacrilege or murder." [48] His insistence on recalling those unjustly exiled, and his complaint that Draco's laws were written "not with ink but blood," [49] exemplified the reasonableness of the Greek approach to crime and punishment. Solon's laws, dedicated to "preventing the perpetuity of discord," were inscribed on wooden rollers, which, Plutarch commented, would last "a hundred years." [50]

It is not to be supposed that punishments meted out in older civilizations did not meet with opposition. The Greek philosophers wrote much of justice and the moral meaning of law. In Plato's opinion, expressed in the Dialogue on Laws,

. . . a law which commanded and threatened but which neither convinced the reason, nor touched the heart must be a most imperfect law. . . .[51]

The effect of such philosophic statements on the actual imposition of punishment is, of course, impossible to determine. One may judge from the writings of the Greek playwrights that the spirit of the populace, for whom the plays were written, was more in the direction of severe penalties than of rational judgment. Their plays cited crime and vengeance in their extreme form. For example, the *Oresteia* by Aeschylus (*circa* 458 B.C.), the tragedy of Pelops' sons, is sprinkled with bloody vengeance. Thyestes, who lost his claim to the throne in favor of Atreus, his brother, returned from exile with his children to visit his ancestral home. (He had been exiled for seducing Atreus' wife.) Atreus invited the family to dinner, murdered his brother's children, and served their flesh for dinner.[52] In retaliation for the macabre punishment visited upon his children, Thyestes put an eternal curse on the house of Atreus.

The early Roman codes gave evidence that the state had replaced the ancient blood feud as dispenser of punishment for crime, especially homicide. From records of the Roman comitia, pronouncements of statesmen as well as the Twelve Tables,[53] a comprehensible picture of Roman law can be elicited. The Twelve Tables (451–449 B.C.) spelled out in detail, as did other ancient codes, specific offenses and specific penalties. Table VIII, for example, stated:

If any person has sung or composed against another person a song [to] cause slander or insult, he shall be clubbed to death.

In the case of thieves caught in the act: if they are freemen, they should be flogged . . . slaves caught in the act of theft should be flogged and thrown from the [Tarpeian] Rock.[54]

So also the Justinian Code, established about a thousand years after the Twelve Tables, contained much from the past—"classical law intertwined with Justinian legislation." [55]

Isolated quotation of a few laws and sentences from the Roman law might imply that the Romans imposed a brutal code upon their own subjects and those of lands they had conquered. The acculturation process can be glimpsed in a statement from the Sanhedrin after the subjugation of Palestine, which decreed that decapitation was performed by striking off the head "after the manner of the Roman government." [56] But a reading of the voluminous material preserved indicates that the Roman tribunes exercised great care in differentiating degrees of crime, in ascertaining guilt, and in apportioning punishment justly. Stephen cites the following to illustrate the brusqueness of Roman law:

Whoever gives false evidence must be thrown from the Tarpeian Rock. . . . If a man kills his parent, veil his head, sew him in a sack and throw him into the river.

Nevertheless, as Stephen points out,

The excessive curtness of these provisions implies the existence of an all but unlimited discretion in those who administer the law. [57]

Other sources of ancient law—the Salic law of the Franks (*circa* A.D. 500), the Theodosian Code of the Goths, and fragments of the Anglo-Saxon law—help to reconstruct the picture of legal punishment during the first millennium in Europe. Scrutiny of these codes reveals a basic interest in protecting the physical person and defending personal honor and reputation. In Anglo-Saxon England, punishments, in part indigenous, in part borrowed from Salic and Roman law, continued to be lethal, although the bot (fine) and wer (the price set by a man's station in life) were freely used for criminal retribution.

It must be remembered that while the Anglo-Saxon kings struggled to control a group of primitive tribes in their kingdom, their laws reflected the introduction of a civilizing influence. For example, the code compiled and established by King Alfred—the Dom-boc (Doombook)—with its laws chosen from the many local statutes already existing, introduced the Decalogue and the "principal provisions of the Mosaic Code" into Anglo-Saxon England. [58] Alfred was forced to combat the "unsettled state of society in Saxon England," characterized by an early historian as a "twilight of mind." The penalties imposed by the Frisians, a tribe that settled in early England, illustrated this primitiveness: their punishment for desecrating a temple was as terrible as that prescribed for adultery.

Whoever breaks into a temple and takes away any of the sacred things, let him be led to the sea and in the sand which the tide usually covers, let his ears be cut off, let him be castrated, and immolated to the gods.

If a woman became unchaste, she was compelled to hang herself, her body was burned, and over her ashes her adulterer was executed. [59]

From an ancient law book, the *Mirroir des Justices,* scholars have established that Alfred sought to improve this brand of justice, protect the rights of jurymen, and mitigate arbitrary punishments. Thus, the king punished several judges for their violation of the rights of the accused:

He [the King] hanged Freberne, because he adjudged Harpin to death when the jurors were in doubt about their verdict: for when in doubt, we ought rather to save than condemn.

He [the King] hanged Markes, because he adjudged During to death by twelve men not sworn.[60]

In many areas, punishments were regulated to a point that betrays the anxiety felt lest severe penalties be misapplied. Consider the graded scale of fines in the law of Alfred and Æthelstan:

If a man's thigh is pierced, 30 shillings shall be given in compensation. . . .

If the first finger be struck off, the compensation shall be 15 shillings. . . .

If the man is wounded in the belly, the compensation should be 30 shillings.[61]

The compensation for bearing false witness shall be 30 shillings. . . .[62]

The welding together of a nation and the codification of provisions for criminal justice and criminal sanctions was no simple task.

BEGINNINGS OF ENGLISH CRIMINAL LAW

During the evolution of English law in the five hundred years following the Norman Conquest, criminal jurisdiction moved slowly out of the king's courts (*curia regia*), with their courtiers, sheriffs, and stewards, into the province of the secular courts (the Assizes, Quarter, King's Bench, Queen's Bench). Gradually the kings ceded their judicial prerogative to the county courts, where representatives of the crown tried cases and dispensed justice.

There seems little doubt that Christianity, with the exception of the witchcraft explosion, did exert a softening influence on drastic punishments for crime. In the earliest code of English laws (Bracton, 1268) this influence is clearly visible. Bracton, who was a lawyer and clergyman (Archdeacon of Barnstable), explained, his editor tells us, to his "savage countrymen, benefits to be derived from an equitable system of law . . . drawing his sentiments from the rich fountain of Roman jurisprudence." [63] A religious tone pervades Bracton's theory of punishment:

But punishments have been invented for the correction and control of human beings, that those whom the fear of God does not recall from evil, temporal punishment at least may coerce and restrain from sin. For God himself corrects men on account of their iniquity.[64]

A tone of benevolence softens his counsel to judges:

The judge ought to keep in mind that nothing be done too harshly or too remissly than the cause requires but should determine with a well-weighed judgment according as each thing demands. . . .[65]

By the twelfth and thirteenth centuries subtle changes in criminal jurisprudence were to have an effect in later centuries on legal punishments. Secular courts and ecclesiastical courts functioned separately; the "privilege of clergy" was established—this removed the clergy from the liability of capital punishment except in rare instances—and literate men were given "benefit of clergy." It was still true during the Middle Ages that men were boiled to death for treason, hanged on "that cursed tree of the gallows" by the hundreds, publicly flogged, strangled, and decapitated for felony offenses. In the centuries that followed, although death was ordered for such oft-cited offenses as stealing sheep, wounding or killing a deer, "housebreaking and putting fear to any person in the house," [66] definite inroads into the frequency of capital punishment were discernible.

In the early eighteenth century "clergyable" offenses were extended to women and illiterates. The Act of 1705 which accomplished this also provided for sentences in houses of correction or workhouses. The bar to "cruel and inhuman punishments" embodied in the Bill of Rights (1689), presented to William and Mary on their accession to the English throne, and the increasing power of Parliament following the revolution against the Stuart kings, formed a backdrop against which attitudes toward inhuman punishment softened.

While criminal judgments on the continent still decreed such monstrosities as "breaking on the wheel" and tearing the flesh with red-hot pincers, a leavening influence was in evidence: transportation to the Colonies and penal servitude were replacing brutish punishments. In England, consignment to the galleys, a punishment dating back to antiquity, gave way to banishment to the Virginia Company and West Indies, and later to Australia. Of the offenders to whom "royal mercy had been extended," some died in convict ships; others, after living out their sentences (from 7 to 14 years), were able to breathe the air as freemen. These "servants of the Plantation" underwent flogging and mistreatment by the overseers and slavemasters, but many lived to cheat the gallows.[67] With the eighteenth century, a wedge had entered the public conscience and the law: the concept of death or mutilation for serious or even casual wrongdoing was losing its unreasoning force. Social attitudes identifying crime with sin, nurtured by religious zeal and loyalty to the Old Testament, were gradually being diluted by a new humanitarianism. But inborn and fundamental concepts change slowly. In the code of laws laid down by the Massachusetts Bay Colony (1640), the Preamble contained a wish to establish "a religious commonwealth in which the laws of Moses were to be supreme."

WITCHCRAFT—PUNISHMENT FOR SIN

The general separation of secular from ecclesiastical courts during the Dark Ages has already been indicated as a significant feature in the evolution of crime management, but the separation proceeded slowly and irregularly. The Church of Rome, which had inherited the institution of ecclesiastical courts throughout Europe, claimed jurisdiction over many wrongs now classed as criminal—adultery, incest, bestiality, heresy, sorcery. It held its position on the authority of the Bible and the Church itself, and the weight of the Scriptures never really freed criminal law from its solemn influence. Sir Edward Coke in the early seventeenth century prefaced his comprehensive treatise on the common law of England by quoting Ecclesiastes:

Because sentence against an evil work is not executed speedily, therefore, the heart of the sons of men is fully set in them to do evil.[68]

Early in the first millennium the Church fathers assumed the task of ridding believers of malevolent demons. As Christianity spread throughout Europe, the suppression of witchcraft—an unholy, organized cult having its roots in the folk religion of prehistoric Europe [69]— required more effort. Depending on the prevailing political situation, many other wrongdoings were considered properly answerable to ecclesiastical courts—simony (traffic in benefices and indulgences), usury, defamation, moral crimes of a sexual nature, heresy, sorcery, and so on. Indeed, the influence of Satan seemed so widespread, his machinations so universal and yet so personal, that an all-out effort by the Church against crime seemed essential in order to preserve humanity itself. Its concern was genuine: rebelliousness against the laws of God and man threatened civilization. As a modern apologist for the Inquisition states it:

. . . Heresy was one huge revolutionary body exploiting its forces through a hundred channels and having as its object chaos and destruction . . . [It] was the same dark fraternity as the Third International, the Anarchists . . . and the Bolsheviks. . . .[70]

Heresy, disease, and crime followed the "incantation, spells, and conjurations" of the Devil. Pope Innocent VIII, in lauding the work of his representatives, introduced the *Malleus Maleficarum* (1484), a medicolegal treatise on witchcraft, with these words:

. . . It has indeed lately come to our ears . . . that in some parts of Northern Germany . . . many persons of both sexes, unmindful of their own salvation and starving from the Catholic Faith, have abandoned themselves to devils, Incubi, Succubi, and by their incantations, spells . . . have slain infants yet in the mother's womb as also the offspring of cattle.[71]

The background for the medicolegal science of witch-hunting lay in the earnest wish of the Church to suppress works of the Devil and so reduce the machinations of the witches. Witch-hunting chiefly delved into those manifestations that we now call mental illness, but such crimes were not exempt; punishments for witchcraft were no less severe than those for murder or treason.

A case is recorded of a man who one day in King James' chambers "suddenly fell into a lunacie and madness," which lasted about an hour. . . . within an hour the patient woke as suddenly as he became ill, remembering nothing of what happened. It was assumed, therefore, that he had been enchanted and that deviles had entered into him. . . . suspicion centered on one Dr. Fian, who was forthwith apprehended and questioned. The doctor denied any compact with the devil, but after considerable discussion and some torture, promised he would quit associating with the devil and signed a paper to this effect. . . . at length he stole the key and escaped the jail where he had been confined . . . Dr. Fian was apprehended and brought back. . . .

Upon questioning, he denied what he previously confessed, *i.e.*, that he had signed a pact with the devil. The court considered his denial was due to a further contact with the devil. King James took a personal interest in the case, and determined to put a stop to the nefarious business. Dr. Fian was tortured.

Under each fingernail two needles were pushed up to the head. His nails were pulled off with a "turkas," which, the notes point out, "in England we call a payre of pincers." Still Dr. Fian did not confess. He was then put in iron boots, his legs twisted, beaten and crushed, so that blood and "marrowe spouted forth in great abundance." In spite of this torture he did not confess . . . [and] he was arraigned as having maintained an indissoluble bond with the devil. . . . Dr. Fian was placed in a cart and dragged through the streets as a public show. After first being strangled in the cart he was burned in the public square.[72]

The methods of inquiry, torture, and punishment used by the witch-finders might well horrify the modern reader; they also horrified men of the Renaissance. Voices of physicians, laymen, philosophers were raised in condemning the mass-delusion of witchcraft. Thus, Johan Weyer[73] exposed the essentially hysterical nature of many demon-inspired symptoms; the German monk Father Spee, in his work *Cautio Criminalis* (1631), called for a halt. The multiplicity of tortures employed led to a multiplicity of crimes discovered. Doubt was arising as to the validity of self-confession by suggestible "witches." Lawyers were examining the legality of ecclesiastical courts and with it the validity of torture in determining guilt and prescribing drastic punishment. Sir Edward Coke, in his discussion of the Church's place in the English courts, commented:

Where some may doubt how we that profess the common law should write of ecclesiastical courts, which proceed not by the rules of the common law, to this we answer . . . that the kings laws of this realme do bound the jurisdiction of ecclesiastical courts. . . .[74]

THE ENLIGHTENMENT

No sudden, drastic change in punishments as the result of dissenting opinions occurred during the Renaissance. The social conscience was not prepared for it; indeed, the social atmosphere was impregnated with the spiritual reality of the struggle between God and the Devil. It is not strange that punishments were so devised as to be severe enough to neutralize the indignities that witches visited upon their victims. The evidence for this attitude was easily forthcoming. It was agreed that witches transported to Hell told tales on their return to earth of what they had seen in Satan's domain. The English historian Henry Buckle sets forth such an account, as preserved by one Reverend Wodrow in Scotland, of common scenes in Hell:

. . . that ther wer great fires and men roasted in them and then cast into rivers of cold water, and then into boyling water: others hung up by the tongue. . . .[75]

But the Reformation was ineluctably forcing its influence on European life and the British deists and French humanists bent their energies and their pens toward dispelling fogs of ignorance. Witch-hunting underwent a decline in the early 1700's: intellectualism, the growing world of science, the "free play of mind" (Shaftesbury) in matters of religion, the civilization of the eighteenth century—all contributed to modify punishment for crime, and paved the way for handling the criminal as an individual. In an indirect way, the original impetus toward the concern with the mind and "soul" of the criminal arose from the accent placed by the Church on the individual's own moral responsibility for his actions. The religious attitude that supported meditation and penitence as the proper antidotes for the equation sin = crime stimulated a reaction that in time led toward exploration of the criminal as a person and, eventually, to our modern interest in the psychology of the criminal. The way from mutilation and death to penitence and meditation, from the witch's burning faggots to solitary confinement in the penitentiary, was long and arduous.

Man's *social contract,* which permitted him to live in relative peace with his fellow beings, began to be studied and clarified by seventeenth-century philosophers. In the process, the meaning of crime and punishment for the individual received attention. Thomas Hobbes, in his *Leviathan* (1651), discussed the rationality of the law in relation to crime, emphasizing the important element of *intention* in the mind of the criminal:

Every crime is a sinne: but not every sinne is crime. To intend to steale or kill, is a sinne though it never appere in Word, or Fact: for God that seeth the thoughts of man, can lay it to his charge: but till it appear by some thing done, or said . . . it hath not the name of Crime which distinction the Greeks observed. . . .[76]

The philosophic search for the distinction between sin and crime, long argued by the Scholastics, led eventually to consideration of the possible rehabilitation of the criminal. But even then, philosophers of the seventeenth and eighteenth centuries were alert to the importance of reforming the offender. Reformation of the criminal carried an important meaning in distinction to that of retribution: "There is not a single ill-doer," wrote Rousseau, "who could not be turned to some good." [77]

Criticism of punishments meted out by the judges led to a reevaluation of the meaning of penalties. Plato's observation that "he who desires to inflict rational punishment . . . has regard for the future . . . he punishes for the sake of prevention . . ." was echoed by Hobbes:

A PUNISHMENT is an Evil inflicted by publique Authority . . . to the end that the will of men may thereby the better be disposed to obedience.[78]

The voices of justice and reason echoed and reechoed in statements of philosophers for a century and more. By the eighteenth century, the humanitarian spirit had gained ground. The criminal offender had been lifted one notch above the doomed human animal who had been burned, beheaded, disemboweled, and hanged for three millennia. But there was a practical side running counter to social theorizing. Crime was prevalent, disturbing, and constant. Macaulay relates the details of a crime wave during the autumn of 1692. Burglary, robbery, and murder swept England:

From Bow to Hyde Park, from Thames Street to Bloomsbury, there was no parish in which some quiet dwelling had not been sacked by burglars . . . A waggon laden with fifteen thousand pounds of public money was stopped and ransacked. . . . There was a sworn fraternity of twenty footpads which met at an alehouse at Southwark. . . .[79]

The Crown reacted immediately. Macaulay states: "Executions were numerous . . . the King resolutely refused to listen to any solicitations for mercy, till the evil had been suppressed."

Although citizens of the eighteenth century listened to and read Rousseau, Beccaria, Voltaire, and Tom Paine, admiring the ascendancy of Reason, applauding the downfall of tyranny, their everyday reaction to wrongdoing was not uncongenial to drastic punishment for crime. Flogging, for example, was a commonplace in the scheme of moral education. Children were beaten in the schools, the military wielded the cat-o'-nine-tails, seamen were lashed, petty thieves flagellated, Negro slaves flogged regularly, jailed prisoners whipped as part of their sentences—the Russians used the knout on Siberian prisoners, the Spaniards invented the bastinado—even the insane were beaten as one aspect of their treatment. "He who spareth the rod hateth his son; but he that loveth him chasteneth him betimes" (Prov. 13:24).

Although workhouses and jails throughout Europe and Great Britain finally reduced physical punishment, other evils remained. John Howard, the English humanitarian, surveyed the condition of jails and hospitals for criminals and reported revolting conditions, ignored by the citizenry. In his inspection of "the men's side" of Newgate Prison he encountered

many boys of 12 or 14; some almost naked. In the men's infirmary . . . 20 sick, some of them naked and with sores, in a miserable condition lay on the floor with only a rug.[80]

Howard's detailed notes spoke frequently of the "itch, scald, sore eyes," "pinched diet," rags, dunghills at the entrance to the cells. In the "Fleet," the infamous debtors' prison in London, he found

liquors sold as usual, notwithstanding the late Act which prohibits keepers from selling liquors, or having any interest or concern therein.[81]

Howard's indignation was largely disregarded in his own day, but in the century that followed his influence was great. In St. Paul's, beneath the statue of John Howard, appears this tribute:

. . . he traversed [the world] to reduce the sum of human misery . . . he trod an open but unfrequented path to immortality.

To criticize Howard's fellow citizens for apathy to conditions around them is to judge them from a contemporary view unsuited to the eighteenth-century spirit. Not only did illegal behavior call for automatic punishment, but the analysis of crime, even its description, in certain cases, was evidently unthinkable. Blackstone, writing in his famed *Commentaries* on Crimes Against Nature (sexual offenses), says:

I will not act so disagreeable a part to my readers as well as myself . . . to dwell any longer on a subject the very nature of which is a disgrace to human nature, a crime not fit to be named.[82]

Although critics have pointed out that Blackstone "revealed skeins of religious ideas governing behavior, tangled with theories of governments," [83] his views were undoubtedly representative of public sentiment in the eighteenth century. The courts dealt with young criminals in cavalier fashion. When Barbara Spence, a young woman in her early twenties, was convicted of "high treason" for counterfeiting a "few shillings"—as Barbara cried out bitterly on her way to Tyburn—the law demanded her death. Being a female, she was strangled and burned on July 5, 1721. She was, noted a contemporary, "of violent temper, behaving, under sentence in the most indecent and turbulent way." [84] A similar fate was the lot of young Peter M'Cloud, leader of a gang of "young villains" who caused a great number of persons "to suffer by their villainies." According to witnesses, after he was brought to Old Bailey, convicted, and sentenced to die,

[he] arrived at the fatal tree [and] begged his jailors to tell his mother he had hopes of [reaching] regions of eternal glory. . . .

The record closes with the remark:

Peter M'Cloud suffered at Tyburn on the 27th of March, 1772.[85]

It was clear that youth needed to be taught propriety and respect.

The accent on corporal punishment lightened early in the nineteenth century. Legislative bodies studied the effects of physical punishment on prisoners. In 1837, testifying before a committee investigating the system of transportation of English prisoners, one Dr. Barnes observed:

I never knew a convict benefitted by flagellation. I have always found him afterwards to be a more desparate character than before. . . .[86]

THE EVOLUTION OF PENOLOGY

Meanwhile, the law itself had become responsive to the newer spirit of decreased sadism. In England during the reign of George III, the judges were finally permitted discretion in commuting a death sentence, and in 1827 an act was passed forming the "nucleus of a criminal code . . . in which punishments were more carefully adjusted to offenses." [87]

"Carefully adjusted to offenses"—so wrote the dignified legal scholars, but the byways along which the institution of punishment passed en route to its present "humane" level were tortuous indeed. When in England the Halifax gibbet replaced the headsman and, in France, Dr. Joseph Guillotin succeeded in introducing the efficient machine that "in a single moment and at one blow" [88] replaced manual beheading, science entered, although hesitatingly, the realm of punishment. Not only medical scientists but philosophers and those precursors of sociologists who wrote on politics, law, and society were active in describing a new approach to punishment. One of the earliest and most influential of these was Cesare di Beccaria, Italian economist and jurist, who protested against the arbitrary power of judges to impose barbarous punishments on criminals. His book on Crime and Punishment (1767) was a plea for abolition of capital punishment; it pointed to the legislature as the source of law rather than to the judges. His work established the so-called classic school with its emphasis on a fixed punishment for each crime. Beccaria, the "protest" writer,[89] was widely read; among others, Catherine II of Russia was influenced by his ideas. He insisted that just punishment, far from calling for one penalty for nobility, another for the common man, was subject to logical and orderly procedure. Beccaria, imbued with the revolutionary fervor of the 1790's, extolled Reason, moral rectitude, humanitarianism:

Would you prevent crimes? Let Liberty be attended with knowledge. When the clouds of ignorance are dispelled by the radiance of knowledge, authority trembles . . . but the force of the laws remains immovable.[90]

. . . the severity of punishments ought to be in proportion to the state of the nation (whether barbarous or civilized) . . . it should be published immediately and necessary; the least possible in the case given; proportioned to the crime and determined by the laws.[91]

The useless profusion of punishments, which has never made men better, induces me to inquire, whether punishment of death be just or useful in a well governed state.[92]

His ideas, embodied in the French Code of 1791, were strenuously criticized because they left no room for consideration of individual differences among criminals. Critics pointed out that human peculiarities—insanity, psychopathology, physical deficiencies—interfered with the exercise of free will and reason, on which Beccaria and the proponents of the Age of Reason based their theories. However vigorous Beccaria's reaction to the wanton punishment of earlier days, it tended to focus, albeit negatively, on the criminal as a person. This came about through a reaction by way of the neoclassic school, followed later in the nineteenth century by the positivists. The ferment which Beccaria and other ethical thinkers introduced into social consciousness in time stirred up a search for motivation, the "cause" of crime, and later brought about the psychologic and physical anthropologic approach to crime.

The classic school influenced sociologic thinking. Jeremy Bentham, the English jurist, ethical philosopher, and chief expounder of "utilitarianism," reintroduced in his work *Introduction to the Principles of Morals and Legislation* (1789) ideas hitherto neglected.[93] One of Bentham's most significant contributions was his analysis of pleasure and pain as a guide toward inflicting punishment:

Nature has placed mankind under the governance of two sovereign masters, pain and pleasure. It is for them alone to point out what we ought to do, as well as to determine what we shall do.

This dictum made it clear why governing bodies should legislate specific crimes: because social *utility,* the social "good," required that painful acts be suppressed. Even more significant for modern penology was Bentham's insistence that the "motives" and "human dispositions" of wrongdoers should be studied individually.[94] "Throughout the middle of the nineteenth century," wrote Bertrand Russell, "the influence of Benthamites on British legislation and policy was astonishingly great." [95]

This may have been so among eager reformers, social thinkers, and advanced legislators, but in practical life the ideas stimulated by Bentham bore fruit slowly. In 1821, Edward Livingston, American attorney, statesman, and diplomat, put into legalistic form his ideas on humane prison administration. He had been invited to draw up a legal code for the state of Louisiana, then plagued by a mixture of Spanish and French archaic law. An admirer of Bentham, Livingston constructed a code which made far-reaching recommendations. He advised readjustment for the discharged convict—a revolutionary idea in the 1820's—a House of Industry for vagrants, prevention of crime through public education, a reform school for juveniles, education for convicts in prison. The Louisiana legislature failed to adopt his code, but Livingston's work was hailed throughout the world as a lawyer's implementation of forward-looking penal ideas—"a fountain of reform." [96]

REVOLUTION IN PUNISHMENT

The social revolutionists who aimed to reduce barbaric punishments struggled with complacent, or worse, social attitudes. It is true that in 1786 the Society of Friends (the Quakers) in Pennsylvania substituted solitary confinement in prison for capital punishment, relying on the effects of enforced meditation to achieve moral reformation. But the relaxation of physical punishment resulted in other horrors. The "Pennsylvania system," as it came to be known throughout the world, was attended by severe moral restrictions under the banner of "reformation." For example, the published doctrine of Massachusetts State Prison (1815) stated that a

. . . prisoner's mind requires to be reduced to a state of humiliation, that all intercourse of prisoners with each other and still more with the outer world should be suppressed . . . that the smallest deviation from duty be severely punished, that the punishment of a convict is incomplete so long as his mind is not conquered.[97]

The rival system at Auburn, New York, on the other hand, stressed employment for the convicts during the day with absolute silence in solitary cells enforced only at night. Discipline was extreme, for the prison officials had little faith in the possibility of reformation of convicts.[98] During the first half of the nineteenth century, the callousness of prison guards and their attitude of contempt (supposedly a factor in promoting humiliation, and hence self-reevaluation, of the convicts) seemed to belie notions of reform.

The state of prison management during the last half of the century was chaotic. There was discouragement and dissatisfaction on the part of wardens and much political favoritism, graft, and corruption. But even so, humanitarian attitudes continued to find expression. By the early 1900's, dedicated reformers had organized the New York Prison Association, Mutual Welfare League, the Osborne Society; church groups, altruistic persons, such enlightened wardens as Thomas Mott Osborne, educators, all spoke, wrote, lobbied, deploring the pariahlike conditions under which convicts lived. In 1870, the National Prison Association in Cincinnati provided a public forum for such men as Z. R. Brockway and Frederick H. Wines.[99] Such prison problems as medical care, the honor system, the indeterminate sentence, prison education, and religious instruction were discussed. A program for total moral rehabilitation of the convict was taking shape in spirit if not in fact.

Many practical issues arose, from the lockstep and the shaven head to the privilege of receiving mail, from the advisability of prison labor to the trusty system. Each point encountered long argument, much scrutiny, consultation, and comparisons by wardens and legislators here and abroad. But easing the wretched life of the prisoner required more than orders from the warden; it required a therapeutic program, taking its authority from an informed, unprejudiced public.

Reform associations and men of good will in and out of penal institutions played an incalculable part in the spotty improvement of prison administration during this period. Substitution of the electric chair and gas chamber for hanging, prolonged discussions surrounding capital punishment and its abolition, erection of special institutions for youthful offenders, were some of the by-products of one hundred years of social therapeutizing.

During the 1930's and 1940's, as a result of outer pressure and inner enlightenment, life within the "grey walls" came to be more tolerable, capital punishment decreased in frequency, and rehabilitation was a hope, a planned program, and often a fact. But the underlying approval of punishment and the attitude that punishment was "something eternal and immutable" [100] exerted its subsurface influence. In 1895, Frederick H. Wines (son of the Reverend Enoch Cobb Wines, a moving spirit in the New York Prison Association reform group), in tracing the struggle to improve prison conditions, wrote:

It cannot be too strongly insisted upon, that there is no righteous law which is not part of the law of nature and in harmony with it.[101]

In this somewhat ambiguous statement lies a strong connotation of morality. The phrase "law of nature" appears to refer to laws related only to the reality of human life, with no hint of supernatural intervention. But in spite of this use of "ethical naturalism" one can sense the moral values inherent in the formulations of early penologists. If punishment is natural, it is also "right."

One curious influence in keeping afloat the unconscious social concept of sinfulness in relation to criminal acts came to the fore as the medical (and mental) sciences joined in the growing interest in the criminal as a *person*. Whereas during the past two thousand years the wrongdoer had been extruded from the body politic, killed or maimed as a sinner or the anti-Christ, denounced as an incurable rebel against the feudal system and the divine right of kings, a new justification now arose: scientific investigators discovered the criminal to be "born . . . an atavistic being who approaches in his person the ferocious instincts of primitive humanity and the inferior animals." [102]

Notwithstanding the finality of the ecological, biological, and psychological findings of the early investigators—altered and minimized in large measure during the next fifty years—there was much of value in the positivists' views. The criminal offender was recognized as a physical, economic, social, and political integer in society. His plight called for painstaking study and consideration rather than indiscriminate punishment "by the book."

In retrospect, this subtle shift in interest appears in sharp silhouette. During the nineteenth century, however, while the reorientation was occurring, the trends and countertrends were not so easily discernible. So many scientific ideas, so many social forces, so many economic and industrial changes were disturbing the homeostasis of the social and economic structure that it was difficult to distinguish the immediate from the later consequences of the revolution.

Although the ethical concept that punishment was inevitable and immutable remained in the social conscience, sociopsychologic stirrings made possible a new focus on the criminal himself. This idea has been expressed in a diagrammatic way by saying that the classic school emphasized the crime while the positivists emphasized the criminal. The shift in accent from punishment to rehabilitation that followed was closely interwoven with the growth of the psychologic and sociological sciences. For "treatment" and "rehabilitation" lead directly to the need to know more about the person being treated: Who is this criminal? What are his potentialities, assets, physical and social background, liabilities, aims, and goals?

Here lay the beginnings of a sociopsychologic revolution. Of prime importance as a corollary of the renewed interest in the wrongdoer as an individual was the *examination of his mind*—including not only his intent to commit crime but also any disturbances (such as insanity) that might obstruct his responsibility for acting on such intent. The newly developed field of alienism, which provided practical aid long needed by the judiciary, served to catapult the mental sciences into criminology. Later, the insights of dynamic psychology expanded the participation of psychiatry in the study of crime and the criminal.

The primary effect of the broadening of social horizons insofar as criminology was concerned was a new awareness of the meaninglessness of severe punishment in the social polity. A valuable by-product of the realignment of man's methods of dealing with evil was the introduction of the social and mental sciences into the morass of crime. Of equal significance in the total picture was a de-emphasis on punishment as retribution, for it paved the way for rehabilitation possibilities in the individual offender. In brief, the reshaping of antiquated attitudes toward criminals laid the groundwork for modern penology and criminology. Centuries of blind acceptance of automatic penalty for crime gave way to a critical examination of the reason for punishment. As a result, the impregnability of the crime = punishment equation decreased. Forward-looking men turned to the social and mental sciences for knowledge of both the environment of crime and the personality of the criminal.

REFERENCES

1. Genesis 3 : 19.
2. Genesis 4 : 10–11.
3. BOSCAWEN, W. ST. CHAD, *The First of Empires* (Harper & Brothers, London, 1903), p. 288.
4. *Ibid.*, p. 297.
5. MURPHY, JOHN, *Primitive Man* (Oxford University Press, London, 1927).
   FRAZER, SIR JAMES G., *Taboo and the Perils of the Soul*, 3rd ed. (The Macmillan Company, New York, 1911; London, 1914).
   MARETT, R. R., *Psychology and Folk-lore* (Methuen & Co., London, 1920).
   FRAZER, SIR JAMES G., *The Golden Bough*, 3 vols. (The Macmillan Company, London, 1900).
6. CODRINGTON, R. H., *The Melanesians* (Clarendon Press, Oxford, 1891).
7. MURPHY, *op. cit.*, p. 168.
8. MARETT, R. R., *The Threshold of Religion*, 2nd ed. (The Macmillan Company, New York, 1914), p. 97.
9. FRAZER, *Taboo and the Perils of the Soul, op. cit.*, p. 132.
10. FREUD, SIGMUND, *Group Psychology and the Analysis of the Ego*, trans. by J. Strachey (Liveright Publishing Co., New York, 1949), pp. 90 ff.
11. FREUD, SIGMUND, *Totem and Taboo* (Moffatt, Yard, New York, 1918).
12. REIFF, PHILLIP, *Freud: Mind of a Moralist* (Viking Press, New York, 1959), p. 198.
13. GOLDENWEISER, ALEX, "Totemism," article in *Encyclopedia of the Social Sciences*, E. Seligman and A. Johnson, eds. Vol. 14 (The Macmillan Company, New York, 1934), p. 657.
   MEAD, MARGARET, "Tabu" article in *Encyclopedia of the Social Sciences, ibid.*, p. 502.
   MEAD, MARGARET, "Totemism," article in *Encyclopaedia Britannica* Vol. 22, ed. of 1962 (Encyclopaedia Britannica, Chicago, 1962), p. 319.
14. MAINE, SIR HENRY, *Early Law and Custom* (pub. 1883), quoted in Arthur S. Diamond, *Primitive Law, (q.v.)*, p. 9.
15. HOEBEL, EDWARD ADAMSON, *The Law of Primitive Man* (Harvard University Press, Cambridge, Mass., 1954), p. 142.
16. LLEWELLYN, K. N., and HOEBEL, E. A., *Conflict and Case Law in Primitive Jurisprudence* (University of Oklahoma Press, Norman, Okla., 1941), p. 22.

17. HOEBEL, *op. cit.*, p. 158.

18. *Ibid.*, p. 131.

19. WALLACE, ERNEST, and HOEBEL, E. ADAMSON, *The Comanches* (University of Oklahoma Press, Norman, Okla., 1952), p. 233.

20. MAINE, SIR HENRY, *Ancient Law* (John Murray, London, 1905), p. 14.

21. WALLACE and HOEBEL, *op. cit.*, p. 228.

22. HOEBEL, *op. cit.*, p. 261.

23. *Ibid.*, p. 142.

24. *Ibid.*, p. 265.

25. DIAMOND, ARTHUR S., *Primitive Law*, 2nd ed. (Watts & Co., London, 1950).

26. REIWALD, PAUL, *Society and Its Criminals*, trans. by T. E. James (International Universities Press, New York, 1950), p. 54.

27. LLEWELLYN and HOEBEL, *op. cit.*, p. 65.

28. POLLOCK, SIR FREDERICK, *Introduction and Notes to Sir Henry Maine's "Ancient Law"* (John Murray, London, 1906), p. 4.

29. HARPER, ROBERT F., *The Code of Hammurabi, King of Babylon* (University of Chicago Press, Chicago, 1904), p. 3.

30. *Ibid.*, p. 11.

31. *Ibid.*, p. 37.

32. *Ibid.*, p. 43.

33. *Ibid.*, p. 55.

34. *Ibid.*, p. 79.

35. DIAMOND, *op. cit.*, p. 39.

36. GURNEY, O. R., *The Hittites* (Penguin Books, Harmondsworth, Middlesex, England, 1961), p. 95.

37. *Ibid.*, p. 97.

38. Exodus 22 : 19.

39. Leviticus 24 : 14.

40. Leviticus 24 : 20.

41. Exodus 21 : 18–19.

42. KASTEIN, JOSEF, *The History and Destiny of the Jews*, trans. by J. Paterson (Viking Press, New York, 1935), p. 12.

43. COHEN, REV. A., *Everyman's Talmud*, American ed. (E. P. Dutton & Co., New York, 1949), p. 315.

44. JOLOWICZ, H. F., *Historical Introduction to the Study of Roman Law* (Cambridge University Press, Cambridge, 1952), p. 177.

45. HARTLAND, EDWIN S., *Primitive Law*, quoted in S. P. Simpson and J. Stone, *Cases and Readings on Law and Society*, "American Casebook Series," W. A. Seavey, ed. (West Publishing Co., St. Paul, Minn., 1948), p. 26.

46. COHEN, *op. cit.*, p. 317.

47. BOTSFORD, GEORGE W., *A History of Greece* (The Macmillan Company, London, 1890), pp. 46, 47.

48. PLUTARCH, on Solon, *International Library of Famous Literature* (International Library Co., New York, 1898), vol. 2, p. 567.

49. *Ibid.*, p. 567.

50. *Ibid.*, p. 573.

51. MACAULAY, THOMAS B., *Plato and Bacon,* International Library of Famous Literature, *ibid.,* p. 671.

52. AESCHYLUS, *The Oresteian Trilogy,* trans. by Ph. Vellacott (Penguin Classics, Baltimore, Md., 1957).

53. STEPHEN, SIR JAMES F., *A History of the Criminal Law in England,* Vol. 1 (The Macmillan Company, London, 1883).

54. NAPHTALI, LEWIS, and REINHOLD, MEYER, *Roman Civilization,* vol. 2, trans. by the authors (Columbia University Press, New York, 1955), p. 533.

55. JOLOWICZ, *op. cit.,* p. 497.

56. COHEN, *op. cit.,* p. 319.

57. STEPHEN, *op. cit.,* p. 11.

58. TURNER, SHARON, *The History of the Anglo-Saxon* (Carey and Hart, Philadelphia, Pa., 1841), vol. 1, p. 474.

59. *Ibid.,* p. 147.

60. *Ibid.,* p. 476.

61. ATTENBOROUGH, F. L., ed. and trans., *Laws of the Earliest English Kings* (Cambridge University Press, Cambridge, 1922), p. 89.

62. *Ibid.,* p. 149.

63. BRACTON, HENRICI DE, *Angliae Legibus et Consuetudinibus,* Sir T. Twiss, ed., vol. 2 (Longman & Co., London, 1879), p. lxvii.

64. *Ibid.,* p. 153.

65. *Ibid.,* p. 155.

66. STEPHEN, *op. cit.,* p. 473.

67. IVES, GEORGE, *A History of Penal Methods* (Stanley Paul & Co., London, 1944), pp. 103 ff.

68. COKE, SIR EDWARD, *Institutes of the Laws of England: Concerning High Treason and Other Pleas to the Crown and Criminal Causes* . . . (W. Clarke and Sons, London, 1817; first printing, Institutes of Law . . . 1st, 2nd, and 3rd Parts, M. Flesher for W. Lee and D. Pakeman, London, 1644).

69. MURRAY, M. A., *The Witch-Cult in Western Europe* (Clarendon Press, Oxford, 1921), p. 10.

70. SUMMERS, MONTAGUE, *The History of Witchcraft and Demonology* (Kegan, Trench, Trubner & Co., London, 1926).

71. KRAMER, HENRY, and SPRENGER, JAMES, *Malleus Maleficarum,* trans. by Rev. M. Summers, from edition of 1489 (Rodker, London, 1928), p. xiv.

72. JAMES I (of England), *Abstract from Daemonologie: 1597 Newes from Scotland declaring the Damnable Life and Death of Doctor Fian, 1597* (John Lane, London; E. P. Dutton & Co., New York, 1924).

73. ZILBOORG, GREGORY, *A History of Medical Psychology* (W. W. Norton & Co., New York, 1941), p. 200.

74. COKE, *op. cit.,* p. 320.

75. BUCKLE, HENRY T., *History of Civilization in England,* Vol. 2, from the 2nd London ed. (Hearst International Library, New York, 1913), p. 302.

76. HOBBES, THOMAS, *Leviathan,* Everyman's Library, No. 691 (E. P. Dutton & Co., New York, 1940), p. 155.

77. ROUSSEAU, J. J. in "Great Ideas," *Great Books of the Western World,*

M. J. Adler and W. Gorman, eds. (Encyclopaedia Britannica, Chicago, 1952), vol. 2, p. 493.

78. HOBBES, *op. cit.*, p. 164.

79. MACAULAY, THOMAS B., *The History of England from the Accession of James II* (E. H. Butler Co., Philadelphia, 1856), vol. 4, p. 214.

80. HOWARD, JOHN, *An Account of the Principal Lazarettos in Europe* (William Eyres, London, 1789), p. 124.

81. *Ibid.*, p. 91.

82. BLACKSTONE, SIR WILLIAM, *The Commentaries on the Laws of England, 4th edition, Adapted to the Present State of the Law by Robert Malcolm Kerr* (J. Murray, London, 1876), vol. 4, p. 218.

83. CLARK, WILLIAM L., and MARSHALL, WILLIAM F., *A Treatise on the Law of Crimes,* 6th ed., revised by Melvin F. Wingersky (Callaghan Co., Chicago, 1958), p. 4.

84. KNAPP, ANDREW, *The Newgate Calendar or the Malefactors Bloody Register* (T. Werner Laurie, Blackfriars, London, 1932), p. 65.

85. *Ibid.*, p. 834.

86. IVES, *op. cit.*, p. 155.

87. STEPHEN, *op. cit.*, vol. 1, p. 473.

88. SCOT, GEORGE RYLEY, *The History of Capital Punishment,* (Torchstream Books, London, 1950), p. 177.

89. VOLD, GEORGE B., *Theoretical Criminology* (Oxford University Press, New York, 1958), pp. 21 ff.

90. BECCARIA, CESARE DI, *An Essay on Crimes and Punishments,* trans. from the French, commentary by Voltaire, 2nd ed. (F. Newbery, London, 1769), p. 167.

91. *Ibid.*, pp. 178–79.

92. *Ibid.*, p. 102.

93. BENTHAM, JEREMY, *Introduction to the Principles of Morals and Legislation* (1789) J. L. Lafleur, ed. (Hafner Publishing Co., New York, 1948).

94. BENTHAM, JEREMY, *The Limits of Jurisprudence Defined,* C. Everett, ed. (Columbia University Press, New York, 1945).

95. RUSSELL, BERTRAND, *A History of Western Philosophy* (Simon and Schuster, New York, 1945), p. 777.

96. MOORE, ELTON H., "The Livingston Code," *Journal of the American Institute on Criminal Law and Criminology,* 19 (November, 1928), 344.

97. WINES, FREDERICK H., *Punishment and Reformation* (Thomas Y. Crowell, New York, 1895), p. 152.

98. *Ibid.*, p. 147.

99. *Ibid.*, p. 282.

100. RUSCHE, GEORGE, and KIRCHHEIMER, OTTO, *Punishment and Social Structure* (Columbia University Press, New York, 1939), p. 4.

101. WINES, *op. cit.*, p. 295.

102. LOMBROSO, CESARE, *Crime, Its Cause and Remedies,* trans. by H. P. Horton (Little, Brown & Company, Boston, 1911).

CHAPTER III

Medicine, Psychiatry, and the Social Awakening

MADNESS, ITS LEGAL DETERMINATION /
LAW AND PSYCHIATRY—A TENUOUS
ASSOCIATION / PARTIAL RESPONSIBILITY—
A PSYCHIATRIC CONTRIBUTION / THE FREE
WILL VS. DETERMINISM DILEMMA / MORAL
RESPONSIBILITY AND PSYCHIATRIC PROGRESS /
PHYSICAL ANTHROPOLOGY AND THE CRIMINAL /
THE "CRIMINAL MAN" AND THE THEORY
OF DEGENERACY / THE "PSYCHOPATHIC
PERSONALITY" AND CRIME / THE SECOND
ENLIGHTENMENT / REFERENCES

The superstition that a deformity or an asymmetrical figure is linked to eccentricity of behavior and to evil deeds has a long history. In prehistoric days, as Frazer has noted, the medicine man "owes his place . . . to strength or weakness of mind." The shaman of primitive societies undoubtedly achieved his status through some difference in structure or mystical quality of intellect. The same idea runs through the medieval cosmology of the witch, whose evil, sin, and crime are brought to an apex in the plaint of the Witch of Edmonton:

> Why should the envious world
> Throw all their scandalous malice upon me?
> 'Cause I am poor, deform'd, and ignorant,
> And like a bow buckled and bent together
> By some more strong in mischiefs than myself? [1]

The clear-minded Greeks, too, joined physical and mental aberrations to misbehavior, as witness Homer's description of Thersites, the repulsive Greek soldier, who was slain by Achilles for his scurrility:

> Thersites only clamour'd in the throng,
> Loquacious, loud and turbulent of tongue;

Awed by no shame, by no respect controll'd,
In scandal busy, in reproaches bold:
In witty malice studious to defame,
Scorn all his joy, and laughter all his aim:—
But chief he gloried with licentious style
To lash the great, and monarchs to revile.
His figure such as might his soul proclaim;
One eye was blinking, and one leg was lame;
His mountain shoulders half his breast o'erspread
Thin hairs bestrew'd his long misshapen head. . . .[2]

Did these rough clinical correlations between misbehavior and aberrations or disabilities of man sway judgments made in ecclesiastical and secular courts long ago? Did the dwarfed, the mentally twisted, the palsied or frenetic receive their just portion of mercy and compassion when dreadful punishments were meted out?

There seems little reason to doubt, from the voluminous writings inherited from the ancient world, that literate men, senators, members of tribunals, judges, were conversant with various forms of madness, yet the earliest legal codes contain no provision for the influence of mental disease on criminal responsibilities. Apparently punishment was visited upon culprits without regard to their mental state. Roman law, for example, made it clear that a "man is responsible for his acts irrespective of his state of mind." [3] Still, exceptions did occur: Clark, a student of biblical law, states as a plausible surmise that in the ancient Holy Land lunatics, or those "possessed of demons," were not punished for crime.[4] Whether questions as to the interference of insanity with criminal responsibility arose with more insistence after the teachings of Christianity had spread throughout Europe is difficult to determine. As will be seen, the ecclesiastical courts of the thirteenth century were already pondering the problems involved in deciding on punishment for the mad.

MADNESS, ITS LEGAL DETERMINATION

From the early pronouncement by Bracton in 1265 of the so-called "wild beast" test (for insanity), it may be assumed that his formulation incorporated much that his predecessors had pondered. Bracton's statement is generally taken as quite primitive:

An insane person is one who does not know what he is doing, is lacking in mind and reason and is not far removed from the brutes.[5]

Presumably this dictum simply meant that an insane man could not reason. As Jerome Hall points out, Bracton "was simply repeating, in a literary phrase, the doctrine that man was distinguishable from other animals by his intelligence." [6] This "wild beast" test apparently held for several centuries, supplemented by a test for mental deficiency (Fitzherbert, 1535):

An idiot is such a person who cannot account or number 20 pence, nor tell who was his father or mother, nor how old he is.[7]

In the seventeenth century, a beginning scrutiny of madness made it appear less an "afflictive dispensation of Divine Providence" than a strange malady that demonstrated certain distinguishing marks. Sir Matthew Hale's "test" (1671) stated:

Such persons as have their lucid intervals (which ordinarily happen between the full and change of the moon) . . . have usually at least a competent use of reason, and crimes committed by them in these intervals are of the same nature, and subject to the same punishment, as if they had no such deficiency. . . .

The effect of "melancholia," or dementia, on reasoning power was thus stated by Sir Matthew:

Such a person as laboring under melancholy distempers hath yet ordinarily as great understanding as ordinarily a child of fourteen years hath, is such a person as may be guilty of treason or felony.[8]

Just when the physician was called into court to determine lunacy and its effect on criminal intent is a matter of speculation. Throughout the witchcraft pandemic in Europe the doctors of the Church were concerned with problems in psychiatric-legal differentiation, and there is evidence that in the sixteenth and seventeenth centuries physicians were consulted as to the validity of self-confessions made by witches brought before ecclesiastical courts. As to this, Father Spee (*Cautio Criminalis,* 1631) wrote: "We who have to do with such people (witches?) in prisons and have examined them carefully (not to say curiously) have sometimes found our minds perplexed." [9] In the main, however, the issue of insanity in its relation to criminal culpability, with its question of how "melancholy distempers" could effect the understanding of the criminal at the bar, lay in the hands of the judges. The medical man, with an occasional exception, had not yet entered the forum.

It is difficult to imagine what perplexity must have assailed conscientious judges who tried to distinguish between normality and insanity in criminal trials. In England the law in respect to delusions of insane persons had centered on whether a man was "deprived of all power of reasoning, so as not to be able to distinguish whether it was right or wrong to commit the most wicked transaction" (Bellingham case, 1812). In America at least, this determination did not in most cases depend upon a physician's opinion. Thus, in New York in 1823, one Eliza Tripler was accused of stealing five silver spoons from the home of Mr. Stonehale. The learned judge in commenting on the case said: "No question can ever come before a court and jury so embarrassing to consider . . . or with precision to determine, as cases of real or alleged insanity." [10] In Miss Tripler's case the defense argued that she had had a fall some years before that "affected her head," and that even the prosecutor thought "her conduct was strange." Medical testimony was apparently not forthcoming, for the judge stated in his decision acquitting Miss Tripler that "insanity itself is calamity enough without inflicting the pain of a convicton."

The old case books are replete with homicide cases in which the issue of insanity depended upon Sir Matthew Hale's criteria for "melancholy distemper." The opinion of lay witnesses was relied on to establish whether the accused was a "reasonable creature of sound memory and discretion." The year 1812 marked the "first departure from the ancient rule." [11] In Bellingham's case, Lord Chief Justice Mansfield stated:

The single question was whether, when he committed the offence, he had sufficient understanding to distinguish good from evil, right from wrong and that murder was a crime against the laws of God [and] against the laws of his Country." [12]

Between 1812 and 1843, as cases of criminal irresponsibility for murder due to insanity were tested in the courts, the legal principle was generally adopted that a knowledge of "right" and "wrong" was crucial in determining whether a wrongdoer should be excused from punishment for crime. During the early part of the nineteenth century, expert medical witnesses began to be called on to translate insanity and "unsoundness of mind" into terms of "right" and "wrong" and the knowledge thereof. The McNaghten case made these principles definitive.

In 1843, in London, one McNaghten,[13] a deluded man, shot and killed Sir Robert Peel's secretary for what he considered a just grievance. He was acquitted as insane. The House of Lords, in response to public criticism, asked for an opinion from the Crown's judges. Lord Chief Justice Tindal, acting for His Majesty's Justices, handed down an opinion that involved two essential questions: (1) whether the accused knew at the time of such a crime that he was acting contrary to law; and (2) whether the "party accused was laboring under such a defect of reason, from disease of the mind, as not to know the nature and quality of the act he was doing, or if he did know it, that he did not know he was doing what was wrong." The justices also decided another question of great significance from the standpoint of psychiatry. They decided that once the facts of a case are admitted, medical science becomes the sole arbiter of the relationship between alleged mental illness and responsibility for an illegal act. "The question becomes substantially one of science alone . . . it may be [then] convenient to allow the question to be put in that general form to the medical man." This, in fact, became the basis for the *hypothetical* question given a witness who did not observe the accused.

This portion of the Chief Justice's opinion established the value of alienists in trials where insanity was at issue. As psychiatry developed stature during the nineteenth century, such conditions as homicidal mania, insanity or imbecility, and paranoia were being recognized clinically, and lawyers used this defense more and more to relieve criminals suffering from mental conditions of responsibility.

LAW AND PSYCHIATRY—A TENUOUS ASSOCIATION

Still, psychiatry's position in court during the 1800's was tenuous, and when medical opinions were advanced in the context of laws which Professor Wechsler called "a combination of enactment and common law that only history explains," [14] less than clarity resulted. It is more accurate to speak of "physicians" than of "psychiatrists" when discussing expert testimony given in many nineteenth-century cases. Medical witnesses were called to aid in assigning criminal responsibility for murder cases, but care was exercised not "to transfer the witness from his stand to the jury box" [15] by limiting his opinion to material tested by "professional skill and judgment." In a sense, the McNaghten decision stimulated the alienist to study medical jurisprudence and enrich medical experience in the world of crime. Analysis of the criminal mind, occasioned by the wish to solve the tortuous problems raised by the McNaghten ruling, passed through many vicissitudes before it arrived at its present level of use in our courts.

The theoretical background of irresponsibility due to insanity relates directly to the doctrine of *mens rea*. This knotty problem with which criminal law deals concerns moral guilt in crime (*mens rea*), the doctrine that criminal *intent* is necessary (in addition to the act itself) before the accused can be punished. Therefore the mental condition of the offender, variously stated as "evil mind," "wrongful intent," "guilty mind," became a proper subject for inquiry. [16] The reasoning went thus: To entertain a wish to injure or kill someone, to steal the property of another, or to do other unlawful acts, requires a mind that can reason, form a wish, and execute it; the insane and idiots do not have the requisite "mind" to form a criminal intent, hence they may be excused from punishment for crime. It became clear at this point that those who deal with lunacy are best qualified to establish before court and jury the presence of insanity or idiocy in the accused. "Doctors in lunacy" therefore became important figures in the task of deciding the applicability of punishment to major criminals in certain cases.

The McNaghten decision had as its intention the obviation of confusion, but it did not accomplish this. Psychiatrists, including the far-sighted Isaac Ray, combated the "right-and-wrong" test as being inconsistent with the reality of insanity: An insane person could be intellectually acute, could "know" what he was doing, yet be completely "unsound" emotionally; on the other hand, madness when emotional in nature does not excuse an individual from criminal responsibility so long as his "faculty" of knowledge is intact. Jurists—the venerable Sir James Stephens, for one—also considered the McNaghten ruling "an antiquarian curiosity," since it virtually divided the mind into intellectual and emotional compartments.

Much of the pressure that psychiatric quarters exerted against the right-and-wrong test arose in connection with the conflict over "moral insanity" and the "irresistible impulse" theory. Dr. Isaac Ray, in his famous work on the Medical Jurisprudence of Insanity,[17] linked moral insanity and irresistible impulse together as evidence of a wider spectrum in mental illness than had been accepted up to that time. He thus brought the issue of free will in criminal acts to the fore, invading philosophic areas not ordinarily of concern to physicians. As Zilboorg phrases it:

Such a broad conception of moral insanity could not but offend the sensibilities of those to whom the philosophic concept of free will was also an empirical, clinical fact, and who therefore were constrained to rise against such revolutionary, if not apostatic, ideas in psychiatry.[18]

Broadening the base of mental illness to include volitional and moral (i.e., emotional) insanity brought the right-and-wrong test under attack from another angle, and enlarged psychiatric participation in criminal trials. Dr. Ray, the earliest proponent of this wider view of mental illness, was joined by many who urged the courts to include emotional insanities under the criminal irresponsibility principle. During the trial of Charles Guiteau, assassin of President Garfield in 1881, the problem of moral insanity and criminal responsibility was thoroughly reviewed before a public tribunal.[19] Much testimony by experts on both sides was heard. Some experts urged the moral insanity plea as a defense against responsibility for the crime; others rejected the diagnosis, insisting that Guiteau was sane. The defense contended that the prisoner, who claimed to have been inspired by the Deity to kill the President, was insane. During the long trial the moral insanity diagnosis was argued at length. Simultaneously, the irresistible impulse theory received a decisive legal test. In both instances the jury made the final decision: It found the prisoner sane, rejecting the plea of irresponsibility on the grounds of moral insanity and irresistible impulse.

This difficult area of psychiatric diagnosis brought alienists into the courts more frequently. The question that arose in many cases of homicide where particularly heinous crimes occurred was: If intellectual impairment (as in delusional insanities) renders the individual not responsible for criminal acts, why should not volitional impairment relieve of responsibility? If the will of the accused was under domination of impulses and emotions that were uncontrollable, why was not a "volitional" disease an adequate defense?

In an oft-quoted case involving the plea of "impulsive insanity" in a woman (claimed to have been produced by menstrual difficulties) the court considered the question of "moral, emotional or impulsive insanity" in relation to responsibility for homicide. The accused, "in the dead of night, while her husband lay sleeping on a common bed, split open his head with a hatchet, without provocation or motive. . . ." Justice Chalmers, in reviewing the case, stated in part:

The law is not a medical nor a metaphysical science. Its search is after those practical rules which may be administered without inhumanity, for the security of civil society. . . . And therefore it inquires, not into the peculiar constitution of the mind of the accused, or what weakness, or even disorder, he was afflicted with, but solely *whether he was capable of having, and did have a criminal intent* [italics added].[20]

A Western court, on the other hand, adopted a less disunited view of the personality. It ruled that an individual who knows right from wrong, but whose mind is so deranged or disordered by mental disease that "it fails to function and cannot direct or control the acts of the person so afflicted, is and should be recognized as being legally insane." The opinion continues:

Volitional ability to choose the right and avoid the wrong is as fundamental in the required guilty intent of one accused of crime as is the intellectual power to discern right from wrong and understand the nature and quality of his act.[21]

This opinion, representing a minority view among legalists, coincided with the theory of partial responsibility that psychiatrists had urged over many decades. Careful clinicians working with mental patients involved in major crimes agree that certain types of abnormality—severe psychopathic personalities, degrees of mental deficiency, severe compulsive states—that cannot be said to destroy completely knowledge of right and wrong, nevertheless do impair criminal responsibility. Sheldon Glueck in discussing this basic idea concludes by saying:

As long as there are borderline conditions of mental unsoundness that are not definitely classifiable among clinical groupings of the psychoses . . . humanity dictates the view that in these cases there is really but partial responsibility, in the sense of *penal accountability*.[22]

Since the irresistible impulse theory involved abstruse questions of freedom of the will, it has been generally agreed that this defense is impractical, unscientific, unprovable, and unnecessary in administering justice. Actually, irresistible impulse has been rejected as a practical defense in a majority of courts in this land but its discussion consumed almost a century of medicolegal debate. Its present status can be gleaned from the New York Penal Law (sec. 34), which states the legal position in this regard succinctly:

A morbid propensity to commit prohibited acts, existing in the mind of a person who is not shown to have been incapable of knowing the wrongfulness of such acts, forms no defense to a prosecution therefor.

PARTIAL RESPONSIBILITY—A PSYCHIATRIC CONTRIBUTION

The pros and cons of the irresistible impulse theory significantly represent psychiatry's inroads on the traditional position of the law concerning mental illness and criminal responsibility. Although the theory lost juristic caste it foreshadowed the demand for recognition of partial responsibility of mental illness (not amounting to insanity per se) as a legal defense. Imperceptibly, the doctrine of *partial* impairment of criminal responsibility has opened "crevasses in the thus far rather solid fortress of public-centered justice with which the judiciary has surrounded itself." [23]

It is not literally true that psychiatry alone opened this "crevasse" of partial responsibility, but the realities of life have forced psychiatry to recognize borderlands of mental disturbance in crime. The psychiatrist observes offenders who experience delusions and hallucinations, yet are clearly aware of right and wrong in social life; he sees others who are free of delusion and intellectual disorganization (know right from wrong) but are clearly abnormal in their reaction to ethical social requirements. To divide the "thinking" from the "feeling" or "willing" categories of the human mind is impossible. A recent case of Dr. Cleckley's concerning a man who almost succeeded in strangling his wife points up this dilemma. The patient "knew" his act was wrong at the time and apparently was not angry with his wife. Influences from within urged him to attempt the murder; he being obviously schizophrenic, his criminal act was in response to hallucinations and delusions, notwithstanding his clear intellectual perception of right and wrong.[24]

The courts have often repeated their dedication to the "all or none" character of criminal responsibility. In a California case, the Court stated: "Insanity . . . is either a complete defense or none at all. There is no degree of insanity which may be established to affect the degree of crime." [25] The psychiatrist, however, perceives that another grade of mental illness, "though not so pronounced as to come within the tests of criminal insanity, may nevertheless negate the particular intent requisite to the crime charged." [26] The case in point was that of a subnormal offender who did not have enough "mind" to entertain an intent to deliberate and premeditate a murder charged in the first degree.[27]

The intrusion of a different view of the criminal mind—its liability toward only partial responsibility for criminal acts—conflicts with the court's duty to inflict punishment impartially under the restrictions and provisions of statutory law. The psychiatric position is to understand human behavior in accordance with the realities of mental life as illuminated by studies of the human personality in action. The premises regarding legal punishment for responsible criminals and the psychiatric position, which urges consideration for partial responsibility, represent disparate views. Careful and dispassionate thinking is required to resolve these differences. Leaders in both the legal and psychiatric fields are aware of this. The American Bar Association committees, the American Bar Foundation, the Group for the Advancement of Psychiatry, and other professional groups are working to reconcile these differently based approaches.

This emotionally controlled and mutually respectful attitude [28] was not so evident in the past. In retrospect, we detect a querulous note in Spitzka's advice in his textbook *Insanity* (1883):

On some occasion the question of defining what is called "legal insanity" may be presented to the reader. . . . When that question is asked, he may safely challenge the questioner to show him a broken leg or a case of small-pox in a hospital ward which is not a broken leg or a case of small-pox in law.[29]

In 1949, Zilboorg appears to have adopted a similarly officious attitude:

It is most pertinent to differentiate between the doctor of medicine who is engaged in the business of detection of crime or who otherwise serves the end of penal justice and the psychiatrist who is called upon to examine and testify as to the mental condition of a given defendant . . . such a doctor of medicine is merely a specialist who hires himself to give his special knowledge to the state for value received; he is not a healer, not a physician, not a servant in the ministry of medical mercy.[30]

For the present, it is important to note that, although judges adhere to the position that the law does not attempt to define what insanity is or to place upon the jury the burden of determining the sanity or insanity of a defendant, the law does request the jury to measure, by legal standards, the responsibility of a person who may be mentally unsound. The law interests itself in criminal *responsibility*, not insanity, even though, through inexactitude or careless thinking, the two terms have become identified with each other.

Psychiatric urging toward use of the principle of partial responsibility has had some influence in legal decisions. For example, in a case involving "feebleness of mind or will, epilepsy or psychopathic inferiority" it was determined that proof of such partial mental disturbance could "be effective in reducing the grade of the offense," or that such a person might even "be incapable of deliberation and premeditation" in a murder case.[31] In the celebrated Durham decision, the test for insanity was modernized and broadened: ". . . an accused is not criminally responsible if his unlawful act was the product of mental disease or mental defect. . . ."[32] Reliance on a "dynamic and changing medical concept of mental disorder" here supplanted the original "static" test.[33] From this point of view, "partial" disturbances may be elucidated, the varying levels of cognitive and emotional disorder may be explored, and a truer, more detailed picture of a sick, misbehaving human being may be presented to a jury.

The actual differences between the limited responsibility of the law and the wider limits which degrees of mental disturbance imply, influencing moral responsibility in crime, are considerable only when viewed in the abstract. In practice, the psychiatrist, with the material at hand and with whatever conceptual model of ego structure he carries in his mind, strives to reconstruct the mental state of the criminal in deciding how strong were the emotional forces that stimulated his choice of conduct. This he does in the legal setting. Hence, to inveigh against "the vacuous psychology of the McNaghten rule and the hypothetical question" (Zilboorg) seems to evade the obvious duty of psychiatry, which is to bring clarity and professional aid to the task of understanding types of misbehavior behind which lie extremely complicated motivations.

The introduction into the courts of the psychiatric viewpoint brought difficulties in its train that should not be underestimated. Among these is the intricate problem of free will in relation to criminal acts, which is rooted deeply in philosophic questionings.

THE FREE WILL VS. DETERMINISM DILEMMA

Many psychiatrists feel that no man can really "choose" a course of conduct, because "free choice" is determined by each individual's cultural and psychological background, his unconscious impulses, identifications, predetermined wishes, and drives. Thus, a criminal offender cannot be considered psychologically "free" in any absolute sense. As with any law-abiding citizen, he can be "free" to prosecute certain behavior, but under stress or internal pressure this "freedom of will" may yield to preformed (unconscious) types of behavior. We quote here a representative view of determinism as viewed from a psychoanalytic position:

[In an] attempt to make a psychological analysis of the concept of responsibility . . . we shall try to avoid the traditional tying up of the problem with religion and the philosophical problem of free will. We shall first approach the concept of *responsibility* from the purely psychological point of view. Psychoanalysis considers the human psychic apparatus as a system which is fully, and without a single gap, determined by psychological and biological causative factors." [34]

It is understandable that psychiatrists can look with greater ease on partial responsibility as a defense against criminal responsibility in selected cases, since the traditional view of absolute free will cannot be supported clinically. It is noteworthy, however, that during the full flood of psychoanalytic influence, an American Bar Association committee "viewed with alarm" the "spread of psychoanalytic doctrines which tended towards determinism." [35]

Although no one can say that determinism has any better claim to final proof than free will, practical problems seem to outweigh philosophic ones. A half century ago, Joseph Grasset advised psychiatrists to avoid the pitfall of the free will vs. determinism controversy. Accepting rules of human conduct whether drawn from morality or social utility, Grasset asked only for a judgment as to whether or not the capability of the organism was impaired.[36]

From the same base line of practicality, Wilber Katz suggests that most people be treated "as if they had free will," leaving those who are mentally ill—those whose ego is partially involved in a given act—to be evaluated as responsible social agents from some mid-position between deterministic and free-will premises. For, Katz asks, with empirical as well as logical propriety, "In determinism is there not a residual element of choice or personal response?" [37]

The answer to Professor Katz's question is, of course, Yes. The converse is also true: that "free will" contains inherently some degree of determinism, in terms of early identifications, subtle cultural influences, and the like. Perhaps the clearest statement of the concordance of two opposing views is contained in a committee statement of the Group for the Advancement of Psychiatry:

Ego impairment would appear to be a direct measure of responsibility. Ego impairment implies lessened control in maintaining behavioral norms of social interaction. In law, such would be the basis of exculpation. On this level of abstraction the lawyer and psychiatrist can agree. The psychiatrist can determine that ego impairment exists and the lawyer can transpose the fact into his terms of intent and responsibility.[38]

In the last analysis, in spite of psychiatric dissatisfaction with the McNaghten rule and legal dissatisfaction with the emancipating Durham decision,[39] it is a generally understood, if not accepted, theory that man is an indivisible whole. The legal scholar Jerome Hall has expressed this perception in words of clarity and human understanding:

Moral judgment [knowledge of right and wrong] is not reified as an outside, icy spectator of a moving self. On the contrary, the corollary is that value-judgments are permeated with the color and warmth of emotion—as is evidenced by the usual attitudes of approval that coalesce with right decisions. Indeed all actions, especially that relevant to the penal law, involves a unified operation of the personality. . . . The McNaghten rules provide an analytical device for dissecting this action.[40]

MORAL RESPONSIBILITY AND PSYCHIATRIC PROGRESS

A century of dissatisfaction on the part of psychiatric experts with the legal tests for insanity has not been without benefit. The legal profession, equally alert to certain illogical aspects of the McNaghten test, has read such amendments as the Durham test into legal being, and has developed an appreciation and understanding of the myriad mental states that lay claim to criminal irresponsibility. There has also emerged a highly significant modification of the public attitude toward punishment of mentally disturbed offenders. Indirectly, with widespread public enlightenment on the mysteries of mental disease, juries have been alerted to the facts of dynamic psychiatry. As indicated by the Durham test, if a criminal act was the "product of mental disease or mental defect," it becomes the responsibility of the jury, with the aid of psychiatric experts, to determine whether mental disease existed, the degree of its involvement, and its relation to the crime in question.

This necessarily involves an appreciation of the place of ego control in a disordered psyche.

The increased tempo of discussion in legal and medical journals, and even in public forums of tests for legal insanity shows the broadening effect of the general dissemination of psychiatric knowledge. This lessens the influence of the older, discredited "faculty" psychology, but it also decreases the sense of authoritarianism inherent in decisions involving mental disease. The psychological relationship between judges and juries today differs extraordinarily from that of a century or more ago due to the increased use of psychiatry in the courtroom and the gradual changes in legal practices. De Grazia quotes a legal scholar in this vein:

. . . there was a vastly greater difference between the intelligence of the court and the jury than there is now, and the tendency was for the learned and great judges to bestow their learning very liberally upon the ignorant and degraded jury by way of instructions. . . . The use of experts as witnesses to give opinions on scientific subjects was comparatively unknown.[41]

In a word, we are witnessing the influence of psychiatric thinking upon the traditional and sacrosanct notion that crime must *always* be visited with punishment. For example, the class of mental conditions that might reduce or mitigate legal responsibility for major crimes has been enlarged. In practice, the doctrine of partial responsibility is usually applied in cases of murder; this, if received in the judge's charge by the jury and accepted by the latter, serves to reduce the murder charge from first to second degree, on the ground that one cannot premeditate if one's intent is modified by a mental disease or condition not amounting to legal insanity. Since there is no more unassailable premise in our law than that everyone not insane, idiotic, or a child is fully aware of the law, the doctrine of limited responsibility may act to weaken our basic insistence on legal punishment. Judge Cardozo has stated in an oft-quoted axiom: "Obedience to the law is itself a moral duty."

But the larger question arises: Is the partial responsibility theory undermining the presupposition inherent in the crime = punishment equation? If public morality is valid, punishment for wrongdoing is valid and any deviation from or slackening of "justice" in assessing penalties becomes a starting point for the disintegration of justice itself. Thus, the solid basis of moral responsibility—"The problem of criminal responsibility makes sense only if human responsibility makes sense" [42]—becomes susceptible to question.

The effect of educative efforts by psychiatrists involved in criminological work is beginning to be noticed. One perceptive attorney writes:

In the meanwhile, as will be seen, the psychiatrist (however unwittingly) is already spinning a web which is entangling the ancient fabric of criminal justice.[43]

The conscientious psychiatrist strives to eschew moral judgments in his therapy and clinical evaluations, but his assault on the presupposition that crime *always* deserves and requires punishment involves morality in its essence. When asked to ascertain whether the accused was able to distinguish "right" from "wrong" during a criminal act, the psychiatrist complains that the McNaghten formula forces him to make a moral judgment. At the same time, he wishes to examine the effect of emotional illness on the cognitive and volitional abilities of the criminal; in this process he must necessarily judge the guilt of the accused.

In a case of murder to which there were no witnesses,[44] the present writer, on examination, developed convincing material that supported a diagnosis of epileptic psychosis (postictal furor) in the accused.[45] (A previous conviction of murder in the first degree had already been obtained.) On retrial, because of this newly discovered evidence, the examining psychiatrist, weighing emotional explosiveness in a furor and its effect in blotting out ego control in the offender, was obliged to judge the guilt inherent in the crime, which occurred during a period of organically suspended consciousness. In more common cases (involving schizophrenic illnesses), a psychiatrist needs to judge the nature of the offense to ascertain the relation between the accused's delusions, or his affective distortions, and the specific crime alleged. Or, more pointedly, in sexual offenses, particularly of a revolting nature, the psychiatrist as a citizen often finds his private moral values exposed to inner questioning as he works with the offender's emotional illness and deviated sexual expression. In any event, the psychiatric expert faces a true dilemma in urging an objective, amoral view of crime as behavior, while he weighs those moral values the law encompasses and enforces. De Grazia puts the situation bluntly:

The dilemma of psychiatry appears to be that on the one hand, it cannot avoid moral questions, and on the other hand it cannot deal with them without seeming to invalidate its claim of being a "science," not a theology.[46]

In spite of this conflict faced by the psychiatric adviser to the court and also by the court (which has the duty of interpreting public values in individual cases), the trend of psychiatric opinion in the courtroom and in medical writings has been in the direction of sidestepping fixed moral values. Especially when the emphasis is on careful psychiatric analysis of criminals, which, it is hoped, will lead to rehabilitation rather than punishment, treatment rather than imprisonment, reeducation rather than custodial restraint.

While alienists and psychiatrists were concerned with those ego disturbances that affected responsibility for punishment and the larger questions of free will and determinism, others were delving into causes of crime. Here the medical man's science was brought to bear on those physical and psychological abnormalities that might explain predisposition to crime.

PHYSICAL ANTHROPOLOGY AND THE CRIMINAL

It is generally stated that Cesare Lombroso, the famed Italian physician, launched the scientific era in criminology. For example, one overenthusiastic commentator wrote:

It seems incredible but it is nevertheless a fact, that, prior to the publication of Lombroso's *The Criminal* which was given to the world in 1876, there had never been offered a serious scientific approach to the study of the criminal.[47]

Here little heed was paid to such pioneer-physicians as Franz Gall, who, initially as a hobby and later as a scientific lifework, scrutinized the criminal's body for clues to his behavior. In the first decade of the nineteenth century, Dr. Gall, a Viennese, interested himself in the anatomy of the nervous system. In the course of his very precise neuroanatomical work, he discovered that the "organs" (lobes) of the brain were represented in protuberances of the skull. These, Gall hypothesized, permitted one to read the mental faculties of an individual in terms of the size of his "bumps." His studies of the human skull as related to mental characteristics were first termed *craniology;* under the later term *phrenology,* fakery became associated with the hypothesis, as charlatans seized on its possibilities. Dr. Gall, nevertheless, was a scientist, and he earnestly sought among the inmates of Viennese jails and asylums proof of his theory that faculties of the mind corresponded to the conformation of the skull, and that the larger a given knob, the more influential in determining behavior was the brain lobe beneath.[48] The faculties of "combativeness," "secretiveness," and "acquisitiveness," which he believed to be the "obvious" causes of criminal behavior, were easily identified by this method. Gall and his followers noted how the higher "propensities" combated the lower, or more depraved, propensities. Thus the organ of "destructiveness" would lead its possessor to murder unless the organs of "self-esteem" and "piety" proved stronger.

Craniology was not without its medical adherents in this country in the first half of the nineteenth century. Diagnoses of criminal tendencies from a phrenological point of view were readily made by physicians. For example, Dr. Cardwell, professor of medicine at Transylvania University in Kentucky, declared that "destructiveness, combativeness, acquisitiveness, secretiveness, amativeness" were specifically responsible for crime and could be demonstrated in criminals.[49] In the 1840's, some American leaders in psychiatry, including Dr. Amariah Brigham, of the New York State Lunatic Asylum, believed strongly in phrenology; Brigham held that criminals were the unfortunate victims of unduly preponderant lower "propensities" without the counterbalancing effect of "higher faculties." [50]

In general, however, the basic hypothesis used by phrenology in explaining crime fell into disuse until Lombroso, in 1876, startled the world with his discoveries of the physical characteristics of the criminal "type." In 1870, Lombroso, while performing an autopsy on the cadaver of a criminal—once a vicious brigand of Pavia, Italy—found a long series of atavistic anomalies in the skull. In recalling this experience Lombroso said:

At the sight of these strange anomalies the problem of the nature and origin of the criminal seemed to me resolved; the characteristics of primitive men and of inferior animals must be reproduced in our times.[51]

In addition to skeletal peculiarities, many other facts supported Lombroso's belief in the existence of the "born criminal." The frequency of tattooing, the blinding, violent passions insisting on vengeance, the wild courage that stands on lack of foresight, and the special argot of the underworld were psychological anomalies coinciding with physical peculiarities. The criminal's conscious avoidance of everything that civilized man holds dear proved to Lombroso the atavistic nature of the criminal man. "They talk like savages because they are veritable savages in the midst of this brilliant European civilization," Lombroso wrote. His studies of 5,900 criminals, their physiognomy, skulls, skeletal structure, teeth, and so on, demonstrated "new analogies between the insane, savages, and criminals." Lombroso's further studies led him to equate "moral imbecility, epilepsy, and the 'born criminal' as belonging to the same natural family." The fundamental notion of specific signs of degeneracy—"outstanding ears, frontal sinuses, voluminous jaw and zygomas, a ferocious look, thin upper lip . . ." become fused, in Lombroso's conclusions, with the "criminal" type: atavism, depravity, and degeneracy in modern society were veritable "causes" of crime.[52]

THE "CRIMINAL MAN" AND THE THEORY OF DEGENERACY

The theory of the structural basis for crime, the atavistic throwback to primitive man, flourished concomitantly with another basic notion, that of degeneracy of the nervous system. Studies on heredity in such families as the Jukes and Kallikaks proved that involution (degeneracy) could occur in the human species as well as evolution to higher levels. The influence of Darwinism spurred investigation of physical evidences of deterioration: head malformations, poor dentition, deformities of the extremities, goiters, dwarfing, and the like among criminals and insane patients. In 1857, Morel, a French physician, published an illustrated text [53] detailing every kind of physical degeneracy in patients that matched their mental deficiency and moral depravity. These findings, confirmed by other investigators, demonstrated the varieties of degeneration afflicting the dejecta of the human race. Morel's museum of misshapen heads, prognathic jaws, flattened ears, liberally sprinkled through his books, was matched by the anomalies found by other workers among the mentally and morally sick: defects of teeth, palate, the Morel ear, small ears, elongated ears, yellow iris giving the eye a "snake-like appearance," crooked noses, scanty beards or hirsutism, flat-footedness, dolichocephalic heads, and so on.[54]

The stigmata of degeneration included such findings as "prehensile toes, defective chest development and weak heart." It all meshed in with Lombroso's "criminal man." Degeneracy of the mind and the moral sense was accepted as the cause of crime: "The closer we get to the marrow of criminality," wrote Lydston, "the more closely it approximates pathology." There were some, however, who withheld their concurrence that crime is a disease, an evidence of degeneration. By the turn of the century this ready explanation of criminality began to lose followers, but still in 1904 Lydston, representative of those who believed in the organic background of criminality, maintained his position: "The essence of degeneracy is neuropathy—usually hereditary." [55] In other areas also the theory of degeneracy was adopted with vigorous approval.

In Europe, the literati of the realist school seconded the findings of Lombroso, expanding them enormously. The theory of degeneracy was accepted by social philosophers. Nordau pointed to the overwhelming degeneration with which every branch of life was infiltrated. Among literary historians, Jean Carrère wrote on "Degeneration in the Great French Masters," tracing the unhealthy germ of thought from Rousseau, the father of morbid Romanticism, through Chateaubriand with his melancholy, to Flaubert, the incurable nihilist, Verlaine, with his moral decadence, and Zola, the pessimist. The notion of degeneration of the human stock filled the European atmosphere for a quarter of a century.

The fields of criminal anthropology and heredity were now interlocked in the minds of many who were more idealistically inspired than scientifically critical. Jurists, ministers, and figures in social life united in pointing to hereditary degeneracy as precursive to a social catastrophe that could only be prevented by sterilizing its progenitors, the feeble-minded, criminal, mentally defective, and antisocial. The sterilization movement gained such support that in America by 1915 thirteen states had enacted laws for compulsory sterilization of major criminals.

The hereditary theory of nerve and mind degeneration was embraced by the public, stimulating demands for improved hygiene and the hope for large-scale eugenics. For criminologic theory, it had the opposite effect, the underscoring of that hypermoralistic attitude toward criminals that had dogged them since medieval days. In the 1870's, Charles L. Brace, author of *The Dangerous Classes of New York,* spoke of the "continued families of paupers and criminals" and the chances for survival of their offspring. Blaming the European immigrants who were swarming into the eastern cities, Brace expressed his faith that degeneracy and social sloth would disappear through the workings of democracy:

the girl [of such families] attains greater height over the sensual and filthy ways of her parents . . . when she marries it will inevitably be with a class above her own.[56]

Poor heredity, poor hygiene, alcoholism, prostitution, and poverty became the shibboleths of the social reformers of the latter part of the nineteenth century. The accepted maxim was: "Alcoholism in the parents equals crime and pauperism in the offspring." In 1901, an eminent penologist, Henry M. Boies, stated: "The cause of crime is the moral depravity of the criminal . . . the restriction of criminality depends mainly upon prevention of the disease of moral depravity." [57]

Drawing on his prison experience, Boies agreed that Lombroso's "criminal man" was indeed a clinical-social phenomenon; he pointed out that "the original barbaric man knew and obeyed no law save the instincts of his own uncontrolled desires. His whole nature was what we now call egoistic and in essence criminal . . . the whole human family was once as lawless as tigers." [58]

However, the minutiae of structural detail uncovered by Lombroso's followers, and their hypermoralism, effectively hid the object of their researches: the criminal as a person. In time, careful studies of prisoners disproved the Lombrosian theories. The most painstaking of these was made by Charles Goring. His report, based on his examination of more than three thousand English criminals over an eight-year period, was published in 1913. It unequivocally denied the significance of the findings of criminal anthropologists: "Our results nowhere confirm the evidence, nor justify the allegations of criminal anthropology." [59]

The degeneration theory exerted an influence on psychiatric diagnosis that is still noticeable. The "criminal man" faded from view, but the keystone of the psychiatric explanation of the chronic wrongdoer remained in the "psychopathic personality" concept. Although Lombroso's ideas, eagerly put to the test by prominent neurologists and alienists on both sides of the Atlantic, were relinquished as the century advanced, the conviction persisted that a form of moral disease, or degeneracy, represented by a psychic morbidity, existed among capital criminals (the "moral insanity" of Prichard, Ray, Esquirol, and other psychiatric leaders of the 1820–1870 period). This notion, that the criminal, the ne'er-do-well, and the misfit were afflicted with a constitutional inadequacy—in their mental patterns if not in their physical structure—betrayed the subtle heritage of Lombrosian thinking. When in 1891 Koch introduced the diagnostic term "psychopathic inferiority"[60] to describe morbid characters prone to social nonconformance, and Adolf Meyer amended it to "constitutional psychopathic inferiority"[61] in 1905, the shadow of the degeneration theory lay across their psychiatric analyses.

THE "PSYCHOPATHIC PERSONALITY" AND CRIME

During the major portion of the nineteenth century, the committing of heinous crimes, especially homicide, was imputed to the explosive, aggressive type of personality that came to be diagnostically termed "psychopathic." Thus, the notion of degeneracy was fused with that of homicidal mania. Even though Lombroso's findings concerning the "criminal man" were disregarded in psychiatric thinking, as closer study revealed that psychogenetic elements were active in the psychopathic personality structure, the idea of constitutional inadequacy remained. Although intensive psychologic analysis of this puzzling group of patients seemed to indicate the presence of neurotic features—Alexander pointed to the "impulse-ridden" nature of the psychopath,[62] Cleckley described their closeness to the psychotic,[63] Karpman recognized the calloused, antisocial psychopath as predominantly a defensive neurotic[64]—a "constitutional defect" was often assumed to underlie the actions of many chronic malefactors and criminals. Their geneses appeared that of the neurotic character. Yet the enormous difficulties psychiatrists and other workers have had with these individuals have not completely nullified the hint that lay behind Lombroso's work, that somehow the nervous tissue and nervous system of certain individuals may have been modified to the small degree necessary to misdirect their behavior.

Attention was focused on the aggressive aspect of this clinical type of criminal. Severe emotional rejection during his early years was held to account for the psychopath's sensitivity and calloused aggressivity.[65] His episodic outbursts of anger, traceable in sudden, impulsive homicidal attacks, were considered by Menninger to evidence an impulse "dyscontrol," wherein the ego could no longer contain the surge of emotion underlying the aggression.[66] Although it has been customary in recent decades to devaluate the clinical concept of the psychopathic personality, few experienced workers in this field have doubted its existence. As Trevor Gibbens, an English authority, puts it, "There are primitive types who develop from a background of family violence and the lowest standards of behavior." [67] The evolution of the psychopath has been traced in children by Szurek and Johnson as arising from a "vicarious gratification" of the parent's "poorly-integrated forbidden impulses," which unconsciously encourage (and are adopted in) "the amoral and antisocial behavior of the child" destined to become psychopathic.[68] In spite of these authenticated studies, and many more, which point toward a psychogenic origin for the violent person, the vital question seemed not to be answered: Why does one child exposed to such noxious environment succumb to it, while his sibling does not?

Furthermore, the relation between epilepsy (or epileptoid constitution) and violent crime could not be conscientiously minimized. The older experts had maintained a relation between epilepsy or epileptic equivalents (fugue states or postepileptic furors) and violent crime on the basis of clinical experience. Most of those who have studied the causal relation between sudden heinous crime and epilepsy (or its equivalents) agree with Banay [69] that such crimes occur without "conscious volition"—evidence of some unknown factor in the brain that predisposes toward aggressive behavior. In any event, the introduction of the electroencephalograph furnished a source of verification for the hypothesis that brain architecture and violent behavior were causally related. During the decade 1940–1950, investigations with this instrument demonstrated specific brain-wave changes among psychopaths in roughly 50 per cent of all cases examined. When one adds to this the verification provided for epilepsy and its variants by the electroencephalograph, the place of organic brain changes in the genesis of the aggressive, criminal-prone individual begins to assume some of the overtones pointed to in Lombroso's theories. For much work by electroencephalographers in the no man's land of the psychopathic personality produced this tentative conclusion: "Psychopathic personality is a mental illness resulting from inborn or early acquired cerebral dysfunction and disturbed parent-child relationships." [70]

With closer study of character disorders, particularly since 1930, a shift toward the criterion of social behavior has been observed in the diagnosis of the psychopath. Thus, the word "sociopath" has more recently replaced the original diagnostic term. This shift did not invalidate theories of the genesis of this type of distorted personality, but it did accent these individuals' social nonconformity and predilection for crime. Generations of psychiatrists have wrestled and are still struggling with the exact definition of the term psychopath. At the present time the clinical presence of the psychopath is not doubted, even though psychogenic elements have been delineated as those of a defensive character neurosis. (The relation between aggressive behavior of the explosive type and the individual who is neither psychotic nor neurotic, to homicide, assault, extortion, and other forms of aggressive crime will be dealt with in detail in Chapter V; its position in psychiatric classifications of criminals will be discussed in Chapter IV.)

With all these studies aimed hopefully at the central core of criminality, the sociopathic or psychopathic personality, it was expected that some final light would be shed on the thorny problem of the nucleus of crime. But more study led to more questions. Recognition of the importance of social influences brought sociologists into the field; the several disciplines found themselves unable to proceed without mutual help. A new science, accenting social, psychologic, and biological causes, was born: criminology. We now turn to a brief review of its early years.

THE SECOND ENLIGHTENMENT

The work of the positivist school of criminologists, named for those who sought concrete medical, social, or ecological influences on criminal behavior, did more than focus attention on the criminal mind. It tended to de-emphasize that subjective view of wrongdoing that placed blame on the moral state of the criminal's soul. The question turned from whether the criminal himself was "bad" to whether his crime represented the "bad" in society.

Years passed before this reorientation found voice. Starting work in 1913, Dr. E. E. Southard, a Harvard psychiatrist, and Mary Jarett, founder of the psychiatric social work profession, expounded the merging of psychiatry and sociology. They wrote a book, *The Kingdom of Evils*,[71] in which they stressed the need for a philosophic view of mental disease, personality distortions, and social maladjustments. Psychiatry and psychiatric social work, regarding moral and social afflictions in a clinical light, sought to aid those whose mute claims for attention, in hospital, jail, and clinic, had been largely disregarded. The significance of this attitude lay in the shift from moralism to realism. Behavioral pathology was treated with a degree of objectivity. The traditional punishment-oriented reaction to crime and delinquency gave way to a pervasive questioning as to the "why" of particular kinds of misbehavior. The second enlightenment was evolving.

As the *cause of crime* enigma was discovered to elude any one discipline, the area of criminology broadened to a multidimensional field. In this atmosphere, punishment as a mass reflex reaction gradually yielded to a studied individualization of the criminal offender. Similarly, the goals of penology changed slowly: the indeterminate sentence, attempts at social re-education of the prisoner (initiated by Thomas Mott Osborne, warden of Sing Sing Prison), programs of industrial training and scholastic education were well launched by the 1920's in this country. Concomitantly, the courts manifested an interest in rehabilitation through probation departments and a sporadic interest in neurologic and psychiatric studies of convicted offenders.

The probation system was of incalculable value in reorienting the attitude that punishment must inevitably accompany conviction for crime. Probation in its present form was initiated by John Augustus, a Boston shoemaker, who in 1841 offered to supervise first offenders "whose hearts were not wholly depraved." [72] Many of Augustus' cases were common drunkards; some were children involved in thievery. In time, probation, first under the aegis of private aid societies, then under court organizations, came under legislative order. In 1878, the Massachusetts legislature placed probation, until then operating under the common law, under statutory authority.[73] Within the next twenty years other states passed statutory laws allowing probation (suspension of sentences) in criminal court practice. The idea of the Boston shoemaker soon attracted attention in England and throughout Europe. Probation was introduced into statutory law in England in 1879, followed soon by similar laws in Australia, Canada, New Zealand. As the probation movement spread it received the collateral support of such lay movements as the National Temperance League (which merged with the Anti-Saloon League of America), Society of St. Vincent de Paul and, later, of the various denominational charities in the larger cities.

Much of the activity in this area of mitigation of punishment for wrongdoing rose from specific efforts to remove children from workhouses, where they breathed the air of crime. Later, truants, delinquents, orphaned and neglected children were brought under the jurisdiction of the special courts that were springing up in all parts of the land.

By the first part of the twentieth century probation was established in principle: "Probation advanced steadily and unsensationally as the courts developed the use of this modern instrumentality." [74] In his study of probation, N. S. Timasheff stated that "since about 1900" probation began frequently to be discussed at conferences "of charity organizations, prison associations, and international penological congresses." [75]

Probation constituted only one implement in the fight that had been waged for recognition of the particular problem of the child offender, the alcoholic criminal, and the neglected child. Simultaneously, social workers, and philanthropists united to improve conditions among the underprivileged. Victims of the triad, poverty, depravity, and crime, were lectured at, abjured, educated, fed, "improved" in as many ways as needs suggested. During the first two decades of this century financial, moral, and legislative support was freely given to correct environmental influences that made for crime in the growing cities.

The complexity of economic and social life in the highly industrialized America of the late nineteenth and twentieth centuries made the lives of many children more precarious and their exposure to crime more probable. Ellen Key, a Swedish feminist, in a book entitled *The Century of the Child,* pleaded for a world in which the child could "receive a [chance for] free self-development." [76] The movement for progressive education, emotional training, permissiveness in handling children, emerged, under the influence of behavioristic psychology and Freudian psychoanalysis, as powerful influences on attitudes toward crime among youthful offenders.

The Juvenile Court in Chicago (1899) was the first embodiment of the trends sketched above. Dr. William Healy, a psychiatrist of note, became director of the Juvenile Psychopathic Institute in Chicago (1909), bringing the first fruits of child psychiatry to the urgent problem of juvenile delinquency.

The study of psychological backgrounds of child delinquency by Healy demonstrated that emotional conflict within the offenders themselves was responsible for specific offenses. Innumerable instances of delinquent behavior, such as petty thievery, car stealing, and running away, were found to stem from distorted, misinterpreted sexual information, from guilt feelings arising from masturbation, and from other emotional traumata to which children are specially subject in environments dominated by ignorance or neglect. Antisocial acts that had been regarded as fortuitous or caused by bad environment proved to be reactions to emotional stresses or to the effect of repressed instinctive urges. Communication of these findings to the court led to revised attitudes toward punishment. Delinquent boys sent to placement bureaus where social workers studied their needs were placed in foster homes with due care for emotional stresses underlying their delinquencies. The new attitude toward crime and punishment made its entrance under the aegis of child-guidance clinics. In the juvenile court the social worker or probation officer presented the delinquent as a problem which had come to his attention rather than as an indicted criminal. This practice removed the sting of criminal prosecution and presented the delinquent in his true light—an individual unable to adjust to his environment.

The union of psychiatry and sociology in the probation field can be epitomized by Healy's statement: "We must look to the delinquent *and* the situation to understand the causes of particular criminal character formation." [77] Criminals as individuals were regarded less fearfully. The spawning ground of criminals—tenements and slum areas—were examined with more care; the social mores of the twenties and the depression era were scrutinized with the insight of reformism grown scientific.

Early objections to the new method of handling offenders through psychological and medical analysis of criminal behavior came from those who espoused the primacy of punishment. Probation and methods of rehabilitation in prison met with opposition on moral grounds. Punishment was made for sin and for crime. Morality, inextricably part of religious ethics, became the guide for social ethics in weighing anti-social conduct. The law, which from earliest days had absorbed moral codes into its rationale for criminal penalties, was not entirely ready for treatment aims. The law's position was stated by one judge in 1899, in commenting on a murder case. The Mosaic law, he said, was

intended for the government of an imperfect, self-willed, ignorant, stubborn and hardhearted people. . . . The morality of our laws is the morality of the Mosaic interpretation of the Ten Commandments, modified only as to the degree or kind of punishment.[78]

In nonjudicial areas, the reaction to forward-looking attempts at rehabilitation was similarly conservative. In 1912, an editorial writer for a popular scientific journal lamented the new approach:

. . . there is a tendency to make prisons so comfortable that one is puzzled why those against whom indictments have finally been secured, do not immediately enter these luxurious institutions, instead of wasting so much of the time of the jurymen. . . . there is . . . constant agitation for the substitution of trepanning for hanging . . . of optometry for trial by jury or [treatment] by the nose and throat specialist, or by the adjustment of proper spectacles. . . . may nevertheless, by the exercise of a little consideration, yield to deep breathing, or the rest cure, or the hot air apparatus, and the like.[79]

The law, dedicated to the principle that punishment upheld moral demands, pointed to the presupposition that in their conduct human beings are free to choose good and reject evil. But, as will be shown in later chapters, dynamic understanding of criminal behavior gave psychiatrists an opportunity to learn the role played by the unconscious identifications and other mechanisms that help fashion the human ego. Choices of conduct, they found, were not free in the sense of being completely independent acts; unconscious forces molding emotional reactions and attitudes beyond the awareness of the offender influenced criminal motivation. Psychiatrists and psychologists were not working to reduce punishment as a total social reaction to criminal activity. They were struggling to understand crime as the product of human behavior, and they wished to formulate their understanding in meaningful terms so that the agreed-upon aims of punishment would be effective.

Within the first half of the twentieth century, the courts have perceptibly moved in the direction indicated by philosophers and mental scientists. In essence, what has happened is a shift away from the concept of *moral* wrong in criminal cases to that of *legal* wrong. In Judge Cardozo's opinion, quoted earlier, the meaning of "wrong" in the McNaghten question—"Does the accused know the difference between right and wrong?"—refers to *moral* wrong. Weihofen has traced the developments that, from 1915, the time of Judge Cardozo's influential decision, reinterpreted "wrong" to mean *legal* wrong in legal decisions.[80] This changed emphasis, which chiefly concerns interpretations of the right-and-wrong test in cases of insane persons accused of murder, has subtly modified social attitudes toward punishment.[81] That is to say, "legal" wrong is less onerous than "moral" wrong. One is against the law of the land, the other against an immutable, eternal principle.

It has always been agreed that punishment for crime is retributive and deterrent in aim. Addition of the modern aim of rehabilitation—and this was contemplated by Aristotle and most other philosophers of the past—has enlarged the aims of punishment. As summed up by a modern philosopher, M. R. Cohen, punishment is reprobative, retributive, deterrent, and rehabilitative. It expresses the disapproval of society for certain prohibited acts (*reprobative*); it is a positive moral duty on society's part, to be carried out by legally constituted agents, to repay evil (*retributive*); it confers social protection to the public by destroying or imprisoning offenders and carries the hope of deterrence of wrongdoing in others (*deterrent*); it serves the hope of reorganization in those sensitive to punishment's meaning (*rehabilitative*).[82]

When this modern statement is contrasted with the ethically based rationale for punishment voiced by Kant in 1785, one becomes aware that an evolution in our conception of punishment has taken place over a century and a half. According to Kant,

juridical punishment can never be administered merely as a means for promoting another good, either with regard to the Criminal himself, or to Civil Society, but must in all cases be imposed only because the individual on whom it is inflicted *has committed a Crime.* . . . The Penal Law is a

Categorical Imperative: and woe to him who creeps through the serpent-windings of Utilitarianism to discover some advantage that may discharge him from the Justice of Punishment, or even from the due measure of it.[83]

Kant regarded punishment as necessary for the "preservation of the balance sheet of justice."[84] He saw little virtue in the ideas of utilitarians, who asked that punishment serve some good or mitigate some evil. Kant's concept of law emphasizing the *categorical imperative,* the logical necessity to conform to that law, still lies at the base of modern legal punishment. In practice, however, the courts give respectful attention to other ideas; in particular, that penalties have as their aim modification of personality patterns in order to achieve the deterrence actually sought.

Fifty centuries of civilization have shown that punishment is lacking in educative value; that is, it has failed to deter others from crime. Psychiatrists in assisting the court to enlarge the class of "irresponsibles" (by urging application of the principle of partial responsibility to the problem of persons mentally distorted short of insanity) are in actuality enlarging the group of those who are punished *meaningfully.* The offender whose mental state includes some perception of his criminal act is thus saved for the process of educative punishment. Punishment without meaning has no positive value for the miscreant, and hence no positive value for society. It is to this view that all persons of goodwill are dedicated whether involved in professional or nonprofessional areas. Psychiatry joins the disciplines of education, philosophy, sociology, and law in underscoring the meaningfulness of punishment when utilized as rehabilitation.

REFERENCES

1. DEKKER, THOMAS, "The Witch of Edmonton," in John Pearson, *Dramatic Works,* Vol. 4 (London, 1873), p. 382.

2. HOMER, *The Iliad,* trans. by Richmond Lattimore (University of Chicago Press, Chicago, 1951), Book 2, p. 81.

3. JOLOWICZ, D. F., *Historical Introduction to the Study of Roman Law* (Cambridge University Press, Cambridge, 1952), p. 177.

4. CLARK, H. B., *Biblical Law,* 2nd ed. (Binfords & Mort, Portland, Ore., 1944), p. 270.

5. BRACTON, HENRICI DE, *Legibus et Consuetudinibus Angliae,* Sir T. Twiss, ed. (Longman & Co., London, 1879), p. 153.

6. HALL, JEROME, "Mental Disease and Criminal Responsibility," *Columbia Law Review,* XLV, No. 5 (September, 1945), p. 689.

7. FITZHERBERT, SIR ANTHONY, quoted in J. Michael and H. Wechsler, *Criminal Law and Its Administration* (Foundation Press, Brooklyn, N.Y., 1941), p. 807.

8. HALE, SIR MATTHEW, quoted in Michael and Wechsler, *ibid.*, p. 808.

9. SPEE, FATHER FRIEDRICH VON, quoted in E. T. Withington, *Dr. Weyer and Witch Mania*, C. J. Singer, ed. (Clarendon Press, Oxford, 1917), p. 204.

10. *People* vs. *Tripler*, in J. D. Wheeler, *Criminal Cases* (Banks & Gould Co., New York, 1854), p. 48.

11. *People* vs. *Schmidt*, Court of Appeals, New York, Judge Cardozo, 1915, 216 N.Y. 324, 110 N.E. 945.

12. Bellingham's case, Old Bailey, 1812, Collinson on Lunacy, i, 636, 671, 673.

13. The McNaghten case, 10 Clark and Finelly, 200 (1843).

14. WECHSLER, HERBERT, "The American Law Institute: Some Observation on Its Model Penal Code," in *Crime and Insanity*, R. W. Nice, ed. (Philosophical Library, New York, 1958), p. 208.

15. *People* vs. *McCann*, Supreme Court, State of New York Appeals Court, Justices Wright and Harris, May, 1857.

16. PLOSCOWE, MORRIS, *Crime and Criminal Law* (P. F. Collier & Son, New York, 1930), chap. 4, p. 81.

17. RAY, ISAAC, *A Treatise on the Medical Jurisprudence of Insanity* (William D. Ticknor, Boston, 2nd ed., 1844).

18. ZILBOORG, GREGORY, "Legal Aspects of Psychiatry," in *One Hundred Years of American Psychiatry*, J. K. Hall, gen. ed. (Columbia University Press, New York, 1944), p. 551.

19. "Case of Guiteau," editorial in *American Journal of Insanity*, XXXIX (1882–83); also Bunker, H. A., "American Psychiatric Literature," in *One Hundred Years of American Psychiatry*, p. 195.

20. *Cunningham* vs. *State*, Supreme Court, Mississippi, 1879, 56 Mississippi 269.

21. *State* vs. *Green*, 78 Utah 580, 599–600, 6P (2nd) 177 (1931).

22. GLUECK, SHELDON, *Mental Disorder and the Criminal Law* (Little, Brown & Co., Boston, 1925).

23. American Bar Foundation, *Report on Mentally Disabled and the Law*, F. T. Lindman and D. M. McIntyre, eds. (University of Chicago Press, Chicago, 1961), p. 347.

24. BROMBERG, W., and CLECKLEY, H., "The Medico-Legal Dilemma," *Journal of Criminal Law and Criminology*, XLII, No. 6 (March, 1952), 729.

25. *People* vs. *Cordova*, 14 California 308, 94P (2nd) 40 (1939).

26. WEIHOFEN, HENRY, and OVERHOLSER, WINIFRED, "Mental Disorder Affecting the Degree of a Crime," *Yale Law Journal*, LVI (1947), 959.

27. *Fisher* vs. *U.S.*, 328 U.S. 463–495 (October, 1945).

28. American Psychiatric Association, the Isaac Ray Award (annual since 1952).

29. SPITZKA, E. C., *Insanity, Its Classification, Diagnosis and Treatment* (Bermingham Co., New York, 1883), p. 23.

30. ZILBOORG, GREGORY, "The Reciprocal Responsibility of Law and Psychiatry," *The Shingle*, Philadelphia, April, 1949, p. 83; also Zilboorg, "Psychiatry and the Problem of Criminal Responsibility," *University of Pennsylvania Law Review*, CI (1952–53), 378.

31. *People* vs. *Moran*, 249 N.Y. 179, 163, N.E. 553 (1928).

32. *Durham* vs. *U.S.*, 214 F. 2nd, 862 (D.C. Circuit 1954).

33. WEIHOFEN, HENRY, "In Favor of the Durham Rule," in *Crime and Insanity*, R. W. Nice, ed. (Philosophical Library, New York, 1958), p. 162.

34. ALEXANDER, F., and STAUB, H., *The Criminal, the Judge and the Public* (The Macmillan Company, New York, 1931), p. 70.

35. KATZ, WILBER G., "Law, Psychiatry and Free Will," *University of Chicago Law Review*, XX (1954–55), 397.

36. GRASSET, JOSEPH, *The Semi-Insane and the Semi-Responsible* (Authorized American translation by S. E. Jelliffe, Funk & Wagnalls Co., New York, 1907), pp. 312 ff.

37. KATZ, *op. cit.*, p. 399.

38. Group for the Advancement of Psychiatry, *Report No. 26, Criminal Responsibility and Psychiatric Expert Testimony* (1954).

39. *Durham* vs. *U.S.*, 214 F. 2nd, 862, 874 (D.C. Circuit, 1954).

40. HALL, JEROME, *General Principles of Criminal Law* (The Bobbs-Merrill Co., Indianapolis, 1947), p. 499.

41. DE GRAZIA, EDWARD, "The Distinction of Being Mad," *University of Chicago Law Review*, XXII (1954–55), 339.

42. HALL, JEROME, "Mental Disease and Criminal Responsibility," *Indiana Law Journal*, XXXIII (1958), 212.

43. DE GRAZIA, *op. cit.*, p. 348.

44. *State* vs. *Hoover*, 54 So. 2nd, 130 Louisiana.

45. BROMBERG, WALTER, *The Mold of Murder* (Grune & Stratton, New York, 1961), p. 181.

46. DE GRAZIA, *op. cit.*, p. 347.

47. KIRCHWEY, GEORGE W., "Criminology," article in *Encyclopaedia Britannica*, Vol. 6, ed. of 1946 (Encyclopaedia Britannica, Chicago, 1946), p. 720.

48. GALL, FRANZ, and SPURZHEIM, J. C., *Recherches sur le systèm nerveau en général et sur celui cerveau en particulier* . . . (Schoell, Paris, 1809).

49. CALDWELL, CHARLES, quoted in Arthur E. Fink, *Causes of Crime* (University of Pennsylvania Press, Philadelphia, Pa., 1938), p. 7.

50. BRIGHAM, AMARIAH, "Journal of Prison Discipline and Lunatic Asylums," *American Journal of Insanity*, II (October, 1845–46), article v, p. 175.

51. LOMBROSO, CESARE, *Crime: Its Causes and Remedies*, trans. by H. P. Horton (Little, Brown & Co., Boston, 1911), p. xiv.

52. LOMBROSO, *op. cit.*, p. 376.

53. MOREL, BENÖIT AUGUSTIN, *Traité des dégénérescences, physique, intellectuelle et morales de l'espèce humaine* (Bailliere, Paris, 1857).

54. FINK, ARTHUR E., *Causes of Crime* (University of Pennsylvania Press, Philadelphia, Pa., 1938), chaps. V, VI.

55. LYDSTON, G. FRANK, *The Diseases of Society* (J. B. Lippincott Co., Philadelphia, Pa., 1904), p. 86.

56. BRACE, CHARLES L., *The Dangerous Classes of New York, and Twenty Years' Work Among Them* (Wyncoop & Hallenbeck, New York, 1872), p. 46.

57. Boies, Henry M., *The Science of Penology* (G. P. Putnam's Sons, New York, 1901), chap. 3, pp. 30 ff.

58. Boies, *op. cit.*, p. 16.

59. Goring, Charles, *The English Convict* (His Majesty's Stationery Office, London, 1913), p. 369.

60. Koch, J., *Die Psychopathischen Minderwertignkeiten* (Maier, Ravensburg, 1891).

61. Meyer, Adolph, *Reports of the New York State Pathological Institute*, Utica, New York, 1904–5.

62. Alexander, F., "The Neurotic Character," *International Journal of Psychoanalysis*, XI (1930), 523.

63. Cleckley, Hervey, *The Mask of Sanity* (C. V. Mosby Co., St. Louis, Mo., 2nd ed., 1950), p. 572.

64. Karpman, Ben, "The Myth of the Psychopathic Personality," *American Journal of Psychiatry*, CIV, No. 9 (March, 1948), 523.

65. Bromberg, Walter, "Dynamic Aspects of Psychopathic Personality," *Psychoanalytic Quarterly*, XVII (January, 1948), 58.

66. Menninger, Karl M., and Mayman, M., "Episodic Dyscontrol: A Third Order of Stress Adaptation," *Bulletin of the Menninger Clinic*, XX (July, 1956), 153.

67. Gibbens, Trevor C. N., "Treatment of Psychopaths," *Journal of Mental Science*, CVII (January, 1961), 181.

68. Szurek, Stanislaus, "Notes on the Genesis of Psychopathic Personality Trends," *Psychiatry*, V (February, 1942), 1.

Johnson, Adelaide, "Sanctions for Super-Ego Lacunae of Adolescents" in *Searchlights on Delinquency* (International Universities Press, New York, 1949), p. 225.

69. Banay, Ralph S., "Criminal Genesis and the Degrees of Responsibilities in Epilepsies," *American Journal of Psychiatry*, CXVII, No. 10 (April, 1961), 873.

70. Maughs, Sidney, "Psychopathic Personality," *Journal of Clinical Psychopathology*, X, No. 3 (July, 1949), 249.

71. Southard, E. E., and Jarett, Mary, *The Kingdom of Evils* (The Macmillan Company, New York, 1922).

72. Timasheff, N. S., *One Hundred Years of Probation*, "Fordham University Studies," No. 1 (Fordham University Press, New York, 1941), p. 7.

73. *Ibid.*, p. 16.

74. Cooley, Edwin J., *Probation and Delinquency* (Catholic Charities of the Archdiocese of New York, New York, 1927), p. 22.

75. Timasheff, *op. cit.*, p. 47.

76. Key, Ellen, *The Century of the Child*, trans. by M. Franzos (G. P. Putnam's Sons, New York, 1909), p. iv.

77. Healy, William, and Bronner, Augusta, *Delinquents and Criminals* (The Macmillan Company, New York, 1926), Preface.

78. *Moore* vs. *Strickling*, West Virginia 515: 33: S.E. 274. Court of Appeals, Apr., 1899.

79. "Lunacy and Morals," editorial in *Scientific American*, July, 1912, p. 22.

80. WEIHOFEN, HENRY, *Insanity as a Defense in Criminal Law*. Commonwealth Fund (Oxford University Press, London, 1933), p. 40.

81. GUTTMACHER, MANFRED, and WEIHOFEN, HENRY, *Psychiatry and the Law* (W. W. Norton & Co., New York, 1952), p. 404.

82. COHEN, MORRIS R., "Moral Aspects of the Criminal Law," *Yale Law Journal*, XLIX (April, 1940), 987.

83. KANT, IMMANUEL, quoted in *The Science of Right*, in *Great Books of the Western World*, Vol. 11 (Encyclopaedia Britannica, Chicago, 1952), p. 489.

84. ADLER, M. J., and GORMAN, W., "The Right to Punishment and Pardoning," in *Great Books of the Western World, ibid.*, p. 491.

CHAPTER IV

The Universe of Crime

CRIME AND THE LAW / THE MAGNITUDE OF THE
CRIME PROBLEM / IS CRIME INCREASING? /
RELATIVE FREQUENCY OF CRIME GROUPS /
PSYCHIATRIC BASIS FOR CRIME CLASSIFICATION /
MENTAL ABNORMALITY AND CRIME /
PERSONALITY ANALYSIS AND ANTISOCIAL
BEHAVIOR / THE OBSERVER'S POSITION IN
CRIME STUDY / THE DRAMA OF CRIME /
REFERENCES

It is possible to study crime, first by analyzing the criminal's activities and contacts with the law. Further scrutiny of the mores, cultural peculiarities, behavior systems, and psychological characteristics of the "criminal group," if such exists, may also serve as a channel for investigation. Finally, a psychosocial analysis of the world of commerce and the heterogeneous society in which crime occurs may yield information as to the universe of crime. All these approaches require, besides detailed information, calibration and interpretation of the empirical material developed.

The first approach encompasses the field of *psychiatric criminology;* the second, the subject matter of *criminal law* and *penology;* the third and fourth are aspects of *cultural anthropology* and *sociology.* In this psychiatric criminologic study, social and legal factors will be discussed as they interdigitate with antisocial tendencies within the individual offender. Such a methodology will not neglect the vast legal and sociological terrain [1] so diligently tilled by several generations of scholars; it will seek, however, to place their work in relation to the criminal-actor himself.

There is little doubt that all the outlined areas of approach to the criminal suffer from research weaknesses. The first approach when applied involves only those criminals who have *permitted* contacts with an investigator; the second encompasses *only* those offenders known to the police; the third and fourth do *not* specifically involve the individual offender. Beyond these relatively narrow areas for criminal study lies the no man's land of unapprehended criminals, of unreported and undiscovered crime—in a word, the "private" criminal, known only to himself and his conscience. Nevertheless, one must deal with whatever material is available if statements about the world of crime are not to be either gratuitous or unsupported.

CRIME AND THE LAW

The complexity of the subject—crime—can be gauged by a consideration of the concept "crime." If the uninitiated looks to the criminal statutes in order to understand this concept, he is bewildered; so simple a task as *defining* crime immediately becomes entangled with ambiguities. It is most commonly stated that a crime is an act prohibited by statute, which statute contains a description of the crime and a penalty to be imposed. This statement, though true, requires qualification. For example, some civil or administrative acts are punished by the state although not listed as criminal offenses, for instance, bankruptcy, misrepresentation in advertising, unfair labor practices. Again, it has been pointed out that definitions of crimes are often inexact; thus, in the description "a person who seriously disturbs the public peace" the exact interpretation of "seriously" is left open. Further, punishments for statutory crimes as set down in penal codes have in recent years been reduced, mitigated, or even suspended.

In general, the common law of England, which forms the basis of criminal law in the United States, has been superseded in many states by legislative statutes; nor have these been uniform by any means. The phrases used to describe certain crimes differ widely; thus, sexual offenses against children have been variously termed "impairing morals of a minor," "lewd and lascivious conduct," "carnally abusing a child," "defilement of girls" (England), "indecent assault," and so on. The classification of crimes varies in each state: Massachusetts employs such headings as Crimes against the Government, Crimes against the Person, Property, the Currency, Public Justice, Peace and Health, Chastity and Decency; [2] California lists such offenses as Crimes against the Sovereign State, Elective Franchise, Public Justice, Decency and Good Morals; [3] Texas specifies Offenses against the State, its Territory and Revenue, Offenses affecting the Right of Suffrage, Offenses against Reputation. [4]

In the common law of England, the listing of crimes fell into three classes, still adhered to: treason, felonies, misdemeanors. Treason is punishable by death; a felony, by death or imprisonment; the misdemeanant, triable by a judge without jury, is punished by not more than a year's imprisonment. The felon loses his franchise, the misdemeanant does not. In the United States, this grouping was generally adopted into the statutory laws of the individual states, some of which have modified the distinction between felony and misdemeanor. In

Pennsylvania, for example, "embezzlement by a servant constitutes a felony, whereas embezzlement by a banker, trustee or guardian becomes a misdemeanor." [5]

It is apparent, then, that crime varies with historical periods, modes of life, economic conditions, and social attitudes. An example of the first modifying factor was pointed out by Cantor in the 1930's:

> . . . in an age of skyscrapers "second-story" men cease to operate. One does not run off with a horse under cover of darkness. It is preferable and more profitable to snatch in broad daylight a portfolio bulging with bonds and escape in a waiting motor car.[6]

Other examples could be cited to illustrate the modifying influence of the factors listed.

In spite of a few ambiguities, however, the common crimes described by statutes are clearly understood by the public. A crime, then, is an act that injures, deprives, deceives, or demeans a person or persons, that is contrary to a law, regulation, ordinance, moral code, or accepted practice, and is generally recognized as such by the criminal's peers.

THE MAGNITUDE OF THE CRIME PROBLEM

The extent of crime in our country cannot be exaggerated. It constitutes a tremendous sector of our national activity—a "universe of crime." The number of crimes committed in a given area during a given time-period is usually taken as an index of crime incidence. The *Uniform Crime Reports* published yearly by the Federal Bureau of Investigation estimates that during 1962 one murder, assault, or forcible rape occurred every 3 minutes, a robbery every 6 minutes, a burglary every 35 seconds, and larcenies of $50 or over at the rate of one each minute.[7] Even more startling is the fact that, according to the same reports, one arrest for felonies or misdemeanors as listed occurred for every twenty-five persons in the general population in 1961. This finding, although tempered by the fact that many offenders are arrested more than once and that many individuals (children and senior citizens, for example) fall outside any crime group, graphically explains our necessary preoccupation with the phenomenon of crime. The exact amount of property loss from crime in 1962 totaled $650 million and the number of crimes reported passed the two million mark. Although these F.B.I. reports are based on careful compilations of offenses reported to law enforcement agencies throughout the country, they cover only "crimes known to the police." Unreported larcenies, extortion, racketeering, and indirect thefts constitute an untold drain on the public purse. Further, the consequences of violent crime in human suffering and anguish cannot be measured in terms sufficiently strong to reflect their poignancy. Nor does America hold a monopoly on crime, which is, of course, endemic throughout the world; this work, however, focuses on crime in the United States.

IS CRIME INCREASING?

In considering the extent of crime in the United States, this question springs to mind: Is crime on the increase? The *Uniform Crime Reports* indicates annual increases exceeding the population growth. The 1962 *Reports* stated: "Crime has increased in the past five years four times faster than did the population." [8] In the breakdown of specific crime categories, the 1961 *Reports* indicated an increase in the urban Murder and nonnegligent Manslaughter category of 11.3 per cent, comparing 1961 to an average of the period 1956–1960, with a rise in Burglary of 22.8 per cent in 1961 over the same five-year period.[9]

These reliable data seem to reflect an increase in crime, but other factors should be weighed before concluding that crime is indeed an increasing menace in present-day America. The records provide an inexact account of crime in earlier periods; nevertheless, a qualitative notion of the incidence of crime in other eras can be gleaned by studying the records of punishment meted out in earlier times (see Chap. III). Actual details of the extent of crime in centuries preceding ours are not available, but it would be an intriguing project if we could compare crime figures for 1660, 1760, 1860 with those for 1960. As it is, in examining old criminal records for early types of crime and punishment the uneasy feeling arises that our forefathers were as beset with the pandemic of crime, as discouraged with its prevalence, as are we today.

From the very beginnings of the New World, officials were plagued with wrongdoers. The records of the Quarter Sessions Court—now the Supreme Court, Criminal Division of New York County—cite many major and minor offenses occurring in Colonial New York County during the seventeenth century. Danckaets, a Dutch visitor to "N york" in 1679, was "disturbed by the 'wild worldly' character of its inhabitants." [10] Let us glance for a moment at the court record of prisoner Thomassen, who one August day in 1684 escaped from jail at the site where Rector Street now runs. Whether Thomassen eluded capture by hiding in the wilderness of what is known as Murray Hill or by camping on the shores of Collect Pond (site of the present-day City Hall) is not recorded. But one can sense the frustration of early law-enforcement officers at their never-ending task of dealing with criminals and upholding justice.

The record reads:

Att the Generall Quarter Sessions of Our Lord the King held att the Citty
Hall in the Citty of New-York for our Sayd Lord the King and the body of
the Citty and County of New-York. That is to say on tuesday the fifth day of
Aug[st] in the thirty sixth year of the Reigne of Our Sovreigne Lord Charles
the Second by the Grace of God. . . .

Citty and County of New York

Anno 1684

The Grand Jury being assembled. The Recorder Aquainted the Grand Jury
that they continue in Service the usuall Tyme of Election. . . .

In the After noone the Court being opened the Indictment of Henry Thomassen was returned to the Grand Jury. Henry Thomassen being called for the
Sherriff returned and said he has Broak Prison and made his escape. Ordered
that the Sherriff doe make Persuite after the said Thomassen to have him at
the next session to abide his Tryal. Jury was dismissed from further
Attendance.

The Sherriff being called upon he bring forth Henry Thomassen to abide his
Tryal Pursuant to the Order of Last Court declared that he had made Pur-
suite and deligent Search after him but can not find him. Court Ord[d] M[r] Cox
to have his Recognizance Delivery up. . . .

The Court Dissolved.[11]

Even before Henry Thomassen "broak" prison, the early Dutch set-
tlers of Nieuw Amsterdam were beset by criminologic problems. Almost
forty years earlier, Peter Stuyvesant was busy promulgating colonial
regulations and setting forth penalties, as in this 1647 example:

To the end that due care be taken to prevent rash drawing of knives, all
fightings and personal injuries, all catastrophes resulting from same . . .
penalty of 100 Carolus Guilders or . . . 300 Guilders if wounded, one half
year's confinement to the most menial labor, with bread and water for their
subsistence. . . .

In 1656 he added to this:

[for] beating and striking of one another, which can occasion calamities, yea
homicide . . . penalty for One Single blow, 25 Guilders and in case blood
is drawn, four times as much. . . .[12]

The following tables tend to differ with claims that point to the
modern acceleration of crime, i.e., the reported increase in crime inci-

dence. To take a recent example, the homicide rate in the United States during the past sixty years, when analyzed from available statistics, seems to show only a slight variation in incidence in the face of the most diverse social and economic conditions over these six decades. Table 1 shows the rate of murders per 100,000 of population in five-year periods from 1900 to 1930, derived from vital statistics of the U.S. Bureau of Census; from 1930 on, the function of gathering crime statistics was assumed by the Federal Bureau of Investigation.

The statistics in Table 1, developed from officially stated figures and subject to certain population calibration, indicate that in the United

TABLE 1 [13]

TREND OF HOMICIDE RATES IN THE UNITED STATES, 1900–1962 (INCLUS.)

Year	U.S. Population*	Registration Areas	Rate per 100,000
1900	79,994,575	Bureau of Census	2.1
1905	84,084,545		4.8
1910	91,972,606		5.9
1915	93,537,024		7.0
1920	106,418,175		6.9
1925	103,108,000		8.5
1930	37,709,965†	Uniform Crime Reports	4.0
1935	57,222,252		6.0
1940	62,715,897		4.4
1945	62,726,936		5.5
1950	69,643,614		5.7
1951	70,608,111		5.1
1952	89,071,906		5.8
1953	89,281,777		4.6
1954	89,281,777		8.5
1955	89,353,115		5.8
1956	89,518,135		8.4
1957	89,921,615		7.6
1958	98,317,123		7.3
1959	99,346,019		4.6
1960–61	182,953,000	Estimated total U.S. population	5.1
1962	185,822,000		4.5

* From 1900 to 1930: Figures based on Registration Areas, Bureau of Census, U.S. Department of Commerce Mortality Studies of reported deaths; (actual population figures used).

† From 1930 to 1962: Figures from Uniform Crime Reports, Federal Bureau of Investigation, Department of Justice, J. Edgar Hoover, Director. Population figures of police-reporting areas used for arrests for homicide.

States the rate of murder per 100,000 population over a 60-year span remained within narrow limits, with a mean of 5.8 homicides per 100,000 population. Another tabulation of homicide statistics (Table 2), gathered by Bloch and Geis (from official mortality reports), similarly demonstrates a relative fixity of national homicide rates. Here, the mean is 6.5 per 100,000 population over a 27-year period.

TABLE 2 [14]

HOMICIDE RATE PER 100,000 POPULATION, 1933–1959 *

Year	Rate	Year	Rate
1933	9.7	1947	6.0
1934	9.5	1948	5.8
1935	8.3	1949	5.4
1936	8.0	1950	4.6
1937	7.8	1951	4.9
1938	6.8	1952	5.2
1939	6.4	1953	4.8
1940	6.2	1954	4.8
1941	6.0	1955	4.5
1942	5.8	1956	4.6
1943	5.0	1957	4.9
1944	4.9	1958	4.5
1945	5.6	1959	4.7
1946	6.3		

* Figures gathered from the National Office of Vital Statistics by Herbert A. Bloch and Gilbert Geis.

There are many factors which require analysis before interpretation of these statistics approaches validity. Although there are waves of increased murder rate (such as followed the depression) and waves of decreased rate (following World War II), no increase or decrease over a prolonged period is visible. Bloch and Geis comment: "Taking everything together, it appears quite likely that the drop in homicide [from 1933 to 1959; see Table 2] represents nothing more than a tribute to modern medical and surgical advances." [15] That improved surgical procedures might necessarily reduce a charge from murder or manslaughter to assault with intent to kill does not seem to this writer a potent factor.

However, if one measures aggression through homicide against other figures of aggressiveness, such as manslaughter due to auto accidents, a different picture of aggressive criminal behavior emerges. For example, Morris shows that there are five times as many deaths from nonnegligent traffic accidents as from homicide; [16] undoubtedly, in the former case much conscious or unconscious aggression is demonstrated. Again, the changing social, economic, and technological life of our country must necessarily alter the expression of aggressive acts. It is obvious to all students of the subject that no ready generalization is possible. If meaning can be extracted from these data, it would be that violent crime represents a relative constant in national behavior. The possibility therefore exists that violent crime, as behavior, represents a more restricted sector of human activity than is commonly believed.

On the other hand, the tables compiled from the *Uniform Crime Reports* of the F.B.I. show that bank robberies have almost tripled in the six-year period 1956–1962; embezzlements nearly doubled during this period, over-all crime increased 27 per cent, while the country's population increased 7 per cent.[17] Whether a six-year period is sufficient to demonstrate the validity of the statement that crime is on the increase is questionable. Gehlke and Sutherland,[18] in utilizing available statistical material to prepare a section on crime for a Presidential report in 1933, concluded that the volume of crime in the United States showed a slight upward movement during the period 1900–1933, with nothing to indicate that the long-range trend was marked by unusual waves of crime or by cyclical distortions. More recent data compiled for special categories of serious crimes by Interpol, the international police agency, for areas throughout the world, suggest higher crime rates for Europe, North and South America, and Asia, with some striking increases in thefts and violent crimes for parts of southeast Asia.[19]

In any case, crime is distressing and expensive, painful to our self-esteem, and to a degree corroding to our citizens and our national morale.

RELATIVE FREQUENCY OF CRIME GROUPS

The universality of crime in time and place having been qualitatively established, the next inquiry might well be quantitative; i.e., the frequency of specific crimes. At this point questions arise: What is the comparative frequency of the various crime groups? Which group if studied would shed the greatest light on the phenomenology of crime? Which is the most significant crime group from the standpoint of society's wish to exert ethical pressures on the young through education? What can we learn from the crime groups regarding prevention?

In estimating the frequency of crime groups, we meet such complications as overlapping offenses, inclusion of misdemeanors, arrests for domestic relations problems (abandonment, desertion), drunken driving arrests, and so on. With these difficulties in mind, some notion of the relative frequency of crime can be gained from the F.B.I. tabulations shown in Table 3.

TABLE 3

CRIMES LISTED IN ORDER OF FREQUENCY, BASED ON ARRESTS BY THE POLICE *

1. Other Offenses (includes misdemeanors as disorderly conduct, vagrancy, alcoholism, and other, not specified felonies) †
2. Larceny (theft)
3. Assault, simple
4. Burglary
5. Gambling (promoting, permitting, or engaging in)
6. Auto Theft
7. Assault, aggravated (felonious)
8. Sex Offenses (includ. statutory rape)
9. Concealed Weapons
10. Robbery
11. Forgery (and counterfeiting)
12. Narcotic Drugs (sale, possession, and use)
13. Prostitution and Commercialized Vice
14. Rape, forcible
15. Murder and Nonnegligent Manslaughter

* Data from the *Uniform Crime Reports*, F.B.I., for the year 1961 (reporting population, 115,412,297).
† This grouping, although generalized, is used by the Federal Bureau of Investigation.

From another source—felony offenders convicted in the Supreme Court of New York County—the frequency of crime groups has been estimated as in Table 4, below.

TABLE 4 [20]

CRIME FREQUENCY BASED ON CONVICTIONS OBTAINED IN COURT OF GENERAL SESSIONS, NEW YORK; RANDOM SAMPLINGS OF ALL FELONY CONVICTIONS OVER A 13-YEAR PERIOD. OFFENSES IN ORDER OF NUMERICAL FREQUENCY *

1948

1. Larceny (includ. car thefts)
2. Assault
3. Robbery
4. Burglary
5. Carrying Concealed Weapon
6. Murder and Manslaughter
7. Narcotics—selling and use
8. Rape ‡
9. Criminally Receiving Stolen Property
10. Forgery
11. Sex Crimes †
12. Violations of Probation
13. Malicious Mischief
14. Extortion
15. Conspiracy
16. Arson
17. Abortion
18. Bigamy

	1954		1960
1.	Grand Larceny (includ. car theft)	1.	Drugs
2.	Assault	2.	Assault
3.	Drugs	3.	Robbery
4.	Robbery	4.	Burglary
5.	Burglary	5.	Grand Larceny (includ. car theft)
6.	Concealed Weapons	6.	Concealed Weapons
7.	Murder and Manslaughter	7.	Murder and Manslaughter
8.	Sex Crimes †	8.	Criminally Receiving Stolen Property
9.	Criminally Receiving Stolen Property	9.	Forgery
10.	Forgery	10.	Sex Crimes †
11.	Rape ‡	11.	Violation of Probation
12.	Violation of Probation	12.	Rape ‡
13.	Arson	13.	Extortion
14.	Abortion	14.	Malicious Mischief
15.	Bigamy	15.	Abortion
		16.	Arson
		17.	Bigamy

---

* Includes all degrees and attempts at, in all crime groups.
† Includes impairing morals of a minor, exhibitionism, sodomy, incest, and so on.
‡ Includes forcible and statutory rape.

The wide variation in two different sets of reported statistics, in Tables 3 and 4 (derived from different sources), makes a definitive statement as to crime frequency impossible. However, it appears that larceny and burglary are quite frequent, the sex crimes category occupies a middle position, and murder and manslaughter are comparatively infrequent in comparison with other crime groups. Assault and drug possession are high on the list in a metropolitan area, whereas gambling looms large on the national horizon. Interestingly, the minor offenses (as reported for the entire country) lead the list, as compiled from the *Uniform Crime Reports*.

Another index of the social and psychologic significance of various offenses may be read into a listing of crimes in order of their punishment susceptibility. This type of classification (Table 5), on which the law rests to a large degree, is in terms of decreasing severity of punishment as prescribed by law. In a larger sense, statutory penalties, though enacted by legislative bodies, reflect traditional public opinion as to the seriousness of a given crime. Here, changes have been introduced in recent years: use of the suspended sentence with probation, the indeterminate sentence, and the parole system. Changes in penologic sentiment toward punishment are clearly seen in the increased adoption of the indeterminate sentence, as in California, where the Adult

Authority decrees the duration of incarceration only after a careful social and psychologic study of the criminal.[21] This procedure has come to supersede rigid punishment schedules in many jurisdictions.

When crimes are listed in order of severity of legal penalties, one can indirectly gain an impression of the danger-status of various crimes. Most of these punishments derive from common law as modified by statutes in the several states. For this reason, there is a unanimity concerning such major categories as murder, burglary, rape. It may be

TABLE 5

MAJOR CRIMES LISTED IN ORDER OF SEVERITY OF LEGAL PENALTIES: NEW YORK STATE [22]

Murder, 1st degree	Life, unless jury imposes death
Murder, 2nd degree	Life to 20 years: Indeterminate sentence
Arson, 1st degree	40 years, State Prison
Arson, 2nd degree	25 years, S. P.
Manslaughter	20 years maximum, S. P.
Assault, with deadly weapon	10 years, S. P.
Kidnapping	Life to 20 years, S. P.: Indeterminate sentence
Robbery, 1st degree	Maximum 30 years, minimum 10 years, S. P.
Sodomy, 1st degree	Life to 20 years: Indeterminate sentence
Narcotics, sale or possession	Maximum 15 years, minimum 7 years, S. P.
Larceny, 1st degree	10 years, S. P.
Larceny, 2nd degree	Maximum 5 years, S. P.
Burglary, 1st degree	Indeterminate sentence, 30 to 10 years (maximum and minimum)
Sodomy, 2nd degree	Maximum 10 years, S. P.
Forgery, 1st degree	Maximum 20 years, S. P.
Forgery, 2nd degree	Maximum 10 years, S. P.
Fraud (felony)	Maximum 10 years, S. P.
Fraud (misdemeanor)	County Jail
Incest	10 years, S. P.
Assault	5 years, S. P., $1000 fine or both
Bigamy	5 years, S. P.
Abortion	4 years, S. P. or 1 year County Jail
Carnal Abuse of Child. Less than 10 years old	1 year, S. P. or $500 fine
(If prior conviction)	10 years, S. P.: Indeterminate sentence
Indecency	Punishment for misdemeanor

TABLE 5 (*continued*)

MAJOR CRIMES LISTED IN ORDER OF SEVERITY OF LEGAL PENALTIES:
STATE OF IOWA [23]

Murder, 1st degree	Death or Life at hard labor
Manslaughter	30 years, State Prison
Robbery, armed	25 years, S. P.
Assault, with intent to murder	30 years, S. P.
Burglary	20 years, S. P.: Maximum 40 years
Incest	25 years, S. P.
Burglar tools	15 years, S. P. and/or Fine $1000
Sodomy	10 years, S. P.
Forgery	10 years, S. P., County Jail and/or Fine $1000
Fraud (false pretenses)	7 years, S. P., County Jail 1 year, Fine $500
Embezzlement	10 years, S. P.
Larceny	5 years, S. P.
Receiving Stolen Goods	5 years, S. P., County Jail 1 year, Fine $500
Kidnapping	5 years, S. P., Fine $1000
Rape (forcible)	Life to 5 years, S. P.
Bigamy	5 years, S. P., County Jail 1 year, Fine $500
Mayhem (assault, grievous)	5 years, S. P., Fine $1000
Adultery	3 years, S. P., County Jail 1 year
Lascivious Acts with Child	3 years, S. P., County Jail 6 months and/or Fine $500
Lewdness (indecent exposure)	County Jail, 6 months, Fine $200
Assault with bodily harm	County Jail, 1 year
Assault and Battery	County Jail, 1 month

interesting, however, to tabulate *all* crimes in order of severity of punishment in three states representing different cultural areas—the East Coast, West Coast, and the Midwest. Table 5 contains such tabulations for (a) New York, (b) Iowa, and (c) California.

It is obvious from the tables here presented that the attitude of the law toward the various crime groups, and that of the public as reflected (in an indirect but positive way) in these punishment schedules, sheds little light on the offender's inner motivations, or the depth of his or her personality disorganization. As has been noted above, it became clear that the discovery of the presence of psychoses, mental deficiency, and other types of subnormal mentality in the criminal population was of minor importance in estimating the vital role that emotions play in crime commission. Hence, psychiatrists in prisons

TABLE 5 (*continued*)

MAJOR CRIMES LISTED IN ORDER OF SEVERITY OF LEGAL PENALTIES: STATE OF CALIFORNIA [24]

Murder, 1st degree	Death or Life Imprisonment
Assault, 1st degree, by Life Convict	Death or Life
Kidnapping, bodily harm to victim	Life without Parole
Kidnapping for Ransom	Life
Sale of Narcotics with prior Conviction	Life to 10 years
Inducing Minor to Violate Narcotic Law	Life to 10 years
Burglary, 1st degree	Life to 5 years
Grand theft	Life to 5 years
Robbery, 1st degree	Life to 5 years
Murder, 2nd degree	Life to 5 years
Rape (except statutory)	Life to 3 years
Sexual Offenses (includ. Sodomy)	Life to 1–3 years
Lewd and Lascivious Conduct	Life to 1 year
Sex Crime against a Child	Life to 1 year
Indecent Exposure	Life to 1 year
Robbery, 2nd degree	Life to 1 year
Incest	50 years to 1 year
Arson	20 years to 2 years
Abortion	5 years to 6 months
Assault with deadly weapon	14 years to 6 months
Bigamy	10 years to 6 months

and in the larger criminal courts [25] began to concentrate on personality deviations in offenders under study, rather than on questions of insanity or mental deficiency per se.* Distorted personality traits, technically called "neuropathic" or "psychopathic personality," were analyzed and classified. The result was a new view of crime, a view that was destined to expand into the field of psychiatric criminology and to indirectly point the way to a changed penology. This new knowledge initially found its way into classifications of criminal personalities.

PSYCHIATRIC BASIS FOR CRIME CLASSIFICATION

In the decades before the epochal report of Bernard Glueck from Sing Sing Prison in New York State (1918),[26] the accent in crime study was on subnormal mentality. Goring, whose careful studies in England dethroned the Lombrosian theory of the degenerate "criminal

* Chicago, Baltimore, Detroit, Cleveland, New York, and Pittsburgh have court clinics in courts of record; Philadelphia has a municipal court clinic.

man," concluded that "the one vital mental constitutional factor in the etiology of crime is defective intelligence." [27] This notion persisted in the literature and in the social mind for several decades. Goddard, who did his early work in 1914, reported that 50 per cent of all offenders were defective; [28] V. V. Anderson reported 28 to 50 per cent defective in 1919; Healy and Bronner, working with juvenile delinquents, found 13.5 per cent feebleminded and 9 per cent subnormal in 1926; [29] Overholser [30] stated in 1935 that 16.9 per cent of all prisoners examined in Massachusetts showed "suggestive or obvious mental abnormality." As psychometric techniques improved, the findings of mental deficiency changed. Thus Murchison [31] in his textbook (1928) concluded that those in "the criminal group are superior in intelligence to the white draft group (World War I)." As studies progressed it became obvious that a disordered personality organization (including psychoses, neuroses, and personality problems) was a more significant factor in crime than feeblemindedness. With increasing rapidity, from the late 1930's to the World War II years to the present, interest shifted away from insanity and mental defectiveness to personality disturbances in analyzing the genesis of crime.

This reorientation among those who dealt professionally with criminals began to be reflected in the various reports emanating from prisons and court clinics. For example, in 1927 a classification that stressed personality distortions and neurotic tendencies among criminals was prepared by Glueck [32] as a guide to legal administrators who saw the wisdom of preparing analyses of criminal offenders. This classification, omitting reference to insane (psychotic) or defective individuals, follows:

PSYCHIATRIC CLASSIFICATION

Potentially psychotic

Neuropathic (Psychopathic)
    Schizoid
    Paranoid
    Egocentric
    Hysterical
    Sexual
    Others

    Psychoneurotic
    Alcoholic
    Drug Addict
    Epileptic
    Postencephalitic
    Other brain-wave abnormalities
      with psychosis

Normal
    Without significant deviation
    With moderate personality deviation
    With pronounced personality deviation
    With intellectual inferiorities
    Borderline
    Asymmetric intellectual development

Other workers devised a more dynamic classification, as illustrated by Foxe's pioneer work. Foxe's character (personality) grouping [33] is given below:

CHARACTER GROUP

Immature character—includes adolescent character and
    psychosexual immaturity
Inadequate character—includes ego inferior or
    constitutional inferior types
Hypomanic character—extrovert
Pervert character—homosexually active or perversions
Nomadic character
Depressive character—hypochondriacal
Litigious character
Paranoid character
Primitive character
Impulsive character
Pathological liar
Criminally gregarious character—outspoken "gangster"

Perhaps the most significant work in this direction was that of the Psychiatric Clinic of the Court of General Sessions in New York, which serves New York County. This relatively new idea to classify each offender according to a personality evaluation combined the insights of psychoanalysis, descriptive psychiatry, and behavioral phenomenology. Each convicted offender presented by the Probation Department, which had investigated the cases sociologically and criminologically, was analyzed in relation to four categories: (1) presence or absence of psychosis; (2) intellectual level; (3) presence of psychopathic or neurotic features; and/or personality "diagnosis"; (4) physical condition. Thus, each offender if he was not classifiable as psychotic, psychopathic personality, or neurotic received a personality evaluation classification in terms of the Predominant Personality Characteristics (see pp. 85, 86 ff.).

This truly gigantic experiment in the psychiatry of crime was initiated in 1932 through the farsighted vision of Dr. Menas S. Gregory, then Director of the Bellevue Psychiatric Hospital (New York),

Cornelius F. Collins, Presiding Judge of the Court of General Sessions, and Irving W. Halpern, Chief Probation Officer of the Court. Mayor James J. Walker and Dr. William Greeff, Commissioner of Hospitals (New York), and a host of prominant contemporary penologists and psychiatrists endorsed the plan.* [34] The project, which has been in effect continuously from 1932 to the present year (1965), has been spurred on by the scientific desire to shed light on the personality types involved in crime, as well as by the responsibility of aiding the judges in their selection of probation risks and probation officers in their supervision and treatment of probationers.

The personality evaluations (called in time *personality diagnosis*) established in the Clinic in 1932 follow:

PREDOMINANT PERSONALITY CHARACTERISTICS OF CRIMINAL OFFENDERS

Aggressive Type—antisocial
Aggressive Type—aggression released by alcohol
Aggressive Type—aggression in reaction to inferiority
Emotionally Unstable type
Unethical (Criminal) type
Maladjusted Adolescent type
Adult Immature type
Egocentric type
Inadequate, Shiftless type
Suggestible type
Adynamic, Dull type
Nomadic type
Primitive type
Adjusted to Low Cultural Level
Adjusted Personality

The personality patterns of criminals far outshadowed the significance of psychotic or defective diagnoses in terms of analyzing criminal behavior and in assisting the court and probation department in estimating the potentials or deficits of the individual offender. A brief description of these personality characteristics, then, based on a dynamic-behavioral orientation, might be clarifying.

The first three groupings, *Aggressive* types, are self-explanatory. The *Emotionally Unstable* group consists of the quick reactors, subject to sudden rages but less intense than those of the epileptoid (psychopathic) individual. The *Unethical* types are obviously those who have adopted illegitimate careers or who persistently transgress the law through sharp business practices. The *Maladjusted Adolescent* type

---

* The staff responsible for development of the original personality paradigm consisted of Drs. Fredric Wertham, Nathaniel Ross, and Benjamin Apfelberg, of the Bellevue Psychiatric Hospital, New York.

manifests the criminal expression of the hyperactivity, impulsiveness, omnipotence fantasies, and discontent with reality limitations characteristic of the adolescent. The *Adult Immature* type shows egocentricity and lack of conventional sentiment carried over to adult life. *Egocentric* types are primarily narcissistic in their way of life. Those characterized as *Inadequate, Shiftless* can best be described as hedonistic by choice. The *Suggestible* type is self-explanatory, as are the *Adynamic* (not mentally defective) individuals. The *Nomadic* types are unattached, schizoid to a degree, whereas the *Primitive* type's behavior is simple and instinctive. *Adjusted* individuals were divided into those adjusted to a low cultural level with its own ideologies and mores and those obviously maintaining a relationship to the so-called stable world.

MENTAL ABNORMALITY AND CRIME

This type of personality analysis has been in effect over thirty years at the Court of General Sessions (New York), comprising examinations of some 83,900 felons. In the 25-year summary report of the Court's Psychiatric Clinic,[35] Messinger and Apfelberg reported some 71,300 psychiatric examinations, including 15,000 psychological tests. Their interest was partially focused on comparing the findings of an early study by the present author and Charles B. Thompson, involving about 9,950 offenders.[36]

In this smaller group the diagnostic categories encountered indicated the following: there were 1.5 per cent psychotics, 2.4 per cent mental defectives, 6.9 per cent neurotics, and 13.3 per cent psychopathic personalities among 9,950 convicted offenders examined routinely in the Psychiatric Clinic.

In reviewing the larger group of cases (71,300), Messinger and Apfelberg reported as follows: about 2 per cent of the criminals so examined were psychotic, 2.5 per cent were mental defectives, and an average of 4.5 per cent were psychoneurotic; the percentage of psychopathic personalities fluctuated from 9 to 24 per cent. The significance of these figures in this sampling of a criminal group lies in the fact that if one includes psychotic, mentally defective, and neurotic individuals as being acknowledgedly mentally or emotionally ill in a clinical sense, then generally about 35 per cent of those individuals convicted of crimes can be considered to be mentally abnormal. The remaining 65 per cent, though psychiatrically "normal," tend to display recognizable personality distortions.

It is not surprising, in view of the publicity given capital and major crimes committed by mentally ill individuals, that the percentage of psychotic individuals (not necessarily legally insane) has attracted general interest. The experience of the Psychiatric Clinic (Court of General Sessions) in this regard has already been cited. On reviewing these figures, Dr. E. Messinger, currently psychiatrist in charge at the Psychiatric Clinic of the Criminal Courts in New York, found a lower percentage of psychotic offenders in a thirteen-year period than previously reported (of 37,771 felony offenders in all crime groups seen by Clinic psychiatrists during the 1943–1956 period, 429, or 1.1 per cent, were committed to mental institutions).[37] This figure included those examined intensively at the Bellevue Psychiatric Hospital as well as those seen at the Clinic.

With regard to the percentages of psychotic offenders in the specific categories of crime (murder, arson, robbery, and so on), the problem of obtaining accurate figures is considerable. Besides the unevenness of study of such offenders, depending on their social importance, type of defense counsel, degree of community interest, revulsion, or sympathy, and other impalpable economic and sociopsychologic factors, there are technical difficulties of a legal nature. For example, many homicide cases are permitted to take reduced pleas (such as assault in many cases), thus altering the meaning of the compiled figures. In this connection, it is noteworthy that Dr. John H. Cassity, a member of the Psychiatric Clinic staff, estimated the percentage of psychotic murderers to be 1.1 per cent of the total murderers convicted and examined in New York County over a period of time.[38]

The classification psychopathic (or its modern equivalent, sociopathic) personality raises many questions. Messinger and Apfelberg point out the variations in emphasis that may account for fluctuations in percentages of psychopaths among the criminal population over the years—19.1 per cent during the period 1932–1935 versus 24.9 per cent during the period 1952–1957. In explanation, they suggest that during the decade 1932–1941, when the percentage of psychopaths remained low, the economic depression with its deprivations and unemployment influenced the pattern of psychopaths in crime. Under depression conditions many "normal" or "average" individuals who had no intrinsic antisocial or criminal inclinations engaged in criminal activity as a means of survival. Consequently, the percentage of psychopathic criminals was relatively low. The increased rate of psychopathy, which began in 1943 and lasted through 1949, is understandable when it is considered that those years covered the World War II period and the immediate postwar readjustment, when virtually no unemployment existed among the stable population. Also, the processes of selection and training for military service drew the more responsible elements of our youth and young manhood into the armed services, casting the psychopaths with their high criminal propensities back into the civilian pool. Undoubtedly, another factor contributing to the high proportion of psychopaths in the last five years of the survey, 1953–1957—averaging 24 per cent—was the element of increased drug addiction in New York City.[39]

In trying to assess the significance of social factors that influenced the emergence of criminal tendencies among character anomalies encountered in this intensive study, it must be recalled that the Court of General Sessions operates in the Borough of Manhattan. Messinger and Apfelberg characterize it thus:

This Borough constitutes the hub of the greater New York Metropolitan district, includes the Broadway theatrical area, the Wall Street financial district and immense midtown business and industrial areas. It also includes residential areas which vary from the slums of the Lower East Side, Harlem and "Hell's Kitchen" on the West Side to the most lavish and luxurious apartments on Park Avenue. It is the center of the greatest seaport in the Western Hemisphere, and is a tourist center attracting hundreds of thousands of visitors daily, thus adding to the permanent population of close to two million.[40]

PERSONALTY ANALYSIS AND ANTISOCIAL BEHAVIOR

The outlined panorama of psychiatric diagnosis and personality analysis of convicted criminals implies that crime is causally related to behavior patterns. This implication leads to some obscurities. First, there is the question, *Can* a person be categorized psychiatrically in a meaningful way? Second, Is a basic psychic state or constellation in fact represented in a given crime? Further, formulations of the personality structure of a criminal population cannot be compared with the personality analyses of a random group in the general, law-abiding population for such compilations are not available. Some persons question the plausibility that a felony offender be evaluated as having a "normal," or "balanced," personality on the ground that anyone who commits a crime is by definition "socially sick." Others have pointed out that a diagnosis or evaluation of personality in a clinic tends to be artificial, since the assertions of the offender are self-serving. Examination in a clinic, critics state, is unrelated to the criminal's milieu; his interview with the psychiatrist is out of context with his own life-stream, and unrelated to the future course of his or her life.

In rebuttal, the criminologic psychiatrist points to his access to court and probation department records; to assistance from psychologists, who work with projective psychologic tests (Rorschach) in which falsification of answers is impossible; to conferences with his colleagues, wherein extreme views and personal biases are ground down; and finally, to his own judgment, seasoned by long clinical experience.

The analysis of personality formations found among criminals suggests still another classification, Crime as Behavior (see p. 90). The conceptual background involved considers criminal action as behavior stated by definition to be contrary to societal requirements. Rather than representing a classification in the true sense, "crime as behavior" offers a *position* from which to understand criminal acts. The phrase conveys the attitude that criminal behavior is first and last a *human activity*, that the personality facets of the offender are visible only through his actions. From this position, arrived at through an empirical study of criminals, crime can be described as a psycho-biologic-social phenomenon, evidenced in and through the criminal's behavior.

Perhaps this phenomenological view, stated above, comes closest to the "behavior system" detailed by the sociologist:

The distinguishing characteristics of criminal offenders are the degree of development of criminal social roles and life organization, identification with crime, the offender's conception of himself, his patterns of association with others, progression in crime, and personality traits.[41]

The empirical approach, based on experience with actual criminals brought before the courts for alleged or proven crimes, dictates the view that crime is a behavioral reaction with many social and psychological concomitants.

Crime, viewed as behavior, falls into three natural modalities. Criminal acts may be in response to *aggressive* drives, to *aggression* under cover of *passivity*, and to *psychophysiological* stresses. (In the chapters following, each modality will be dealt with in depth.) Thus, the proposed "crime-as-behavior" classification, presented below, meets the practical needs of discussion in that crimes listed in accordance with broad categories of behavior exhibit in their modus operandi the particular behavioral components denoted as basic.

THE OBSERVER'S POSITION IN CRIME STUDY

Although much has been learned of the antecedents of crime within the offender's psyche, relatively little is known of the influence of punishment on the psyche of the offender. Clearly this is a most difficult area, hardly accessible to the investigator. Direct study of the effect of punishment on convicted criminals would naturally meet with practical obstacles and emotional distortions; those not yet apprehended and potential offenders are obviously unavailable for study. These are areas in which in the absence of empirical data, we project ourselves, intuitively, into the prisoner's inner world.

In addition to objectivity, psychiatrists have fostered the practice of

CRIME-AS-BEHAVIOR CLASSIFICATION

Crimes essentially Aggressive in Nature
Murder and Manslaughter
Assault
Rape (forceful)
Extortion
Robbery
Libel and Slander
Professional Crime (racketeering, and so on)

Crimes essentially Passive-Aggressive in Nature
Burglary
Larceny
Forgery
Embezzlement
Swindling
Arson
Bigamy
Gambling
Conspiracy to Defraud
Carrying Concealed Weapons

Crimes essentially Related to Psychophysiological Stresses
Sexual crimes, homosexuality, exhibitionism, statutory
rape, pedophilia, obscene telephone calls, pornography, indecencies in public, prostitution
Narcotics, possession, use, and/or sale

empathizing with the patient; this intuitive use of human sympathy and understanding helps to attain a perception of the criminal's inner world. To regard the individual offender as a "behaver" rather than a wrong-doer offers a freer view of the actual interaction between the criminal's psyche and "his" society. The moral overhang to which society pays homage, and which necessarily influences the investigators' attitude, would thus be minimized in an analysis of crime. It is to this orientation that Judge John Biggs alluded when he suggested that "we must stop laying so much emphasis on guilt, the 'guilty mind,' in planning regenerative treatment for the criminal." [42]

Unburdened by the preoccupation with guilt and punishment such a view would come closest to that emotional neutrality to which the objective observer aspires in the emotion-laden experience of crime. This orientation has been largely influenced by dynamic psychiatry in its growth during the last sixty years. Accent on "crime as behavior" permits a clinical approach to the offender, whose crimes are considered not as examples of atavism or inhuman acts, but as a recognizable form of very human behavior. As "behavior," crime is purposive, self-enhancing or self-defeating, highly personalized—a crucial act in a human drama. Every crime represents the resolution of an inner struggle between instinctual desire and the residue of moral and ethical ideals seated uneasily in the conscience. The details and movements of this conflict form the substance of the science of psychopathology.

THE DRAMA OF CRIME

It was Freud who first recognized that a neurotic symptom in a patient constituted a statement of the history of an intensely human conflict, not a static, inexplicable human oddity. The drama of mental illness and neurosis is a personal one involving the patient and his family; the drama of criminal behavior involves the individual and his society. Drama, like crime, is a function of conflict, timing, and emotional involvement. The offender chooses, or has thrust upon him, his moment of dramatic impact. The psychic factors beneath can often only be unveiled by psychopathologists who have scrutinized the emotional life pattern of the criminal, and found there his long preparation for the moment of crime.

In crime, as in drama, situations develop, conflict is present, issues are defined, tension increases, crises erupt, resolutions occur. Sometimes the denouement is successful for the criminal, sometimes it is calamitous. Many unanticipated elements arise in the course of a crime; catastrophe may arrive before the expected success. Each crime, whether against the person or property, carries the possibility of an abbreviated life through an unexpected turn of fate. The seasoned criminal knows this; the first offender is dimly and instinctively aware of it. For punishment looms at every turn—a brief detention, a life of incarceration, or death. The unknown factor in this drama is time. Other moves and countermoves of the criminal act fit into a pattern that the criminal weaves with skill, with loving finesse, clumsy inattention, or wild abandon.

These observations should now be put to the clinical test by examining the psychic life stories and life threads, so far as can be ascertained, of actual offenders. In the illustrative cases to follow it should be pointed out that, since psychiatrists are requested by the courts or attorneys to evaluate mental illnesses chiefly as they influence "right" and "wrong" behavior, the criminal material available to the psychiatrist becomes weighted with cases whose psychopathology may be more obvious than obscure.

Jurisprudence requires this delicate evaluation of the influence of psychopathology on criminal responsibility. But the psychiatrist sees beyond his technical task of assessing mental disorganization and responsibility, perceiving the psychic drama inherent in each crime. Hence, the mode of presentation will be dramatic in the hope that the essential *humanness* of crime will thus be more easily realized.

REFERENCES

1. CLINARD, MARSHALL B., *Sociology of Deviant Behavior* (Rinehart & Winston, New York, 1957), Chaps. 6, 7.

2. *Annotated Laws of Massachusetts,* annotated by the editorial staffs of the publishers, Gabriel V. Mottla and others (Michie Co., Charlottesville, Va. and Rochester, N.Y., 1956) Vol. 9, chap. 264 *et seq.*

3. *Penal Code, State of California* (Bancroft Whitney, San Francisco, 1955).

4. *Penal Code, State of Texas, Vernon's Texas Statutes, 1948,* Vol. 2 (Vernon Law Books, Kansas City, Mo., 1948).

5. MIKELL, WILLIAM E., "The Proposed Criminal Code of Pennsylvania," *University of Pennsylvania Law Review.* LXXI, No. 2 (January, 1923), 99.

6. CANTOR, NATHANIEL F., *Crime* (Henry Holt & Co., New York, 1932), p. 40.

7. "Crime in the United States," *Uniform Crime Reports* (1963), issued by J. Edgar Hoover, Director, F.B.I., U.S. Department of Justice (Washington, D.C., 1963), p. 14.

8. *Ibid.* (1962), p. 1.

9. *Ibid.* (1961), p. 83.

10. KOUWENHOVEN, JOHN ATLEE, *The Columbia Historical Portrait of New York* (Doubleday & Co., Garden City, N.Y., 1953), p. 39.

11. Records of Court of Quarter Sessions (1686), Court of General Sessions of the Peace (1813), in Archives of Supreme Court, Criminal Division, New York County.

12. DAWSON, H. B., *Records of the City of New York,* trans. from the Dutch (Common Council of New York, Morrisania, N.Y., 1876), pp. 3, 69.

13. BROMBERG, WALTER, *The Mold of Murder* (Grune & Stratton, New York, 1961), p. 210.

14. BLOCH, HERBERT A., and GEIS, GILBERT, *Man, Crime and Society* (Random House, New York, 1962), p. 259.

15. *Ibid.,* p. 259.

16. MORRIS, ALBERT, quoted in *ibid.,* p. 259.

17. "Crime in the United States," *U.S. News and World Report,* August, 1963.

18. GEHLKE, C. E., and SUTHERLAND, EDWIN, "Crime and Punishment," *Recent Social Trends,* XX, 1123–35.

19. *International Criminal Statistics, 1955–56,* International Criminal Police Organization (Interpol) (General Secretariat, Paris, France, 1957).

20. Probation Department files, Court of General Sessions, New York, I. W. Halpern, Chief Probation Officer, 1940–1960.

21. State of California, Board of Corrections, Minimum and Maximum Terms and Initial Adult Authority Appearance, September 19, 1959.

22. GILBERT, FRANK BIXBY, and CLEVENGER, JOSEPH K., *Criminal Law and Practice of New York, Penal and Correctional Law*, official 46th ed. (Matthew Bender & Co., Albany, N.Y., 1963).

23. *Code Annotated, State of Iowa*, Vols. 54, 55. (West Publishing Co., St. Paul, Minn., 1950).

24. *Penal Code, State of California, ibid.*

25. GUTTMACHER, MANFRED S., "Adult Court Psychiatric Clinics," *American Journal of Psychiatry*, CVI (1950), 881.

26. GLUECK, BERNARD, "A Study of 608 Admissions to Sing Sing Prison," *Mental Hygiene*, II (January, 1918), 85.

27. GORING, CHARLES, *The English Convict* (H.M. Stationery Office, London, 1913), p. 369.

28. GODDARD, HENRY H., *Feeblemindedness, Its Cause and Consequences* (The Macmillan Company, New York, 1914).

29. SUTHERLAND, EDWIN H., quoted in "Mental Deficiency and Crime," chap. XV, of *Social Attitudes*, Kimball Young, ed. (Henry Holt, New York, 1931), p. 357.

30. OVERHOLSER, WINFRED, "The Briggs Law of Massachusetts, A Review and an Appraisal," *Journal of Criminal Law and Criminology*, XXV (March, 1935), 865.

31. MURCHISON, CARL, *Criminal Intelligence* (Clark University, Worcester, Mass., 1928), p. 57.

32. GLUECK, SHELDON, "Psychiatric Examination of Persons Accused of Crime," *Mental Hygiene*, II (1927), 287.

33. FOXE, ARTHUR N., "Classification of the Criminotic Individual," in *Handbook of Correctional Psychology*, R. M. Lindner and R. V. Seliger, eds. (Philosophical Library, New York, 1947), p. 24.

34. GREGORY, MENAS S., "Psychiatry and the Problems of Delinquency," *American Journal of Psychiatry*, XIV (January, 1935), 773.

35. MESSINGER, E., and APFELBERG, B., "A Quarter Century of Court Psychiatry," *26th Annual Report, Psychiatric Clinic, Court of General Sessions*, New York, 1958.

36. BROMBERG, W., and THOMPSON, C. B., "The Relation of Psychosis, Mental Defect and Personality Types to Crime," *Journal of Criminal Law and Criminology*, XXVIII, No. 1, (May–June, 1937).

37. MESSINGER, EMANUEL, personal communication to the author, 1958.

38. CASSITY, JOHN H., "Personality Study of 200 Murderers," *Journal of Criminal Psychopathology*, II (1941), 296.

39. MESSINGER and APFELBERG, *op. cit.*, p. 12.

40. *Ibid.*, p. 2.

41. CLINARD, *op. cit.*, p. 201.

42. BIGGS, JOHN, *The Guilty Mind* (Harcourt, Brace & Co., New York, 1955).

CHAPTER V

Crimes of Aggression

Crimes clearly aggressive in nature include murder, manslaughter, assault, forceful rape, robbery, extortion, and, from the standpoint of verbal aggression, libel and slander. Thus, behavior exhibited by the offender and the personality makeup of the behaver are equated. This, briefly stated, is the working hypothesis upon which the clinical analysis of criminals has proceeded in this work.

The "crime-as-behavior" classification proposed (see p. 90) does, however, show inconsistencies, as does any attempt to compress human behavior into specific categories of feeling and thinking. For example, all crimes involve actions contrary to the wishes and interests of the victims; hence, they may uniformly be termed "aggressive." Thus, sexual molestation of a child involves aggressive action but the psychic motivation of such an offense is psychosexual in nature; a lust-murder is obviously aggressive but the stimulus is chiefly, at least initially, sexual. Again, forceful rape results from sexual excitement, but the modality employed is essentially aggressive. Burglary is acknowledgedly an aggressive intrusion on the victim's privacy but the psychologic motif within the offender at the time of the crime is one of passive aggression through stealth.

These complexities, however, do not invalidate the design of the classification offered, which represents a model upon which to integrate the results of clinical analyses.

THE MEANING OF AGGRESSION

What is aggression, about which we speak so easily? We may say that clinicians know more about the results of aggression than they do of its genesis. To begin with, "aggression" is derived from the Latin word meaning "to attack." Hence, aggression signifies injurious, destructive, or lethal behavior. Combined with the drive to injure are such attendant emotions as rage, hostility, anger, frustration, and humiliation. Criminologically speaking, this type of aggression eventuates in homicide, assault, rape, robbery. A second meaning of aggression is equally significant: aggression as acquisitiveness. In ordinary usage, the acquisitive aspect of aggression is behaviorally represented in terms of grasping, mastering, acquiring, winning. The criminal reflections of this type of aggression lie in such acts as larceny, forgery, embezzlement. In addition to the emotions clustering around the aggressive urge there are motoric tendencies (movement tendencies) that become part and parcel of the aggressivity per se, represented in behavior involving speed, force, and power—for example, homicide or assault.

In general, aggression of either destructive or acquisitive type is considered to have an aim and an object. A third type of aggression, however, appears to be without aim; it might be termed movement-for-its-own-sake. This latter type, also of criminological significance, can be seen among adolescents prone to overactivity (hyperkinesis), expressed in car thefts, joyrides, gang fights, or "rumbles," and so on.

The genesis of aggressivity in human beings has been acknowledged to be almost unfathomable. It is generally agreed among mental scientists that we are dealing with an indigenous tendency in animate and human organisms. Its resemblance to fundamental biological capacities of animate organisms—for example, irritability (responsiveness to stimulation)—qualifies aggression as a function of life itself. In this sense aggression is a fundamental characteristic of humankind, directly attributable to its physiological substrate. The energy for this fundamental quality, commonly called *instinctive*, derives from the body processes; its direction is preformed—laid down, so to speak—in the tissues of the organism. Thus, the "instinct" of self-preservation and the sexual "instinct" are inherent in living substance; they utilize the

mechanical equipment of the organism to maintain, protect, and reproduce its kind. The aggressive tendency is channeled through both
these instincts and in so doing it achieves the status of instinctual
behavior. Anna Freud describes the situation by stating that "aggressive impulses have an independent origin to which frustration becomes
an additive rather than primary cause of such impulses." [1]

Other investigators, especially sociologists and anthropologists, have
disputed the instinctive nature of aggression, imputing it to learned
reactions. Thus Kardiner,[2] in studying primitive cultures from the
standpoint of social influence on character development, found that a
supposedly basic instinct like aggression varied in consonance with
altered values of aggression in a given culture. Among the Zunis, for
example, a "rock-bound series of guarantees" to control mutual aggression made aggression "less necessary and rewarding." Among the
Kwakiutl, however, the security of the culture depended on the culti-
vation of "effective forms of aggression." Anthropologists and social
scientists are beginning to favor the notion that since culture creates
the human ego, rather than the reverse, "instinctive" aspects of the ego
are really "learned" ones. To put it in diagrammatic words: "Anger is
born in social intercourse," [3] not in the germ plasm.

THE GENESIS OF AGGRESSION

Stating either that aggression originates in human instincts or that it
is a learned reaction does not explain it. Theoretical problems remain.
One intriguing explanation is Freud's construct regarding the genesis
of aggression. In his attempt to formulate the mental mechanisms
whereby aggression serves the organism, Freud [4] developed the theory
that two opposing sets of instincts were operative throughout the life
of an individual; one, the *death instinct,* operating silently, tended to
bring the organism to a standstill. This instinct when directed toward
the external world manifested itself as a destructive, or aggressive,
tendency. The other, the *libidinal instinct* (or *life instinct*), operated to
maintain life and promote its "higher development." In general terms,

Life would consist in the manifestations of the conflict or interaction between
the two classes of instinct; death would mean for the individual the victory
of destructive instincts but reproduction would mean for him the victory of
Eros.[5]

Not only did Freud, who suggested the terms Thanatos and Eros for
the death and life instincts, respectively, find the destructive instinct at
work in the unconscious of neurotic patients, but he recognized its
pervading presence in war, daily strife, and in the excessive cruelties

recorded in human history—the martyrdom of the early Christians, the Inquisition, the Nazi extermination of Jews, the Indian massacres in our own West, wholesale killings in many lands and in many time-periods throughout human history. In a letter addressed to Albert Einstein (1932), entitled "Why War?" Freud agreed to the innateness of aggressive drives in men. "There is no use in trying to get rid of man's aggressive inclinations," he wrote; "We can only think of diverting or sublimating them." [6]

In the narrower world of clinical observation one can readily witness the universality of aggressive tendencies. To see a child's inner glee at the destruction of toys by his own hand or his satisfaction in pushing dishes off the table is to see aggression in its physiological-psychological *anlage*. Such action represents a sense of power, as yet unchanneled by emotional education. Studies by Schilder and Bender [7] of the aggressiveness of children show biting, hitting, and smashing to be unrestricted and obviously pleasurable in children to the age of three years. Psychoanalytic study of adult patients and direct observations of children and infants have pointed to destructiveness as an extremely early mental element in human life. In infants, feelings of hatred and fantasies of destructiveness toward the mother's breast are well known. As Melanie Klein,[8] an English psychoanalyst, has pointed out, the infant's fantasies of injuring the mother by tearing or biting her are such basic mental elements as to be "tantamount to the death wish." The object (mother) who both nurtures and frustrates the infant becomes the object of destructive wishes. Later in life, guilt reactions rise from this buried aggression, often remaining active in adulthood and developing into distressing neurotic symptoms.

Studies of newborn infants have been undertaken to establish, if possible, the origin of aggression. René Spitz made meticulous observations on deprived infants as they exhibited the "hospitalism syndrome," [9] occurring among infants who had been separated from their mothers for periods of six months to a year. Studying their reactions to nurses who fed them and to other attendants who did not (the "good" and "bad" mother-figures), Spitz could trace the communication of an aggressive intent by a shaking of the head, meaning No. These frustrated, sick infants greeted the nurse or attendant who did not feed them with the No movement of the head, which, Spitz concluded from many experiences, was the earliest *anlage* of anger reaction to frustration. The No head-shaking, which had been imprinted in the process of numerous experiences with unpleasure, had "become a suitable vehicle to express aggression." [10]

From such studies as those cited, the possibility that anger and hate were reactive in nature in the earliest days of life gained plausibility. Other clinicians working with adult neurotics—Horney, for example [11]

—felt that hostility and urges to kill or injure were reactions to early feelings of humiliation, abuse, or threatening danger. In her own patients, Horney pointed out, self-assertion—a natural channel of aggression—had often been blocked unconsciously, and, she noted, such a patient when relieved of his inhibitions was actually less hostile than before treatment.[12] Many other workers have agreed that aggression is essentially reactive to frustration rather than arising as an instinct *de novo*.

The universality of aggression in social and, especially, criminal areas brought another view of aggression to the fore. Schilder advanced the idea that aggressivity is a function of the psychological development of the body-image. As the child grows, he proceeds to master his object-world through activity—handling, touching. Soon he examines his own body, then that of others. As the body-image builds, emotional charges become attached to activity:

Aggressivement very often becomes sexual aggressiveness . . . the openings of the body become overemphasized . . . feces and saliva acquire a similar significance. Parents respond to this fusion of motor and sexual aggression with still more vigorous suppression. [13]

The child's behavior, which follows his or her mastery of self and others through aggressive (and destructive) experimentation, finally becomes controlled in familial and social situations. Thus, aggression attains a psychosocial function. Hence Schilder wrote: "Aggressiveness and activity do not exist outside of situations in which they come into play. There is no instinct of aggressiveness." [14]

In time, as the child matures, aggressive behavior comes to attain a special meaning, depending on the value systems of his society. In this evolutionary development, destruction through activity could represent one aspect of a constructive process. As Schilder puts it: "In general, activity and aggression are primarily constructive" in that these elements represent an interest in, and a reaching for, objects in the child's world. This constructive reaching is subject to learned cultural values superimposed on the infantile "pleasure in having power over objects." [15] Moreover, aggressiveness and destructiveness have been awarded a positive, masculine value in our culture, just as femininity has been endowed with a passive value. Keiser and Schilder in an early study of murderers and assaulters found a substratum of unconscious passivity in committers of violent crimes, which the offenders covered by excessive "masculinity." [16]

In sum, the trend of opinion on this thorny question is that "aggression [is] in large measure a learned reaction" consonant with the "twentieth-century view that man . . . [is] a plastic, symbolic animal shaped by culture." [17] This attitude has been consolidated by anthropological studies of cultures other than our own. Against this culturalist view, however, must be placed the clinical impression (which coincides with the commonsense attitude of many lay observers) that the degree of aggressive capacity in each individual is unique; in some persons, as judged by social standards, it is simply excessive. This rule-of-thumb measure of degrees of aggressive capacity resulted in such labels among earlier writers as "aggressive psychopath," "primary aggressive psychopath," or, more dramatically, "enemies of society." Karpman's "anethopath"—his term for the "essential psychopath" who remained after he had eliminated all individuals with neurotic backgrounds—belongs to the group of persons endowed with an innately high intensity of aggression. These persons, Karpman states,

. . . [are] characterized by a virtual absence of any redeeming social reaction [or] conscience, guilt or generous emotion . . . while purely egoistic, uninhibited instinctive trends are predominant. They are as close to the constitutional as can be found.[18]

Satten, Karl Menninger, and associates [19] found a group of murderers who, although not psychotic, carried a "surcharge of aggressive energy or an unstable ego defense system that periodically allowed the naked and archaic expression of such energy." Karl Menninger has developed this concept to explain episodic outbursts of murderous aggression as examples of "ego rupture and episodic dyscontrol." In simpler terms, the aggressive impulse is so intense in these individuals that a "temporary insanity" supervenes at the moment of the murderous assault. This principle, says Menninger,

is no more obscure than flooding an area to relieve an overtaxed dam, or incising an abscess to prevent it from bursting. From the standpoint of society, an explosion of murder is disastrous, but from the standpoint of the individual it may be the way to survival, the only solution, which at the moment of decision, the crippled ego could find.[20]

At all events, those (like the present writer) who have dealt with aggressive offenders at many stages following the criminal act—at trial, conviction, during incarceration or hospitalization—are convinced that excessive quanta of aggressive energy exist in certain persons that cannot solely be accounted for by the learning process.

Whether aggression is an instinctive drive or a learned response, it may be assumed that moral teachings and religious exhortation, which attempt to curb aggression, rest on the premise that the destructive tendency is a learned response. The spiritual doctrine that love conquers force, that peace and brotherhood can be secured through adherence to the Golden Rule—basic to the ethical principles of both Judaeo-Christianity and Eastern religions—seems to imply that destructive action will yield to moral teaching. The empirical handling of aggression long preceded the scientific analysis of the origin of this force.

However that may be, little doubt exists on one point, that there is a regular emotional concomitant to aggression. The discharge of any instinctual energy results in feelings of satisfaction, and the relief of frustration is accompanied by satisfaction. In a sense, society well understands this reaction: one of the immediate results of aggressive acts is the infliction of punishment. Children are trained, and criminals are punished, with this principle in mind. Society is clearly girded to curtail the pleasure or satisfaction that follows injurious acts by inflicting punishment therefor. There are, of course, exceptions: warfare or certain athletic sports (for example, boxing, bullfighting) where destructiveness is a revered social value. In almost every other aggressive situation—fighting, assaults, mayhem, homicide, verbal aggression (as in angry squabbles or heated arguments)—sanctions are imposed for the excessive display of physical aggression.

There is another aspect of aggression to be considered: destruction employs the ultimate power of the individual in a final definitive act. Destruction, like love, touches the outer limits of human capacity. Its closest competitor in producing human satisfaction is the urge to create. A creative act is equally definitive in purport and as immensely satisfying to the individual. However, the destructive urge (in crime) is most often sated in one effort, whereas the creative urge grows. In the area of homicide or assault, the criminal act may be the expression of an emotional storm, the so-called "occasional" or "accidental" crime. Such a crime—the once-in-a-lifetime crime—is rarely repeated. The aggression responsible for it is exhausted in one outburst. In the area of creative work, on the other hand, new accomplishments inspire others.

What is suggested is that a destructive crime may signify a creative act in terms of the inner dynamics of the murderer. In this unconscious realm, destruction becomes creation. This paradoxical situation has been phrased in another way by an English analyst who found, in an intensive study of several murderers, that their deeds did not merely represent the acting out of impulses but a "dramatization . . . of the whole internal situation upon the external world." [21] The dramatic essence of crime leads, then, to a closer approximation of the criminals' inner world, which may in time prove of value in treatment.

For the present, though the existence of the creative aspect of a criminal act may be granted, at least on a philosophical level, society is little concerned with this view. Its concern is with punishment for crime accomplished and with the suppression or diversion of such urges before the crime. But it is essential to consider these basic elements in the criminal if our understanding of crime is to have validity in terms of the criminal's inner world. In this direction, the following case of precriminal aggression in a man who struggled with his inner conflicts illustrates the criminal's dim awareness of that basic aggression, with its subsurface of creativity, which lies within him.

PRELUDE TO MURDER

Several years ago, I received a series of letters [22] from a man who disclosed only that he was of mature years, an attorney who had once taught at a large university; he also stated that he was emotionally distraught. The unseen patient's decision to write these numerous anonymous letters had been prompted by his having read one of my articles, "The Treatability of the Psychopath." [23] In it the idea was advanced that treatment of this type of individual could only proceed with the knowledge that "society played a vital role" in the evolution of the psychopath's calloused attitude and defensive personality structure. It pointed out that society's congealed hostility toward the sociopath was perceived unconsciously by the latter and reacted to by hardness, egocentricity, and aggressiveness. The psychopath's toughness signalizes the boomerang of society's rejection of the hated one. Thawing the defensiveness of the psychopath toward society by a recognition of society's aggression, its "parental" anger at him as an incorrigible, was a first step in the psychotherapy, or rehabilitation, of these unyielding members. "One wonders," the article concluded, "whether psychiatry has not been frightened by the sardonic, snarling mask of the psychopath, behind which lies the frightened, lonesome face of a neurotic character."

My anonymous patient opened his correspondence by writing: "I have a vision of knocking your head off and seeing it rolling in the gutter. . . . I would be assailed as a murderer, but it was only because I wanted to defend myself. If only the psychiatrist years ago had been able to talk to me about my wanting to fight."

It soon became apparent that his aggression was beamed toward psychiatrists, since several whom he had consulted had recommended his committal to a mental institution. "What would you do [wrote my correspondent] if you are faced with these words: You are a menace to yourself and others; you should be committed."

Out of the mass of material in the letters certain facts, and a personality, began to emerge:

I pulled a jackknife and defended myself when three fellows got me cornered (age 7–8). That was when I was sent to the school for feeble minded. . . .

I learned to box well enough so I could hold my own with almost anyone. At one time I was sparring partner of a fellow who was training for a fight in Madison Square Garden. No one could understand why a fellow of my size had such a weak punch. (They didn't know I "pulled" it.) It is more of an art to "pull" your punches in such a way that it cannot be detected than it is to kill a man. (Enclosed is one of my famous "letters," it should be of value to you in your investments.) . . .

I had a constant urge to hit someone with my fists: he tried to have the children kept away from me. . . .

Apparently my "patient" had successfully suppressed his rage and learned to adjust to society, eventually achieving a law professorship. Interspersed with expressions of an old anger were statements to the effect that he had "determined to cure myself in spite of all the psychiatrists in the world." From boyhood on, he had struggled with his resentment at being adjudged "feebleminded" and "psychopathic" (according to him) by psychiatric examiners. "There is only one person in the world I trust—me."

Scattered through the letters of Mr. Anonymous were discussions of philosophy, the law, poetry, the problems of semantics, and many remarks about "quacks, cheats, dirty bastards, cheap windbags," referring chiefly to psychiatrists.

When I combined imaginative action, emotionalism and expression (written expression) and clipped you (imaginatively) in the jaw, I was shocked and amazed that your head went rolling down the gutter though you remained standing. Then my adult thinking took over and I laughed.

In one letter he summarized the point made in "The Treatability of the Psychopath" by accepting the theory that the term "psychopath" is itself a semantic weapon that society hurls at the nonconformist. He quotes these ideas with approval:

He [the psychopath] is a rebel. (The question as I see it is based on his rebellion against a "then society" his instinctual being knew was wrong.) . . . He has a deep antagonism against anyone associated with his "now society," particularly in an official position. . . . He listens to the "tone" of peoples' voices rather than literal interpretations. (He uses words as weapons and expects others to do the same.) . . .

As letters continued to arrive from my anonymous correspondent, interlarded with threats to "chop you in the jaw," "see your head rolling down the gutter," a more moderate tone became evident. His rages decreased, his relationship improved, as he wrote out his feelings. He no longer felt as he had at first, when he wrote:

The psychopath will fight to the death rather than obey, submit or sublimate. Those are words of death and not of life. The rebel had a cause and believes he still has it, in a negative society. . . . Until I punched you and saw your head rolling down the street I saw no error in myself; only in society. I was half right. The rebel had a cause.

A year after he commenced writing, he stated:

It is about a year since I knocked your head off and saw it rolling down the gutter. Possibly if I had a fist fight then my therapy would have been hastened—but I did not. The outstanding change has been that people no longer seem to be members of society but are increasingly personal as individuals. My attitude toward society has changed from hostility to a rather sympathetic contempt; I am avoiding meeting an ex-governor and a present Chief Justice I have known for years lest I show how little respect I have for them.

A playful manner, hiding under a sort of grim humor, began to make its appearance:

How was that from a graduate of the school for feeble-minded? Oh, how my enemies would like to know what you know about me.

Nearly a year and a half after the first letter was received, he signed himself, "Cum laude, school for the feeble-minded." Gradually his language became more moderate; small clippings were enclosed in the letters, relating to university courses in sociology and social relations; a warm attitude developed—"Tonight I am just drunk enough to want to brag, but not drunk enough to give you any clues." He then admitted that his teaching of law was becoming more effective:

Whereas my former lectures were given from the contra-moral point of view my present lectures are more tolerant of morality. However, I still tell my students that they are living in a legal world and not in a moral one.

Mr. Anonymous began to develop a warmer relationship to people; he admitted, somewhat reluctantly:

The new world that I am living in, since I hit you in the jaw and saw your head rolling down the gutter, is disconcerting. By the way, _____ is the other doctor who examined me and wanted me committed. He has a new book out and when I saw the jacket I remembered his name. . . . I am having the damnedest experiences. Hardly a day goes by that three or four people fail to stop me on the street and ask some question or other. I seem to exude some kind of friendliness.

Apparently the suppression of his anger was successful, because he related that on two occasions he refused judicial appointments from two governors.

As my correspondent's defensive aggression thawed, feelings of dependence became evident. The process was not uniform, however, being punctuated with surges of anger at his earlier psychiatrists and threats to "roll your head in the gutter." The unilateral correspondence continued. The homicidal impulses did not disappear, however.

The knowledge that I would probably be a KILLER if I ever get loose, had its value. I never had a feeling that the other fellow could beat me if I really let go. But of course, knowing that I was a killer, I never let myself go but only boxed with my opponents. I had to protect myself from you and protect you from me.

Finally a letter arrived in which my anonymous patient proposed that he be examined. The judgment that he was "a menace to himself and society," made thirty years ago, still irritated him. He now wrote that he would reveal himself for an examination to see if the same diagnosis would be made. At the same time he displayed the sensitivity, the paranoid attitude, and the reactive aggression that characterized all his letters:

I might regret removing those who tried to take me from this terrestial sphere, but they would not take me alive. As long as you do not know that I am the one who is "a menace to myself and society (or others) who should be committed" then we could meet, spend an afternoon together, have dinner and go our ways in peace. But if you knew who I was I would not let you get behind me; I would not eat any food you could dope; I would not enter any private building where you might have me seized and I would watch you like a hawk for the first sign of a hostile move.

The threat of intimacy through a possible meeting had stimulated anxiety with its consequent aggressive defensiveness. The alternate play of dependence and aggression, so commonly observed in therapy of disturbed persons, was unmistakable in this "patient." When a meeting was proposed, guarded by plans to preserve his anonymity, he promptly withdrew. In his next letter he wrote:

There is no sense in my flying out to see you. One of three things would happen if I did.

1. As an individual, aside from your role as a psychiatrist, you might attack me and I would have to kill you in self-defense.
2. As a psychiatrist you might try to treat me but you would first have to get me committed. I might have to kill you to prevent this.

3. You might say, "You are as crazy as a bed bug; don't bother me." In that event the trip would be a waste of time.

But his retrospective anger continued, albeit more mildly:

Had either _____ or _____ been willing to discuss my feelings about fist fighting with me I might have corrected it then. But they treated me and talked to me in tones of reproof when I had no feeling of guilt.

A year and a half after the first letter arrived, the correspondence stopped abruptly, with a "good luck; thanks for listening":

I am firmly of the belief that the psychiatrist should take seriously the viewpoint of the psychopath and SUPPORT IT. If "the rebel had a cause" he still has it.

This case of an unconsummated aggression leaves us with a subtle commentary on society's use of punishments and threats of punishment to control its unstable members. The psychopath is an outspoken member of society. It is he who acts out, it is he who voices, through his behavior, the underlying attitude of all people toward forceful restraint. It is he who rejects punishment because he feels his position is right. He understands, nevertheless, the need for maintenance of a civilized law-regulated society. As our attorney-patient put it, the offender perceives the moral implication of society's rules but only grudgingly accepts them. Through the printed word—a chance reading of a technical paper in which the writer expressed empathy for the psychopath and an appreciation of *his* burden—the potential offender was able to release aggression against psychiatrists, relieve pent-up hostility, and adjust within the limits of allowable behavior.

Were this entire production of letters a piece of fantasy, a macabre practical joke aimed at one psychiatrist as an image for the others, it still would demonstrate the feelings of an "oddling," a misfit, a rejected man, and the evolution of a defensive attitude of aggressiveness. Indeed, in many persons the fantasy of destructiveness can be as poignant as its actuality.

MURDER DE FACTO

The discussion of unconsummated aggression, or, more accurately, the discussion of chronic, destructive aggressivity without consummation, brings to attention those cases that do eventuate in violence. All aggression does not necessarily result in personal injury; what starts as a neurotic outburst may end in a homicide statistic and that which starts as a destructive drive may be transformed into a creative act. Let us plunge into the case story of a moon-struck, quiet high-school student whose masked aggression catapulted him into the most capital of crimes—murder.

Lee Parker at the age of seventeen felt a little ill at ease with his high-school classmates, who, in this smallish western town, found him interesting, but referred to him as "cockeyed" or "goofed-up." He preferred the more poetic term "moon-struck." In general, Lee was a successful student, competent and interested in his avowed purpose of becoming a science teacher. While his middle-class parents complained that he was a little too quiet, preferring to go fishing by himself and rarely rowdy with his fellow adolescents or robust siblings, Lee always thought of himself as being romantically moody; he treasured opportunities to meditate. Large of frame, but not athletic; slow-moving, but strong, no one doubted that he was a "good boy." Usually he remained home with his parents, reading perpetually. His teachers liked him, perceiving the beginnings of a student in this large, self-contained, in-dwelling youth.

Of himself, Lee said: "I never did like people . . . life was like a plan drawn up for you . . . you eat breakfast, go to school, do your work, but it's all so insincere." Only two girl-friends, whom he idolized, were concerned about the trace of emotional disturbance evident in Lee during the last few months preceding his crime. True, the school authorities reported his marks had become poorer but his "steady" girl, Toni, felt uneasy at his persistent and tense romanticizing, although she was pleased that he was so different, so poetical. As the school term rolled on, Lee's attachment to his girl became a major preoccupation with him. He wrote long, rambling love letters which reflected his gathering moodiness. "I'll never find anyone so devoted and truthful as you," he wrote Toni. His letter went on:

I adore you. I was a fool to mistreat you. I caused the problem that split us and then I made the cut . . . Your love was so tender and true . . . I have experienced the worst disaster possible to my heart. I feel like I could lie down and die. . . . Well, the moon and stars no longer shine. The dream is gone I thought was mine.

So intense an attachment to one girl suggested a peculiar situation, even for mooncalf love. Lee sensed its inappropriateness. Then clarity broke over him like a wave. It was obvious he couldn't continue to belabor his girl with such overwhelming "mooning." There was only one way out—a death pact: death for her, suicide for himself. It seemed so natural a solution to his problems. He would be bound in everlasting love to Toni; the troublemakers—"the guys I didn't like"—would be out of the way, the adults who bore down on him would be circumvented.

I always daydreamed I could be anything I wanted. . . . I felt like I would like to tell them off. . . . the women were stupid on the job . . . they make a bigger mess . . . I can do a better job myself than listen to the teacher . . . this goes for my mother too but not Toni. . . . when I was with her it was like being myself.

His subservience to his teachers and parents merely concealed his contempt:

The teacher would ask me how I felt about things; the Civics teacher had me grade papers with him . . . would try to get me to talk about politics, religion . . . he liked some of my ideas . . . I would be real nice and pleasant to the minister but I would never be real. . . . I would force myself to be the way he wanted me to be.

His hostility shielded from casual observation, Lee's plans soared: He wouldn't kill any of the boys he knew, but some casual person, or anyone who tried to stop him—maybe an older man—no children or women. An old man had lived his life; what's the harm in it? Or perhaps he could escape with Toni; then they would die together. Sometimes, lost in reverie, Lee replaced his suicide and murder fantasies with plans for world destruction:

I think of ways to get rid of people by poisoning them . . . putting poison in cans . . . poison in wells . . . starting wars on purpose with bombs. . . . I think opposite things . . . I would straighten things out by the wars . . . introduce some good in life . . . get rid of the bad and make people good.

If he didn't commit suicide, he could fall back on murder and thus be executed by the State: "It was all quite simple if you used your brains and things worked out properly." He wrote to his girl on the eve of the homicide. "I feel wiser than I have ever been in my life. Everything can come to my mind at once and I can control it, until my mind comes back home . . . to you."

The confusion in Lee's mind grew deeper as his apparent mental clarity increased. Destruction via suicide, homicide, world wars, holocausts blobbed together in his mind: what Lee considered a clear course of action was a chimera resulting from a psychotic episode into which he was sliding. The "clarity" was that of the individual whose fantasies were now unhampered by reality.

By midnight, his farewell note written, Lee slashed his left wrist with a razor. The bleeding was minimal but enough blood spattered on the note to alarm his parents when they awoke the following morning to find him missing from his room. By 1:00 A.M. Lee, waiting for death from hemorrhage, decided the suicide attempt had failed; he took his rifle and drove off into the night. He pulled up in a country lane, hoping to asphyxiate himself in the car. He parked, turned on the motor, and waited; early in the morning he woke up, "very much alive," as the local paper commented the next day. Grasping the rifle again, he attempted to shoot himself: it failed, so Lee carried out the alternate plan he had devised. Sighting an elderly workman walking along a quiet street, Lee pulled up the car, aimed the rifle, firing four shots: The old man collapsed, and expired without a sound. The youth drove to his girl-friend's house, where police, called in by Toni's parents, were waiting for him.

The curious statement that Lee freely offered the police, that he had shot a complete stranger "for the avowed purpose of having the State execute me," arrested the attention of his defense counsel. Counsel urged the judge, who agreed, to remand Lee to a state hospital for examination. The psychiatrists reported him legally sane, but noted the history of frequent depressions. In view of this finding, the judge of the juvenile court felt the charge merited his being bound over to the county court, where a charge of first-degree murder was entered.[24] He was placed in solitary confinement because of attempted suicide.

During the three months Lee sat in jail awaiting trial he experienced the full flowering of his fantasies as they flitted in and out of his depressive state. Plans to escape suffused his mind. "I could break out of here, ride up to Toni's house, take her away, and finish the original plan," he daydreamed. But the steel bars in his cell cooled his daring. He reviewed his alternate plan: shooting the old man; his own request for the death penalty. Tension mounted in him. At night anger surged through him as he imagined the best years of his life being spent in prison: "How stupid and helpless I feel," he would tell himself. Then his immaturity would rise to the surface: he observed with satisfaction that he had changed since the "case" and that his parents now treated him with awe and respect.

The psychological tests gave Lee a chance to amplify his fantasies. In the Thematic Apperception test he told stories of great loneliness and rejection; nearly all involved death, suicide, or destruction. One character killed himself because of remorse, following the death of a friend; another character (female) killed her lover. The test stories constantly reminded Lee that persons who are "scorned" will kill. Lee saw himself as Cain. He explained how he often would entertain himself with "hate spells," during which he had strong impulses to destroy and kill.

When one examined Lee's preoccupation with aggressive actions toward women, one became aware that his aggressive impulses covered an underlying (unconscious) dependence on the female sex. These relationships (mother, teachers, girl-friends) entailed tremendous dependence, of a leaning, needy type—the so-called anaclitic reaction.[25] Here, the child needs continuous emotional support and nurturing from the mother, characteristically in early infancy, but bespeaking a severe emotional disturbance when persisting into adolescence. It seems clear in this case that Lee's suicide plan was aimed psychologically at his girl—the girl to whom he wrote:

If I had any guts I would kill myself—my thought of never seeing you again bothers me too much. If you were to die there would be no problem. . . . The seriousness of my separating [from you] was more than I expected.

His last note to her spoke of a "death pact . . . this all seemed natural for everybody to die."

Looking back on Lee's psychic state before the homicide it is worthy of note that these fantasies both preceded and followed the offense; it was as if the homicide had not occurred. The act of murder did not sate the vigor of his hate. The youth complained that often he seemed an "actor" rather than a real person "living the situation." Depression and thoughts of suicide had plagued him for some time. Beyond his extremely immature dependence pattern, elements of *depersonalization* could be clearly seen. Yet in one way (cognitively) he could be said to have understood the meaning of reality, to have known right from wrong. But the detachment of affect, the separation of emotional feelings from intellection, which occurs in the condition called depersonalization, rendered Lee's judgment unreal. Inner convictions of depersonalized patients do not share the same psychic solidity and integrity, of realness about thoughts and actions, experienced by normal persons.

Since the presence of legal insanity was disavowed, the issue of murder in the first degree was raised, and with it the questions whether the offender had the requisite capacity to premeditate and deliberate and whether he committed the homicide with malice aforethought. Inasmuch as the issue of malice aforethought was decided in the negative in Lee's case, he was committed to a state institution that had been reserved for active therapeutic and retraining programs.* Examined a year later in the institution, he appeared calm, described no further rage episodes, and regarded his offense as an act of immaturity. One received the impression, however, that the benign, sometimes amused, expression with which Lee regarded the interest of the investigator in

* California Medical Facility, Vacaville, California.

his further progress covered an emotional flatness. In any event, the acute tension occasioned by his conflicts at the time of the homicide had dissipated; the adolescent schizophrenia had, for practical purposes, subsided to a considerable extent. What the future held in store for him and his society would depend on the nature and balance of the forces within his ego in the years ahead.

MURDER, SUICIDE, AND THE IDEAS OF DEATH

The close relation between the suicidal thoughts in Lee's mind and his homicidal act leads to a consideration of these twin psychologic phenomena. It has been noted frequently that the mingling of suicidal and murderous impulses eventuates in double killings: the "death pact" combines a suicide on the part of one following the murder of the other. Curiously, the perpetrator of planned double destruction often survives because his suicidal attempt is clumsily executed. The psychologic association between murder and suicide has been clarified since murders by ambulatory schizophrenics (including the adolescent group of schizophrenics) have been studied psychodynamically. Zilboorg,[26] Menninger,[27] Reichard and Tillman,[28] and the present writer [29] have demonstrated, as does the case just outlined, that suicide and murder are equated in the disordered psyche.

Among psychotic individuals, the victim often represents the murderer's self in the latter's unconscious mind. This formulation explains the so-called senseless or wanton murder, where a slaying of a person unknown to the murderer occurs. These occur among schizoid and schizophrenic persons especially; here the act of murder, due to an explosion of unbearable psychic tension, can be regarded as a symbolic suicide. Reichard and Tillman point out (in the study cited above) that the murder (or suicide) may represent an internal defensive act that has the function of warding off the progression of the schizophrenic process. Fenichel put the situation axiomatically, stating that "nobody kills himself who has not intended to kill somebody else," [30] to which we must add from criminological experience that the reverse is also true. It should also be noted that in the "philosophical" suicide, where incurable disease or the decision that life is not worth living, or the adolescent's poignant *Weltschmerz*, motivates a suicide, aggression toward an intolerable fate or a seemingly inhospitable, unloving world is really against the self for not changing that world.

Since murder accomplishes the death of the victim, to understand the psychology of the murderer in all its implications it would appear necessary to plumb his or her philosophic notions of death. It is obvious that very few of those who commit a murder consciously philosophize about the death of their victim at the moment of killing. On the other hand, within all humans (whether articulated or not) thoughts of death are present as a central fact of life. Sometimes these thoughts obtrude in most unexpected ways: a sudden accident, an unexpected tragedy—then reality evokes that soundless voice that speaks of death running like a faint theme throughout our lives. Small wonder, then, that poets from the days of Homer and philosophers from the time of Plato were concerned with death and its meaning. "Speak not smoothly of death," sang Homer,[31] and Sartre, the modern existentialist, expounds: "Death tells us about ourselves . . . [but] we have to realize the absurdity of death."[32] Great philosophers and ordinary men alike have been perplexed by this eternal enigma—death.

Common as these thoughts and wonderings may be, the opportunity seldom presents itself for psychiatrists to study empirically the attitudes toward death of actual and potential murderers. In an attempt to arrive at some notion of attitudes toward death in persons *not* involved in aggressive crime, Schilder and the present writer empirically analyzed attitudes toward death in a number of normal[33] and neurotic[34] persons at New York's Bellevue Hospital. The questionnaire method was used, and some of the patients were interviewed later in depth. Our investigations were aimed at understanding attitudes toward death in terms of conscious and unconscious personal experiences.

We found that for those investigated, death had several meanings: (1) escape from an unbearable life situation; (2) a means to force others to give more affection than they are otherwise willing to grant; (3) the equivalence of final sexual union in intercourse; (4) the promise of final narcissistic perfection and unchallenged importance of the individual; (5) gratification of the masochistic tendencies, since self-punishment is eternally satisfied in death. Indeed, we concluded that all the desires of life found intensive expression in the idea of death. In the simplest terms, we think of death as fulfilling the desires, wishes, drives, and feelings of the living. It is clear, then, that inflicting death on another or contemplating it (except in cases of illness due to organic brain disease) tends to solve some intrapsychic problem in the assaulter.

It is obvious, however, that the assaulter or assassin has at the moment of the offense no perception or appreciation of the psychological meaning of death attitudes; he is only aware of the overpowering impulse, the urge of his muscles and senses. But though the murderer has no obvious interest in the philosophy of death ideas, they do bear a direct relation to practical problems of homicide. This is especially true where the concern is with killings by adolescents and youth, a significant aspect of modern criminology. The adolescent whose fantasy life may—paradoxically, in the face of vigorous sexual and activity preoccupation—be thickly strewn with death preoccupation commits senseless and unexplained crimes. They may be committed under the shadow of psychosis, as in the cases of Lee Parker and others, to follow. Adults seldom realize how familiar adolescents may be with problems that have vexed thinkers down through the ages. If one studies the fantasy life of adolescents as expressed in their gang organizations, their games and spontaneous play, their fights, it will be readily seen how ubiquitous are death ideas among youths. Even though association with criminal elements in delinquent areas (*i.e.*, gang fights, gang killings) does help to substantiate these feelings, they nevertheless exist in all youths to varying degrees.

The "death" psychology of the adolescent and that of the adolescent schizophrenic (or schizoid individual) leads to action: This action forms a spectrum, at one end of which lies assault and homicide and at the other, the normal contact sports and interest in daring play activities, such as hot rod racing. The vast majority of adolescents and youth rarely suffer the breakthrough of hostile impulses and death fantasies into the reality of murder and assault.

ADOLESCENCE, SCHIZOPHRENIA, AND DESTRUCTIVE AGGRESSION

Adolescent schizophrenia, or adolescent "breaks," as psychiatric slang has it, often lies behind inexplicable assaults and homicides. To a degree every adolescent or young adult experiences the breakthrough of hostile impulses that to the individual ego appear to be ethical and right. The adolescent is aware only that he is thwarted by adult values; from his position his impulses are "right." Indeed, every adult as well as adolescent is subject to these temporary "breaks," but whether these episodes amount to mental illness or transient psychotic outbreaks or even "blow-ups" will be determined after an intensive analysis of each case.

It should be remembered in assessing adolescent aggression that social pressures are also exerted on the youth. He has had the strictures of society dinned into his ears since childhood. The social values of "right" and "wrong" echoing interminably in his ears seem remote, even slightly ridiculous. The only right or wrong is that which issues from a fist, a knife, or a gun. To kill, to destroy are the natural ends of activity; but punishment is likewise the natural end of destruction. Anticipated punishment paves the way for depression, or at least a depressive affect, appearing in a persistent current of self-defeatism, feelings of inferiority, and depression. The ethical problems arising within the neurotic adolescent appear to him as insurmountable. Often he may ponder or attempt suicide but at the crucial point, the inconvenience or pain are more than anticipated. Better, he feels, to shoot, to kill, another, to offer another's life for one's own.

Ensconced in an unyielding, defensive emotional shell, the patient is unable to see reality, or sees it in a blurred light. The ego cannot contain the impulses that seem to bombard it in a steady stream. Ego stability falters; reality and fantasy merge. Fantasy seems so real and gratifying that death takes on a clean, natural glow; it is punishment at its best. The fear and anger that gripped the disturbed person have been shunted aside and he feels at ease for a brief moment. The notion of crime may at this point enter his isolated mental world. The pattern of control that is ingrained in the average adult, upon which rests our mutual interdependence in this complex world, presents a hazy outline to the adolescent schizophrenic. All he perceives is his pattern, which must be followed to its conclusion. What appears to the outsider as sadism is merely a natural culmination of the patient's appreciation of his own power, its destructive strength, and its meaninglessness to anyone except himself. Power calls for use, for enjoyment of that primitive kinesthetic sensation that emanates from healthy, active muscles. If one could enter into the adolescent criminal's psyche, one could sense how congenial is the genre of force in his world.

When the object of aggression is fragile or young, an added feeling of triumph ensues. The schizoid or psychopathic adolescent yearns for beauty but cannot permit its presence within himself: It would be contrary to the social conserve of masculinity with its accent on force and its denial of esthethics. The natural repository of the artistic or the esthetic in the universe of adolescence is women or homosexuals. Early feelings of rejection, originally aimed at the mother or mother-figure, become projected to women and girls, an added reason for not permitting beauty to exist. Bergler, in investigating the psychic situation of the masochistic neurotic, comments on the presence of the hurt that certain infants feel because of fancied or real rejection. This analyst utilized the name Herostrates to signalize the unconscious need of these persons to do some heroic deed that would center attention upon them.[35] As Herostrates burned the Temple of Artemis (356 B.C.) in order to become renowned, so the "criminotic" (neurotic criminal) unconsciously forces the (infantile) mother-image to recognize that he is not really helpless, that he is indeed capable of revenge. In the adolescent who kills, early infantile complaints against women, long since buried in the unconscious, thrust a clenched fist up through a tottering ego, signalizing an onrush of aggression toward their female victims.

This is often the source of hostility where attractive young women have been murdered for no apparent reason and without obvious sexual reference. Such "senseless killings" have been described as the "despoiler reaction."[36] The case of Lee Parker, described earlier, demonstrates this; death to the old man (symbol of the denial of sexual power) becomes a symbol for death to Toni, and thus, remotely, to Parker himself. For the sick adolescent, nurtured in a culture that directs men to be protectors of women and to enshrine them in the romantic tradition, the struggle to maintain this fiction proves too great for an ego that cannot permit beauty to exist.

Even in nonpsychotic adolescents, outbursts of destructiveness or aggressive sexual interest spring from a generalized hostility that may not find expression beyond occasional vandalism, malicious mischief, or, in some cases, gang fights or rape. In young men described as "despoilers" the conflict lies deeply buried and is more strongly defended, that is, less open to perception. The case that follows demonstrates a savage crime by a young man clinically mentally well. The outcroppings of destructiveness displayed in the murder speaks for the strength of his unconscious hostility toward women.

THE DESPOILER REACTION IN YOUTH

At twenty-two, Cecil Horton was a well-developed youth, neither very bright nor dull. Of an unexceptional family, his behavior record was clear except for a tendency to drink with bravado and to excess. His life centered around the enjoyment of girls and the company of beer-drinking, but generally law-abiding, youths. A marriage contracted at the age of eighteen was followed by divorce and remarriage. There was no history of brushes with the law; Cecil worked steadily as a mechanic's helper. There was little in his workaday life, as detailed by the parents, to predict the offense. The details of his sexual life provided a picture of vigorous but normal drives: His wife and girl-friends, in retrospect, considered him somewhat oversexed, but never brutal. As an attractive youth in a semirural area where opportunities for recreation were not lacking, Horton might have been considered a high-spirited and adventuresome, but not necessarily psychopathic, young man.

So the situation stood one midsummer evening when Cecil and a few friends consumed perhaps a dozen beers in friendly camaraderie. Just before midnight, his companions invited a young waitress from one of the bars for a ride, placing her in the back seat with Cecil. The group drove about at random, chatting gaily. Then, without knowing just why, Cecil began to strike the young woman. Her tearful protests were taken by the others to be part of the fun. Finally, the driver glanced back and saw that the girl was nude. He and the others left the car precipitately at this point. Alone with the girl, Cecil pushed her into the front seat and, while he drove slowly, pelted her with blows. He recalled vaguely, with some complacency, that he had also struck her neck and head with judo chops. Soon he became aware that his victim was unconscious. He drove out of town along the river road where he stopped; dragging her from the car he saw that her face was covered with blood—she was dead. He continued dragging her body to the river bank, where he pushed it into the current, hoping it would sink. Instead, an eddy swirled the body back to shore at his feet; he recalled the full moon that illuminated the scene. With his pocketknife he punctured the lungs and abdomen several times so the body would sink. He then pushed it back into the current, where it disappeared from sight. He washed the blood from his hands, threw his victim's belongings into the river, and went home to sleep. For a week, he kept silent about his night's work, but when the police arrived, a week later, he readily confessed.[37]

Cecil's examination revealed no signs of psychosis or emotional disturbance. His partial amnesia of the murder itself was accounted for by the drinking that evening. The offender's history offered little of psychodynamic significance. He could contribute nothing of his inner feelings to explain his much regretted actions. The insanity issue was denied and the defendant pleaded guilty to first-degree murder, with the stipulation that he would not get the death penalty.* The judge sentenced him to life imprisonment.

The behavior displayed by Cecil was more suggestive of wanton brutality than of sexual excitement. This type of behavior, commonly called "sadistic," resembles rather the delight in destruction displayed by boys of prepuberty age, the wing-pulling, body-rushing, compunctionless aggression against nature so characterisic of boys during their latent sexual period. This reaction, carried to inanimate objects, forms the material of malicious mishief or destruction of property. In felony offenses it crops out in assault, murder, and mayhem, often involving attractive females. The crime of the "despoiler" lies upon a symbolic matrix, appropriation of the dual function of creator and destroyer, a function associated predominately with women.

There is a striking parallel between child-murders by psychotic women and young despoilers; both invoke the fantasy of creativity and its counterpart, destruction. In men the crime lies upon a background of despoiler attitudes, joined with sexual dissatisfactions and profound hostility toward women, who in their embodiment of beauty and dress symbolize human appreciation of esthetic sensitivity. The murderer displays in his act the same symbolic ambivalence as that shown toward their own offspring by women who have committed infanticide. The "despoilers" add their sadism to that fraction of femininity within them that parallels the (unconscious) psychological privileges that women appropriate to themselves. Interestingly, this same reaction is observed among homosexual murderers of youths; it will be discussed

* This is permissible under a 1947 ruling in California.

in a later chapter as will infanticide by women. Here, the assailants almost universally are men with psychosis or neurosis.

It may occur to the casual observer that sexual excitement predominates in the motivations of the despoiler type of murderer. Experience shows, however, that sexual drives function as a channel through which destructive power is expressed. There are, of course, lust-murders, in which sexual desire is combined with aggressive behavior and sadistic outbursts. Criminologically speaking, it seems of little moment whether the form of libidinous activity is heterosexual or homosexual. Among disturbed adolescents or young men under the influence of alcohol, the object of the libidinous drive may be homosexual in type: the drive, initially sexual in nature, suddenly swerves into a purely aggressive act. This mechanism is the basis for the frequent robberies of homosexuals by gangs of young men, or groups of two or three, who openly express their contempt for homosexuals. Beneath this socially "desirable" action which the masculine code approves, lies a complex emotional syncytium. It is woven from skeins of unconscious fear of uncovering their own homosexual interest, a total denial of the anxiety caused by the implication of homosexuality, and compensatory, violent aggression.

There seems little reason to doubt that assaults and homicides by young men perpetrated on persons they meet by chance, and for whom little or no enmity exists, are motivated by reactions to buried homosexual elements. The "adjusted" homosexual is rarely involved in murder. It is the individual who may be struggling with homosexual tendencies, or whose ego is poorly integrated, who is triggered into an aggressive act.

THE SEXUAL ELEMENT IN MURDER

The case now to be considered illustrates one aspect of the relation of sexuality to assault: the murder of a bisexual young man, following his chance acquaintance with a stranger. This case must be prefaced by remarking on a finding not common in this type of murderous assault, the complaint of a "dream state" in the offender, experienced during the assault. At the interrogation, the offender often alleges that his mind "went blank," or that he didn't know why he committed the murder. The prosecutor commonly regards this statement as an attempt to evade guilt, or at least to mitigate punishment. What appears at first blush to be a self-serving maneuver, on study develops another significance. This type of "absence," accompanied by partial amnesia, ultimately proves to be an indication of inadmissibility by the ego of the fact of assault. As will be seen, the "absence" has a complex origin. The original motive, homosexual activity, becomes blurred by an outcropping of revulsion against homosexuality and the partner. Fury against the self, covered by a psychic defense structure (in this case a messianic fantasy), is displaced from its real object, and explodes against the victim. The dream state that overcomes the offender is the result of repression of strong feelings, permitting an unconscious transposition of emotion to an automatic assault or murder. But let the case speak for itself:

The evening was well advanced when Henry Peters folded his apron after his stint as fry cook and prepared to leave the restaurant. Placing his prized meatcutting knives inside the apron in the manner of cooks before him, Peters strolled leisurely toward town. He had no special plans that night except to enjoy the soft air and the walk to his lodgings. On the way, a car stopped for him, picked him up, and drove on. The driver, curiously, was dressed in silken pajamas; it wasn't difficult for Henry to infer that adventure was in the wind. That kind of situation was by no means novel to him. The conversation rapidly veered toward possible sexual intimacies. Peters' account to the District Attorney was freely given. . . .

Somehow conversation drifted around to the usual—women. He began to get a little closer and made remarks indicating he needed some sex. I went along with it: pretty soon he turned off the main road. We found ourselves on a country road. It was late, about midnight, and the driver started to touch me, asking if I minded. . . . I said I didn't care one way or another. Then he touched my privates and asked me to remove my pants.

Peters recounted the story as one relates a casual incident.

By this time—well, he was "down on me" his head on my lap, leaning over from the driver's seat. Something went on in me, kind of revolted. . . . I remember reaching over to where my cook's tools lay on the right side of the seat. I grabbed the handle—it was the big knife. I plunged it into his back, blood spurted out, all over my legs, the seat, the floor of the car. He turned and gasped, something like "I told you a lie—I have a family"—I don't remember the rest, but they tell me he was stabbed thirteen times with a boning knife; the big knife remained stuck in his back.[38]

Peters looked at the District Attorney with a bemused expression, as if inwardly checking off the facts of his report. He continued: "Then I dragged him out of the car, pulled him into the woods."

Peters drove back to town, bought a hamburger, and was about to eat it when he noticed blood on his hands. He was astounded to make this discovery; he turned to look into the car—blood covered the seat. Complacency was replaced by the first crinkling sensation of fear. He drove home and slept for two hours. Then he arose, abandoned the car in town, and fled the city. For a month he wandered around the West, living on the proceeds of the burglaries and robberies he committed freely. Meanwhile, alarms went out for his arrest. Finally, in the Midwest, the police picked Peters up, and returned him to the West coast. Police easily obtained his written confession. He spoke in detail of the night of murder, but the dreamlike quality of his speech was not what the police expected from a seasoned felon. "I don't know exactly why I did kill him," he said, "but I did. . . . robbery wasn't my purpose."

When the facts of Peters' apprehension and extradition were published, public indignation ran high in the city where the murder had occurred. The vicious stabbing aroused the District Attorney's office to make an intensive search of Peters' background and that of the victim, to check literally hundreds of friends and co-workers of the victim. They checked Peters' every movement, his life of robbery, burglary, and petty and major thievery, his slaying some four months before of an admitted homosexual in another city under similar circumstances, his release on probation after a series of fifteen armed robberies in Southern California. The District Attorney's files enlarged the picture of an unconscionable, calloused criminal. There was no doubt they were dealing with a dyssocial personality—a conscienceless criminal.

His background featured complete chaos in the formative years, including complete rejection by his father and, to some degree, by his mother. The psychologist reported Peters as having an uneven but adequate intelligence, and described him as a psychopathic personality with features of weak integrative ability and "underlying primitiveness of thinking, emotional blandness, a basic callousness and inability to empathize with others," impulsiveness, and preoccupation with antisocial behavior. During these hours of study, Peters was calm: "I know I am destined for the gas chamber . . . I have an inclination for that."

The psychiatric examination agreed with the psychologic analysis. Peters was found to be egocentric, impulsive, pleasure-seeking, and also, curiously enough, interested in religion and poetry. All examiners (for the District Attorney and the defense) agreed on his completely antisocial bent. The examiners' conclusions seemed reasonably based on Peters' clinical history: "A characteristic disregard for consequences that stems from infantile striving and wish for omnipotence."

Since the crime had been admitted, even depicted, by the prisoner in the cold sentences of a clinical report, there was no question of insanity as a defense; there was only the question of the meaning of the crime. Peters' legal defenders were piqued by his ready confession; there was also the vital legal point of premeditation, which might mean first-degree murder and execution. Further analysis was suggested.

On the surface Peters seemed almost disassociated emotionally. He expressed no hot resentment or remorse, no open contempt for the homosexual victim, little guilt. Much of his behavior was characterized by jauntiness and self-interest. Nevertheless, there were several unusual aspects to Peters' confession and discussion of the crime. When he "discovered" the blood on his hands he "came to," as out of a reverie. "It was kind of like being drunk . . . things start to come back to you and you remember what you've done," he said musingly.

He then drifted off on his favorite topic, a book he was working on, called "The World-Creation of God," composed in a curious, stilted style, the handwriting overdecorated with curlicues and with one side of each letter accentuated, with no variation in the markings as the lines spun out. More than one observer remarked that the writing suggested a paranoid individual.

Peters' flip, remorseless, egocentric attitude during the trial, as during the crime, aroused the enmity of the community. In the courtroom he appeared euphoric, almost elated. During the lengthy trial, he alternately listened quietly, showing excited pleasure when homosexuality was discussed, or wrote long notes on a pad—one of them turned out to be a lengthy letter to a pretty blonde he had once met. Sometimes Peters spoke feelingly of wanting to tell only the truth. When his hearers would listen, Peters spoke in detail about his desire to be a "Christ-like figure who gives everything to everyone." He rarely let slip an opportunity to mention Oscar Wilde's fairy tale "The Happy Prince," [39] which seemed to him to epitomize the life-direction of his fantasies. In the story, Wilde describes the gilded, bejewelled statue of a prince, standing in the square of a medieval town. As he gazes on the townspeople he becomes aware of the poverty and misery about him. To a friendly bird that nestles in the folds of his mantle, the Prince expresses his feelings: "Give this poor student my sapphire eyes; to this widowed mother, my gold leaf; to this sick child, the precious jewels in my sword handle." The swallow did as he was bid, until little by little, nothing but base metal remained. The town burghers, on seeing the drabness of their once resplendent statue, cried, "Let's do away with it." The statute was consigned to the furnace. Its substance shrank in the flames, but its heart of lead would not melt. The Prince, who had given everything else to the townspeople, still offered his heart.

It was a curious coincidence that Peters, chancing upon this tale, had recognized his masochistic identification with Wilde's prince. To Peters, the tale was his own—the denouement belonged to his deepest desires. Although he recognized his criminal aggression, he felt comfortable inwardly with the image of the selfless Prince. The Wildean drama, only dimly suspected by Peters until he came upon the Happy

Prince story, became his own. It will be recalled that he had said: "I know I am destined for the gas chamber . . . I have an inclination for that." Whatever the court decreed would be anticlimactic.

But his conscientious defense counsel *was* concerned with the anticlimax—the death sentence. The prosecution could not forget that Peters had wantonly taken a life. The examinations had failed to disclose any interference with the prisoner's knowledge of right and wrong; hence there was no possibility of a defense of legal insanity. The issue then hung upon premeditation, requisite for a first-degree murder charge.

THE CAPACITY TO PREMEDITATE AND ITS IMPAIRMENT

At the trial the effect of psychopathy or schizoid personality on the capacity to premeditate was thoroughly aired. An analysis of the prisoner's personality became requisite material for consideration by the jury. Accordingly, witnesses were asked to describe Peters' background as it contributed to his personality distortion: First, his chaotic early life, his broken family life, ever-changing home environment, the fact of never being close to his mother or her inability to be close to him, his father's habitual violence, Peters' inability to form stable attachments for anyone. More than half his life, it was pointed out, had been spent in prisons, reformatories, and institutions. The experts agreed that Peters presented a classical picture of a psychopathic personality. They outlined the historical factors that explained the inadequate balance existing between his impulses, drives, and the control mechanism in the superego. They showed how an X factor—a basic disturbance in the tissues of the brain (sometimes demonstrated by the electroencephalograph)—may underlie this personality type, how egocentricity, pleasure-seeking tendencies, emotional thinness, a paucity of abiding feelings for others, are all bound up in the psychopath's personality structure.[40] Under questioning, the psychiatric witnesses declared that such persons may engage in homosexual acts without really experiencing appropriate, if only temporary, feelings of warmth or excitement toward their partners.

The issue turned upon whether a person in an emotional wasteland, a partial emotional vacuum, can indeed deliberate. Deliberation and premeditation require sufficient "forethought" to commit a crime. Although he was not insane, did Peters possess this forethought? The transcript of the testimony as to this point follows:

Q. Now, Doctor, do you attach any true significance to the fact that this particular event happened during the commission of a homosexual act?

A. Yes, I do. I think that the impact of a homosexual act somehow started the train of reactions which resulted in this impulsive killing. Some sort of a sudden realization occurred, a revulsion, that set off in its train this impulsive act and that interfered with whatever deliberation might have been possible. That is why I say his capacity to deliberate was impaired.

In the cross-examination as to the deliberation issue, the District Attorney focused on the grasping of the knife (as apart from any other cooking utensil—for instance, a spatula) through which the slaying occurred:

Q. It would likewise then be possible that in reaching for the knife he would be reaching for something he would recognize as a potentially lethal weapon?
A. You are asking about knowing [his knowledge]?
Q. Yes, sir.
A. With respect to knowing, I think he knew what a knife was when he saw a knife; he possibly knew what a knife was when he felt that knife.
Q. Could you give us your opinion as to the point after the incident, or during the incident, when the defendant did regain his full capacity, when his capacity was no longer impaired?
A. We are speaking about capacity to premeditate and deliberate?
Q. Yes.
A. Which is different than knowing?
Q. Yes.
A. The point at which he regained his capacity to deliberate, I think, was when he came to in the drive-in.

The issue then narrowed down to premeditation and deliberation, apart from the capacity to know. In the testimony that followed, relating to that which tripped the impulsive reaction in the psychopath, the expert tried to avoid the atomization of emotion and act which legal logic utilizes in determining the presence of deliberation:

Q. Is it correct to say that when the defendant is confronted with frustration he acts it out by this antisocial behavior we have discussed?
A. You can't say it is a one-to-one relationship, that every frustration is reacted to each time. I say he has a personality structure that is patterned by instability, that he has a thin relation to reality and what frustration does to him depends on the situation at any given time.

Other experts, however, did not agree that the defendant's emotional explosiveness impaired his capacity to premeditate. One expert witness pointed to behavior after the crime that disclosed an apparent rationality and with it a capacity to premeditate. The cross-examination of this witness by the defense follows:

Q. Now, the fact that he is leaving the scene—you said he did all these things, went to the car, drove away—the fact that he scattered the belongings from the wallet throughout the area and the fact that he dropped some of his own objects that would identify him, you say that tells you that he had the capacity to premeditate?

A. That is one of the points, yes.

Q. And that indicates to you, Doctor, that he had the capacity to premeditate and deliberate. Is that right?

A. Yes, he was wanting to get rid of the objects.

Q. . . . does it appear strange to you that a person who had this tremendous capacity wouldn't go back and remove these instruments and hide them?

A. Yes, I think here we have to realize that a psychopath, a character neurosis, is a very egocentric person and they feel that many times they would not be apprehended, whereas somebody else would. This is a part of their psychopathy.

Q. And did you take that into consideration in formulating your opinion in this matter?

A. I did.

Q. Will you tell us, Doctor, what indicates to you that the defendant did have the capacity to deliberate and premeditate?

A. Well, I found no evidence of any mental illness; he didn't feel there were any outside influences that had any bearing on him. . . . In fact, he is the least unstable person that has taken the witness stand in this trial. . . . he has restraint and calm and speaks to the point.

Another expert witness agreed on the serious personality distortion present, stating that Peters "did have the ability to premeditate and deliberate the killing." He could not say, however, that the prisoner "actually had so deliberated or premeditated."

After prolonged argument and summation by counsel for both sides, instruction by the judge, and consideration by the jury, a verdict of second-degree murder was brought in, indicating agreement that Peters could not be guilty of first-degree murder in view of impaired capacity to premeditate his crime. The jurors were reported to have said: "None of us was too happy about the decision but we felt under the law there was no other choice."

Public reaction was immediate: Not only the crime but the verdict aroused strong feelings. The press stated editorially:

The verdict of second degree murder returned by a jury of seven men and five women against Henry Peters was, to put it mildly, an outrageous miscarriage of justice. If ever a defendant deserved the death penalty for a cold-blooded and fiendish killing it was Peters.

What in the defamed name of justice could the jurors have been thinking of in returning the comparatively lenient verdict of second degree murder? On what ground was he entitled to the slightest compassion? [41]

A competitive paper editorialized in an opposite vein:

_____ has been torn asunder in recent days by the murder trial of Henry Peters. At the height of the trial feeling was so aroused that the Public Defender was subjected to abuse and threats. . . . Inside the courtroom, personal feelings became so involved at one stage that there was an outbreak. . . . The Jury was made up of men and women of substance in the community who gave of their time and knowledge. They alone had the benefit of all the testimony . . . and an opportunity to study at close range the conduct of the witnesses on the stand. . . . We commend the Judge, the Prosecutor, the Public Defender and members of the Jury for their contribution to the cause of Justice in the community.[42]

In a letter to the editor, one citizen commented on this latter editorial:

Let it be hoped that your close calm reasoning will have a sobering effect on those who with muddled heads and churning guts demand blood sacrifice of the offender and would abandon both evidence and law for a chance to engage in a tribal orgy of retribution. . . .[43]

So ran the public battle. To an observer it was evident that in a case of homicide the utilization of psychological analysis, which tended to explain the psychological background for murder, ran counter to deep public feelings, feelings that sprang from a conviction that the punishment should "fit the crime"!

DEGREES OF GUILT AND PARTIAL RESPONSIBILITY

The case of Peters illustrates some crucial problems arising from major crime in mental situations *not* amounting to insanity. In these murky areas, dynamic psychiatry can be of aid to a discriminating judiciary and conscientious jury. Apart from the juristic importance of psychological analysis of mental conditions not attaining the degree of legal insanity, the Peters case and its resolution demonstrate the humanizing influence of psychiatric efforts to understand and explain motivation in crime. Psychiatry does not have a prima facie interest in relieving offenders of criminal guilt, but the intricacies of human behavior are such that motive, intent, and act in crime are in tight relationship to each other.

It is important to bring into relief the larger question that lies behind the ascertainment of degree of crime; namely, that it revolves around the extent of punishment to be inflicted. If a crime is the result of an "abandoned and malignant heart," punishment is justified, in effect. If a mental disturbance of any degree alters "criminal intent," the penalty to be inflicted will be modified. In this sense, "motive," "intent," and all the factors bearing thereon are significant for psychiatric study of criminals. On the other hand, motives in crime are not of primary concern to the law, for, in the words of Justice Jackson,

courts sometimes must decide whether an act was committed intentionally . . . or whether the action was taken in malice, or after deliberation or with knowledge of certain facts. But in such cases the law pries into the mind only to determine the nature and culpability of an act.[44]

The crucial question in a crime is that of "intent"; if "malice" is conjoined with intent (the word malice being used "in its broadest sense [to] mean the state of mind of a person, irrespective of his motive"; that is, a "hostile" mind, as in ordinary usage), he is consciously violating the law.[45] The question of estimating the influence of a mental condition *on* malice aforethought in a crime passes, then, into the realm of psychologic motives; and distortions of motives fall into the field of psychopathology. Thus, Bernard Diamond in his exhaustive article on "Malice Aforethought" states:

The psychiatrist's job is to make a thoroughgoing investigation . . . searching for the hidden psychodynamics which will explain the unique act of criminal behavior. . . . The questions raised by the elements of premeditation and malice aforethought offer a special opportunity for the application of psychodynamic psychiatry.[46]

The well-documented Gorshen case,[47] in which Dr. Diamond and his associates (including the author) were active, brought these issues to light. Gorshen, a longshoreman, shot and killed his gang boss after being told to leave the job, with no evidence of old or recent ill will toward the victim. Witnesses agreed that there was insufficient incentive for killing. After hearing the evidence, the trial judge commented, "There was no evidence whatsoever that he had a violent temper or anything of the sort."[48] The shooting demanded some explanation, and Dr. Diamond, after a thorough psychiatric examination, established the presence of a long-standing paranoid schizophrenia in Gorshen. He had entertained delusions and hallucinations of satanic influence and fears of bodily changes and sexual perversions being forced on him for many years without his fellow-workers being aware of his mental disturbance. His mental illness was uncovered only through the probing of a knowledgeable psychiatrist. This type of illness, called occult schizophrenia, on its demonstration, was sufficient to base an appeal from a conviction of first-degree murder: premeditation and malice aforethought were manifestly impossible in a person in such a mental state. Gorshen's attorneys, in their appeal, noted that cases of schizophrenia and alcoholism of marked degree and severe states of tension "cause high sensitivity to external stimuli," i.e., exaggerated reaction to external provocation. Such cases could not be said to entertain malice aforethought.[49] A brief filed on behalf of eighteen psychiatrists (amici curiae) requested the Appeal Court to permit probing into the chain of psychological and circumstantial events, to understand the pathological distortions between the inner mechanisms of a sick mind and the external world of reality.[50]

MURDER AND PSYCHOSIS

The discussion up to this point has focused on homicides wherein the relationship between the act and the underlying psychopathology has been demonstrable. The extreme of this group covers homicides committed as the result of paranoid delusions; these have been amply dealt with in the literature. Here, the relation between the emotional state (the psychosis) and the crime may be clear, as with the murders by the "Mad Sculptor," [51] or in triangle murders where infidelity observed *flagrante delicto* arouses acute emotional explosions with resulting killing. But many cases of homicide or assault are encountered in which the ego of the offender is distorted by mental illness to the point where the dynamic motivation is not traceable.[52] In such cases the relation between crime and the psychic mechanisms involved is shadowy and elusive of description. This group does not include the many homicides committed by delusional persons but does include a class of psychotic persons who commit manifestly wanton homicides or assaults.

Aggression in wanton murderers has no well-defined psychic meaning, represents no obvious infantile (unconscious) acting-out mechanism, and presents no recognizable symbolism. If meaningful trends, which would elucidate the architecture of the crime, are discernible they are buried in the chaos of the offender's insanity. From the standpoint of describing crime as behavior, we are in a no man's land however much we may wish to read meaning into these acts of wanton murder. This is not to say that study of insane criminals has not yielded a rich harvest of clinical observations and conclusions. Scores of studies by competent students of criminology (Wertham, Menninger, Karpman, Zilboorg, and many others [53]) have shown the psychologic correlates of a variety of crimes by psychotic persons.

Psychiatry has benefitted by these clinical studies in that the literature has been enriched with descriptions of cases of organic brain disease, schizophrenia, mania, paranoia, epilepsy, alcoholic psychoses, mental deficiency, severe psychopathic (sociopathic) personalities, and severe obsessional and compulsive neuroses whose mental aberrations have propelled individuals into crime. Articles and treatises in the hundreds, ranging from Prichard [54] to Isaac Ray [55] in the nineteenth century to Guttmacher and Weihofen [56] and Roche [57] in our time, have given details of psychiatric interest, chiefly from the standpoint of legal culpability. Since this work is devoted more specifically to crime and punishment as individual behavior and social response, it would be irrelevant as well as repetitious to categorize the cases illustrating the types of mental illness represented in crime. The accent here will be on those subclinical states—lesser grades of recognized mental conditions and distortions of "normality," whether culturally or individually determined—that form the psychologic substrate of the majority of today's criminal offenders.

The following case is a wanton killing by a man who, all examiners agreed, was psychotic at the time of the crime. But even in this clearcut case of a schizophrenic individual there was room for suspicion that the aggressive urge, in some unexplained way, utilized the ego rupture (the psychosis) as a defensive structure to symbolically deny the actuality of a deliberate murder. One comes away from a deep study of this offender with the feeling that aggression is so egosyntonic, so congenial to the human psyche, even in mental disease, as to manipulate the ego defenses in its own favor. One glimpses here that hazy borderline where biology and dynamic psychiatry meet, where raw instinct erupts through the obscuring and defensive movements of the ego in acts of violence. Such cases are properly diagnosed as "insane," and yet——

THE WANTON KILLER

There is in this land an army of strong, quiet men whose names never reach the newspapers, who fill the construction camps, operate the heavy machinery, grease the wheels of communication, and weld the steely sinews of industry. They are lonely men, unmarried or separated, living unpretentiously in small hotels or single rooms, working quietly and efficiently, asking little more than a union scale of wages, a neighborhood bar, an occasional evening of mild adventure. Their clothes are utilitarian, their food substantial, their ideas practical, their perceptions clear and simply stated. Such men are more at home with jackhammers and gaskets than with the best-seller list; they make no claim to refinements, living lives without desperation but with the solid satisfaction of a job, a pickup truck, and perhaps a hunting rifle.

Claude Girard was such a man; he came of a good working-class family. Always a lone wolf, his recreations were limited to reading magazines on firearms and practicing with his rifle on a range, or hunting alone in the hills. Few knew him, for he avoided friends and when drinking in a bar was unobtrusive and asocial rather than antisocial. His life had been lived in small hotels and rooming houses. Claude's work record was excellent; all his employers reported him to be a solid, efficient worker—a man to depend on. During World War II, he did a shipshape job in the Navy until, at the age of about twenty-three, he suddenly developed an acute mental condition. During this episode he was facetious, destructive, and incoherent. Hospitalized, he was treated as an acute schizophrenic. There was no recourse but to discharge him from the Navy.

Within a month, Claude was back at work as a welder. For the next eight years his life consisted of a steady diet of work, of solitary hunting trips, and six schizophrenic episodes followed by treatment. After each of the treatment periods, during which he was placed in state or federal hospitals, he emerged mentally clear, the same cheerful, workmanlike Claude—silent but willing, his foreman's pride. His brother, who rarely saw him except when called to the hospital when Claude developed an acute illness, never understood the reason for these attacks of insanity. When Claude returned to his small hotel, recovered, there was little need to probe his psychologic state. Claude never discussed his mental troubles and his silent return to routine life excited little comment. No one seeing Claude in a state of remission from illness could have anticipated the occurrences of that foggy morning when he committed a wanton murder.

One Christmas Day a farmer and his wife were driving along a main highway in the mountains. Fog slowed down their progress. When they saw a truck pulled up at the side of the road, they stopped as the occupant of the truck hailed them. Hunting rifle in hand, the man told the farmer, briefly but lucidly, that his car had broken down and that he wanted a lift to the closest garage. The farmer's wife noticed four cans on the road in front of Claude's truck, set in a rectangular formation. She saw the stranger throw a piece of metal under the car as he spoke. His behavior, and the gun, unnerved the farmer slightly, but with presence of mind he said he would be back shortly, having an errand to do, and drove off slowly. When they were twenty or thirty feet away, the farmer's wife heard the crack of a rifle. Glancing at her husband she saw him drooping over the wheel; the stranger was standing calmly on the road behind the farmer's truck. The bullet had come from his gun; the shooting was deliberate, precise, and deadly on that quiet Christmas morning.[58]

The victim's wife, paralyzed with fear, managed to stop the truck. "I heard the gun, but I really didn't realize that my husband had been shot until his glasses hit the floor. The truck was going along with nobody driving. I tried to put my foot on the brake. We swerved—it was horrible."

Claude Girard stood near his truck quietly, deer rifle in hand. He waited patiently for the sheriff, who gingerly disarmed him. Although his apprehension was accomplished without difficulty, the investigation progressed less easily. Girard spoke disconnectedly, his manner unpretentious, his behavior neither excited nor elated. When asked why he had shot the farmer, whom he could not have known, he replied, "That's none of your goddamn business." During the long, meticulous interview the investigating sheriff observed that Girard's tone was alternatingly smart-alecky and serious. He described how he had lined up the gun through the window of the cab. He said simply: "I missed, or he died, I don't know which." The interrogation and answers continued in this unresponsive, desultory vein:

Q. What reason can you give for shooting this man?
A. I just thought it would be a good idea at the time.
Q. Why did you think it would be a good idea?
A. Because I never had no time.
Q. What reason was there for you to shoot him?
A. None.
Q. Why did you shoot him?
A. Made a mistake.
Q. Had he done anything to you in the way of harm?
A. Not that I know of.

The interrogation developed no motivational material that would shed light on the killing. Girard readily agreed that he fired the one, accurate shot that shattered the base of the victim's skull. His manner was bantering, occasionally grotesquely jocular, his speech garbled:

Q. What did you do?
A. I tried to flag down a man's car and almost got knocked down.
Q. Who was in the car?
A. There were three people in it, all men.
Q. Were they men or women?
A. One was split and one ain't . . . that's how they tell, don't they?

A rapid check of Girard's record revealed the fact that he had been hospitalized several times. Within a few days, his manner became agitated, his speech more disconnected, the information which he offered, confused. Further legal preparation being impossible, Girard was transferred to a state hospital where it immediately became necessary to treat him for destructiveness, agitation, obscene and noisy shouting, and disturbed behavior. From breezy, amusedly laconic speech, the prisoner changed to mutism. A series of shock treatments rendered the offender quieter and more disposed to speak of the offense. His responses, however, remained quixotic and incoherent. For example, when asked why he was in the hospital, he answered:

I'm not sure, a friend of mine brought me here. . . . I shot at somebody . . . my hand was full of nothing . . . my car was stuck on the curb. I parked it and one wheel went over the curb.

Continued questioning in the hospital produced the same sort of obscene witticisms that the investigators had encountered. When asked if he carried a rifle, Girard answered with a snort:

I have taken enough bullshit around here. . . . eat a couple of tons of it and see. Some eat it, some smoke it, and some chew it. With a crop duster you can spread it around.

In other areas, Girard's irritability relaxed and he conversed with apparent interest and intelligence. He gave an accurate description of the shock-treatment process, spoke of his work record, discussed his Navy experience and previous hospitalizations. When comment was made that his word usage on general topics was adequate, he responded: "Well, every word you utter is true, false, or has a deflated meaning . . . like a tube inflated."

Throughout long examinations Girard smiled at times in consonance with his pithy, disconnected statements, at times inappropriately. There was a flight of ideas, a jumpiness in his speech, and considerable winking and smirking accompanying his rough, barroom repartee. For example, when pressed for an answer to the casual question as to what he liked to eat, Girard answered: "The main course, the second, third, or fourth." When a specific answer was again requested, he answered: "Prune whip."

Time passed; Girard was treated intensively by psychiatric methods. A careful recheck of the history, interviews with his brother, fellow workers, employers, landlords, neighbors, and casual acquaintances filled in the picture of this lonely man, lonely out of choice and out of the inhibitions of his restricted personality. All informants agreed that he was not an aggressive person, that he was usually immersed in reading hunting magazines, received little mail, spoke to others briefly but pleasantly, was a hard worker—"The best I ever hired," said one employer. There had been periods during the past fifteen years when he disappeared from what could charitably be called "haunts," then reappeared, the same quiet, smiling, "working stiff." Only brother Andrew knew that he entered hospitals, received shock treatments, remained several months, and was discharged as improved, the diagnosis usually reading schizophrenia or depression. His psychotic episodes started with nervous, highstrung behavior, never with violence. Even on the day before the murder, nothing untoward was observed by acquaintances who met him before he left for a holiday in the mountains.

Reexamination a year later revealed a totally different man. His expression was pleasant, his smile a little set. He remembered nothing of the occurrences of that Christmas Day; he recalled nothing up to the following April, when he "came to" in the hospital. Soberly, he judged his situation as it was reviewed for him: "If I shot a man, that's murder. . . . I don't remember anything of it, but if I shot a man I have to be punished."

Q. What if you get the gas chamber?
A. I'd have to go. . . . I know right from wrong . . . but I can't understand how it happened.

It was of some significance from a medicolegal point of view that no delusions of persecution were ever elicited from Girard, that his amnesia for the offense never faltered in either his sick or well periods, that his bantering, grotesquely jocular periods were suggestive of the hebephrenic form of schizophrenia, whereas many of his answers after treatment seemed reasonable.

It could be readily imagined that the superficial layer of his perceptive ego dealt with the external world through the mechanism of denial through jocularity (a mechanism often seen in wit), while the disjunction of the deeper portions of his ego (schizophrenia) effaced his aggressive impulses. When these impulses erupted during the crime, the ego was overrun and a psychotic picture rose to the surface. The law does not permit an offender who was insane at the time of the crime to be punished, no matter what wishes the prisoner expresses in his sane moments. This wanton killing seemed to represent an outburst of aggression within the psyche of the offender, which sought egress during the periodic psychotic episodes that represented periods of ego-disorganization. To speculate on the dynamic meaning of these aggressive explosions erupting during these periods of ego-disintegration is not especially satisfactory in the absence of "material" from the patient that might explain his underlying thoughts. Yet it could easily be imagined that his aggressive explosion (the murder), though expressed in an apparently calm manner, was a silent complaint against the emotional sterility of his life.

MURDER AND THE DISORDERED BRAIN

It has been recognized for many years that organic brain disease of certain types may underlie violent behavior just as do functional mental diseases, such as schizophrenia. Crimes secondary to chronic alcoholic deterioration, epilepsy and its variants, mental defect of congenital type, cerebral syphilis, brain tumor, brain injury, and so on, have been described in these pages and elsewhere.[59] In addition to this array of brain conditions, subclinical states (where the disease is not advanced sufficiently to justify a "diagnosis") also influence behavior to the point where the issue of criminal irresponsibility arises. These situations have been discussed under the doctrine of partial responsibility (Chapter III). In this sense, epilepsy and its mental effects constitute a special case of subclinical conditions, not yet called "mental disease," lying behind criminal actions. Here arises the vexing problem of disturbances of consciousness, as opposed to insanity impinging on criminal responsibility, for consciousness is a necessary element in crime. In California, for example, the law states:

When a person commits an act without being conscious thereof, he does not thereby commit a crime even though such an act would constitute a crime when committed by a person who was conscious.[60]

Sanford Fox has pointed out that this "expanded noninsanity defense," [61] as apart from the insanity plea with its direct involvement of the "knowledge of right and wrong test," does not exist in other than the Western states. In any event, the question of unconsciousness bears directly on crime in organic states, particularly in epilepsy, where unconsciousness and subsequent amnesia are present. The peculiar effect of brain disease on the "knowledge" of a criminal-actor may be illustrated by the complex of epileptic conditions. Before these criminological implications are discussed, however, it might be well to define the various types of epilepsies:

The *grand mal* type of epilepsy is characterized by a major convulsion, often preceded by an aura, associated with unconsciousness and skin-color changes, followed by amnesia. Individuals afflicted with this condition rarely become involved with violent crimes, except in the condition called *postepileptic furor* (postictal furor), in which the patient strikes out blindly with violent force, unaware of what he is doing. The various forms of epilepsy, *petit mal, jacksonian epilepsy, somnambulism* (a designation of older authorities), are ordinarily not involved with criminal acts.* The *epileptic equivalent,* a state in

* Hysteroepilepsy is sometimes included; this is now questioned by modern authorities.

which extreme irritability, irrational anger, sudden, inexplicable rages, or even habitual faultfinding without reason occur, "awareness and consciousness being maintained," [62] also may be accompanied by momentary unconsciousness. The condition may be characterized by *fugue* states, or "absences," in which the patient wanders from his accustomed haunts without perception of what he is doing. The fugue states do result from hysterical mechanisms also, as witnessed by the numerous cases of amnesia for which no head injury or epileptic condition is responsible. During the fugue, automatic behavior, which is characteristic of the patient's personality pattern, is displayed; no conscious awareness of the aimless or even complicated movements is present; amnesia follows the behavior enacted. *Psychomotor epilepsy,* now considered as temporal lobe epilepsy, features coordinated, automatic movements, dreamy states, etc., approaching the fugue. It is this group of seizure patterns and reactions that brings us close to the problem of irresponsibility for criminal activity. Finally, the *epileptoid personality* has been described (and denied by some [63]) as classical in its self-righteousness, egocentricity, poverty and restriction of outside interests, marked religiosity, diminished respect for reality, and emotional intensity. The epileptoid personality may exist with or without actual epilepsy. And finally, the *epileptic psychosis* is considered an extension of postictal confusion, being characterized by delusional or hallucinatory experiences that are relatively short-lived. This type includes the post-epileptic furor.

For a century and a half it has been agreed among alienists that epilepsy and epileptic insanity give rise to fugue states in which vicious and senseless crimes have occurred. Psychiatric pioneers of the nineteenth century recognized clinical variants of epilepsy in their relation to aggressive crime. Basing their understanding on the condition of "masked epilepsy" (described by Esquirol [64] in the 1830's), in which mental automatism may replace an epileptic seizure, observers recognized the special character of epileptic homicides. The English neurologist Sir William Gowers, echoing the opinion of clinicians of his time, wrote:

These automatic actions . . . have the aspect of voluntary actions. It is, indeed, often not easy to convince observers that these actions are not deliberately volitional.[65]

In more spectacular language, Trousseau, the French clinician, stated: "Whenever there is a revolting and motiveless crime I suspect the existence of epilepsy." [66] In fact, prior to the development of the electroencephalograph, it was virtually a clinical axiom among alienists that heinous murders or assaults, otherwise unexplained, were attributable to hidden forms of epilepsy. As late as 1906, the Italian psychiatrist Bianchi, in speaking of mania senses this relation:

In the typical and severer form of mania (furor) . . . the desire for violent destruction . . . is accentuated . . . resembling somewhat the excited and sinister mind of the epileptic.[67]

These clinical impressions of competent alienists were buttressed by a long history of attitudes toward epilepsy. It cannot escape notice that the conception of epileptic behavior as "sinister" (Bianchi) betrays the older idea of degeneracy as the background for obscure brain diseases, as, for example, Lombroso's "epileptoid criminal condition." In spite of modern criticism these clinical correlations cannot be ignored. Hence, when unnecessarily violent aggression is evidenced in crime we must look at the broad spectrum of those conditions which may underlie this behavior. Extreme care needs to be taken to relate brain disorder, if any exists, to violent behavior; for example, the aggressive, destructive outbursts among aggressive psychopaths who are neurologically normal. This is a group of individuals whose emotion, once stimulated, leads without inner controls to violent behavior. The question that suggests itself is whether such persons, known as "acting-out individuals," "aggressive psychopaths," "enemies of society," "dyssocial personalities," and so on, show diagnostic brain-wave changes.

Since the 1930's, the electroencephalograph has helped to pinpoint actual cerebral functional irregularities that might predispose to aggressive behavior. It is thought that the aggressive psychopath could be more accurately diagnosed by its use. According to the best authorities—Gibbs, Silverman, Knott, Gottlieb—roughly 50 per cent of all clinically diagnosed psychopaths show abnormal electroencephalographic tracings. Indeed, these authorities have set down as an etiological axiom:

Psychopathic personality is a mental illness resulting from inborn or early acquired cerebral dysfunction and disturbed parent-child relationships.[68]

It remained, then, to relate aggressive and violent crime among psychopaths to cerebral tissue disturbances: thus, a population of 452 offenders convicted of major crime was examined with the brain-wave instrument.[69] In this crucial study Gibbs and his associates found no significant changes in the electroencephalographic tracings. Hence it seemed reasonable to conclude that clinical forms of epileptic disorders are not, in any significant fashion, crucial factors in a convicted criminal population. (In these studies, electroencephalographic changes of any grade or type were considered positive.) Evidence for a direct relation between cerebral dysrhythmia (organic brain disorder) and violent crime is ambiguous. However, Gibbs and his associates still state that "epileptics occasionally commit crimes during psychomotor seizures."

To further investigate the relation between epileptic states and violent crime, the author studied more than 27,000 consecutive cases examined clinically in the Psychiatric Clinic, Court of General Sessions, New York, over a ten-year period. These persons were examined after conviction of major crimes (felonies) and represent the *total number* of felony convictions in New York County from December 24, 1931, to December 24, 1941. Thirteen qualified psychiatrists examined these individuals within these ten years. Their diagnoses were made in terms of intelligence, mental capacity, presence of mental illness or abnormality, and personality structure. This tabulation of *routine* examinations discloses that .035 per cent of all those convicted of major felonies in this 27,693 sample of a criminal population were diagnosed as demonstrating types of the epileptic complex. Table 6 (page 135) shows the relation between the type of crime and the variety of epileptoid disturbances diagnosed *without* the use of brain-wave tests.

In recent years, since the electroencephalograph has aided the evaluation of brain conditions, the criminologic literature evidences a continued interest in murders by epileptics. Psychomotor epilepsy has particularly claimed attention; thus, Podolsky[70] reports from the records of twenty murderers who claimed amnesia for their crimes a definite relation between psychomotor epilepsy (autonomic diencephalic epilepsy?) and violent crime. English authorities[71] recognize that automatic behavior may follow this condition and have urged relief of criminal responsibility for those suffering from this condition. In a case heard in Ireland,[72] the issue was whether psychomotor epilepsy was validly a "defect of reason from disease of the mind," and hence sufficient to excuse one Bratty for strangulating his victim during a "blackout." The judge refused to instruct the jury that automatic behavior during such a blackout was sufficient to acquit unless an insanity defense was urged, even though the doctors agreed that "psychomotor epilepsy was a defect of reason due to disease of the mind."

In spite of the position of the law, clinicians have found evidence of a distinct relation between epileptic variants and violent crime. A Polish investigator[73] analyzed a large series of 250 cases of epileptics concerned with crime, concluding that "epilepsy, compared with other diseases, is not so haphazardly connected with delinquent behavior as was previously thought." An Australian psychiatrist[74] reported a recent case of psychomotor epilepsy with positive electroencephalographic findings in a man whose previous character made his criminal act quite unlikely (except due to automatism following a seizure). Similarly,

FROM THE RECORDS OF THE PSYCHIATRIC CLINIC, COURT OF GENERAL SESSIONS, NEW YORK, COVERING PERIOD OF DECEMBER 24, 1931, TO DECEMBER 24, 1941

Clinical Diagnosis (without E.E.G.)	Idiopathic Epilepsy, includes History of, Also traumatic	Epileptoid Personality	Epileptic Equivalent incl. Psychomotor	Hysteroepilepsy
Aggressive Crimes				
Assault 17	9	6	1	1
Manslaughter 5	—	5	—	—
Murder 9	2	6	—	1
Robbery 21	12	8	—	1
Carrying Concealed Weapon 4	4	—	—	—
Total 56	27	25	1	3
Passive-Aggressive Crimes				
Larceny 21	9	12	—	—
Burglary 15	13	2	—	—
Bigamy 1	1	—	—	—
False Registration 1	1	—	—	—
Violation of Probation 2	1	1	—	—
Forgery 1	1	—	—	—
Total 41	26	15	—	—
Grand Total 97 *	53	40	1	3

* .035% of 27,693 offenders examined Dec. 1931 to Dec. 1941

Italian workers [75] find a correlation between antisocial behavior patterns and the localization of epileptogenic foci. In the words of these authors, "the epileptic personality represents a mental condition which decreases the subject's will power at the moment of the crime."

The total effect of these studies underscores a dual conclusion: (a) that cases involving the epileptic complex are directly related to criminal acts—more particularly, violent crime, and (b) numerically, this relationship is not impressive. The systematic investigation done in the Court of General Sessions by the author (Table 6) indicates only a slight preponderance of aggressive crime over passive-aggressive crime among epileptics. However, the frequency of epilepsy among criminals is *not greater* than the frequency of epilepsy in the law-abiding population. It must be concluded, therefore, that the incidence of crime due to the epileptic complex is not greater than it is among nonepileptics. That this relationship exists, however, is undoubted.

This relationship between seizure states and violent behavior becomes a moot point from the standpoint of establishing legal responsibility. The issue revolves around whether the convulsions, their aftermath, or their equivalents impair or remove the offender's cognition during the criminal act, whether he knew what he was doing, and so forth. The answer depends on a minute investigation of the individual case. The relation between emotional explosions, associated with cerebral dysrhythmias, mental obfuscation, and criminal acts, requires careful interpretation, as the following case will demonstrate. It is that of Jack Ruby, who at close range shot and killed Lee Harvey Oswald, President Kennedy's alleged assassin.[76]

PROFILE OF A KILLER

At the age of fifty-two, Jack Ruby represented an anachronism reaching back to the American melting pot of the early 1900's. Born into the turmoil and uncertainties of the life of an immigrant's son, he lived with little perception of how atypical it was compared with that of the average American boy. To young Jacob Rubenstein, life was defense and attack. Hardships and underprivilege gave way to the pounding of fists, swagger and daring were the currency of social relatedness, loyalty to one's self the keystone of personal worth. His life of activity touched on the fringe of the American ethos but did not borrow its relative stability. Somehow, Jacob, who became "Jack" as boyhood advanced, never understood the interplay of aggression and restraint that spells social adjustment. However, a strong sense of patriotism grew within him, acting in part as a cover for the shoddy adjustment he was to make.

Jack's father, a noisy, bibulous carpenter, proud of the "Cossack" spirit he had absorbed from his early service in the Imperial Russian Army, brought up the eight children in his own patternless way. He depended upon his more socially attuned wife to provide any hint of softness in the home atmosphere. Jack's mother, who spoke of herself as having higher tastes (*edel* was the word she used, meaning "noble" or "high-born" in German), was nevertheless capable of argumentativeness also. Tension, arguments, brutality characterized the Rubensteins' family life; separation followed separation until Jack was twelve years of age. About this time, his mother developed a depression, was treated in the state hospital, and died several years later. The home now broken, the children were sent to various foster homes scattered throughout the Chicago area.

In retrospect, the sons and daughters united in complaining of the pressure of poverty and of the constant turmoil at home, some siding with the father, but most with the mother. After the dispersion, the children went their separate ways, although still, potentially, at least, interested in one another. Of them all, Jack and his sister Eve were especially close. They both agreed that they had inherited their father's unstable temperament; neither, however, was alcoholic.

Jack dropped out of high school in the first year. If his home ever had a central motif, it was perhaps the desire to escape poverty. Money now became the important thing in life for him. As a boy he had sold shopping bags on a street corner to family shoppers. When the opportunity presented itself, he became an entrepreneur: if balloons sold well in the ball park, Jack took them on; if there was money in fake watches, he sold them also. As huckster, dealer in novelties, salesman, assistant union agent, Ruby roamed the Chicago area, and later the West Coast. He always made a "buck" because, in his Damon Runyanesque phrase, "I used a little ingenuity." Most of his work career consisted of selling trinkets, scalping tickets or selling refreshments at sporting events, house-to-house canvassing, selling salt and pepper sets, operating a mail-order business—he made a living wherever and however he could. Actually, he was never far from the periphery of the underworld. An aspirant to the life of a racketeer, but too obvious and undisciplined to be trusted by other racketeers, Ruby admired the universe of force.

With the advent of World War II, Ruby's itinerant business career was halted. After serving in the Air Force and receiving an honorable discharge, he aspired to an improved social status. "I wanted to go first class," he said. Settling in Dallas, he believed his place in society was fixed. Although he felt like a "foreigner in Texas," he considered himself a "positive thinker," an admirer of "class"; now he could move ahead socially. Ruby had acquired a veneer of positivism that covered his unstable personality: "I used a dominant attitude with people," he explained. "I was a constant challenge [in Dallas] for sixteen years."

But his explosive reactions, quixotic behavior, and malapropisms earned him only the reputation of being a "character." His circumstantiality and unrealistic reliance on physical strength were the first faint indications of a mental disturbance. As will be shown, the distortion of his behavior, even allowing for cultural coloration, progressed to the level of a virtual psychotic divorce from reality. But in his own estimation he was a success: "To run the biggest hillbilly place in Dallas, for a Jew is something . . . coming from a ghetto in Chicago," he said, with sudden tears in his eyes.

In spite of this favorable self-evaluation, Jack's criminal record suggested an abnormal personality, even before he came to Texas. On analysis, it reduced to ten minor offenses for battery and assault, for minor infractions, for suspicion of pandering and abduction, and the like. His explanations were always unrealistic. For example:

They tried to shake me down in Chicago and beat me with a pistol. . . . I got a day in jail for that. Or the time I clipped a fellow who cheated me out of some money and then they made it assault, but I got out the same day.

One year he took a six-year-old Negro boy to New York ("I was negotiating for TV") to introduce him to show business. Since the boy had dancing talent and Ruby had promised his grandparents that he would be a quick success, he saw nothing unusual about this bit of promotion. A charge of abduction resulting therefrom was dropped. But the early seeds of defect-in-judgment displayed in this episode evaded Jack; he followed this account with another: "When I was in San Francisco I saw a camel hair overcoat. I took it and gave it to a friend. The friend sold it for seventy-five dollars," he said with an inappropriate smile.

By the time Ruby was in his early thirties, fifteen eventful years were behind him. He had received two head injuries, the second of which had been diagnosed as a brain concussion in a Chicago hospital, lost the terminal joint of one finger (bitten off in a street fight), had amassed a reputation for being a tough, "wild" man. Barney Ross, the boxer, brought up with Ruby on Chicago's West Side, recalled the quick temper that earned Jack the nickname "Sparky": "He would turn blue with rage," recalled Ross, "when someone didn't agree with him." Childish tantrums, which subsided a moment later, were also recalled by Dallas acquaintances. On one occasion Ruby became so enraged at a cabdriver that he ended in beating the man's head on the concrete sidewalk. Suddenly, he stopped and asked, "What am I doing?" as his rage rapidly melted away.

Embarked on a business career in Dallas, he was in contact with gamblers with whom he tried to arrange all sorts of "big deals," the details of which were never very clear to his auditors. Apparently business associates felt the same because, aside from the two clubs he operated in Dallas and the one that failed (Silver Spur), the facts are obscure as to actual business ventures in which he was engaged. Illustrative of this was his trip to Cuba, which had been explored by the authorities for a possible Communist connection. In association with a certain gambler who operated in Havana and other Gulf cities, Ruby spent ten days in and around a club in pre-Castro Havana. He was elated to be considered not only a "tough Jew" but an associate of "classy men." "They taught me how to eat, to dress." They talked "big money" but eventually they dropped him from consideration in the "deal."

His complaints that his competitors in the striptease business "took advantage" of him are interpretable as reflecting their opinion that he was a bungler in business. But bungler or no, Jack warmed to the fact that he was "in the know":

They used to say, "Jack is a right S.O.B."; they loved me. Some of my competitors wanted to run me out of town . . . they wanted to get something on me for a stripper, Candy Bar . . . and one time they talked about Honey Cup . . . she was colored . . . something about the Mann Act, but believe me I'm no pushover. Their greatest victory [this he said with emphasis] was that somebody should put me in a hospital . . . if you start trouble with Ruby [and here he smiled expansively] I'm simply ready for trouble.

His accounts of fights were legion; some of these smacked of fabrication, although associates vouched for their authenticity. In his club, he broke up fights, knocked guns out of his rougher customers' hands, jumped over the bar to quell a troublemaker, street-fought men a head taller than himself, and so on and on. "I'm a man geared for action and fight. . . . I can't take ribbing. . . . I lived in a jungle; this town [Dallas] is homicidal; people do murder in Dallas and pay a ten dollar fine." Ruby's preoccupation with fights, homicide, guns, and his position as an arbiter of conflict denoted a persistent paranoid air. At one time he had business relations with a man who was later convicted of a felony and sentenced to eight years in the state prison. Jack felt he himself was suspected of being a member of a Chicago syndicate; his fears ran rampant: "They wanted to run me out of town."

Ruby talked readily, compulsively. He didn't talk to his auditor, he just talked as he moved—physiologically, so to speak—bobbing his head forward like a boxer, rolling up phrase after phrase, which became entangled with malapropisms, flashes of aggression, and self-aggrandizement. His verbalizing outdistanced his ideas: it was circumlocutory, it was aggressive, paranoid, and just beyond the firm ground of reality. One had to listen a long time to catch the thin line of inconsequentiality and the confused thinking behind it. He spoke of himself as a phenomenon, without conscious appreciation of any inappropriateness. A messianic tendency peeped through the tangle of immature bragga- docio: "Inwardly I was a representative of the Jewish people." Action and idealism were smudged in his mind: "I'm a guy geared to fight . . . a little Heb being a big guy. One fellow, Mac, he said I was the tough- est Jew he ever knew." This latent paranoid trend gained strength as the years passed.

The epileptoid personality is egocentric and, simultaneously, by a strange quirk, religious and altruistic. Ruby demonstrated this charac- teristic. He never tired of reporting how generous he was and how frenzied his generosity became when somebody was injured or killed accidentally. The prisoner's religious interests, which started with a Jewish education, waned in early years, but increased during the last twelve years. He was active in a Conservative synagogue, but took time to interest himself in an older, Orthodox synagogue in South Dallas. Although not learned, he had great respect for Orthodoxy and a kind of hysterical interest in religion. He felt himself a messiah, a saviour of the Jewish people in the South—a saviour without portfolio!

It would be expected that his sexuality was more casual than intense, interspersed with transitory sexual contacts over the years. Although homosexuality was never an overt problem, there were signs that a psychoanalyst might discern of a struggle with unconscious homo- sexuality—in his sexual techniques, predilections, fears, and so on. Several attacks of venereal disease had impaired his potency over the years, but the strippers still "looked good to him" and he had a dim plan that some day he would marry the girl to whom he had been "engaged" for ten years; "after ten years, you know, you've got to get promiscuous, but she was a clean, moral girl." But sexuality took second place to the world of fight. To be a "right guy," to be loved by the police and by his associates, to lead the Jewish people militantly prom- ised more than love—more than womanly love.

The type of narcissistic defensiveness that Ruby displayed could be expected to be reflected in his body-concern. Always a crank about food and nutrition, he had a ritual of physical exercise and an interest in stimulating drugs that occupied much of his attention. For about two months before the murder he had taken a drug for weight-reducing; for two years he had taken a drug that combined Dexedrin and a sedative that "makes you a positive thinker." He took Preludin for a nonexistent weight problem: "It helped me handle things." He would buy drugs from pharmaceutical agents and sell or give them to friends, to "share my happiness." He would embark on "magic menus," on food preparations with names like CDR, Concentrated Protein, and the like. His body-concern, his emphasis on physical strength, the faintly feminine air about his conversational manner produced an impression of personality disintegration on his listeners. It was the curious mixture of instability, impulsiveness, and unreality in the midst of a world of dollars, deals, hurly-burly fights that suggested an aura of psychosis around this man.

But there were other, positive mental signs: three depressions in his life. The first occurred in 1940 following the killing of one Leon, an attorney friend, during a union altercation. Ruby was held overnight for questioning. He was so hurt and heartsick over this that he mourned for months, even adopted "Leon" as part of his own name. He sought no medical help and gradually came out of the depression.

The second depression followed the failure of a business venture, the Silver Spur nightclub in Dallas. He became overpowered with suicidal feelings, developed a prolonged apathy, and hid away in a hotel room for two months, deeply depressed. The third depression occurred after the assassination of the President.

In addition, there was a fourth curious episode which had never been explained. Considered in retrospect, it appeared to be an "absence." Ruby, at ringside, was watching his friend Barney Ross fight in San Francisco. When Barney was knocked down, Ruby fainted. In the general excitement, little was made of this inexplicable episode. Later, after the assassination, when a brain-wave tracing showed evidences of cerebral dysrhythmia, this occurrence assumed a degree of significance.

THE PSYCHIATRIC EVALUATION

The picture that emerged required a longitudinal view to fully appreciate its meaning. This unstable, impulsive, defensive, and narcissistic man was fighting a losing battle. His weak ego, gathering about itself the mechanisms of psychic defense, was gradually exposing its inadequacy. His depressions were transitory, but they pointed to his powerlessness to withstand rushes of emotion. His friends called him a "kook," a "character," but no psychiatrist had yet examined him to find the disjunct psyche underneath. Those who came in contact with Jack Ruby knew he was quixotic, that his moods were fiery and gentle in turn. Not until the time came to probe into his mind did psychiatric analysis and psychological tests reveal the true nature of his chaotic mental condition.

The picture presenting itself to the examiners * over many hours was

* The psychiatric examinations were conducted by Dr. Manfred S. Guttmacher, Chief Psychiatrist of the Supreme Bench, Baltimore, Maryland, and the present author. The psychological tests were performed by Roy Schafer, Ph.D., Clinical Psychologist, Yale University.

that of an unstable, impulsive man displaying hypomanic behavior and evidence of intellectual defects in judgment, conceptualization, and discrimination, intermixed with a definite paranoid coloring and serious personality defects. Without the defenses of hyperloyalty, hyper-activity, expansiveness, constant promotion of new interests, he would never have been able to maintain an intact ego. He, in fact, was a psychological failure, although this failure did not present itself im-mediately. The three depressive episodes evidenced his inability to maintain an ego balance—a type of ego decompensation.

A remarkable evidence of his intellectual disjunction was found in his use of words. Even beyond a cultural slovenliness of word use and a predilection for slang terms, was a lack of understanding, a semantic dementia (Cleckley), in which words bore little relation to deeds. In malapropisms, this type of word misuse or affectation ordinarily carries within it the nub of an idea. In Ruby's case, the words were no longer symbols of ideas; they were fragmented, as were the ideas, sometimes approaching incoherence. Thus, in talking about handling some rough customers in his bar, he said, "I told them, I'll show you what muscle is." Similarly, about his feelings concerning the anti-Kennedy whispering campaign in Dallas he said, "He is one of ours. . . . inwardly he was a representative of the Jewish people." In prais-ing his writing of ads for his club in the newspaper, he said, "I know the semantics of words." In explaining his impulse to buy somebody food, he said, "I wanted to get drunk on kosher food"; of his sister's mourning when they cried together, he said, "She was contagious to me."

The significance of these and other phrases is in their indication of an actual intellectual disorder that is not readily visible on the surface. It is noteworthy that the psychological tests revealed him to have an IQ of 110, well above average. His performance in the face of this intel-lectual potential pointed toward some impediment, probably organic in nature.

The projective tests, the Rorschach, Draw-a-Person, Thematic Apperception, and others, resulted in several significant findings. Fluctuation between appropriate responses at one moment and loosely organized, confused, and arbitrary responses a moment later, as well as perseveration, difficulties in memory of uneven type, and emotional dyscontrol, were all clearly evident in test situations. The tests that measured these underlying changes could be easily obscured in casual contacts with the prisoner. For example, the Rorschach test showed how Ruby experienced his own body and how he reacted thereto: he felt it was damaged, impaired, repulsive. His description of his body, however, was quite the opposite; he often exclaimed over how strong, virile, and vigorous he was. On the test he proved not to have a well-integrated perception of his own body, could not clearly register sex differences, and was not always in control of his body.

In this connection, the Draw-a-Person test, which is completely undirected, demonstrated unconscious fears of homosexuality. The psychologist who interpreted the drawing * (see Plate I) found indications of homosexual conflict in the "open crotch area, avoidance of a seam in the sexual area, the phallic tie, the treatment of the feet in the drawing (one shoe is cut vertically, the other opens in front), the lack of hair, indicating doubts as to virility. . . ."

Again, the tests showed that which was obvious to the psychiatric examiners: the presence of a basic mistrust of others, an irrational grandiosity; they showed that his alleged capacity to establish warm relations with people gave way quickly to suspicion and outbursts of irritation. In brief, the tests confirmed his paranoid tendencies as well as impairment of insight into his own inner mental world and of the capacity for mature judgments concerning reality. The psychologist commented that "his test responses were very similar to those obtained from patients with psychomotor seizures."

A thorough neurological examination disclosed no overt signs of neurologic deficit except the significant findings on the electroencephalogram of cerebral dysrhythmia of the psychomotor type (F. A. Gibbs). Whether the cerebral dysrhythmia was due to an inherent defect in the brain, the result of head injuries or drugs, or a variant of epilepsy could not be determined.

From the material accumulated, the examiners constructed an hypothesis to account for the murder, somewhat as follows: a strong emotional charge, whether it be anger, guilt, hate, or sexual emotion, may trip off the electrical charges in the brain in those predisposed to convulsive activity, the so-called epileptogenic persons. An epileptic convulsion or its equivalent (as, psychomotor epilepsy) results from the electrical discharge in the brain. In and through this cerebral activity, aggressive impulses emerge. If the convulsion is of the grand mal type and the motor activity disorganized, no violent behavior occurs. If, instead of disorganized muscle movements, the convulsive seizure produces automatic behavior, violent, criminal acts may ensue. In these cases, the organized movements, accompanied by lack of awareness, are called a fugue.

With this generalized hypothesis in mind, the examiners inquired into the details of Ruby's account of the fateful days which preceded his crime. This can best be paraphrased from the mass of material developed by the examiner as well as by the Warren Commission.[77]

* A blind analysis of the drawings was done independently by Professor Tarmo Pasto, Director, Ars Gratia Hominis Project, Sacramento State College, Sacramento, California.

THE DAY OF SUDDEN DEATH

On the morning of President Kennedy's visit to Dallas on November 22, 1963, Jack Ruby was in the advertising office of the *Dallas News,* preparing to file his weekend ad. He became aware of a hush in the ordinarily bustling room; then came the sudden announcement, "The President has been shot." Advertising copy in hand, Ruby gasped incredulously. He felt something akin to a physical blow; he felt sick, blurred, and could only think of one thing—to call his sister. His throat felt choked as he spoke over the phone; Eve was babbling and crying inconsolably. Jack remembered only a few words of the conversation: "He was precious," cried Eve. He himself cried, sobbed, moved quickly, not knowing just what to do. Frequently, during the day, he was heard to say, "Dallas is ruined." He thought aloud: "I'll have to leave town. I feel like a nothing person. . . . I don't want to live any more. The world has ended."

Ruby closed his beloved Club Carousel. During the next forty-eight hours he wandered from home to synagogue, to radio station, police headquarters, his sister's apartment, back to his own. It was a moody, distraught, agitated forty-eight hours. He cried, he talked to his sister, he rocked with grief. "Such a fine person, such a great family, such a wonderful wife." Suddenly he felt a need to be helpful. He thought of the harassed police. Impulsively, he brought them sandwiches, kosher sandwiches. The radio and TV people were working overtime under tense conditions—he also brought them sandwiches. Nothing relieved him. Over and over, he said: "I felt like a nothing person. . . . Such a beautiful man and wonderful family." Ruby's wailing wall was the streets of Dallas.

His world had ended, but he kept moving, talking, doing. After a time he found himself at police headquarters in the midst of reporters, police officials, the District Attorney, and the Chief of Police. In the assembly room he caught a glimpse of Oswald, surrounded by cameras, microphones, and questioning reporters. Suddenly Ruby's feelings changed. Elated and excited, he stood in a corner of the room, assisting the correspondents, identifying officials for them while the news-hungry crowd stared at Oswald.

I felt like a somebody. I pointed out who was who, even passed out some of my cards for the Club Carousel. I'm in on the deal, the only lay person in the room. I didn't think of Oswald then, I was too excited to be there. I had my gun with me but never gave it a thought. I had a feeling I never had before. . . . I was "in," a big man.

A ferment of feelings moiled through Ruby's mind: depression, anguish, fury, noble sentiments, righteousness, hopelessness succeeded each other. The anti-Semitic posters and leaflets, the newspaper advertisement, bordered in black, that had appeared in the press the day before the President's arrival, the posters that called for Justice Warren's impeachment, all danced in obsessive rapidity through his head. The hint of tragedy in the newspaper welcome addressed to the President and signed with a Jewish name, Bernard Weisman, echoed and reechoed in his frenzied mind. He couldn't sleep, he felt he had to do something. At 4:00 A.M. on November 23rd, he woke his roommate, called for his Polaroid camera with its flashbulb attachment and drove to the spot where he had observed the anti-Warren posters. Someone should be told about this; the radio station must know; it was a national "story" and it was his duty to relate that story. In the early dawn, in the company of his roommate and the Club porter, the pictures were taken. But Jack's activity didn't cease: Weisman's post-office box was investigated, post-office employees interrogated, the radio station manager contacted, rival clubs, which had remained open in defiance of the general mourning, were checked. The day wore on; Ruby watched television, grieved, and talked. "He aged ten years that day," commented his roommate.

On the 24th of November, Ruby awoke rather late and dressed leisurely. He then drove downtown on a brief errand, and found himself at the entrance to the loading platform of the police station. Out of curiosity, he walked down the ramp. No one opposed him and as he reached the bottom, the image of Oswald, handcuffed to two officers, appeared. Two strides brought him within three feet of Oswald. Ruby remembered nothing until he found himself on the concrete floor, crying out with concern, "You don't have to beat my brains out. I'm Jack Ruby." He recalled thinking, "I'm a known person . . . not somebody who is a screwball."

In contradiction to this alleged amnesia stood the accounts of witnesses and the photographs of the murder, scrutinized by millions of persons. One remarkable photograph (Plate II), apparently taken as the bullet entered Oswald's body, shows Ruby hunched forward, squeezed gun in hand, an intensity of effort mirrored in his broad back and tightened neck muscles. The movement portrayed is the forward thrust of a body in gear, a synchronized physical block of movement. The facial expressions of the officers handcuffed to Oswald reflect their utter amazement as the shot rings out; Oswald's face is distorted with acute pain; surprise transfixes the faces, torsos, and arms of the dim figures that line the ramp and surround the killer and his victim.

The trial * produced definite statements by eyewitnesses that clearly implied Ruby acted and spoke like a sane man.[77] One of the officers to whom Oswald was handcuffed heard his assailant say, immediately after the shooting, "I hope the son-of-a-bitch dies." At the moment of shooting, another officer heard Ruby say, "You rat son-of-a-bitch, you shot the President." However, a third officer, also shackled to prisoner Oswald, did not hear these words. One of the newsmen, standing almost as close to Oswald and his escorting officers as Ruby, also did not hear these words of hate from Ruby. In fact, a microphone thrust up to Oswald's face at the moment of shooting picked up the sound of the shot, the sound of scuffling, but no word from Ruby. However, a detective who brought Ruby up on the elevator from the scene of the killing minutes later heard Ruby reply to the statement "Jack, I think you killed him": "I intended to shoot him three times." Other witnesses, who had been standing close to the melee, then and subsequently testified that Ruby said: "You rat son-of-a-bitch, you shot the President," as well as the comment, "I hope I killed the son-of-a-bitch." Other officers reported that Jack explained later, "I meant to get three shots off, but you moved in on me so fast I couldn't get the other two away." There were still other witnesses who quoted Ruby as having stated that he had planned the crime two days before and that he had intended to use three bullets "to avenge" the President's death. At another time Ruby explained that he killed Oswald to save Jacqueline Kennedy and her daughter Caroline the trouble of coming to Dallas for the trial.

Discrepancies surrounded the actual wording of Ruby's statements: one officer stated that after the shooting, in the police questioning room, Ruby said, "You don't think I was letting him get by with it?" This officer later retracted this and the "I hope the son-of-a-bitch dies" statement. Yet another detective testified that the murderer had decided to "kill him the first chance I got" when he noticed the "sarcastic sneer" on Oswald's face on the night of his exposure to the newsmen at the police station. It is true that Ruby had said to the psychiatric examiners, some days after the shooting, "He had a very smirking expression —vicious like a Commie, like an animal, like a rat," and, on another occasion, "He had a smirky, cunning, vicious look on his face, a Commie, a rat." These characterizations also occurred to Ruby at the time of the shooting. Of this, more later.

Another disputed issue, belonging rather to the psychiatric and neurologic examination than to the account of eyewitnesses, was the finding of cerebral dysrhythmia on the electroencephalogram. Dr. M.

* The defense attorneys were Melvin Belli, of San Francisco; Sam Brody, of Los Angeles; and Joe H. Tonahill, of Jasper, Texas. The prosecuting attorneys were Henry Wade and William Alexander, of Dallas.

Towler, of the University of Texas, Department of Neurology, had described distinct abnormalities in the brain-wave tracing, diagnosable as that of psychomotor epilepsy, as originally described in the literature by Dr. F. A. Gibbs. At the trial, several competent neurologists, associated with renowned universities, denied the specificity of the electroencephalograph findings. Some of the experts agreed that a nonspecific "mild abnormality" was evident in Ruby's brain tracing, but none agreed that psychomotor epilepsy was diagnosable. Finally, Dr. Gibbs at the trial confirmed the finding of psychomotor epilepsy in the Ruby tracing as a "clear" indication of a rare form of epileptic variant.

At the end of the presentation of evidence, by lay and medical witnesses, the testimony as to Ruby's mental condition was almost equally divided between those who felt he had committed the murder with premeditation and those who believed he had been subject to a physiological change in the brain that had altered his consciousness. As one reporter sitting through the entire trial wrote in its final day: "And there we were again, thirteen medical experts later, where we had started at the beginning." [78]

The question of motivation for the crime absorbed much attention. The District Attorney of Dallas County believed that Ruby shot Oswald in the mistaken belief that the act would lead to "fame and fortune." It was even jocularly suggested that the criminal expected to open a "Jack Ruby on Broadway" in the yet unnamed future. Opinions were voiced that Ruby was in league with Oswald; that these two assassins had been seen together on occasion; that Ruby was in the employ of communists to erase the shadow on the world communist movement because of Oswald's experience in Soviet Russia; that Ruby was part of a plot of the Dallas police force; that he was acting for the underworld, enemies of the President, and so on. The European press appeared to be convinced of a political plot to which Ruby was privy, or of which he was the agent. The American public at large, so far as can be judged, turned away from these devious explanations within a short time of the tragic double murder.

AN INTERPRETIVE RECONSTRUCTION OF AN ASSASSINATION

There are two steps in an estimation of an offender's mental state at the time of commission of a crime: (a) an analysis of statements of witnesses, and interpretations thereof, and (b) reconstruction of this evidence by one who was not a witness. The latter position is that of the juryman and the expert witness. The remarkable aspect of the Ruby case was that few citizens of this country had not been witnesses to the murder, either by virtue of a motion picture made at the time or by examination of the crime photograph. In the approach to an analysis of the criminal's mind, subjective impressions necessarily enter. Judicial procedure is aware of this circumstance in the very process of jury selection. The psychiatric criminologist is similarly keenly aware of possible artifacts.

Under our jury system the accused is entitled to be judged by his or her peers but the latter are unused to analyzing intricate elements of consciousness. They apply a common-sense view of behavior that appeals to the rational man. One of the tenets of the common-sense view is the notion that the most simple and direct explanation is the correct one. Therein lies the strength and weakness of the jury system, especially in cases complicated by obscure mental conditions. Psychiatrists, as witnesses, may only present their findings on examination together with their opinion as to the mental state at the time of an offense. Nevertheless, a detailed study of an offender does permit the development of a reconstruction that might well be presented to a jury for their understanding.

The reconstruction that seeks to interpret the described behavior and the inner workings of the accused's mind starts with the events immediately preceding the shooting. The actual entrance of Ruby into the ramp at the Dallas police station, which within a few seconds brought him face to face with Oswald, alleged slayer of the President, was apparently not a timed maneuver. The ramp was unguarded, Ruby walked unchallenged. Clearly, since minutes before he had conducted some business in sending a money order to an employee through a Western Union office, he was in possession of his mental functions at the moment. As he approached the point where the platform and down-ramp met, he was aware of the presence of a crowd of newsmen and police officials in the immediate area. When Ruby reached that point, as a matter of pure happenstance, Oswald appeared before him about twelve feet away, shackled to two officers. In that instant a surge of emotion swept over Ruby, tripping off a physiological reaction in his dysrhythmic brain. He advanced two strides forward, his gun in hand. His emotional set, his body reactions, and impaired mental functions were already under the influence of a wave of cerebral irritation. The squeezing of the trigger of the gun and the forward movement were of a piece, occurring as an automatic movement.

The expletives uttered by the murderer at the time of the shooting were taken at the trial at face value as motivation for the murder. In the ordinary course of events, what is said by a person is assumed to be a voluntary utterance expressing what they mean to say. This examiner has no reason to disbelieve the reported obscene remarks that Ruby was heard to make. However, experience and experiment have shown that perception of visual and auditory occurrences may be shaped by the mental content and attitude of the viewer or hearer. Cantril says that "perception itself is modified, if not created, on the assumptions we bring to the particular occasion." We are all, Cantril noted, subject to insecurities in relation to other persons; hence, "we try to pigeonhole people according to some role, status, or position." This very important problem of how a person interprets motives as he witnesses certain actions is a difficult-to-interpret-psychological process. To phrase it in Cantril's more technical terms:

. . . the more one studies perception, the more one sees that what we label "perception" is essentially a process which man utilizes to make his purposive behavior more effective and satisfying, and that this behavior always stems from and is rooted in a personal behavioral center.[79]

The present writer has no hesitation in concluding that Ruby's statements were subject to confabulation, filling in details in accordance with his interest in a given subject. For example, when he reported that he had seen a "smirky and vicious expression" on Oswald's face (a statement that altered slightly on different occasions), it is impossible to say whether this was not a later fabrication to cover a hiatus in memory, or possibly a projected feeling of his own self-image; similarly, his explanation that he killed Oswald to protect, by preventing, Jacqueline and Caroline Kennedy from attending a future trial in Dallas. From the lengthy interrogations by the present writer the impression was gained that Ruby's need to rationalize his aggressive acts was great. In any event, it is in such situations that words—their meaning, connotation, and associations—taken on faith may still require calibration and interpretation.

Ruby's emotional reactions, the depression, the instability elaborated on above, in addition to his feelings about the President and his family, deserve special consideration. There seems little question that Jack Ruby was depressed beyond what one would expect by the President's assassination. The prisoner's description of the President, of Mrs. Kennedy, of their children, and of the First Lady's charm, cannot be reproduced specifically here; essentially, it arose from unconscious sources. His hatred of Oswald was also determined by unconscious feelings. Psychologically, it is felt, Ruby's lifelong aggressiveness was in the service of deep unconscious conflicts over his own masculinity and his racial origins. Somehow, the images of Oswald and of Kennedy became entangled in this psychologic morass. The complex psychological situation can best be restated briefly by saying that Ruby was torn by his unconscious love for the President and his unconscious identification with Oswald. The conflict was too great for his ego to control, especially in view of his paranoid disposition.

It is quite conceivable that Jack Ruby in the early stages of his psychosis was deluded to the extent that he believed there was a plot hatching in Dallas to assassinate the President. This is not to say that there was such a plot in fact, or that Ruby was involved in it if there had been. What is meant is that Ruby's psychotic fear for the safety of American Jews, itself a delusional idea, was extended to the President, and that the actual assassination coincided with the development of his paranoid trends. This would account for his seemingly normal talk of vengeance against Oswald, heard by the police shortly after Oswald's death in the police station. Only later, within the ensuing year, did Ruby's actual delusional state regarding his family and American Jews in general come into clear focus.[80] In fact, at the last examination (March 1965), Ruby believed more strongly than ever that American Jews were being systematically destroyed, and that their final elimination would benefit the "great society." [81]

In this man of quick movements and quick reactivity, shooting was automatic, beyond conscious control. This condition among individuals with cerebral disturbances amounts to a *fugue state*, wherein consciousness is impaired while physical acts consonant with a person's customary behavior occur. The fugue has been observed in boxers who fight on automatically after being knocked out on their feet; it has also been seen in cases of head injury and in unstable persons whose irritable brain tissue allows the emergence of aggressive impulses. Karl Menninger has described this type of reaction as "episodic, impulsive, aggressive dyscontrol." Other observers have described it as of the character of a fugue. This writer has seen it in one case of murder [82] following an epileptic furor and in other cases with brain injury due to car accidents.

The examinations by Dr. Manfred Guttmacher, Dr. Roy Shafer, and the present writer revealed sufficient material to conclude that Ruby's mental state was such as to indicate impaired consciousness during the killing of Oswald. In such condition, he was unable to premeditate his crime and hence was not responsible for murder in the first degree. However, since the law in most states, including Texas, requires that the accused to be relieved of criminal responsibility shall be so mentally deranged as not to know right from wrong and the nature and quality of his acts, the issue of impaired consciousness was not in point. The analysis of the case presented here indicated a lack of consciousness and an impairment of "knowledge" at the moment of shooting. The verdict of the jury was that Ruby was able to distinguish right from wrong at the moment of murder and hence was liable for the supreme penalty.

It is the duty of the psychiatrist called by the prosecution or the defense or the court to illuminate, out of all the knowledge he can acquire and with all the objectivity he can muster, the happenings in the body and mind of an accused criminal. In this way, psychiatric criminology may contribute to an eventual understanding of human violence and aggressive crime, and therefore, perhaps, to the processes of justice.

REFERENCES

1. FREUD, ANNA, "The Significance of the Evolution of Psychoanalytic Child Psychology," abstract in *Annual Survey of Psychoanalysis*, Vol. I (International Universities Press, New York, 1950), p. 5.
2. KARDINER, ABRAM, *The Individual and His Society* (Columbia University Press, New York, 2nd printing, 1943), p. 127.
3. SULLIVAN, HARRY S., quoted from E. Becker, *The Birth and Death of Meaning* (Free Press of Glencoe [Macmillan], New York, 1962), p. 134.
4. FREUD, SIGMUND, *Civilization and Its Discontents*, trans. by J. Strachey (W. W. Norton & Co., New York, 1961).
5. FREUD, SIGMUND, *The Libido Theory*, in *Collected Papers*, Vol. V (Hogarth Press, London, 1950), p. 135.
6. FREUD, SIGMUND, *Why War*, in *ibid.*, p. 273.
7. SCHILDER, PAUL, and BENDER, LAURETTA, "Studies in Aggressiveness, II," *Genetic Psychology Monograph*, XVIII, No. 5–6 (1936), 546.
8. KLEIN, MELANIE, and RIVIERE, JOAN, *Love, Hate and Reparation*, "Psychoanalytic Epitomes," No. 2 (Hogarth Press, London, 1953), p. 61.
9. SPITZ, RENÉ, *No and Yes: On the Genesis of Human Communication* (International Universities Press, New York, 1957).
10. *Ibid.*, p. 47.
11. HORNEY, KAREN, *New Ways in Psychoanalysis* (W. W. Norton & Co., New York, 1939), chap. VII.
12. *Ibid.*, p. 129.
13. SCHILDER, PAUL, *Goals and Desires of Man, a Psychological Survey of Life* (Columbia University Press, New York, 1942), p. 27.
14. *Ibid.*, p. 48.
15. *Ibid.*, p. 279.
16. KEISER, SYLVAN, and SCHILDER, PAUL, "Studies in Aggressiveness, Aggressiveness in the Male Criminal," *Genetic Psychology Monograph*, XVIII (1936), 361.
17. BECKER, ERNEST, "Anthropological Notes on the Concept of Aggression," *Psychiatry*, XXV (November, 1962), 328.
18. KARPMAN, BEN, "The Myth of the Psychopathic Personality," *American Journal of Psychiatry*, CIV (March, 1948), 523.
19. SATTEN, J., MENNINGER, K. M., ROSEN, I., and MAYMAN, M., "Murder without Apparent Motive, A Study in Personality Disorganization," *American Journal of Psychiatry*, CXVII (July, 1960), 48.
20. MENNINGER, KARL M., *The Vital Balance* (Viking Press, New York, 1963).
21. WILLIAMS, HYATT A., "A Psycho-Analytic Approach to the Treatment

of the Murderer," *International Journal of Psychoanalysis,* XLI (July–October, 1960), 532.

22. Personal communications to the author, 1957–58.

23. BROMBERG, WALTER, "The Treatability of the Psychopath," *American Journal of Psychiatry,* CX (February, 1954).

24. *People* vs. *Parker* [*sic*], Superior Court, State of California, County of Yuba, 1962.

25. FREUD, SIGMUND, *On Narcissism,* in *Collected Papers,* Vol. IV (Hogarth Press, London, 1934), p. 30.

26. ZILBOORG, GREGORY, "Psychoanalytic Aspects of Suicide," *International Journal of Psychoanalysis,* XIV (1933), 387.

27. MENNINGER, KARL M., "Some Sidelights on the Psychology of Murder," *Journal of Nervous and Mental Disease,* LXXXI (1935), 442.

28. REICHARD, S., and TILLMAN, C., "Murder and Suicide as Defenses Against Schizophrenic Psychosis," *Journal of Clinical Psychopathology,* XI (October, 1950), 14.

29. BROMBERG, WALTER, *The Mold of Murder* (Grune & Stratton, New York, 1961), pp. 195 ff.

30. FENICHEL, OTTO, *Psychoanalytic Theory of Neurosis* (W. W. Norton & Co., New York, 1945), p. 400.

31. Quoted in Jacques Choron, *Death and Western Thought* (Collier Books, [Macmillan], New York, 1963), p. 32.

32. Quoted in Choron, *op. cit.,* p. 242.

33. BROMBERG, WALTER, and SCHILDER, PAUL, "Death and Dying, A Comparative Study of the Attitudes and Mental Reactions Towards Death and Dying," *Psychoanalytic Review,* XX (April, 1933), 133.

34. BROMBERG, WALTER, and SCHILDER, PAUL, "The Attitudes of Psychoneurotics Towards Death," *Psychoanalytic Review,* XXIII (January, 1936), 1.

35. BERGLER, EDMUND, *The Basic Neurosis* (Grune & Stratton, New York, 1949), p. 305.

36. BROMBERG, WALTER, "The Murder and the Murderer: The Destroyer and Creator," *Archives of Criminal Psychodynamics,* II (1957), 523.

37. *People* vs. *Horton* [*sic*], State of California, County of Yuba, Superior Ct., 1961.

38. *People* vs. *Peters* [*sic*], State of California, County of Sacramento, 1958.

39. WILDE, OSCAR, *The Happy Prince and Other Tales* (Gerald Duckworth & Co., London, 1913).

40. CLECKLEY, HERVEY, *The Mask of Sanity* (C. V. Mosby Co., St. Louis, Mo., 3rd ed., 1955).

41. Editorial in *Sacramento Bee,* December 20, 1958.

42. Editorial in *Sacramento Union,* December 24, 1958.

43. Letter to the Editor in *Sacramento Union,* December 26, 1958.

44. *American Communication Association* vs. *Douds,* 339 U.S., 382, 437, 70 S.Ct., 674 (1950).

45. CLARK, WILLIAM L., and MARSHALL, WILLIAM L., *A Treatise on the Law of Crimes,* 6th ed., rev. by Melvin F. Wingersky (Callaghan & Co., Chicago, 1952), p. 248.

46. DIAMOND, BERNARD, "With Malice Aforethought," *Archives of Criminal Psychodynamics*, II (1957), 43.

47. *People* vs. *Gorshen*, Dist. Ct. of Appeals, 1st Appel. Dist., Criminal 2423, 326, P. 2nd, 188, California, March, 1959.

48. *Ibid.*, Appellant's Brief, p. 3.

49. *People* vs. *Wells*, 33 California, 2nd, 330 (1949).

50. *People* vs. *Gorshen*, Brief, Amici Curiae, Sup. Ct., California, Criminal #6310.

51. WERTHAM, FREDRIC, *The Show of Violence* (Doubleday & Co., Garden City, N. Y., 1949), pp. 120 ff.

52. BROMBERG, WALTER, "A Psychological Study of Murder," *International Journal of Psychoanalysis* (London), XXII (1951), 117.

53. WERTHAM, FREDRIC, "Catathymic Crisis," *Archives of Neurology and Psychiatry*, XXXVII (1937), 974.

MENNINGER, KARL, and SATTEN, JOSEPH, "Development of a Psychiatric Criminology," *Bulletin of the Menninger Clinic*, XXV (1961), 164.

KARPMAN, BENJAMIN, *Case Studies in the Psychopathology of Crime*, Vols. 1, 2 (Mental Science Publishing Co., New York, 1939).

ZILBOORG, GREGORY, "Some Sidelights on the Psychology of Murder," *Journal of Nervous and Mental Disease*, LXXXI (1935), 442.

54. PRICHARD, JAMES C., *A Treatise on Insanity* (Haswell, Barrington & Haswell, Philadelphia, Pa., 1835).

55. RAY, ISAAC, *A Treatise on the Medical Jurisprudence of Insanity*, 1871 ed. (Little, Brown, Boston, 1838).

56. GUTTMACHER, MANFRED, and WEIHOFEN, HENRY, *Psychiatry and the Law* (W. W. Norton & Co., New York, 1952).

57. ROCHE, PHILLIP Q., *The Criminal Mind, A Study of Communication Between Criminal Law and Psychiatry* (Evergreen Book, Grove Press, New York, 1959).

58. *People* vs. *Claude Girard* [sic], Superior Court, State of California, Placer County, 1961.

59. BROMBERG, WALTER, *The Mold of Murder* (Grune & Stratton, New York, 1961), pp. 158 ff.

GUTTMACHER, M., and WEIHOFEN, H., *Psychiatry and the Law* (W. W. Norton & Co., New York, 1954), pp. 243 ff.

60. *California Jury Instructions, Criminal*, prepared under the direction of the Superior Court of Los Angeles County, California, rev. ed. (West Publishing Co., St. Paul, Minn., 1958), supps. p. 743.

61. FOX, SANFORD J., "Physical Disorder, Consciousness and Criminal Liability," *Columbia Law Review*, LXIII (1963), 645.

62. LENNOX, WILLIAM G., *Epilepsy and Related Disorders*, Vol. 1 (Little, Brown & Co., Boston, 1960), p. 56.

63. DeHAAS, LORENTZ, A. M., "Epilepsy and Criminality," *British Journal of Criminology*, III, No. 3 (January, 1963), 248.

64. ESQUIROL, J. E., *A Treatise on Insanity*, trans. by E. K. Hunt (Lea & Blanchard, Philadelphia, Pa., 1845).

65. GOWERS, SIR WILLIAM, *Epilepsy and Other Convulsive Disorders*,

quoted in S. V. Clevenger, *Medical Jurisprudence of Insanity* (Lawyers Publishing Co., New York, 1898), p. 1040.

66. TROUSSEAU, L., quoted in Clevenger, *op. cit.*, p. 1047.

67. BIANCHI, L., *Textbook of Psychiatry* (William Wood Co., New York, 1906), p. 766.

68. Quoted from Sidney Maughs, "Psychopathic Personality," *Journal of Clinical Psychopathology*, X (July, 1949), 249.

69. GIBBS, F. A., BAGGHI, B. K., and BLOOMBERG, WILFRED, "Electro-encephalographic Study of Criminals," *American Journal of Psychiatry*, CII, No. 3 (November, 1945), 294.

70. PODOLSKY, EDWARD, "The Epileptic Murderer," *Medico-Legal Journal* (Cambridge, England), XXX (1962), 176.

71. LEIGH, L. H., "Automatism and Insanity," *Criminal Law Quarterly* (Dept. of Justice, Ottawa), V (1962), 160.

72. *Bratty* vs. *Attorney General for Northern Ireland*, 3 Weekly, L. R. 965 (1961).

73. USZKIEWICZOWA, L., "Criminality of Epileptics and Some Questions of Giving Opinions in Cases of Epilepsy," *Archiwum Medycyny Sadowej, Psychiatrii Sadowej i Kryminalistyki*, XV (1963), 1.

74. STEVENSON, H. G., "Psychomotor Epilepsy Associated with Criminal Behavior," *Medical Journal of Australia* (Melbourne), L (1963), 784.

75. AMATI, G., and RAGOZINO, D., "The Epileptic Personality and Its Criminologic and Forensic-Psychiatric Aspects," *Folia Psychiatria*, III (1963), 269.

76. *State of Texas* vs. *Jack Ruby*, Criminal Court, No. 3, County of Dallas (1963), No. E-4010-J.

77. The Warren Commission's Report (*Report of the President's Commission on the Assassination of President John F. Kennedy*), Associated Press, reproduced from an official text (U.S. Government Printing Office, Washington, D.C., September 27, 1964), pp. 348 ff.

78. BEDFORD, SYBILLE, "Violence, Froth, Sob Stuff—Was Justice Done?" *Life*, March 27, 1964, p. 32.

79. CANTRIL, HADLEY, "Perception and Interpersonal Relations," *American Journal of Psychiatry*, CXIV (1957), 119.

80. BELLI, MELVIN M., and CARROLL, MAURICE C., *Dallas Justice, the Real Story of Jack Ruby and His Trial* (David McKay Co., Inc., New York, 1964), pp. 261 ff.

81. WEST, LOUIS J., personal correspondence, June 10, 1965.

82. *State* vs. *Hoover*, 54 So. 2d. 130, Louisiana.

CHAPTER VI

More Crimes of Aggression

ALCOHOL AND AGGRESSION IN SUBCULTURES /
VIOLENCE DU JOUR / A NODE OF CRIMINOLOGIC
ADVANCE / THE USES OF AGGRESSION /
SLAUGHTER OF THE INNOCENTS / CRIMINAL
ABORTION AS INFANTICIDE / THE HAND OF
MEDEA / INFANTICIDE BY THE MALE / THE
GREEKS HAD A WORD . . . / THE CRIME OF
BARABBAS / EMOTIONAL REACTIONS AMONG
ROBBERS / ASSAULT BY WORDS / THE WORD
AND THE MAILED FIST / REFERENCES

The cases recited thus far have involved aggression in persons suffering from neurotic or psychotic processes of varying degrees. There are, of course, homicides or assaults falling in the group of aggressive crime; these include a host of motivated murders—infanticide, parricide, and matricide, paranoid homicides, triangle murders, forceful (sadistic) rape or lust murders. In these situations, the offense may also lie upon a neurotic or psychotic basis, or it may not. Then there are crimes in which the offense represents for the miscreant a reality-need rather than a neurotic need, as in professional killings, assaults by strong-arm men, racketeering, and extortion with its accompanying threats and brutality. In addition to the reality aspect of certain types of homicide, account should be taken of cultural modes that encourage aggressive action, where assaults and homicides are, if not congenial to the culture, at least not unheard of.

ALCOHOL AND AGGRESSION IN SUBCULTURES

Aggression as a behavior pattern is not limited in its expression to abnormal psychic states; it is prevalent also in areas where fighting and aggressive retaliation for slights are normal social patterns in daily life. In such situations the basic low level of tolerance (emotional instability) in the assailant and his readiness to use aggressive measures coincide with the socially accepted values of a particular subculture. Certain rural areas in the South; underprivileged minority-group areas in large Northern cities; and areas in the West where a "frontier spirit" of personal defense is still characteristic demonstrate this coincidence of cultural mores and personal aggression; particularly, behavior among youth—characterized by callousness, egocentricity, ruthless action, apparent lack of conscience—joins with behavior systems where the value placed on life cedes to larger values given to prestige, personal honor, and physical valor. Here alcoholism is frequently a stimulating factor. The issues occasioning the assault may be women, money, gambling debts, personal slurs, and so on. Values given the need for retaliation differ in various parts of the country. Brierley,[1] in studying provocations to murder, found personal honor to rank high in the South. These differential values[2] form the basis for many murders. Aggressive intent in the offender is in part a reflection of subcultural attitudes, in part an expression of personal inner hostilities nurtured and stimulated by neurotic feelings of inferiority shared by minority groups, who keenly sense their pariahlike position in society.

Pedro Gomez started his "lost weekend" on New Year's Day by "pub crawling," in perfect consonance with custom. In the first bar he consumed fifteen beers; in the second, he switched to whiskey. Hours later he dimly recalled visiting a third bar; the next thing he remembered was waking up with a headache, in a cell. His drinking companions could only say that Pedro suddenly seized a bottle, broke it over a man's head, and jabbed the broken end into the victim's eye. There was no provocation for the attack, not even a quarrel. The police were forced to turn a hose on Pedro to quiet him; he remembered nothing of the struggle to subdue him. The officers added the information that when quieted he urinated in the street.

Born to a Mexican family, one of twelve children, Pedro started drinking at the age of twelve. His first official "drunk" was on wine at age thirteen. From school days until the assault in the bar at age twenty-four, Pedro's life was punctuated by fighting, roistering, and arrests, the early ones sending him to the Juvenile Detention Hall. Later, a robbery charge, a period in a boys' reformatory, and several arrests for vagrancy brought his record up to date. He was the "black sheep" of the family, Pedro explained; he learned to be tough and aggressive in "order to survive." For about a year he had visited the Alcoholic Rehabilitation Clinic in an effort to reduce his drinking. His wife, a frequent victim of his rages, described periods of tantrum, during which he would fall on the floor or smash furniture in a blind rage, or on occasion attempt to burn the house down; once he tried to hang himself. Pedro was able nevertheless to hold his job as foreman, but his weekends belied his apparent stability.

There was no question of legal insanity or even of psychosis. Evident was a pathological intoxication, an occasional explosive emergence of bitterness and aggressivity under alcohol, which served to prevent exposure to himself of his inner pain and isolation; to Pedro, it was the "bad" in him. The psychological tests demonstrated an average intelligence, with areas of capacity higher than average. His attitude of marked dependence and a sense of isolation could be detected during the examination. With some insight, Pedro explained how as a boy in the West he played with Indian boys, thereby seeking consolation for his inner insecurity. He was engaged in a struggle for ego identification and survival; punishment would accomplish nothing.

A recommendation of probation with psychiatric guidance was accepted by the judge.[3] After a year, Pedro sought admission to a state hospital on a voluntary basis; he left within two months and eight months later was arrested for drunken driving. The struggle was too great for Pedro. He was unable to raise himself from the pariah position he fancied himself in: he never wiped out the "black sheep" image.

It is a clinical axiom, even a conversational commonplace, that with drinking violence comes to the surface when the sense of elation, lack of social concern, feeling of limitless power, and free-flowing courage subtly perfuse the drinker's psyche. Indeed, the Old Testament anticipated today's clinical findings: "Wine is a mocker; strong drink is raging." Physicians, psychiatrists, lawyers, and judges too numerous to list have written tracts and volumes, pleaded cases, and delivered opinions based on human behavior as modified or stimulated by alcohol. The law has long since come to a settled conviction as to the significance of alcohol in crime. Where "drunkenness falls short of a proved incapacity . . . to form the intent necessary to constitute crime," [4] the law, from the days of Sir Matthew Hale, has considered

. . . a drunken man as fully responsible for his acts as a sober man though he may have been so drunk as to be temporarily deprived of his reason.[5]

Mental disease due to alcoholism (delirium tremens, alcoholic hallucinosis, Korsakow's syndrome, and the like), which extends beyond chronic or acute alcoholism, has been considered more specifically to lie in the province of psychiatry. Many authors,[6] including the present writer, have traced the effect of alcoholic psychoses and severe states of intoxication on emerging aggressive impulses in violent crime. The sociological literature is replete with studies of social customs, group attitudes, drinking patterns, and behaviorial responses in alcohol addiction.

Our interest in this section is in the association of drinking with aggressive crime in those subcultures where alcohol stimulates aggression, through a display of violence, as an accepted, even treasured, personal asset. In the subculture to be illustrated in the case to follow, behavior patterns differ from those generally accepted by society. Drinking is not constricted within definite social periods; behavior is not restricted by rules of social deportment; routine drinking is a way of life, part of a generally indolent, hedonistic, socially unformed world. The effect of this pattern is that in these subcultures alcohol forms a background for acceptance of violence as a norm. The ongoing personality is *expected* to be aggressive as a basic fact of existence.

VIOLENCE DU JOUR

At thirty-three, Courtney ("Bobo") Jones, of Alabama, had an unenviable record for a Southern Negro. He had earned two arrests and convictions for assault with a deadly weapon, one for resisting arrest, and several for disturbing the peace and gambling. His noncriminal record was even more inglorious. He finished the sixth grade in a rural school, spent seven months in the U.S. Navy earning an "undesirable" discharge, then settled down to gambling and drinking, interspersed with bouts of work. He generally drank wine, as did most of the group with which he consorted in a Western town. Some years before the murder for which he was convicted,[7] he had been committed to a state hospital for delirium tremens, where the staff had good reason to suspect a paranoid background as well.

Married to a hardworking colored girl, Bobo broke up with her on occasion. At one time during a "fuss," he broke the furniture and refrigerator with a hammer. Such behavior was admittedly not unusual for his "crowd," who devoted themselves to gambling, drinking, and "studding" around. For Bobo, there was the usual history of syphilis and five or six gonorrheal infections. Although powerfully built, he had the scars of gunshot and knife wounds over his chest, face, and arms— mementos of many casual knifings at the "club," where the crowd spent their evenings and often their afternoons.

The immediate stimulus to the murder was the liaison that sprang up between Bobo's wife and "Sugar Boy," although it was true that Bobo himself was living with a white girl, Opal, in retaliation. The "street" accepted these rearrangements, but Bobo was seething inwardly. There was much arguing, boasting, and blatant name-calling around the club, where Bobo and Sugar Boy were regarded as destined for a fight. Bobo had been drinking steadily for a month, and finally he couldn't take it any longer:

I was in the club with a girl. My wife, she put me out and I met Sugar Boy coming out of *my* house with a butcher knife. . . . I goes home to Opal's place . . . I take a rifle . . . Sugar Boy was looking for trouble so I shot through the door. . . . he come out at me with a knife and I shoot him again. . . . he don't say nothing . . . he just fell. . . . everybody knowed he was a doublecrosser. . . . it's been eatin' on me all these four months.

In the county jail, Jones was obviously self-protective, tense, actually delusional. He complained to the jailer that the other prisoners were making fun of him. He could hear them saying, "That's the nigger who killed over a white girl. . . ." Bobo professed to know nothing of Sugar Boy's shooting; he wasn't sure why he was in jail awaiting trial. He would discuss only the "bad time" the other inmates were giving him. Enough paranoid trends were demonstrable to suggest a psychosis, but careful analysis ruled out the plausibility of legal insanity. Chronic drinking to the point of an alcoholic psychosis was urged by the defense as mitigating Bobo's intent to kill his rival, but this was disbelieved by the jury. They convicted the offender of first-degree murder with a recommendation of life imprisonment.

A NODE OF CRIMINOLOGIC ADVANCE

It seems a fair assumption that where the subculture permits, even encourages, aggression to be the norm of behavior the eventuality of punishment is encompassed in the folkways and folk psychology of the group. The paraphrased dictum that "those who live by the gun, die by the gun" expresses the underlying psychological formula of many subcultures today, as it did in the gangster world of the 1920's. This world appropriated the mores of a remote period in history—justice served through private vengeance. But in modern times the courts assume the function of punisher; the degrees of crime, with corresponding degrees of punishment, are set down in the law in their infinite variety. Yet this codification does not signify rigidity. The combined efforts of realistic law, dynamic psychiatry, and a clearsighted judge do, on occasion, achieve humane justice. In the cases reported and in the one to follow, the supreme penalty, death, was not merited because analysis of the offenders uncovered mental factors precluding premeditation and malice aforethought.

It should be recalled at this point that the essential aims of legal punishment are generally given as *retribution, deterrence, rehabilitation,* and *treatment.* Some authors add *reprobation* (society's reproof to the criminal). From the cases discussed, it is clear that retribution and reprobation have been directly satisfied by punishment, while the third, deterrence, remains more a pious wish than an actuality. As a result of a more objective view of crime as behavior, the last two aims have recently come into view as practical outcomes. Quoting Curtis Bok, "The determined and growing thrust of psychiatry against current notions of criminal responsibility and treatment" [8] has broadened criminalistic philosophy. The case now to be outlined illustrates this crucial juncture of humanitarian, legal, and psychologic principles in some detail.

In this case, that of the Garfield brothers, the Court, while functioning as the protector of society, openmindedly chose to utilize punishment in the direction of rehabilitation.[9] This case presents a picture of advanced judicial practice, in which psychiatric concepts of the genesis of behavior were considered and utilized. Since the situation included kidnapping, murder, and attempted rape, the requirements of justice could have been met by a stark death sentence. Instead, the whole physiology of the crime and the lives of the two offenders were exposed and scrutinized, as one might stop a motion-picture reel to study the action in a single frame.

The soft valley breeze filtering through the earthbound heat of an August day found the Stevens family in their trailer, preparing for early bed. The father, Bob, recently recovered from a stomach ailment, needed his rest. Carol, his wife, settled their children for sleep, then turned to the lounging-chair in the small living room. They were parked off the highway; the trailer was comfortable, the countryside quiet. Carol smiled contentedly and picked up a magazine. "Tomorrow we'll be on the ranch"—enough travel for this summer, a peaceful prospect.

Someone rapped sharply on the door. A gruff voice, manly, but with an amateurish ring, Carol realized later, said, "Open the door in the name of the law!" Startled, Carol opened the door. Maybe it was the Highway Patrol; maybe they were on someone's property. A young man, tall, wearing blue jeans, entered, pistol in hand. "Give me your money," he said, swaying a little. He spoke as one who, though drunk, wishes to be impressive. Carol shrank back; Bob, awakened by the noise, came forward, his tall frame silhouetted in the half-light. "Get back in that closet," the intruder told him, pressing the gun into his side. He backed Bob into the closet, shut the door, and locked it.

Carol became panicky. She knew her husband had been cautioned against excitement; another hemorrhage could be fatal. In a small voice she said, "We haven't got much money—lost it in Reno." Slim, the intruder, glanced around the small trailer room, then back at Carol. He started toward her and she recoiled. It was then she realized that the trailer was moving. The car picked up speed, swerving around sharp turns, sometimes slipping into the roadside gully. Slim walked to the window and fired two shots into the air.

At once, whoever was driving slowed up, then stopped, and the driver suddenly appeared at the trailer door. "Okay, Tex," Slim said to him. "Two shots means go ahead; one, stop." Tex slipped back in the car and the wild ride continued.

Carol turned to Slim. "We have very little money," she pleaded. "Take it and get out. My husband is ill." A few minutes passed; the trailer was careening from side to side. "What do you want?" she cried in alarm, as Slim moved toward her. "Take off your blouse," he ordered. Later, Carol recalled: "He put me on the bed and sat next to me, but he didn't seem really determined to do much. He did touch me, but then stopped. At one point he touched my breasts, but I had my clothes on. I suddenly saw he was a boy, maybe seventeen to twenty, and somehow he looked more frightened than I did. He kept talking about money."

Carol became more alarmed as Bob finally forced the closet door lock and burst out and immediately grappled with Slim. Carol seized a flashlight and impulsively smashed it down on Slim's head. Bob, six feet three, puffing and straining, continued to wrestle with the intruder as the trailer rocked crazily along the road. Carol heard herself repeating mechanically, "We don't have any money." The intruder, his powerful muscles rippling, was overpowering her husband. She saw the glint of the gun barrel pointing toward him.

Slim shouted an order to Tex through the window, as the vehicle slowed down: "Go on driving!" he yelled.

A fury seized Carol. She rained blows on Slim's head. Bob was losing in the struggle. The gun was visible again and Carol thought madly, "This is a cap-gun." She called out to Bob, "It isn't real!" There was a shot, and her husband moaned, "I'm shot, I'm shot."

Freed from Bob's assault, Slim fired two more shots out the window. The car stopped. Bob slumped to the floor, blood spattering his shirt, and Carol screamed. Slim ran out the door, jumped into the car with Tex and drove off, pulling the trailer. To Carol, the next few minutes were a maelstrom of confusion. She ran to the sink for water. She ran back to her husband. Through the curtained window, she saw Slim aiming his gun at her from the car ahead. Nothing happened; the gun was empty. She turned back to Bob—and then it struck her: her husband was dead. The rest was one mass of blackness, of distant lights, of yelling, of sickening feelings, of silent prayers for help.

The two youths were arrested without difficulty by the sheriff, who had followed the trail of the wildly careening trailer. There was no struggle.

Slim and Tex told their story rather clinically: "We had been drinking beer all day and most of the evening while working on a car. It was a nice evening. While we were driving back we saw a trailer by the road."

Slim paused and smiled faintly: "We were pretty drunk. At least I was, and I said, 'Tex, how about taking over that trailer?' Tex nodded—he never says much. I had the gun on the seat. I picked it up. I walked over to the trailer and said, 'This is the law! Open up the door.' I had a glove on—I read that somewhere.

"A young lady opened the door; she let us in. I just thought we could use a little money, so I asked her for it. I didn't mean nothing. We were on our way home to see my wife. I guess it was the beer. I had no idea to get into trouble. I tried to back out. As a matter of fact, I was pretty scared. I didn't want any woman; I wouldn't know her if I saw her again. I just wanted to lock up the man—get some money—but when he started wrastling, something exploded—I felt a pain. [Slim had been shot in the right shoulder.] I stuck the gun out the window to get my brother to stop. I had this man whipped when he grabbed me. The gun went off all of a sudden—the gun went off. I thought I broke a bone or something. If I had known that he had been shot, I would have taken him to the hospital. He was behind me. I didn't see anything. My thought was to run. I wished the bullet had hit me instead."

The detective questioned him: "Did you ask the woman for money a number of times?"

"Yes."

"Do you remember what she said?"

"I don't remember what she said. I remember thinking it was not worth it anyway. Then I felt this guy grab me from the back. I was just trying to get away."

The District Attorney could do nothing but charge first-degree murder, kidnapping (Penal Code Section 209, State of California, the "little Lindbergh law"), robbery, burglary, and assault with intent to rape. There could be no other legal solution: the law fixed the penalty at death.

Court officers sent for a full account from the Garfields' home county in Texas. The background of the two bandits read like a textbook case history: They had been involved in robberies, burglaries, juvenile delinquencies from the age of sixteen. The younger one, Tex, had once escaped from a reformatory in Texas. Obviously, these were not beginners at antisocial conduct.

The Garfields were two of nine children. The family had been perennial problems in their local area. "Pappy" Garfield was an alcoholic. There had never been enough food. The home was unsanitary. There were unmerciful beatings, turmoil, and truancy. Mrs. Garfield could no longer control the situation; she divorced the father when the boys were young.

It was not that Slim and Tex were dull; their school records showed more than adequate mental capacity. In class the boys seemed orderly, but the truant officer was struck by the unfavorable home conditions. It didn't seem inappropriate that Slim and Tex spent more time in Juvenile Detention Hall than in the school room. Slim's teacher commented, in retrospect: "Slim was a good student and a fine citizen, but always looked so unkempt, unloved, and sadly in need of parental attention and care." This was in their eleventh and twelfth years. Within a year or two, changes occurred. The teachers reported that from attentive students who were good "listeners," the boys at thirteen and fourteen became bullies and toughs.

The authorities in the reformatory were properly skeptical. These youths were bound for trouble. Slim and Tex looked to others rather than their teachers for guidance. They found pals in the pool hall and in the reformatory who were also unloved and unkempt. They learned something about "clouting" (burglarizing) cars, about stickups, and how to saw a gun barrel to fit a bullet; they learned how to lie and how to keep a straight face before the "fuzz" (the police).

They were still learning when they found two girls who thought marriage at eighteen and sixteen was a career worth following. They married, had children, and came to California.

The examinations by the court-appointed psychologist and psychiatrist disclosed good intelligence, especially in the older boy: Slim's IQ was 112. The psychiatrist found evidence of impulsiveness, of a loosely formed personality integration, of ruthless aggression and calloused hardness in Slim. He also found evidence of a born leader.

Tex, on the other hand, was more compliant, more a follower, and more placid in his makeup.

Several psychiatric examiners scrutinized the youths: some felt that Slim was willful, self-centered, and power-striving—in short, a psychopathic brute whose brother Tex obeyed him like an automaton; others agreed that both were strong-minded, socially rootless, bright, and aggressive. All in all, there were sufficient features in the psychological profiles to diagnose both as psychopathic personalities. Alcohol was, of course, a factor in the murder and kidnapping, but in the background was the loose social and familial organization, with its pattern of inconsistency and instability. None of the examiners found evidence of insanity in either of the defendants. When Slim's degree of mental clarity had been established, this inner fantasy-life became the subject of study. Upon probing, it became clear that Slim himself was aware of the lack of impulse control that he experienced, and which was encompassed in the psychopathic personality concept.

More material developed as the study progressed. Slim was able to describe a type of anxiety he had experienced for many years, which took the form of head pains and odd head sensations. Slim's description of his anxiety spells was dramatic, even melodramatic, to the point where feigning was suspected: "It is like the presence of something terrible and fearful in the way this thing visits me." The "thing," as close as one could visualize it, was a corporeal representation of aggression. Slim explained that it was like "standing on some high building and some urge would come over me to jump." The analogy was apt: the compulsion described by the prisoner masked his impulses to attack, to rob, to injure. In one sense his sensations, embroidered with adolescent fantasies, were of a hysterical nature. At one time he described the "thing" thus:

I was lying there one time and it seemed that I could feel the presence of it and then—this sounds funny—but one of my upper left teeth seemed to explode and it actually drowned out all other inside noises. . . . I often wondered what would happen if I just kept my eyes shut, if it would explode in there.

Behind the masked anxiety infiltrating Slim's inner experiences lay a feeling of omnipotence, expressed in words reminiscent of those used in describing the poetical, transcendental effect of hallucinogenic drugs. As is well known, such drugs as mescal, peyote, lysergic acid developed pleasurable sensations in users that are dependent on psychophysiological changes in the body image. With the inner perception of these changes, inexplicable feelings of "really existing," of some sort of cosmic union, occur, to be followed soon by anxiety involving fears of bodily disintegration, of insanity, and the like. Schilder,[10] who studied body-image representation under many conditions (normal and pathological), comments that we are "so intent on living in reality that we tend to neglect" what goes on in our bodies; certain drugs simply project into consciousness those perceptive changes that are already registered subliminally. The anxiety that hysterical sensory changes aroused in Slim was accompanied by ideas with transcendental implications. For example:

My mind has no walls, no roof or floor, no up or down, or no start or end. . . . I don't know if this could be physically so. There is a comet that orbits my mind which at one time was expanding from the time of my birth. I don't know if this is some power or talent, or some terrible thing, as no one I have discussed this with has this thing. . . .

Compare this report of Slim's, entirely unsolicited, with the words of Fitzhugh Ludlow, who, hailed as a "minor De Quincey" in the 1850's, thus reported his experience with hashish (chemically equivalent to the drug in marihuana) to the literati of the Romantic period:

The sublime avenues in spiral life, at whose gates the soul in its ordinary state is forever blindly groping are opened widely by hasheesh. . . . there is a majesty surpassing the loftiest emotions aroused by material grandeur. . . .[11]

Or compare it with the more recent words of Aldous Huxley, the modern apostle of mescaline:

To [some] . . . is revealed the glory, the infinite value and meaningfulness of naked existence, of the given unconceptualized event. . . . The percept has swallowed up the concept. . . [These experiences] were inexpressibly wonderful, wonderful to the point of being terrifying.[12]

In the absence of evidence that the prisoner had read, or had any knowledge of, Ludlow or Huxley, it was concluded that what he perceived in mystical form was a hysterical reaction to his anxiety. It is eminently plausible that the struggle raging within Slim, between aggressivity and his ego, gave rise to a dramatic formulation of a "thing" that possessed him:

. . . it also has a separate will to come as it wants. . . . If this took over completely . . . would it be some vast knowledge, or fear . . . and hate . . . ?

Impulsive aggression and anxiety alternately struggled within Slim: he could not have known of this inner titanic turmoil, but he could feel the pressure of aggressive feelings. The presence of anxiety in this prisoner was significant in one respect: it indicated sufficient ego fluidity to favor the possibility of treatment and rehabilitation.

The problem posed to the presiding judge by these two youths standing before the bar of justice touched on social, legal, and psychiatric problems of great complexity. Legally, they were guilty of offenses that carried the death penalty. Socially, they were misfits, as yet unable to profit by punishment. Psychiatrically, they were sane, not defective, but seriously psychopathic. On the *surface*, the prisoners demonstrated a feature that one authority has described as characteristic of psychopaths: an "extraordinary poise rather than jitteryness or worry, a smooth sense of physical well-being instead of uneasy preoccupation with bodily functions." [13] In attempting to visualize what lies *below* the surface, therefore, one bears in mind the concept that the pathological personality "merely expresses his anxiety in a different way [than the neurotic]. . . . his behavior has the structure and function of a symptom." [14] They could be considered "rebels without a cause," [15] as Lindner has pithily expressed it, wearing "sardonic, smiling masks behind which lay the frightened, lonesome faces of neurotic youths." [16]

The issue lay clearly before the Court: whether the state should take two lives for the one snuffed out. Since a jury trial had been waived, the Court had the discretion of choosing the sentence: death or life imprisonment. After studying every aspect of the case, the presiding judge declared, in a thoughtful summation:

It is possible, through anger, to reach a harsh judgment; it is possible, through pity, to reach a sort of judgment. . . . we avoid arbitrary judgments . . . and reach out for such objective standards as are available.

The judge then reviewed the objects of punishment: retribution, protection of society by execution or imprisonment, deterrence of others, and, finally, correction and rehabilitation; each of these he analyzed in turn:

Were retribution a primary factor . . . the Court might impose the death penalty . . . as the expression of an outraged community. . . . [however] enlightenment tells us that retribution is no longer a desired objective of punishment. . . .

[Concerning] the objective of protecting society . . . certainly their deaths will accomplish that aim, but will life imprisonment do any less? . . . Now, deterrence must be a prime objective of the sentence . . . the hard fact is there are no facts to sustain a choice between life and death for the purpose of deterrence . . .

In reaching the final objective, rehabilitation, the Court reviewed the psychiatric testimony as to the offenders' personalities and early environmental influences. He discussed the absence of fixed sadistic elements, the question of premeditation and malice aforethought in the shooting, the issue of the kidnapping (under the "little Lindbergh law"), and the penal code direction that the defendants' backgrounds be inquired into. As to this, the Court commented:

If . . . social forces did their share to twist these boys, then it would ill behoove society to put them to death. . . . In a proper setting, the doctors say, their personalities may be reshaped to more socially acceptable forms. . . . These observations do not excuse the defendants or palliate their crime. . . . Their background . . . explains but does not excuse their actions. . . .

From this full consideration of all factors, the Court passed final judgment:

The determination [is] that these defendants shall not suffer the death penalty but shall be imprisoned for life.

In Slim's case, the possibility of parole was specifically excluded; for Tex, parole is possible after twelve years' incarceration. There is always the possibility, however, of the parole of any felon by executive clemency if rehabilitation shall have been effected.

This, then, is a node of criminological growth, a meaningful weaving into the law of human, and hence necessarily psychological, elements within two criminals with which society, against its own resistance, must contend. No abstract principle for or against capital punishment was involved; the nodal point transcended this principle. It dealt with human practicalities: Can these prisoners, these two egos, be rehabilitated? In terms of the common weal, is rehabilitation in prison possible? Is it practical? Is it good? The enlightened jurist answered in the affirmative, and the law permitted pragmatism to replace fruitless debate about principle.

THE USES OF AGGRESSION

The summation by the judge presiding in the Garfield case touched on a growing change in attitude toward death for first-degree murder. The concepts expressed by the judge did not evade the duty of punishment, but they did pave the way for possibilities of rehabilitation and treatment. This orientation necessarily brought a crucial area of concern to the fore; the psychologic and behavioral meaning of aggression to the offender. The cases so far discussed illustrate conflicts surrounding masochistic tendencies, suicidal and homicidal urges, oversensitized attitudes toward personal "honor" and social integrity, and so on. A corollary of the dynamic investigation of crime is contained in the generalization that aggression is the coin of social relatedness. Further, aggression, through the motor apparatus of the individual, serves the purposes of body satisfactions: in muscle movements in the young, for example, and in sexual activity among adults. In other words, aggression serves certain aspects of the ego structure in its relation to the world about it. In the criminal field, the sexual function is a background for aggressive crime to a degree that warrants attention.

There are crimes of a sexual nature in which aggression is a more weighty motivating factor than the sexual drive per se. Many cases of forceful rape, on examination, demonstrate the mechanism of strong hostility toward women, the sexual act being in a sense a substitute (and accommodation) for the deeper aggressive drives. This situation occurs in rape-murders where either the victim, in struggling, is killed or mutilated, or the homicide takes place after the sexual act. Here the latter act represents the true aim of the rapist. The fantasies and behavior of the offender revolve around destructive wishes and urges, in spite of an increased sexual appetite. Let us look at young Korner, who was convicted of rape, assault, and intent to murder at the age of twenty-one.

After a boyhood punctuated by juvenile offenses of various types, Korner, when he was sixteen, married a girl of fourteen. From this time on, his life was oriented around sexual relations—with his wife, girl friends, prostitutes, and pickups. There was no doubt that the loose organization of his own family—his father and brother had both been involved in cases of incest—formed a background wherein sexual license had attained a fixed social value. As Korner himself stated, he could not be content with fewer sexual contacts than several times a day. Often he would meet women in bars who were willing to have sexual relations with him, but this fast became child's play. What he yearned for was an aggressive mastery of the women with whom he had relations. As in the current case, he was not satisfied until he threatened them with injury. When Korner determined to have intercourse he always carried a knife with which to threaten his sexual partner, sometimes assaulting her by punching her with his fists. The essence of his sexual pattern was this: Once stimulated, he could not rest until satisfaction was obtained. As a result, according to his statement, his life became devoted to sexual satisfaction rather than work. Actually, Korner felt a considerable amount of guilt during and after the rapes he described. In a less boastful moment, he recognized his compulsive drive and asked to be treated for it.

In the case for which he was examined,[17] Korner while having intercourse with an acquaintance cut his victim's throat. Initially, the affair proceeded according to barroom rules. Presently, however, Korner produced a knife. His excitement increased when his partner, a woman in her twenties, became frightened and resisted him. Force led to counterforce. As Korner's sadistic fantasy took over, excitement mounted with it. Carried away with the power given him by the knife, he slashed the girl's throat. The charges brought against him were serious ones: forcible rape, assault with intent to murder.

The examination revealed Korner as sane, but clinically this youth of twenty-one suffered from the sexual neurosis termed satyriasis. The drawings that he offered the examiner unsolicited, those of an untutored artist, are mirrors of sexuality turned to destructiveness and sadism (see Plate III). The drawings themselves describe more vividly than any word-picture the direction of Korner's fantasies.

In connection with Korner's case it should be noted that in the crime of forceful rape, the aggressive aspect of sexuality, though it occupies a secondary position in the thoughts of the rapist, actually determines the criminal behavior evidenced. Normally, in the male, the fusion of aggressive and sexual urges are bound together in the orgasm. The aggressive and sexual instincts fuse into a psychosexual state that meets the requirements of passion, love, pleasure-giving, romance, and physical necessity, as well as gratitude and tenderness when satisfaction has been achieved. In cases of forceful rape or lust murder, however, this fusion becomes unbalanced. The object from which the male demands sexual gratification is the object he unconsciously seeks to injure or destroy. (The significant relationship betwen sexuality and crime will be discussed in detail in Chapter IX. The brief reference at this point to sexuality and aggression is meant to round out the panorama of aggressive crime.)

SLAUGHTER OF THE INNOCENTS

Among crimes associated with physical injury, that of infanticide is of great psychological interest. Infanticide is related to impulses deeply repressed in the average adult.

Those who deal with infants are impressed with the apparent fragility of these budding organisms, the utter helplessness, the complete dependence on adults. Behind an adult's expressed delight at these miniature replicas of grown human beings may range, in the preconscious and unconscious regions of the mind, unrecognized feelings of power and control, transformed under neurotic or psychotic pressures into aggressive impulses toward infants. At all events, the psychology of infanticide runs counter to the usual sentiment toward the very young. For children are prized by people by virtue of being mirrors of their progenitors or for their own elusive charm of innocence and trust. Children carry our hopes for the future. The educational system in this country, its insurance programs, health enterprises, defense systems, safety regulations, and so on, are largely fashioned with children in mind.

It may be set down as an axiom that the number of infanticides encountered by legal agents is far in excess of that which the criminologically inexperienced might suppose. In this respect, infanticide by women, especially mothers, might conceivably be culturally significant, for children are a vitally important segment of the psychological structure of society. It would be instructive to compare the authoritarian social attitudes toward children of the eighteenth and nineteenth centuries with those of our time with respect to infant assaults and homicides. There are no figures available for these periods but undoubtedly child-beatings occurred then; one can assume only that infanticide was less frequent than now reported. Whatever the reason, since the child has assumed a central place in our social planning and family life, child-beating and infanticide have increased alarmingly.

A recent article (1962) by a group of physicians (pediatricians) has drawn attention to an alarming number of deaths and cases of physical abuse of children, generally under the age of three years. These authors, Kempe and others,[18] coining the term "The Battered Child Syndrome," indicate that subdural hematoma (head injuries) and fractures of the femur are the most frequent findings in these cases. The editorial writer of the *Journal of the American Medical Association* (July 7, 1962) comments that child and infant murder and assault "may well rank with automobile accidents" as the cause of disturbances of the central nervous system among young children.[19] In these cases, and in those seen by this author and his colleagues, both natural parents and step-parents are involved, and mothers more frequently than fathers. That mothers, intimately concerned with procreation and the tender emotions surrounding it, should negate this fundamental feeling by injuring or killing their offspring, seems paradoxical. Psychotic conditions, depression, and schizophrenia often lie behind infanticide by mothers. In fathers, extreme immaturity or psychopathic emotionality are frequently observed. Two psychiatric investigators [20] who studied seventeen cases of infanticide encountered a condition in the mothers which they called "child-centered obsessional depression," while Lauretta Bender [21] found depressed mothers utilizing the children psychologically as hypochondriacal "organs." These mentally ill mothers identify with their children to a point where murder becomes a symbolic suicidal act.

The paradox of maternal aggression toward infants is related to a concept ancient in the human race: those who create may destroy that which they have created. This primitive idea is rooted in prehistory, stretching back far beyond law, custom, religion, or eithics. Aboriginal women who gave birth killed their offspring without too much compunction. Anthropologists have pointed out that other cultures do not place the same restrictions on infanticide as those of this civilization. There is considerable evidence, according to Marston Bates,[22] that among prehistoric man, even as remotely as the Pleistocene Age, "infanticide has been general among food-gathering peoples." It even has been suggested that early man spaced infants by killing alternate ones in order to spread the available food among those living.

Similarly, in some primitive tribes the convenience of the mother seems to have determined infanticide, in spite of certain taboos. For example, among the Mohave Indians, Devereaux [23] observed, infanticide is looked on askance if a child has been put to the breast. The overtones of recognition of this pristine mother-child relationship can be seen in the Infanticide Act (1922, revised in 1938 in England [24]), which, in recognizing the clinical fact that a disturbed mental balance may occur in recently delivered mothers, reduced the charge in infanticide from murder to manslaughter.

The primitive attitude toward infanticide that has been outlined is not much different from that reported in a case in Old New York. Here, emotional reactions to the crime of infanticide seem to reflect the ethics of that period. A case from a court * in Colonial America sheds light, through the language of the indictment, on social attitudes toward infanticide in those days:

One Hannah, a negro woman, slave and property of James J. Beekman of the North Ward of the said city on the 10th day of our Lord 1785 being big with male child . . . by the providence of God did bring forth the said child alive of the body of her the said Hannah alone and secret. But Hannah being moved and seduced by the instigation of the devil afterwards . . . the said Hannah with both her hands about the neck of said child then and there feloniously wilful of her malice aforethought choak and strangle, of which said choaking and strangling the said child then and there instantly died. And said Hannah . . . did kill and murder against the peace of the people of New York and their dignity.

Although in our time infanticide offenders are more frequently mentally ill women, the emotional dynamics lying behind the crime are not always obvious. Occasionally epilepsy is found, where the killing occurred during a state of epileptic fugue.[25] On the surface, those psychotic women who commit infanticide offer explanations derived from their delusions: that they wanted to save their children from an expected dread fate, that God wanted it as a sacrifice, and so on. In the mentally ill mother, motherhood itself is unconsciously negated as too great a price to pay for distortion of her body image, an assault on her narcissistic integrity, and a drain on her impoverished emotional life. The psychosis itself represents a denial of the child's birth. The aggressive components in these patients are warded away from the ego; hence, the homicide occurs under a cloud of confusion or in a depression. On the other hand, Lauretta Bender, in her study referred to above, states that infanticide is "not primarily an expression of conscious or unconscious hatred against the child."[26] Often the child serves as an object of displaced aggression aimed sometimes at the husband, sometimes at the marriage itself. But in the last analysis, the infant *does* bear a meaning to the mother (whether mentally ill or not) who kills; often the meaning is that of intolerance of life.

CRIMINAL ABORTION AS INFANTICIDE

The problem of induced abortion is tangential to that of infanticide, while involving other psychological implications. The midwife who

* The Court of General Sessions in New York originated in 1683, when it was called the Quarter Sessions. A charter was granted in 1686. The Court continued to sit until June, 1774, and reopened in February, 1784, after the close of the Revolutionary War. It was renamed "The Court of General Sessions of the Peace" in 1813.

commits criminal abortion unwittingly carries in the dim recesses of her psyche the primitive idea of a prior right over birth and death. In the evolution of medical history this preconscious attitude was challenged in a professional struggle as male physicians invaded the field of mid-wifery in the seventeenth and eighteenth centuries. The care of child-birth cases passed from midwives to trained male obstetricians during the 1700's in Europe. Garrison quotes the opposition of a Haymarket midwife to Dr. William Smellie, pioneer English obstetrician, in the course of which she called him a "great horse godmother of a he-midwife." [27] One finds occasionally, even today, this anachronistic atti-tude among some midwives, especially of European extraction, toward physicians. The ancient struggle for control of midwifery may be interpreted from the frequency with which midwives are charged with inducing criminal abortion.

The money involved in criminal abortions (and it is considerable) is not germane to this discussion. The point is that those elements of aggression toward infants uncovered by psychiatric scrutiny of female abortionists borrow their strength and persistence from the mythic preoccupation of women with creation and destruction. This hypothesis, suggested by ample clinical criminologic experience, helps in under-standing the psychology of infanticide and, tangentially, the psycho-logic motivations of criminal abortion, which are more readily traced in the women, rather than men, involved in this offense. With these generalizations in mind, let us examine a longitudinal section of the life of a midwife abortionist.

Greta Handtuch looked the part of the practical nurse: There was nothing indecisive in her manner as there was nothing skimpy about her figure. Surprisingly agile for a woman of her amplitude, Greta spoke with corresponding verbal agility. Her absence of diffidence and fear matched the machine-gun rapidity of her speech. There was an air about Mrs. Handtuch during the psychiatric interviews in the court clinic not unlike that of one colleague discussing medical matters with another; she discussed technical points freely, while dismissing lightly her previous arrests for suspected abortions:

. . . In 1934 it was practically the same thing as this, only it was worse. I was convicted and sent away for six months in the House of Detention. About twelve years ago, I was arrested again—it was for the same kind of case; that case was thrown out because it was proved that I didn't touch the girl.

Greta did not mention the fact that she had been charged with criminal abortion on five other occasions over nine years, including one charge of homicide in connection with an abortion. She dwelt feelingly on her graduation from the Midwifery School at Bellevue Hospital, on her practice as practical nurse and midwife in a neighborhood of predominately foreignborn people, and on the fact that she had been "framed the first time." In her words:

I don't know why I was framed the first time. I can't imagine why: somebody sent a letter in; I don't know who it was. The first time I know that another midwife framed me. All the midwives were jealous of the others because one had more business than others.

A first felony charge [28] provided an opportunity really to know Greta. There had been hints for years in the neighborhood of her activity as an abortionist, but proof of the overt act was missing. Her first five indictments, made on insufficient evidence and so dismissed, were lightly covered by Greta; but she was voluble regarding the current charge:

This is just a frameup. Some women come to the house and said they were recommended by someone whom I treated when I was a midwife. She told me that her stepdaughter was pregnant and wanted me to help her get rid of it. She told me that she was unmarried; but it turned out to be that it was two policewomen. I took this girl to the bathroom and the older woman stayed with my daughter. . . .
There were two men waiting downstairs—policemen—and then they came up and arrested us. The policewomen said a Mrs. Schmidt had referred them to me; I didn't remember anybody by that name. They were looking around the place—for instruments, I suppose. They found a speculum, sheets, pillow cases, small clamps, and they took a lamp, pillow, bed sheet. They found a package which wasn't even open; I was holding it for someone—there was catheters in it. This woman was a midwife and she died and that was the package she left.

During a pause in this recital, one of the examiners read aloud from the official indictment:

On February 1, 1940, without lawful authorization, the defendants unlawfully practiced medicine on Carol Benton by holding themselves able to diagnose and treat and prescribe and by offering to do so and have conspired to unlawfully practice medicine in order to procure the miscarriage of a woman. . . .

Greta listened gravely to the ponderous phrases; with a gesture of disdain, she remarked, "It's all jealousy between women, I suppose."
Discussion of her background yielded little of psychologic or socio-

logic interest. Born in Germany, deserted by her first husband, Greta had one daughter, now married and apparently adjusted on a low economic level. A second marriage in this country ended in divorce. The issue of this marriage, a second daughter, lived with Greta and helped her in her "medical" work. Both women painted a picture of a quiet life in a modest flat, working as domestics and seamstresses with little recreation and few friends. Greta was of average intelligence, perhaps brighter, and unquestionably superior to her daughter. Both women presented bland descriptions of a continuously unethical life, the recital shaded only by righteous evasion and indignation. The social investigator was less charitable in his characterization. The report stated:

Greta Handtuch . . . is dominating, aggressive, cunning . . . lacks a sense of guilt . . . without moral considerations . . . there was no economic urgency to perform the abortions.

There was nothing to be gained by further probing. Greta's attitude was fixed; she accepted the interrogation and psychiatric evaluation as part of the difficulties of "having trouble." She was placed on probation for five years.

Seven years later, under the name of a third husband, Greta was rearrested and charged with manslaughter in the first degree,[29] following an abortion on a young woman who subsequently died. By this time she had been arrested ten times, placed on probation twice, and acquitted eight times. The examiner noted the same breezy defiance of legal interference with her activities, commenting that Greta was well preserved for her age, an alert and hardy 63-year-old woman. He noted also that she was as evasive and circumstantial in 1948 as she had been at the 1941 examination.

Later, her probation period for the manslaughter charge satisfied, Greta moved to Florida, then returned to New York, where she was arrested in 1955 for unlawful practice of medicine: aborting a young woman and prescribing for her.[30] Now a hale sixty-nine, Greta shook off any questions. Her stability and self-assurance were "remarkable," according to one examiner. Whereas in the past Greta had complained of being "framed," now she spoke bitterly of friends "betraying" her, by which she meant they had not cooperated properly in protecting her. Her attitude was: "I've always worked hard. This is just one way of making a living. Why not?"

Greta's position had concretized into a reality. No longer did she evade the issue of abortion, but boldly held her own. She indicated that she had given fair service, exploited no one, did her job, and gave little cause for being penalized. Her struggle with man's law had reached an impasse after thirty years. Greta remained the apostle of independent action, the solver of problems of creation and destruction. In spite of having served prison and jail sentences, there was no change in her attitude toward punishment or crime. In a sense she had contributed her mite to the cause of freeing women from the tyranny of unwanted conception. To Greta Handtuch it was a simple situation of service. She might have felt a little repugnance had she known she was being classified as an Unethical Personality type by her psychiatric mentors. Without so stating, Greta believed in her "cause." She died of cancer at the age of seventy-three, while living in retirement in Florida.

This primitive matriarchal aggression—implied in the case of Greta—which places woman's function beyond the reach of man's law, may be seen in other situations also. The case of a Negro woman of forty who was charged with the murder of her third, common-law husband demonstrates this attitude with a directness that is unmistakable.

She was an attractive, buxom woman, known as a roisterer and drinker, who had murdered her second husband some years ago in a Southern state. Now, in the case against her for the killing of her third husband, the evidence was convincing but circumstantial: a blood-streaked room, a bloody knife at the scene, signs of a severe struggle, witnesses who had heard loud, obscene arguments between the pair prior to the homicide. The accused simply denied all this evidence, stating: "I woke up from a nap, saw the blood and the man dead. I have no idea what happened. I don't know the man." Because of a devious paranoid trend—she insisted that she had been followed by two men, had been given rat poison in her tea, and so on—she was committed to a state hospital as having been insane at the time of the "accident." [31]

For a year and half she maintained a complete denial of the evidence gathered. Her attitude was gentle and dignified, her manner controlled and stable. The original condition, diagnosed as schizophrenia, if it had been present, had improved by the time she was reexamined a year and half after the offense. As stated, she denied not only the well-documented evidence of the homicide but her entire life of unstable, boisterous, aggressive behavior, her arrests for prostitution, disorderly conduct, and the like. As is well known, offenders who deny an offense persistently come to believe it so intensely as to confer the coloring of reality to the denial. In this case the offender's denial reached even deeper: it approached an amnesia. One had the impression that she excluded the world of men from her consciousness, rejecting the prized rationality behind law and legal procedure in order to wreak that vengeance on her common-law husband that she deemed proper. Her aggression was compounded of her own sense of social fitness, her cultural standards, and a subterranean wish to outwit the values that society had enshrined in the name of law and order.

THE HAND OF MEDEA

The digression into criminal abortion during the last few pages sheds an indirect light on the psychology of infanticide. We now turn to a case that more immediately illustrates this crime, that of Mary Haller, housewife, thirty-three years old, mother of four. Mrs. Haller was taken into custody after a workman, glancing through a bedroom window, reported her seven-year-old son lying unattended in what appeared to be a coma. Examination proved the boy dead, strangled a few hours earlier, presumably by his mother.

It was obvious to the authorities that Mary was ill: she appeared wan, pale, and confused. "People," she said, "were laughing at me. . . . They said my family was mentally retarded." Investigation demonstrated the telltale signs of forthcoming trouble in her early history. Married at twenty-one, her first child died immediately after birth. Mary took it stoically but careful questioning of her family revealed that she had had a tendency toward depressions in her high-school days. Her mother had noted that she often complained of not feeling "right." Still, her marriage seemed routine enough. A second child was born and all seemed well, although it soon became apparent that this child, a girl, was afflicted with a brain injury. A psychotic episode followed this birth, which was treated successfully by shock therapy. The following year, after bearing a third child, Mary developed a minor depression, during which she scratched her wrists in a suicide attempt.

In her depression, Mary complained of being totally unworthy of her husband's ideals. He, toughened by family cares, mistook her suicide attempt and complaints for lack of robustness. His intolerance left little room for emotional support. Nevertheless, the birth of a fourth child left her only mildly depressed. However, with the advent of the fifth baby, the situation became serious.

Two days after that delivery, Mary developed hallucinations and delusions: she was the resurrection of the Christ; she could perform miracles. The children were neglected at home; turmoil reigned as her husband tried to control her odd behavior by impatience and loud advice. Finally, a minister's counsel was sought. He recognized the psychotic nature of her speech; Mary spoke to him of suicide, even homicide. There was no doubt now of her need for medical care.

Hospitalized, she looked fatigued and pale, but spoke with exhilaration of the "power of Christ" that filled her. There was little talk of the children, little concern with anything but this divine aspiration. Things were different, she said, "the TV was reversed." Between bursts of ecstatic talk about her "reincarnation," depressed periods occurred. The patient often spoke of dying. Treatment was instituted; improvement seemed to follow and leave of absence was proposed. At home again after several months away, Mary went about her household duties apathetically. The homicide occurred soon after.

In custody and under observation again, Mary's delusions faded as the reality of her plight was borne in on her. A weighty sense of remorse filled her mind, which appeared clearer. "Nothing can bring my Hughie back," she said. "I'll probably go to the electric chair this time [*sic*]. . . . I deserve anything they do to me. . . . Wherever I go, I see the boy's face."

Her husband, for his part, maintained an attitude of righteousness, emphasizing the "disgrace brought on the family." The deep, unexpressed conflict between a depressive woman and a rigid husband suggests the psychologic motivation for this tragedy: the acting out of hostilities that could not be faced or controlled by a weakened ego.

Like Medea, her ancient counterpart, Mary Haller, although ill enough to be relieved of standing trial for her crime,[32] began slowly to feel the pain of her acts. Euripides permits his heroine, Medea, "luckless Medea," no protective madness to cover her anguish. She faces her pain and shame barefacedly. When Medea's husband Jason betrays her by choosing a Greek princess to wed, thus bestowing noble rank on the children born to him and Medea, her ensuing emotional storm is unavoidable:

NURSE: . . . with a husband who now holds her in contempt. . . . She hates her children and has no pleasure in the sight of them. I fear she forms some new and horrible resolve.

MEDEA: O cursed sons of a hateful mother, a plague on you! And on your father! Ruin seize the whole household! [33]

The crime of Mary Haller seems to be one that lies external to punishment, external to criminal law. As Wertham in another case history says, "The legend of Medea is no pale myth or fable." [34] Her story is as much a psychological reality today as in antiquity, when Euripides showed in stark outline the inner struggle of the humiliated woman who slew her children in feminine fury. The great playwright has Medea say, as she writhes in her mental torment:

I shall not let my hand be unnerved. . . . Ah, ah, stop, my heart. Do not you commit this crime. . . . In any case they must die. And if die they must, *I* shall slay them, who gave them birth.[35]

As might be expected, Mary Haller was remanded to a hospital for treatment, a deeply disturbed woman.

INFANTICIDE BY THE MALE

Fathers and stepfathers—particularly the latter—who injure children are prone to display serious personality disturbances rather than psychoses as in the case of their female counterparts. Aggression in fathers toward their infant children seems more clearly based on direct antagonism to the child, spawned by immature feelings of jealousy. Uncontrollable crying by the infant, excessive admiration of the child by the mother, temporary neglect of the husband by the wife-mother, become the stimuli for sadistic slapping of the child or other forms of assault on it. The character of the feelings behind the blows, as analyzed after the crime, remind one of the prepuberty sadism so characteristic of boys from nine to thirteen years of age. The stark, almost inhuman, predilection of boys in this age-group for destroying animals, crushing and mutilating insects, ostracizing and hazing unpopular playmates is generally known. The animality of their play, which floods into primitive aggression in a gang, is notorious; it lies upon a renunciation of the tender feelings and sentiments so carefully instilled in boys by the ethical forces of church, home, and school. This attitude, seemingly inexplicable to the adult, who sees only the savage in the boy at this period, is evidence of the *latency* period, usually soon outgrown. Among normal boys, it evidences itself sporadically; among adolescent gangs, it may erupt in force; and among neurotic men, it emerges in solitary instances of assault and homicide, including infanticide.

The young serviceman, looking more like a junior auditor than a soldier, answered with glibness and assurance the questions put to him by the psychiatrist. Harry was not unused to analysis; he and his pert wife had discussed the problems of life in depth during their brief engagement. They would manage their money wisely, live in a modest apartment, and Cynthia would continue to work. At twenty, there was no need for a family. All the courses in marriage at the state university agreed that planning should take precedence over passion. To Harry, the path lay clear: "Finish your military 'time,' resume your studies at the University, take the proper courses, get that coveted degree in business administration, you'll make the grade," he told himself. The plan was conformist and sensible; it fitted the times. On that note, the marriage started auspiciously.

But Harry's parents were not so pleased. His father, a university graduate, joined Harry's mother in discounting the social level of the young bride, her wish to have a child at once; her plebian ideals, which threatened to upset Harry's plans, her distant manner with her in-laws. Both parents agreed that Harry had changed during the two years of marriage before the baby came. He had complained about their miniature apartment, the extravagances of his wife, and, above all, Cynthia's delight over her pregnancy.

After the birth of his child, Harry, growing testy, often complained that Cynthia "threw the baby in his face"—nothing was too good for baby and nothing mattered except the baby. He felt rejected. But his young wife and *her* mother were pleased beyond their dreams.

Several evenings a week, Harry was left to watch over the child while Cynthia worked overtime feverishly, trying to earn enough for baby's first Christmas. Alone with the infant, Harry brooded on his psychic bruises. One evening he found himself striking the infant in its crib with a flurry of blows. He felt his arms "working automatically" as if, Harry explained, "my mind stepped aside from what I was doing." The child took the blows without too much effect and Cynthia, although surprised at the unexplained bruises on the child, accepted them as part of the hazards of childraising. A few weeks later, Cynthia came home to find the baby unconscious. Her physician advised her that a subdural (cerebral) hemorrhage was present: he was also at a loss to understand why it should occur to a healthy infant. Treatment brought the child around, but the cause of the trouble could not be ascertained. Harry did not reveal that on a second evening he had struck the child repeatedly on the head, and had also stuck pins into the baby's arms and legs in a burst of automatic fury. Again he wondered why his arms functioned "one way" while his mind asked, "What are you doing?"

A month later, the baby suddenly became listless and the doctor insisted on hospitalization. Cynthia was beside herself. The baby gradually weakened, then died. Harry confessed a third series of blows on the child's head. He didn't know why he had done it; something must be wrong. He even voluntarily requested a month's observation in the psychiatric division of the hospital.

The examiners agreed that Harry was impulsive, immature, and probably psychopathic. "There was no motive for the offense except a disordered mind," his attorney asserted at the court hearing,[36] and the examiners concurred that Harry's mind was disordered, but that he was not legally insane. The examining psychiatrists noted a tendency to blame his wife and mother-in-law quite unrealistically for their preoccupation with the wife's first child. At times one saw a true prepuberty sadism shining through his account of the assaults. He spoke of the infant as something external to himself. His description of an episode of automatic behavior bore an hysterical character, a repressive mechanism that protected his ego from a full realization of his acts.

An outstanding finding of the examination lay in the emotional thinness the offender demonstrated toward his wife and child. He seemed to have had none of the pride or interest a young father usually develops in a first son. This callousness and lack of appreciation of the emotional aspects of the marriage relationship reflected a serious immaturity. Details of the offender's psychologic pattern were revealed by a Rorschach test, which showed strong impulses to immediate gratification. He generally maintained rather rigid controls, although he showed a tendency to be ruled by his own immediate needs for gratification, while his affectional needs threatened to swamp his entire personality. A primitive sort of compulsiveness associated with anxiety and insecurity was evident.

The total family reaction to the crime shed some light on Harry's personality structure. His mother gave the impression that she was antagonistic toward the wife on a social level, while actually she sought to prevent her son from maturing. The father was simply hurt because the family status had been injured. He was much more interested in the familial intellectual level than in his son's emotional problem; he thus betrayed his belief that the boy was duller than he actually was. Harry adopted his father's pride without the latter's capacity to back it up; he also seemed to have borrowed his derogation of his wife from his parents.

THE GREEKS HAD A WORD . . .

Infanticide, viewed as criminal behavior, presents no special facet of aggression in action. Viewed psychologically, however, it is involved with the central core of those human emotions that are almost mythic in their scope and strength. Crimes of father against son, of brother against brother, and of son against father (or mother) bear an epic stamp: They represent the deepest layer of human feelings. The earliest literature, from the Old Testament to the Greek tragedies, dealt with these tragic themes. When Freud found the nucleus of neurosis in the Oedipus story, the legend of the son who slew the father in aspiring to his place,[37] he further speculated that this son became a hero, who himself was deified, assuming the position of Father, so perpetuating the eternal cycle of son and "never forgotten primal father." The common saying that "a man is not a man until his father dies" expresses this psychologic progression; myths, fairy tales, and legends in many lands and times support these speculations. As Philip Rieff has phrased it:

The primal murder signaled not merely the beginning of political society but also the beginning of all ritual.

From the parricide motif, we are lead to examine other aspects of killing within the family. In this connection Rieff goes on to say:

The murder of the father is but one theme in the myth literature extant; the fratricide motif occurs quite as significantly as that of parricide.[38]

Many scholars have traced the vicissitudes of emotions within the family group. Gilbert Murray,[39] in examining the universal passions (among prepsychiatric writers the word "passion" embodied the meaning now given to "emotion"), contrasted the legends of Orestes and Hamlet. He noted similarities in the life of Orestes, son of the slain king, Agamemnon, and that of Hamlet, son of the assassinated king of the Danes, comparing Euripides' Electra and Shakespeare's Hamlet. Murray concluded that "this gradual shaping and reshaping of a primitive folk-tale, in itself rather empty and devoid of character . . . issues [forth] in a great tragedy which shakes the world." [40] Imaginative literature, he went on, reflects passions as old as time:

The things belonging to old stories and old magic rites, which stirred and thrilled our forefathers five and six thousand years ago, set them dancing all night on the hill, tearing breasts and men in pieces, and joyously giving up their own bodies . . . to keep the green world from dying and to be the saviours of their own people. [41]

These pristine passions, Murray suggests, even before they involved parricide or king-slaying, fulfilled the "prehistoric and world-wide ritual battle of Summer and Winter, of Life and Death."

Familial homicides are as old as man; this primitive overtone itself brings the heart of such tragedies to the fore: the conscious, yet unconscious, hatred of those loved. One can understand these homicides or assaults psychologically if one understands the basic ambivalence underlying parricide, matricide, fratricide, even infanticide. These crimes involve a primary type of hate, an intimate kind of violence expressed in behavior which, because of its closeness to the core of the ego, all humans instinctively understand. In particular, the crimes of parricide and matricide convey an organic coloring that reaches to those archaic levels of the ego where blind emotions, love and hate, dwell in secret.

In recent years, parricide, even more than matricide or fratricide, is met with in criminal practice in increasing frequency. Usually it is perpetrated by adolescents and youths. These youths explain that they were "angered at the father," had a sudden "urge to kill someone," felt they had been "reprimanded unjustly," and so on. Sometimes they prove to be mentally dull or have a history, given by associates, teachers, and parents, of being "good" boys with no discernible psychiatric problems.

From a theoretical point of view, the psychological motivation of parricide should be transparently clear. The father-slaying immortalized in Sophocles' tragedy *Oedipus Rex*, wherein Oedipus unwittingly fulfills the dreadful prophecy of the oracle, was taken by Freud as the nuclear neurosis, the unconscious psychosexual problem of all men. Among neurotic patients, material interpreted by psychoanalysts abundantly exemplifies the Oedipal conflict.[42] When Oedipus becomes aware that he has fulfilled the oracle's prediction when he acceded to his father's throne, this unhappy being voices his anguish:

> But other grievous things he prophesied,
> Woes, lamentations, mourning, portents dire;
> To wit, I should defile my mother's bed
> And raise up seed too loathsome to behold,
> And slay the father from whose loins I spring.[43]

The emotion behind this tragic myth is buried in the average man: it exists only in deep-laid fantasies and dreams. Normally, the resolution of this unconscious drama occurs when the boy identifies with his father and relinquishes his incestuous fantasies and murderous instincts toward him, replacing them with love and admiration. In certain cases, however, the substrate of hostility toward the father persists throughout life: the Oedipal conflict, because of parental cruelty, abnormal home environment, an excessively domineering father, and so on, is unevenly resolved, or fails of resolution. Indeed, some workers, for example, Robert M. Lindner,[44] feel that the unresolved Oedipus conflict, with its hostility toward the father-figure, projected onto society, becomes the basic mechanism of the psychopathic personality. In one case of a young psychopath, convicted of such crimes as assault, robbery, burglary, larceny, and in five prisoners whom he had studied through the method of hypnotherapy, Lindner found the "special feature of the psychopath to be . . . a profound hatred of the father" [45] persisting throughout life.

The ready transliteration of the Oedipus myth into the unconscious emotional life of a boy has been questioned by several investigators. Some have modified the Oedipus complex to mean a *symbolic* rather than an actual killing wish toward the father accompanied by a *symbolic* sexual wish toward the mother. In this construct, as a recent commentator [46] notes, the Oedipal attachment within the child uses a "body zone" for the emotional closeness needed. In other words, "he [the boy, especially] has learned to relate using primarily his body for cues" until he finds other "socially responsible symbols" with which to force society to satisfy his inner emotional needs. This discussion of the Oedipus conflict in the psychic life of the parricide would suggest altering the older formula of unconscious sexual interest in the mother and aggressive trends toward the hated rival (father) as the unconscious motivation of parricide.

Examination of youths who have killed one or both parents often reveals no previous indication of aggressive tendencies in their relations with their parents. One does find thinly veiled feelings of contempt for the parents, rebelliousness masked by an attitude of aloofness toward the family, inner rage hidden by an air of compliance and passivity, deep feelings of inadequacy covered by a strong attitude of independence of parental control and impatience with adult precepts. It may be that such cases have not been studied as deeply as was Lindner's—although here one must be cautious of insinuating theoretical considerations into clinical material. For example, the primal scene reported to have been witnessed by Lindner's patient, at the age of seven months, was interpreted as having initiated the prisoner's hatred of his father, and so his criminal tendencies.

It seems to this investigator that it is more plausible to look to the democratization of aggression, the ubiquity of assertion, the decreased bond of dependence of the young on the old in our time for an explanation of parental homicide. Perhaps these tendencies, so long repressed by a rigid moral ethos, are coming into expression. Fantasies, universally infiltrated with movement tendencies, are acted out more readily. The accent on motility and aggression in the social atmosphere lends its support to this acting-out tendency. Static, stationary, formal institutions in society provide little satisfaction for youth.

Another factor comes into play here, namely, the problem of achievement in the world. The current social climate, which accents accomplishment, tends to denigrate nonachievement: the more potent the status symbol of achievement, the more difficult it is for youth to withstand frustrations that block success. In those whose threshold of emotional tolerance is low, not to achieve status through accomplishment and motility stimulates reaction through assaultive acts. It is this subtle attitude in his society that impels the neurotic, mentally dull, or schizoid youth to commit such crimes as parricide or matricide. But a social atmosphere is an abstraction until it reacts upon and through a personality. The sociological influences making for criminal aggression often thrive in the soil of poor ego-integration. Ralph Gruber is a case in point.

Not especially gifted intellectually, Ralph perceived the world with both simplistic clarity and blurred distortion. His ambition to be a musician had little possibility of fulfillment. Insight was lacking in Ralph; his inner universe was poorly differentiated from the adult world of reality. Nevertheless, the boy did recognize a world in which people "read books—like doctors, for instance." They, he remarked, "were better than most folks. They wanted a better life, money." And there were stage people, like Arthur Godfrey and Steve Allen: "I used to pretend I was them. . . . I would laugh to myself and make up my own world. But that was when I was sick and went to the state hospital."

It would have been obvious to anyone but the family that Ralph's dream of becoming a performer on the accordion contained little promise of realization. His school record proved this, but the accordion course which Ralph assiduously followed for twelve years contained the promise of glory. "I played *Poet and Peasant,* Debussy, and Bach," he said proudly. "Practiced three and four hours a day, but my father thought that wasn't enough." Ralph enlarged on this in that intimate, yet slightly muted tone that the dullard employs:

I got no free time. . . . Father never thought three or four hours was enough. He kept pushing me. "Get a better technique," he used to say. Then he would listen and say, "It don't sound like you practiced." My mother, she stuck up for me. My father, he never slapped me but he kept on . . . practice all day long . . . three hours ain't enough. . . . I got mad.

Perhaps Ralph's fantasies of future fame bore a dim relationship to his father's success as a graduate engineer. Ralph's father knew the meaning of work: when Ralph spoke of wanting to be a musician, his father approved—"But you will have to practice—eight hours a day."

Ralph's report concerning his family members was given in the same staccato way, as if he were checking them off mechanically, the sooner to be rid of the chore: "My father graduated college. My older brother, he is a salesman; my sister, she is married; my half-sister lives in Arizona."

His account of his two admissions to psychiatric institutions was given in an equally mechanical manner. He didn't like the hospitals or see the necessity for the shock treatments administered. "I couldn't wait to get out of the hospital," he said. "I used to talk and laugh to myself, but not any more."

The neighbors agreed that he was quiet, very polite, and docile. They could hear his father harping on his practicing, belittling his practice. Ralph played his accordion fitfully, but his daydreams of success rolled on. Although by the age of nineteen he still had not finished high school, his mother encouraged his musical ambitions. His older brothers and sisters later remembered how she overprotected Ralph. His odd manner was overlooked by his parents; in fact, when he complained that his classmates discriminated against him because of his constant interest in music, his mother thought it best to remove him from school. Both parents encouraged him to stay home and take correspondence courses, sheltering him against an inconsiderate world. Thus, the atmosphere in which Ralph grew up did not correspond to that recommended for the typical American boy. But he tried to be "regular." Borrowing five dollars from a neighbor, Ralph selected a .22 caliber rifle from a local store, to " go hunting." His father objected to the purchase and removed the gun from the home.

A month later Ralph stole a revolver from the same store, secreting it at home. His life of practicing, daydreaming, idling continued. His rebellion at his father's attempts to control and guide him did not impress the parents too much. One day, Ralph admitted, "I got mad. They said I was chasing around because I didn't practice eight hours a day. No free time. I got mad. I wanted to hit him." Ralph went to his room and returned with the revolver. He saw his father standing in the living room; he raised the gun——

Ralph's story of the homicides [47] was told in a cool, clinical manner, as indicated in the investigating officer's report:

I asked him if he lived with his parents and he said yes. I asked him where they were and he said at home. I asked if they were all right. He said, "Yes." I asked him what they were doing and he said, "Oh, they were just around the house." I asked if he had talked with them and he said yes, he had. I said, "Did your father talk back to you?" He said, "No." "What was he doing?" "Well, he was just lying there on the floor."

In order to explain this oddity, Ralph continued simply:

My father was standing in front of me; I shot him in the face. All he said was "Ow." My mother ran into the bedroom. I shot her in the back of the head. Then I got kind of scared. I tried to get some money: sell the silverware and the phonograph. I slept in the house for three days before anybody bothered me. My father lay on the floor about ten feet away. He began to look black; but mother, she was frozen white.

At one point Ralph described the breakfast he cooked while his parents lay mutely in an adjoining room. "I had breakfast and supper with them," he said with disarming simplicity. The emotional flatness of his speech varied little as Ralph described his situation in retrospect:

I just try to figure out what happened, to see if anything is wrong. . . . I think of what happened before . . . drinking tea, watching television, going to the store, taking the dog out, writing music . . . one minute and the next minute something tragic happens. . . . it makes the heart sad.

Ralph's report of the murders had almost a third-party detachment. It reminded one of those hebephrenic schizophrenics who speak of themselves in the third person—the "transitivism" described by Eugen Bleuler years ago. This attitude reflected Ralph's whole psychological life; as the psychologist read the picture of Ralph's ego in the projective tests, "Ralph must stick to simple, common-sense views of things because he is not capable of a more integrated view. His inner resources are limited." His fantasies were childlike, escapist in nature. Little material of a sexual nature appeared in the tests. The clichés in his speech brought Ralph as close to the nuances of life as he was able to perceive; they were total phrases that he borrowed from the world of adult conversation. He himself lived on a level of emotional and intellectual imperception. Since he was psychotic and unable to confer with counsel in his own defense, Ralph was unable to stand trial. The judge ordered his commitment to a state hospital for treatment, on the presumption that if and when he recovered he would be tried for the crimes.

THE CRIME OF BARABBAS

The psychology of robbery shares some of the elements of the psychology of physical aggression, as in assault or murder. Although financial gain is basic, robbery is essentially an aggressive crime. In robbery, acquisitive aggression and destructive aggression often meet. The usual robbery does not necessarily encompass physical assault, whether by gun or knife, yet their combination is common enough, as every law enforcement officer knows. The potential robber is always ready for physical assault, either to defend himself or to give meaning to the robbery. Indeed, the psychology behind robbery, that of outright aggression, is so closely related to assault that, behaviorally, they may be considered as of one piece. The legal definition of the crime of robbery mirrors this combination of acquisitive and destructive action in its actual wording. Thus, in the common law robbery constitutes the

felonious taking and carrying away of the personal property of another, from his person or his presence, by violence, or putting him in fear.[48]

The essence of the crime resides in the last two aspects; hence, the various degrees of robbery depend on the degree of injury inflicted, the use of a deadly weapon, and the extent of fear induced in the victim. If the crime is done "privily, without the person's knowledge"—as, for example, a pocketbook snatching, where violence is not an essential part of the robbery—the crime usually falls under the category "larceny from the person." Robbery may involve the taking of property from a person, an institution (as, a bank), or a group of persons (gathered, for example, at a card game), and in modern times almost always involves the use of a weapon or a substitute for a weapon.

The use of a weapon involves deep feelings within the potential robber that subtly influence his behavior; the gun (or its facsimile, a toy gun) or knife is considered a masculine symbol of power, being interpretable as such by its very form and nature. To arm oneself with a gun immediately betrays a lack of security in one's aggressivity because the certainty of resistance by the victim is obviously implied. There are few self-respecting robbers who would agree with this idea, that a gun or knife is carried as a defense against strong fears of being vanquished by a selected victim. And many robbers, especially young ones, would strenuously disagree with the finding that deep feelings of inferiority and passivity lie beneath their bold actions.

Nevertheless, careful analysis of the emotional substrate in robbers demonstrates that feelings of inferiority are the mainspring of many robberies, especially among the immature. In addition, organic defects or constitutional deficiencies may give rise to inferiority reactions that may lead to compensatory aggression, reflected in robbery. Shortness of height has been found clinically to be one of the structural anomalies that stimulates prestige-sensitivity among youths.

The neurotic robber is often sensitive to his "social" status among his fellows. He has a strong need to uphold prestige values as he perceives them. In the robber's special community, prestige rests on clothes, motor cars, drinking, the company of women, and money. Antisocial groups are united by specific social values and cultural attitudes, just as the accepted social community holds prescribed allegiances. The criminal scurries, under the pressure of anxiety, to conform to the standards of conduct and prestige accepted and set before him by his group.

This underlying inferiority feeling can be observed from another angle. Robbery as a forthright crime carries the special implication of public recognition for daring. Not only among the public but among criminals, robbery ranks high in prestige value. Within the hierarchy of prisoners in a penal institution, the robber ranks himself far above such operators as burglars, arsonists, embezzlers. The robber is impatient with pettiness, disillusioned with slow gains, and driven to desperation by powerful, unconscious cravings for approval. On the surface the equation seems simple: higher stakes imply greater risks. Vigor, daring, and courage belong to the young—free souls who are imaginative, fast-moving, bold, yet withal quite human. In no other crime does the coloration of gallantry or chivalry enter into the psychology of the crime; in no other crime is the ego-ideal of the offender, and the public image of the criminal, so warmly cradled by the unconscious of the victim-public. Small wonder that Robin Hood, with his sense of justice and humanity, his daring and high courage, is the symbol of the robber, a symbol loved by a victim-public, who dramatize their own acquisitive impulses in the sublimated form of a cult of robber-heroes. To Robin Hood may be added Black Bart, Jesse James, John Dillinger, and the romantic figure of Jean Lafitte, or the Highwayman, so touchingly depicted by Noyes:

> One kiss, my bonny sweetheart, I'm after a
>   prize tonight
> But I shall be back with the yellow gold
>   before the morning light,
> Yet, if they press me sharply, and harry
>   me through the day,
> Then look for me by moonlight,
> Watch for me by moonlight,
> I'll come to thee by moonlight, though
>   hell should bar the way.[49]

The romanticized figure of the eighteenth-century highwayman or pirate bears an inner relation to the modern holdup man, in spite of the mechanistic and organizational, rather than individual and impassioned, frame of reference in which he is viewed. The romance lies in planning grandly, operating efficiently, and escaping detection cleverly. The techniques of speedy depredation and competent disguise or precise timing form the lifeblood of the crime of robbery. Further, the elaborate plans of the stickup man or gang betray elements that also suggest those of a game. The game ostensibly aims to outwit the police and public, but beneath the gambits, moves, defenses, and speedy action one may recognize psychological motives not unlike those of players in a sport. The wish to win—in this case, large sums of money—is present, but even more compelling is the hidden wish to be admired for daring and cleverness. The robber collects psychological dividends because he symbolizes the secret wish of the law-abiding population to revolt against the frustrations and restricting minutiae of daily life.

For the organized gang, robbery is a spectacle wherein victory is to the swift and the sure. As a way of criminal life, robbery is remunerative for a short time in comparison with some types of larceny (confidence swindles, pickpocketing, burglary) that can provide lifelong livelihoods. The very brevity of robbery adds impressively to its sportlike quality. Robbery is the last roll of weighted dice against odds, a desperate last-minute play against an implacable rival, a final maneuver as the shadows lengthen over the field.

The robber himself would be the first to scoff at the implied romance in robbery, and no self-respecting robber or successful "heist man" would admit to the psychological motives discussed here. His hard exterior, crusty manner, efficient technique, and aplomb in the face of police officers bespeak a denial of any dependence on the dramatic aspects of his acts or on the public's apparent approbation of his derring-do. Yet a modus operandi that befuddles and confuses the agents of the law and enlists public interest, even for only a time, offers tremendous gratification to the robber-criminal.

The theory advanced above has been constructed from hints gathered in the examinations of robbers. Robbers are not free in their explanations of inner motives or feelings, and the convicted robber yields very little personal material from which to corroborate the theory. Analysis of young robbers gives a clearer picture of the underlying dynamics of the crime; here one sees some of the hidden elements in the psychology of robbery. But in the main one must rely on the occasional case studied, even though the psychopathology present may distort the picture of the routine robber somewhat.

EMOTIONAL REACTIONS AMONG ROBBERS

The average robber, because his behavior is in the currency of aggression—he is direct, often brutal to his victims, and acts rapidly in the execution of the crime—reveals little of psychologic interest. But the frequency of emotional reactions among these offenders speaks for them. Direct lying about the crime, denial of many elements of their behavior, mutism, rage reactions, and, finally, symptoms characteristic of the Ganser syndrome (to be described later) are common among robbers under study in jail or while serving sentences in prison. It is these emotional reactions, some amounting to psychosis, some being extensions of neurotic reactions, that illuminate the psychology of the crime.

Denial, a natural defensive maneuver, is an expected answer from all persons accused of crime. Among robbers, however, it has been observed with unusual frequency, probably because the outright aggression of the crime constitutes a trauma to the ego. The enormity of the aggression, the effrontery of the robbery react upon the ego, reflexly causing a repression of the entire episode. This reaction approaches a psychotic state known as Ganser's syndrome (also variously called buffoonery syndrome, pseudo-imbecility, prison psychosis, and so on). This condition has been noted among robbers since 1898, when Ganser [50] described the "hysterical twilight state."

Originally considered a specific mental illness, the syndrome to which Ganser drew attention is characterized by approximate answers to the point of absurdity. Thus, a patient will say, "2 and 2 make 3" or "New York City is in New Jersey" or "Chicago is in Indiana," thus betraying specific knowledge that is distorted within approximate limits. This sort of pointed stupidity is seen during incarceration, in jail preliminary to trial, but rarely at the time of apprehension. Ganser's syndrome, in both pure and impure forms, may range from obviously foolish behavior of infantile character to grotesque movements that suggest conscious malingering. This is seen in the case of Daniel Covington, a thirty-year-old Negro, who attempted to rob a bank with a simulated gun and a note asking for money from the teller. When the bank manager came forward to talk to him, Covington broke a window with his fist, making no attempt to escape. He spoke quietly when a sheriff arrested him. While awaiting trial, he developed a Ganser syndrome.

During the psychiatric examination, Covington was vague, acting in an exaggeratedly boyish manner. He answered questions with a sing-song lilt. When asked for the name of the President before Eisenhower, the prisoner answered, "Ike, Truman, Hops, Buck, Robinson, Kiddo, and Clay." When asked about the duration of previous hospital admissions, he replied, "Must be twenty years, that's how old I am." When questioned about his family, particularly his mother, he spelled "M-o-t-h-e-r," and when asked a question which required a negative answer he spelled out "n-o." Covington was asked what time it would be if the hands pointing to 4:00 P.M. were reversed; he replied, "About this time."

It soon became apparent from his alternating states of excitement and mutism, as well as his apparent hallucinations, that a psychotic state had developed. The record indicated two previous state hospital admissions. His criminal record was also extensive; since the age of nineteen, he had been charged with burglary, sodomy, grand theft, and suspicion of robbery and gambling.

The interplay of defensiveness that takes the form of the Ganser syndrome and the encroachment of a disorganized mental state are frequent findings in robbers. It can easily be imagined that an inner perception by an offender of an unsuccessful criminal act may precipitate a state of denial that, in turn, gives way to a psychosis. Cases of the Ganser reaction evolve into definite psychoses on occasion because the repression of a frustrating experience is sufficient to cause an ego rupture. This was the situation with Covington. After observation, he was diagnosed as schizophrenic, the robbery charge was dropped, and commitment to a state hospital was ordered by the Court.[51]

This symptom complex, often puzzling to court attachés, occurs more frequently than some investigators have indicated. Guttmacher, for example, states from his long court experience: "It [the Ganser syndrome] is now a rather rare condition."[52] In indicating that some mental conditions vary from one historical period to another—as with the grande hystérie of Charcot's time (the 1870's), now clinical rarities —Guttmacher points to the periodicity of the Ganser reaction. It is generally agreed that some disease conditions do wax and wane in incidence over different periods. But in the Ganser syndrome, rather than speak in terms of historical cycles, the present author feels that a dynamic view of the condition would explain its fluctuations more satisfactorily. Since the condition is essentially a denial reaction, the social attitude toward the crime that is resisted through the syndrome might explain its prevalence in some periods. Further, since the buffoonery syndrome does not occur exclusively in robbery offenders, as shall soon be seen, it stands more closely related to the offender's ego than to the type of crime. It is, one might say, a "function" of the social-psychologic image that the offender carries of himself. The denial inherent in the Ganser reaction is compounded partly of shame and partly of self-anger at being caught; but this does not necessarily mean that the offender has experienced remorse for his wrongdoing.

The example of an offender of twenty-six, arrested for criminally receiving stolen property, comes to mind. The indictment cited the purchase for three dollars of several typewriters and an adding machine from two youths who had previously burglarized the items from a furniture store.

The offender, John Olney, left the seventh grade in school when his mother died. He then led a vagrant existence, roaming throughout the Eastern, Midwestern, and Southern states seeking employment. During these nomadic years, Olney was arrested on twenty-one occasions for such offenses as vagrancy, soliciting alms, and suspicion. However, there was no record of actual arrest for a major crime until the current offense.[53]

John's social profile might have suggested mental deficiency, or at least marked dullness—indeed, his behavior during the examinations would seem to substantiate this reconstruction. He was unable to understand the questions put to him; he seemed confused, dazed, childish. Sometimes this attitude was mixed with a desire to be playful—the buffoonery syndrome. For this reason, the examiners determined to try to get beneath this reaction and find its cause. The offender talked of his "bumming around" for years, telling his story with wide-eyed amazement at people's not believing him. He said people laughed at him, called him "stupid," and made fun of him; he himself thought he was "mentally defective." Occasionally during the interviews, in the midst of his bewilderment, he laughed in an embarrassed, inappropriate manner. He told isolated bits of the story, professing not to know the answers to simple questions, trying to show his complete confusion with the world around him.

Probing beyond his playful attitude showed that he was not defective; a basic emotional block became demonstrable, which was his habitual, defensive personality characteristic. As a matter of fact, on the Bellevue-Wechsler test he rated 95 on the IQ (an average performance), with a verbal IQ of 102 and a performance level of 88.

The psychologists who conducted the test reported that the perceptible "clowning" shown by John was an attempt to disguise his inadequacy. Beyond this was the implication of an emotional flatness perfusing his personality, akin to simple schizophrenia. But, as often happens, the dynamic changes incident to clinic handling, or therapeutic management, released those emotional forces making for the Ganser clinical picture. Within a few days the examiners reported Olney much more stable. He claimed that his clowning attitude disappeared because he felt free and at ease with the examiners.

ASSAULT BY WORDS

The strains of aggression are pitched in other keys than that of physical injury. Not the least of these involves verbal aggression in the form of the shrill voices of slander and libel. Slander comprises the uttering of a statement that tends to defame or otherwise calumniate a person's actions or behavior; libel is the publishing of

. . . malicious [material] by writing, printing, picture, effigy, sign or otherwise than by mere speech, which exposes any living person or the memory of any person deceased, to hatred, contempt, ridicule or obloquy . . . or has a tendency to injure any person, corporation or association . . . in his or their business or occupation.[54]

The offense of criminal libel involves publication of an article or book that defames by pointing maliciously or falsely to a racial or religious characteristic, a personal idiosyncrasy or type of behavior so as to injure the victim's reputation, business, or profession. The verbal aggression involved in slander and the wordy aggression in libel are of destructive nature: they aim to injure directly by false statements or association. In this discussion, it should be borne in mind that in the maelstrom of everyday life verbal aggression is more frequent than physical action. The rich and changing vulgar vocabulary that serves to castigate and symbolically injure our neighbors, co-workers, and even members of our intimate circles is testimony to the need to siphon off anger and reassert the self-esteem of the one uttering these imprecations. Usually, slanderous remarks are absorbed in an atmosphere of general banter, but occasionally slander rises to an insufferable level, motivating assaultive behavior.

The psychological background in such offenders rests on hypersensitivity in matters of personal honor and low tolerance of thrusts at their self-esteem. The slander or libel usually proceeds from a person whose personality contains a paranoid fraction. When a series of slanderous statements fan into a situation where maliciousness is extreme, or assault and battery occur, the case comes before the criminal court for judgment. More often, the victim takes civil action to recover damages as recompense for injuries inflicted by libelous spoken or published statements. Although cases of slander and libel occur relatively infrequently in our criminal courts, the psychological features of aggression as behavior are transparent. The following case involves both physical and verbal (slanderous) aggression. In it were elements of a feud, a crime, a civil wrong, and a tinge of paranoia.

The local newspaper carried a small item stating that a local jury had awarded Mr. and Mrs. Hans Holzmann damages to the extent of $3,000 in a suit against their neighbors, the Walkers.[55] It had been charged that the latter had used insulting language, had mocked and mimicked Mrs. Holzmann, discrediting the reputation of the Holzmann family. The simple statement covered ten years of aggressive provocation and angry responses.

It all started when Mrs. Holzmann, a native of Germany, and, she claimed, victim of a Soviet concentration camp in Europe, became upset by too pointed references on the part of her neighbor to her Teutonic origin. Swastikas were being displayed near the house and her two boys, earnestly trying to adopt American attitudes and shed the traces of a Teutonic accent, were openly taunted. This insulting behavior was tolerated for months until Mrs. Holzmann could stand it no longer; she pelted her neighbors with rocks and shouted obscenities at a few who were antagonistic to her. The neighbors complained and the sheriff arrested Dorothea Holzmann on the charge of disturbing the peace. A considerate judge dismissed the case, and she returned to her home.

But the verbal assaults did not cease. From time to time, the Holzmanns overheard muttered remarks, in which the government was called on to "clean out the dirty Nazis" or to "kill the Germans." Sometimes their children were subjected to snide, barely audible, remarks— "Send them back where they came from." Mr. Holzmann, trying to maintain an objective attitude, paid little attention to his wife's complaints; he wanted only to live and let live. Dorothea vowed she would get revenge if it took her ten years. Nevertheless, in time, amity descended on Maple Street. The Walkers went out of their way to befriend the Holzmanns. When Mrs. Holzmann was hospitalized for severe diabetes, Mrs. Walker brought flowers to her bedside. They had long talks; Dorothea described in detail her bitter life in Germany during the war, told how the Russians had cut off one of her fingers, and dwelt on the horrors she had witnessed in a concentration camp. Thus, the Holzmanns attained the level of being "interesting neighbors" and bygones became bygones.

But peace did not last long. Mrs. Walker is said by other neighbors to have characterized Mrs. Holzmann as a "gossip"; there had been some talk concerning Dorothea's trying to "break up" other couples on the block, and Mrs. Walker remarked, rather archly, to a neighbor, "People don't change, you know."

A few months went by before Mrs. Holzmann received word of Mrs. Walker's attitude. "Ja," she thought, "prejudices don't die easy." For some time, in fact, she had noticed that the floodlight on the Walkers' driveway was turned in such a way as to illuminate her bedroom brightly. For one thing, the lamp needn't have been so large, and, for another, why was a floodlight needed through the night anyhow? There followed heated discussions between the parties on these points. Then once more a form of peace descended.

With the advent of the Christmas season, the Walkers bedecked the trees in front of their house with lights that, curiously enough, were timed to blink on and off *almost* as if they were meant to irritate Mrs. Holzmann as she sat in her favorite chair before the window. More discussions, more explanations; oil was poured on the troubled waters. The lights were dimmed; ivy vines were trained to obscure the lights; the dove of peace redescended on Maple Street.

The years rolled along: the Holzmann-Walker truce remained an uneasy one. Dorothea noticed that the innuendoes, which had continued, were rarely voiced in front of her husband. Sometimes when the Walkers "got to drinking," the old taunts were heard. Pebbles were thrown at their cars, the Holzmann boys were pelted with rocks (Dorothea said). The situation flared up again. Mrs. Holzmann demanded an explanation of the continued persecution. The Walkers said she was a "gossip" and other things more pointed. An altercation developed one day while the Walkers were watering their lawn. Mrs. Holzmann, demanding explanations, became infuriated. She struck Mr. Walker, inflicting small lacerations on his chin and behind his ear. Walker insisted that Dorothea be arrested for battery and assault. Again the charge was dismissed.

The issue had gone too far to be left hanging in limbo; there were loud voices, complaints, charges and countercharges, obscenity, threats, and vows of eternal vengeance! There was one recourse left: the courts of the United States, or at least the county court! Through their lawyer the Holzmanns demanded $300,000 because of the Walkers' malicious prosecution of a battery complaint against Mrs. Holzmann, and for

. . . alleged wrongful, unlawful, malicious and intentional conduct. . . . As a direct and proximate result of the alleged conduct, behavior and actions of the defendants, [the plaintiffs] have suffered injury to their nervous systems and have been caused great mental, physical, and nervous pain and suffering. . . . [etc.]

The Walkers filed a cross complaint for damages to the extent of $100,000.

The point at issue was the extent of nervous "damage" suffered by Mrs. Holzmann and, secondarily, by the Walkers. Both attorneys agreed to psychiatric examination of their respective clients. The parties were examined carefully: In the case of Mrs. Holzmann, a physical review indicated that she suffered from diabetes and a heart condition. She cooperated during the interviews, talking rapidly when things went in her favor, but a little averse to being pinned down to specific dates. She traded heavily on her concentration camp experiences during the war. She had suffered so much, and then to have *this*—words like "dirty Nazi," the fighting among the neighbors' children and her own, the lights flickering and shining in her windows—it was too much; even reciting the facts made her tense, fearful, disgusted, and gave her "poor vision."

A study of the Walkers indicated that they also were unwilling to be specific, but upon being pressed they did give rather detailed information. They minimized the fights among the children. Regarding the disturbing lights, these were used without malicious intent. It was clear, however, that Mr. Walker took a certain amount of pleasure in irritating Mrs. Holzmann on whatever basis she presented—mainly her sensitivity about her race. It could be readily seen that a certain subtle capacity for aggression was present.

Each side accused the other of being irritating, gossipy persons, vengeful, and "looking for trouble." The truth lay in the demonstration of an interesting crosscurrent of social aggression issuing from both sides. Mrs. Holzmann was undoubtedly a sensitive, emotionally unstable woman with a paranoid coloring, Mr. Holzmann was a somewhat passive individual who followed the trend of his wife's feelings, unable to dissuade her from emphasizing the Walkers' attitudes. Mr. Walker, on the other hand, got a covert satisfaction from Mrs. Holzmann's continued complaints, and unconsciously provided provocation for them. Mrs. Walker supplied silent support for her husband's attitude. Mrs. Holzmann misinterpreted or exaggerated the expressed and unexpressed feelings of the Walkers, and in so doing permitted an airing of her own latent hostility and possible inner guilt.

The court in its wisdom awarded damages to the plaintiff and, after a thorough airing of the distress caused on both sides, trusted that the "long and sometimes sleepless neighborhood feud" would end.

THE WORD AND THE MAILED FIST

The area of verbal aggression into which the discussion has moved contains many elements of criminological interest. Perkins in his standard text on criminal law makes the point that "words are acts in the juridical sense," that is, they can *injure;* thus, the words of a perjurer may serve to convict an innocent man and so injure him through unjust punishment. Other crimes (as, extortion) bear a distinct psychological relation to that of malicious libel, even though the surface wish to injure or defame is replaced by the demand for money. In the psychologic drive to belittle and denigrate his victim, the blackmailer, extortionist, and slanderer are motivated by the same psychologic aggression.

Although the legal definitions of *extortion, libel,* and *malicious mischief* are clear-cut for purposes of prosecution, the types of aggression expressed in cases of this sort range from ransom notes in a kidnapping case to crank letters and obscene phone calls. One may also include here the malicious painting of obscene words on churches or synagogues and the painting of swastikas on Jewish synagogues. In such cases, the satisfaction felt in doing injury does not extend to the point of demanding a monetary reward, as in extortion.

The aggression involved in extortion and blackmail has a special quality of remote power. The blackmailer arms himself preliminarily with knowledge of his victim's character defects: sexual irregularities or other indiscretions not generally known by the victim's friends. It may be that the weak chink in the victim's armor consists of racial concealment, a past indiscretion in sex or business, or some private habit best held secret. The blackmailer wields this knowledge as a threat against the victim. Aside from monetary gain, the power held over the fate and fortune of another person through acquisition of intimate facts feeds the omnipotence fantasy in the criminal himself. There are even more flagrant illustrations of this principle among group extortionists who impersonate officers or profess other identification with authority.

It is worth comment that persons who engage in extortion tend to be, but are not necessarily, paranoid in personality structure. This is readily seen in the very technique of assumption of authority by extortionists. For example, notes left by an extortionist utilize the magic power of the written word in the service of omnipotence feelings. The control over another person through the agency of the written word is, again, a symbolic representation of the grandiosity found at the core of every paranoid individual.

Some time ago the president of a large department store received a series of threatening letters, written crudely in pencil and demanding $6,000. The first letter demanded that the money be paid immediately or the store would be "blown up." The second letter, written a few days later, stated:

We felt sorry for you so we didn't blow up the store yet but your time will come. This time you have to pay $1,000 more. If you inform the police, inform your undertaker.

Elaborate instructions were added for paying the money. The letter was flamboyant and full of semihumorous quips.

By employment of a ruse, the extortionist was easily apprehended. He proved to be a sixteen-year-old boy.[56]

Anton was one of seven children, whose father, an alcoholic, died when they were very young. The family was known to many social agencies. When Anton was four years old, he and four of the other children were sent to an orphanage. At fourteen, Anton was caught by the police when he entered a building from the skylight. At that time he made extravagant statements about his ambitions. He fancied himself in all sorts of roles; sometimes he was a trainer of horses in the West, sometimes an expert "yegg man or just all-round cook." He stated definitely that he was exactly what he wanted to be and had no intention of changing, indicating that he was prepared to live a self-willed life of antisociality. Some time later, Anton busied himself writing letters to the department store head.

Brought before the judge on the extortion charge, Anton requested ten days to prepare his own defense. During his examination, he said he knew he talked "crazy," but insisted that everything that happened to him was part of his plan. He spoke of blowing up public buildings with explosives that he could extract from ordinary substances, such as matches, or by telephone by secret processes known only to himself. At one point he burst out to the examiner:

I know more about chemistry than anybody in the world. . . . If you knew the secret you could be as powerful as I am. I can give it to any of the boys in any of the institutions where I have been, no matter how dumb they are; if I told them how, they could be the biggest criminals in the world.

His bizarre statements and his emotional superficiality were striking. He was jocular in an exaggerated, aggressive manner, with a marked push of speech and flight of ideas bordering on a psychosis. With the cessation of this period of excitement, the basic picture became clearer. Anton's frustration at his obvious weakness in the face of reality gave rise to a transitory psychotic reaction. The youthful extortionist utilized the magic of his fantasy to deny his inner perception of a deprived childhood. The object he took for blackmail, the department store, was clearly a symbol of magnitude and plenty that served his unconscious need for a magical denial of early deprivation. His oral aggression, extravagant speech, and flamboyant boasts were also evidence of his striving to overcome overwhelming feelings of inferiority. The crime committed by Anton was a replica in actuality of his psychological problem and an attempt to solve it through the magical power borrowed from words.

The paranoid coloring that runs through cases of blackmail and extortion is unmistakable, especially in younger offenders. Even where money is not involved, where malicious exposure of another person is the desired aim, paranoid ideation is evident, as is illustrated in the following case of libel.

The instructor in economics and political science, a man of wide intellectual interests and liberal views, permitted his students to hear several sides of certain public issues. In an area noted for its extreme conservatism, rooted in an agricultural ethos, Professor Goldstein could be misunderstood and labelled a radical by those whose political knowledge was scant. Finally, the professor received by mail eighteen scurrilous letters. At the same time, a group of hate-mongers, stimulated by Gerald K. Smith, had found eager readers of the *Defender* in the area in which the professor lived. The *Defender's* anticommunistic and anti-Semitic propaganda echoed in many homes. So, not surprisingly, the letters which Goldstein received, some crudely written and some typed carefully, all stressed a sinister relation between Jews and communism. A typical sentence from one stated:

Well, I'm sure glad that the imbecile Jew Bastard fell for the trap. . . . now H bombs will fall and Red Dog Goldstein shall die. . . . the only way to kill a Red Jew is to use his tactics.

The letters varied very little from this theme; they threatened death, they threatened ostracism, they contained obscene statements joining Jews and communism. Several members of the community were suspected, but the choice narrowed down to a twenty-year-old student who had often stated that he wanted to "change the Professor's opinion." The letters were put in the hands of federal authorities, the arrest was made, and young Wendell Allen was brought up for questioning.[57]

The investigation showed that Wendell's parents were conservative, cooperative people who related the youth's offense to an early nervousness. Both parents had been impressed and puzzled by his difference from his brothers, his talkativeness and lack of normal interest in girls and sports. His concentration on politics and on the Bible also differentiated him from his classmates. Wendell talked freely; he described how he wanted to be a "crusader" in wiping out communism. He spoke in an almost professionally engaging manner, except that he used crude clichés in describing how the country needed to be rid of Jews and communists and other "dangerous characters." Although his expressed wish was to change Professor Goldstein's opinions on political issues, some of the phrases used, he himself admitted, were clearly threatening. When these were repeated to Wendell—"He must die . . . must be crushed . . ."—he did not feel he had meant to make direct threats. His letters to the professor and his general attitude coincided with other material discovered. It was found that some months before Wendell had engaged in a campaign to torment a fellow student on the campus, as well as a dwarfed girl, whom he made the butt of his jokes in letters.

It is clear, however, that this youth was paranoid in tendency, if not psychotic, and that he was a skittish, loosely integrated personality of definitely schizoid makeup.

The results of the psychiatric study presented to the judge suggested a period of confinement at a federal corrective institution. After Wendell returned from a six-month period of study at the institution, where a similar diagnosis was made, the judge placed him on probation. For a period his paranoid tendency continued, but never to the point of a definite psychosis. As the influence of the lunatic-fringe literature on Wendell waned, some of the youth's paranoid ideation decreased. A sympathetic and trained probation officer helped to provide him with new and more stable identifications. For more than three years, there was no recurrence of his antisocial activity; he was therefore finally released from probation as no longer a menace.

REFERENCES

1. BRIERLEY, H. C., *Homicide in the United States* (University of North Carolina Press, Chapel Hill, N.C., 1932).

2. NISBET, ROBERT A., "The Study of Social Problems," in *Contemporary Social Problems*, R. K. Merton and R. A. Nisbet, eds. (Harcourt, Brace & Co., New York, 1961).

3. *People* vs. *Gomez* [*sic*], State of California, County of Sacramento, Superior Court, September 1, 1958.

4. CLARK, WILLIAM L., and MARSHALL, WILLIAM L., *A Treatise on the Law of Crimes*, 6th ed., rev. by Melvin F. Wingersky (Callaghan & Co., Chicago, 1952), p. 384.

5. HALE, SIR MATTHEW, quoted in Clark and Marshall, *op. cit.*, p. 385.

6. EAST, NORWOOD, *Society and the Criminal* (Charles C Thomas, Springfield, Ill., 1951), chap. 18; also texts on psychiatry by Noyes, Henderson and Gillespie; Strecker & Ebaugh; and others.

7. *People* vs. *Jones* [*sic*], State of California, County of Stanislaus, Superior Court, 1961.

8. BOK, CURTIS, *Problems in Criminal Law* (University of Nebraska, Lincoln, Nebr., 1955), p. 59.

9. *People* vs. *Garfield* [*sic*], State of California, County of Sacramento, Superior Court, 1962.

10. SCHILDER, PAUL, *The Image and Appearance of the Human Body* (International Universities Press, New York, 1950), p. 86.

11. LUDLOW, FITZHUGH, "The Hasheesh Eater," *Putnam's Monthly Magazine,* VIII (July, 1856), 233.

12. HUXLEY, ALDOUS, *The Doors of Perception* (Harper & Brothers, New York, 1954), pp. 26, 53.

13. CLECKLEY, HERVEY, *The Mask of Sanity* (C. V. Mosby Co., St. Louis, Mo., 3rd ed., 1955), p. 359.

14. NOYES, ARTHUR P., *Modern Clinical Psychiatry* (W. B. Saunders Co., 4th ed., Philadelphia, Pa., 1953), chap. 32, p. 495.

15. LINDNER, ROBERT M., *Rebel Without a Cause* (Grune & Stratton, New York, 1944).

16. BROMBERG, WALTER, "The Treatability of the Psychopath," *American Journal of Psychiatry,* CX (February, 1954), 604.

17. *People* vs. *Korner* [*sic*], Sup. Ct., State of California, County of Stanislaus, 1962.

18. KEMPE, C. H., and others, "The Battered Child Syndrome," *Journal of the American Medical Association,* CLXXXI (July 7, 1962), 17.

19. "The Battered Child Syndrome," editorial in *ibid.*, p. 42.

20. McDERMOTT, G., and WINKLER, E. G., "Psychopathology of Infanticide," *Journal of Clinical & Experimental Psychopathology,* CXVI, No. 1 (January, 1955).

21. BENDER, LAURETTA, "Psychiatric Mechanisms in Child Murders," *Journal of Nervous & Mental Diseases,* LXXX (1934), 32.

22. BATES, MARSTON, *Human Ecology in Anthropology Today,* A. L. Krober, ed. (University of Chicago Press, Chicago, Ill., 1953), p. 700.

23. DEVEREAUX, GEORGE, "Mohave Indian Infanticide," *Psychoanalytic Review,* XXXV (April, 1958), 123.

24. EAST, SIR NORWOOD, *Society and the Criminal* (Charles C Thomas, Springfield, Ill., 1951), p. 52.

25. VICTOROFF, VICTOR, "A Case of Infanticide," *Journal of Clinical & Experimental Psychopathology,* XVI (July, 1961), 217.

26. BENDER, *op. cit.*, p. 33.

27. GARRISON, FIELDING H., *Introduction to the History of Medicine* (W. B. Saunders Co., 3rd ed., Philadelphia, Pa., 1921), p. 343.

28. *People* vs. *Greta Handtuch* [*sic*], Ind. #224930, Ct. of Gen. Sess., N.Y., 1941.

29. *Ibid.*, Ind. #1407–48, 1948, N.Y.

30. *Ibid.*, Ind. #1871–54, 1955, N.Y.

31. Stockton State Hospital, Stockton, California, 1962.

32. *People* vs. *Mary Haller* [*sic*], U.S. Dist. Ct. for Northern California Dist., 1962.

33. Euripides, *Medea,* in *Ten Plays by Euripides,* trans. by M. Hadas and J. McLean (Bantam Books, New York, 1960), p. 34.

34. Wertham, Fredric, *The Show of Violence* (Doubleday & Co., Garden City, N.Y., 1949), p. 235.

35. Euripides, *op. cit.*, p. 55.

36. *People* vs. *Harry K.* [*sic*], State of California, County of Sonoma, 1961.

37. FREUD, SIGMUND, *Group Psychology and the Analysis of the Ego*, trans. by J. Strachey (Liveright Publishing Corp., New York, 1949), p. 114.

38. RIEFF, PHILLIP, *Freud: The Mind of a Moralist* (Viking Press, New York, 1959), p. 195.

39. MURRAY, GILBERT, *Hamlet and Orestes, a Study in Traditional Types* (Oxford University Press, London & New York), 1914.

40. *Ibid.*, p. 24.

41. *Ibid.*, p. 25.

42. MULLAHY, PATRICK, *Oedipus, Myth and Complex* (Hermitage Press, New York, 1948).

43. Sophocles, *Oedipus the King*, trans. by F. Storr (Wm. Heinemann, London, 1912), vol. 1.

44. LINDNER, *op. cit.*

45. *Ibid.*, pp. 285, 286.

46. BECKER, ERNEST, *The Birth and Death of Meaning* (Free Press of Glencoe [Macmillan], New York, 1962), chap. 6, p. 57.

47. *People* vs. *Ralph Gruber* [*sic*], State of California, County of Sacramento, Superior Court, 1959.

48. CLARK and MARSHALL, *op. cit.*, p. 781.

49. NOYES, ALFRED, "The Highwayman," in *Standard Book of British and American Verse*, Christopher Morley, ed. (Garden City Publishing Co., Garden City, N.Y., 1932), p. 711.

50. GANSER, SIGBERT J. M., "Ueber Einen Eigenartigen hysterischen Dämmerzustand," *Archive für Psychiatrie*, XXX, No. 2 (1898), 633.

51. *U.S.* vs. *Covington* [*sic*], U.S. Dist. Ct. for Northern California, Dist., C., 1960.

52. GUTTMACHER, M., and WEIHOFEN, H., *Psychiatry and the Law* (W. W. Norton & Co., New York, 1954), p. 42.

53. *People* vs. *John Olney* [*sic*], State of New York, County of New York, Court of General Sessions, 1941.

54. Penal Code, State of New York, Section 1340.

55. *Holzmann* vs. *Walker* [*sic*], State of California, County of Yolo, Superior Court, 1960.

56. BROMBERG, WALTER, *Crime and the Mind* (J. B. Lippincott Co., Philadelphia, Pa., 1948), p. 59.

57. *U.S.* vs. *Wendell Allen* [*sic*], U.S. Dist. Ct. for Northern California Dist. (18 US CA Mailing Threatening Commun.), 1957.

CHAPTER VII

Aggressive Crime Among Juveniles

THE BEHAVIOR CALLED DELINQUENT / THE
LEGAL POSITION OF JUVENILE DELINQUENCY /
THE INDIVIDUAL DELINQUENT / THE ANTISOCIAL
GIRL / AGGRESSION AS DEFENSE / SADISM IN
THE YOUNG / SEXUAL AGGRESSION AND THE
JUVENILE / THE DEMOGRAPHY OF JUVENILE
AGGRESSION / "GOOD NEIGHBORHOOD"
DELINQUENCY / EMOTIONAL IMMATURITY AND
CRIME / REFERENCES

A special quality of shock attends the report of an aggressive crime committed by a young person. Murder or serious assault by a youth, an outcropping of vicious mischief and destruction by a group of children touches on sensitive areas within us all. Adults secretly share the hope that in the young, aggression has been repressed and regulated. When crime by youth assails us in its incredible, naked cruelty, the fiction that humanity's hostile impulses are at least controllable in the young is badly shaken. To meet brute hostility face to face is unsettling for any individual who lives in a culture where strict control of aggression is not only essential for success in life, but also for the very existence of the community. To meet aggression among those carbon copies of ourselves, the young, is doubly painful. As two workers in the field of adolescent delinquency express it:

Negative attitudes of the community toward mental illness and delinquency are based on a vague recognition of certain central elements of the pathology of both—defective reality contact of the psychotic—and hostility of the delinquent.[1]

THE BEHAVIOR CALLED DELINQUENT

It has been generally observed that aggression is a basic aspect of childhood. Patterns of maturation are intimately interwoven with motility and with physical and sexual aggression among children. It seems hardly necessary to dwell on the overactivity of children, chief cause of the unspoken cold war between screeching children and adult standards. The new importance of children has not materially lessened parental exasperation with hyperactivity, though it is now generally accepted that preadolescent children are entitled to rebelliousness in life and aggressive contact in play. Particularly shocking and revolting to parents are those sex activities and interests that mirror sexual perversion in children: with boys, mutual masturbation and homosexual play; with girls, seduction and intercourse early in life.

The list of crimes in which adolescents and preadolescents are involved is increasing. Whereas two generations ago juvenile behavior disorders were limited largely to petty thefts, disobedience, and possibly some minor sex play, juvenile delinquencies today embrace every aspect of crime, from murder to mayhem, from extortion to infanticide. We are thus forced to examine anew the individual psychopathology of preadolescents and adolescents, as well as the special circumstance of gang psychopathology.

Psychopathology, however, is not the sole determinant of juvenile aggression. The influence of neighborhood patterns and cultural modes in the specific areas where social disorganization occurs has been cited as the chief cause of delinquency among the young.[2] More subtle cultural influences—particularly television and comic books featuring violence and sadistic sexual activity—have also been held to account for aggressive delinquencies.[3] In fact, Fredric Wertham, a formidable advocate of the deleterious effect of comic books on young minds, states flatly: "Up to the beginning of the comic-book era there were hardly any serious crimes such as murder by children under twelve (*circa* 1930)."[4] The specific, deleterious influences that are present in today's world impress the child to an as yet unmeasured degree. To date, there is no empirical study of the effect of violence in comic books or on TV on the young. As Peck and Bellsmith note:

To demonstrate a simple, direct interrelationship between bad conditions in a neighborhood and severe psychopathology in a delinquent is not easy, even where the connection appears a close one.[5]

Running through the discussion of aggression in the young is the vexing question of the exact nature of aggression and hostility. Also, in trying to assess objectively the problem of juvenile delinquency and its genesis, the psychophysiological structure of the individual cannot be ignored. Lauretta Bender provides a succinct statement of the genesis of hostility in children:

Aggression is a symptom complex resulting from deprivations which are caused by developmental discrepancies in the total personality structure such that the constructive patterned drives for action in the child find inadequate means of satisfaction and result in disorganization of these drives into hostile or destructive aggression.[6]

Although this author subscribes to this statement, he feels that deprivation, even fancied deprivation, is so ubiquitous in childhood—it is, indeed, an emotional substrate of *all* human beings—that it must occur in relatively psychologically well children. Hence, deprivation cannot be the sole basis for aggression. It would seem logical, in fact, to say that aggression is part and parcel of the maturation process of the human young, developing on the basis of an original somatic energy endowment, as indicated by Freud (see Chapter V).

The child, with its quantum of aggression, is under constant sociologic pressure from parents, school, religious teachings, television, movies, social patterns and fads, world events, political upheavals, and the like. To separate psychologic from social influences in estimating children's behavior and misbehavior seems futile. For today's child is exposed to all the subtle influences that agitate adults in this world, whether they are consciously aware of them or not. One of these influences is parental. For example, Johnson and Szurek trace the genesis of antisocial action in some children to gaps in the conscience of the parents. As a result of unconscious defects in their own development, parents may tacitly suggest, or assent to, antisocial acting-out by their children. Such behavior usually fulfills the repressed wishes of the parents, who thereby experience vicarious gratification.[7]

THE LEGAL POSITION OF JUVENILE DELINQUENCY

What are the crimes of the young and what is "delinquency"? The term itself (from the Latin, 'to commit a fault') reflects a general description of behavior, not a specific criminal act. From the standpoint of the child, acts of delinquency include many acts resulting from normal impulses—curiosity, prankishness, excessive motility, revenge, the expression of one's rights. From the standpoint of the law, delinquency occurs when one or more of these acts results in injury to persons or property. But juveniles are held accountable for behavior far removed from the type of behavior accounted as crime among adults. For example, a child may be held for "incorrigibility, habitual truancy, running away from home, being wayward or ungovernable," whereas the crimes of adults do not encompass these classes of misbehavior. It is a basic axiom that what the adult *does*, if contrary to law, is accounted a crime; what the juvenile *may* do becomes delinquency without his having committed a specific crime.

It is clear, then, that the viewpoint from which adolescents and children in the puberty group are judged accents prevention of crimes through control of behavior rather than punishment for crimes committed. There are, of course, exceptions, as in cases of grievous assault, murder, rape; these may be dealt with in the criminal courts or remain in the Adolescent Court. It is generally true, however, that, in theory, the courts are less punitive than directive in the case of juveniles. In this connection, Bloch and Geis state:

In effect, what has transpired in this century in the United States in the children's courts is that they have been compelled to arrogate to themselves functions for the care and protection of children in the face of a situation where other community institutions, notably the family, have either failed or refused to assume traditional responsibilities of child care.[8]

This reorientation is slowly altering the face of criminal law as applied to juvenile crime. Jurisprudence in the Children's Court has presaged a tremendous change in social philosophy. As Edward J. Sacher recently stated, the new criminology reflects the psychiatric viewpoint:

For a basically crime-centered system, in which the penalty fits the crime, the psychiatrist would substitute an offender-centered system in which the treatment would be designed to effect change in antisocial behavior.[9]

Changes in social philosophy occur slowly. Meanwhile, more and more children run afoul of the law; it has been proved that the participation of the young in serious crimes has increased during the past three decades beyond their representation in the population.

Take the crime of auto theft, which ranks high in the F.B.I.'s *Uniform Crime Reports* (see Chapter IV). Although stealing an automobile is listed as grand larceny in the statutes of most of our states, investigations show that the great majority of auto thefts serve the purpose of pleasure through movement rather than that of financial gain. A study of this group by Wattenberg and Franklin [10] showed that the term "auto thief" is misapplied to these boys, since they fit the pattern of "socialized delinquents"; they come from good neighborhoods and have little relationship primarily to antisocial groups. Such delinquents, the above writers state, represent the exact "opposite of the unsupervised" type of auto thief. The present author's studies over many years reflect a similar finding, as indicated in the following composite example of a car theft, its details culled from experience with hundreds of such crimes committed by youths in metropolitan cities.[11]

After preliminary inspection of an empty automobile, several youths seat themselves in it, talking of the cost of the car, discussing its make and model, and the thrill of driving. Presently, one of them, toying with the ignition switch, starts the motor by crossing the wires. The first satisfaction they feel is that of driving slowly through the neighborhood in the commandeered car. This sense of heightened social prestige gives way to the urge for speed. As hyperkinetic impulses assert themselves, the drive becomes a joyride that increases in tempo until it is terminated by apprehension of the car by the police, or by an accident.

The motorcar, like the rocket, is the modern symbol of speed, the former for the individual, the latter, for the nation. For the immature person behind the wheel, the psychobiologic drive toward movement can become a compulsion that is unhampered by adult considerations of danger or driver responsibility. Driving a car entails movement without an object, an intransitive act encompassing an identification of the driver with the apparently unlimited power of the mechanism he controls. Compulsive joyriding is now quite common. In one such case, a youth of twenty-three, twice arrested for driving without a license, was apprehended for stealing a new car, which he had driven as fast as 108 miles an hour on the highway. He boasted that he never drove less than 100 miles an hour in any car where possible. "It's in my blood to drive fast," he explained.

Car thieves are often easily apprehended because their joyrides finish with destruction of the vehicle they have stolen. There is conceivably a psychological meaning to the wreck that frequently terminates such stolen rides. The speed of the car is absorbed into the driver's psyche and tends to express his destructive aggresssion as well as the pleasure principle or larcenous tendency. An act of aggression without an object, like movement without terminus, is a frustrating experience. The terminal smashup, often caused in part by alcoholism, is frequently an unconsciously determined act aimed at ending the frustration of objectless speed. The car thief, working alone or in groups, who strips a car of tires or mechanical parts is sublimating his movement gratification in financial rewards, thus illustrating another psychologic mechanism. This is signalized by the frequent petty thefts of car parts—hub caps, batteries, tires and wheels, distributor caps, and other removable parts. This activity provides the erring adolescent with cash and hence involves the same psychologic considerations as found among youthful burglars.

In this group of offenses the hyperkinesis referred to above is repressed, although groups of boys often refurbish or rebuild their own cars (the so-called jalopy or hot rod) with the proceeds of their activities. Finally, the game of outwitting the adult owners of cars plays a significant role in car-stripping: in this sense, the offense is a variant of juvenile delinquency with its overt and covert rebelliousness and aggression.

THE INDIVIDUAL DELINQUENT

The juvenile who persistently gets into difficulty with the law, providing he or she is not under the direct influence of a gang, is usually found to be neurotic or schizoid. Their emotional rigidity and constriction impels them into misbehavior in a world where emotional gratification is a highly prized asset.

The very process of maturation brings in its train the normal "neurosis" of childhood. The anxieties and insecurities in children, many of whom are bewildered by a world of adult realities, symbolize the emotional valleys through which childhood must pass to emerge as ongoing personalities. Myths, fairy tales, fables, and stories have externalized these "normal" child anxieties into manageable form, as witness their anxiety-ridden dwarfs, the beneficent fairy, the bad witch, the devouring beasts, the slain dragon, the vanquished giant; and today's fantastic assortment of space monsters, supermen, hypertrophied creatures, robots, resuscitated primordial gargantuas. These symbolic representations of childhood neuroses pass for amusement, enriching (or impoverishing) our literary and cultural heritage, providing a channel for the working-through of neurotic elements. The average child can release his aggression and anxieties through this world of fantasied entertainment. The child who for some reason is not well integrated, or has only weak defenses at the disposal of his ego, may emerge as a delinquent from his unsolved infantile neurosis.

From a tremendous store of material that every clinic or institution for behavior disorders could amass, one can choose only a few cases to illustrate the psychopathology of individual juvenile delinquents.

One afternoon, a housewife was backing out her car when she became aware of a youth's face at the car window. Suddenly pulling the door open, a seventeen-year-old, brandishing a knife, ordered her to drive them to a "lonely spot." While complying, the housewife induced him to allow them to return home; there the youth insisted that she "draw the drapes and disrobe," explaining that he had never seen a "naked lady" before. The victim refused, whereupon he placed a knife at the throat of her three-year-old child, repeating his demand. With desperate courage, the mother responded with a well-placed blow on her tormentor's head, after which he left the house quietly.

With police aid, Larry Silver was picked up and his record reviewed.[12] It revealed trouble since the age of twelve: waywardness, incorrigibility, armed robbery, and kidnapping. He had already served about eighteen months in an institution for boys, without much progress. When placed on parole from a youth-training school, he lapsed into further aggressive behavior. Nothing seemed to have altered his temper, his tendency to molest small children sexually, his threats of assault with deadly weapons. Foster homes had had as little effect on him as institutions. Accordingly, his parole was taken up and Larry was sent to the California Youth Authority's Classification Center for study.

The history of his delinquencies had a most ominous ring. Three years before the current offense Larry had ordered a girl of eight, at knife-point, to disrobe and dance for him in an abandoned building. He tried to set fire to the child's hair, then forced her and her five-year-old brother to accompany him to a rest room adjoining a motel, where he attempted intercourse with the child unsuccessfully.

To questions about these incidents Larry reacted with silence, flushing, and great embarrassment. Later on, he explained ingenuously, "That is something I do not want to talk about." In describing his offenses, he says, "I get crazy notions and then I do it. I am plain no-good." In discussing his background, he gave a very realistic appraisal of his father, showing considerable respect for him, but revealing a warmer relationship to his mother. He said his father used "big college words" and was therefore distant from him somehow. His mother "argued at everybody" but she loved him, he said.

From his mother came the report that Larry had been "tempermental" since the age of two; that he had an ungovernable temper. Others pointed out that his father was discouraged by his son's development and wished to have nothing to do with him. All agreed that he was a lonely boy, close to neither parent. He was abusive toward a small sister and "impossible" at school. This latter proved to depend on a total inability to benefit from schooling. Although an early psychological test indicated an IQ of 98 on the Binet-Simon test, he was unable to write, print his name, spell, or read. This scholastic difficulty, hidden under bizarre, aggressive behavior, was readily uncovered. The unusual complication of total absence of school achievement was analyzed; it was found that Larry had not the slightest notion of the phonetic value of the letters of the alphabet.

Selected for study, Larry was recognized as an "anxiety-ridden" boy with emotional thinness and quixotic manner. He revealed a curious mixture of infantility and adult behavior patterns. His sexual exploits, on the surface quite daring and sadistic, of which he was admittedly ashamed, were fraught with the quality of a secret sex world. It was a world with which he would like to be familiar, but one in which he had little true libidinal interest. Although this split in feeling and behavior suggested schizophrenia, there was little else to support this diagnosis in this desperate, "impulse-ridden" boy.

The extraordinary social behavior of this Jewish boy was so out of

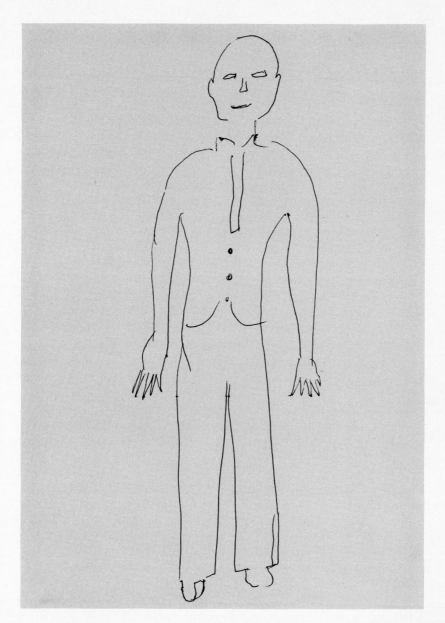

PLATE I

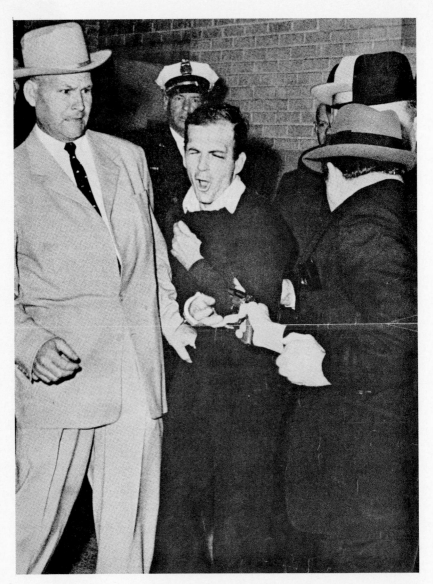

Photograph © 1963, Dallas Times-Herald and Bob Jackson.
From Saturday Evening Post

PLATE 2

PLATE 3

PLATE 4

PLATE 5

PLATE 6

conformity with youths of his cultural group that an organic element was suspected. Careful psychological examinations with the Bender Motor-Visual test and the Graham-Kendall Memory test demonstrated erratic designs. The psychological test revealed an IQ of 83 at this time (age 17) with lower performance scores on visual-motor tasks and high achievement in arithmetical reasoning. The psychologist concluded that Larry functioned as a retardate, but was not one.

Several of the examiners were impressed with his bizarre behavior and schizophrenic attitudes during the testing. The finding made two years earlier by other examiners—that motor incoordination was so extreme as to suggest a diagnosis of organic brain disease—was reviewed. Few children who are not mentally defective display such rudimentary responses to reading as did Larry. For example, when asked how he managed to read words, he replied, "I try to sound them out. If I can't say it, I say the closest thing to it. Sometimes I get it." This produced, as might be imagined, "some amazing reading mistakes." His reading deficiency was so severe as to keep him from identifying with adults, imprisoning him in a world of noncommunication; this further stimulated his basic insecurity and may have been a strong factor in impelling him into sexual misbehavior.

The treatment recommended for Larry included a return to a Youth Authority institution for prolonged retraining, since he was ill equipped to return to the social world. For a year and a half, he was given academic training in remedial mathematics and remedial English, as well as industrial training in garment-making. As time progressed, Larry's senseless aggression seemed to decrease markedly; his emotional relationship with his parents improved and his sexual interests faded to a sexual curiosity more normal for a boy of his age. The daydreams of bizarre sexual conquests were replaced by a more natural attitude, attended by normal emotion.

By the time Larry attained his nineteenth birthday he showed a semblance of stability, although to some observers he appeared emotionally retarded. But an organic brain defect was no longer suspected. Without the tools of social relatedness (the ability to read and write), Larry had frozen on a quixotic, schizoid level. Having acquired a few tools of communication the beginning, at least, of social adjustment appeared possible. The rapist and sadistic torturer had become a reasonable, well-motivated youth. The replacement of punishment in a reformatory by three years in a training school with a therapeutic accent was well worth the effort involved.

THE ANTISOCIAL GIRL

The female counterpart of Larry becomes involved in behavior that is not so blatantly aggressive, but that is nevertheless distinctly anti-social. The aggression displayed is social, not personal; it flouts society, but threatens no individual, except herself. Among girls, one sees a more direct rebelliousness with less neurotic symptomatology. Although such girls become involved in many varieties of delinquency, their prime misbehavior is in the sexual area. Here the direct appropriation of the adult female's role is signalized by their indulging in sexual adventures willingly, repeatedly, and with unconcern. Thereby the intricate psychological problem of identification with adult women is readily solved.

Contrast the freedom with which Darlene Jackson, a winsome colored girl of fourteen, entered into what she considered a woman's world with the tortuous route traveled by Larry in order to realize his fantasied sexual potential.

In her fourteenth year, Darlene had changed from a docile child to a sexually promiscuous, incorrigible girl. Her misconduct came before the juvenile court when she was discovered to have charged a nineteen-year-old youth with "molesting" her, when in fact she had been promiscuous with him and several boys in the neighborhood for months.

Two days after she was cited as a juvenile delinquent by officers in a juvenile division, a policeman, catching up with an erratically driven car, was surprised to find an intoxicated fourteen-year-old girl at the wheel. Questioning brought out the fact that she was equipped for spending the night with a certain boy of sixteen. Investigation of Darlene's behavior led to a recommitment to the juvenile court on a charge of "being in danger of leading a lewd life." [13] Darlene, blasé, her expression immobile, but willing to talk, described her sexual free-dom with several boys in her group. She told how she masturbated two boys in the presence of three other juveniles, how she led a gang of openly promiscuous girls into petty larcenies. Her gang—she called them "my own personal gang"—made capital of their newfound free-dom; they were obscene and completely undisciplined, truant from school, rarely at home at night. Their routine of escapes included stealing liquor, getting "dead drunk," and having intercourse with any boys who presented themselves. In Darlene's case, contact with a psychiatrist, initiated by an anxious mother, had produced little help: the doctor suggested an early marriage, a solution that the mother considered impractical. The judge of the juvenile court, recognizing the need for a thorough study, committed Darlene to the Youth Authority.

An adequate social investigation proved Darlene's accusation, that her mother was aggressive and unloving and her father a "namby-pamby," to be generally untrue. When the child was examined directly with a full dossier at hand, some significant factors came to light. Proudly, Darlene said that she had been dubbed "Sweater Sophie" by her gang. She spoke disparagingly of her mother, calling her an "old grapefruit." With fine sarcasm, she expressed the opinion that her mother was a "phony" because she wore "falsies" and spent much time and energy "prettying" herself. The mother, a tense, anxious, but well-meaning person, smartly dressed in comparison with the studied sloppiness of Darlene, entertained no perception of the basic struggle between her daughter and herself on the ground of sexual attractiveness. The girl, reveling in her greater physical gifts, was pleased to confide that she was also called "Rotten-Crotch Annie" by her gang, in admiration and pride. The essence of her rebellion lay in the simultaneous degradation of her sexuality and expression of superiority over her mother. Surprisingly, Darlene perceived the unconscious struggle going on between herself and her mother; she did not know why, but she knew her erring ways were defeating her mother. She was a "rebel *with* a cause," a cause in which she was joined by her juvenile allies.

It was apparent from the examinations that Darlene possessed an adequate intelligence; she was characterized by one examiner as "very astute." Although she impressed several of her interrogators as "emotionally flat," it was obvious that her inner aggression could be released if she was unable to easily manipulate her environment. On the surface she appeared self-assured, but underneath there was a marked sensitivity and a marked aggression, particularly toward parent-figures. She regarded her sexual exploits in a naturalistic way; she felt there was nothing particularly antisocial about them, because of the changing attitudes in girls throughout the nation. For example, she said virginity is no longer a prized asset. The social aggressiveness evidenced by Darlene was built on aggression that she intuitively considered "safe." She obviously felt superior because of her sexual endowment and her general conversation derided all but the "sexual woman." In our culture this attitude earned Darlene Jackson commitment to a juvenile institution as a sociopath. Here one sees a "psychopathy" that is more situational and environmental than it is an individual character-illness—a direct appropriation by an intense girl of selected, and socially approved adult attitudes.

AGGRESSION AS DEFENSE

Aggression among male adolescents has serious social consequences, as has been indicated. Verbality does not so easily serve the boy; he is more prone to physical acts. Hostility is tightly woven into his character structure; hence, difficult to verbalize and to thaw out. The attitude one sees in these boys is that of a closed circuit, within which their impulses, moods, and needs are expressed directly in a world in which adults, with their mores and laws, have no part. The rigidity that causes such boys to close their psychic universes to the adult world is a part of the defensive position of every child; it is seen in full flower in the adolescent schizophrenic. It is this rigidity that makes the adolescent period, with its complete absorption in fantasy-life, so difficult for teachers and parents.

David Peebles was a big boy. His delinquencies, although not serious, were persistent and uncontrollable. Weighing two hundred pounds, six feet tall at the age of sixteen, he had been considered incorrigible since the age of twelve. His grandparents, with whom he lived, said he was beyond control. David went out of his way to irritate his grandfather, who, at the age of sixty-seven, was far from disabled; he held a job as a stevedore. David delighted in telling his grandfather to "drop dead"; he often waked him from a nap with a kick or a threat. He kept both grandparents in constant fear of physical injury. Such behavior resulted in charges of "incorrigiblity" for at least four years before David arrived at the Classification Center. There had been no serious crime—just a negative adjustment at school, in the home, and in juvenile agencies.[14]

As with other boys of this type, direct questioning yielded little information about his fantasy-life, his emotional feelings, or attitudes. Chiefly, one met a vague toleration of parental figures. David's attitude at first was aloof, yet polite. With the police and during the examination David described his grandmother as the "nicest old lady he ever met." He admitted that he could not concentrate in school, that he couldn't learn anything because he needed to converse with "kids on an intellectual level, higher than the average run." David's choice of words was meant to imply he lived in a "real educated" environment. He was glib, yet rather manneristic. When questioned as to specific details of his alleged incorrigibility and intolerable aggression, he resumed his vagueness.

The psychological test showed him to fall in the superior range, but his verbality added a note of grandiosity; his intellectuality was clearly in the service of defensiveness. In the institution he would (to quote the supervisor's words) "twist and scream until he could prove that the instructions, requests, or orders were given to demean him." The paranoid coloring was readily apparent: "What you are trying to do is to make me refuse the punishment. . . . I want to go into isolation." It was obvious that this was an extremely emotionally disturbed youth.

After futile attempts to penetrate his defense, a diagnostic experiment was tried: the young patient was pushed by persistent questioning and by an authoritarian position on the part of the examiner. With this he became even more involved, contemptuous, argumentative, and aggressive. The hint of nervous excitement in his verbal aggressiveness gave the impression that behind this flurry of words was a mass of uncontrolled, wild aggression. The stimulation had provoked an atmosphere that seemed to correspond to what his grandparents said they felt in his presence at home.

Then a rapid change in approach, using a friendly, benevolent manner toward David, permitted him to explain how he felt inwardly. Withdrawn over the years, he preferred to be placed in isolation in the institution; he "could not stand to be around the others." It was acknowledged that his life with his grandparents had been the source of his feeling of rejection, although they had tried in every way to understand him and to supply the emotional warmth he needed. As with other boys of this type, he retreated into a pseudo-intellectualism, quarreling with his teachers about the interpretation of philosophy, of Freudianism, and so on. David's rebellious behavior was recognized as a defense against a schizoid illness. He was referred to a mental hospital for treatment.

Let us look now at the case of Carl Kude, who at sixteen had been before the courts for the past four years on such varied offenses as burglary, petty theft, possession of lewd literature, and incorrigibility.[15] The juvenile judge sitting on the case was impressed with the seriousness of his antisocial development since the age of twelve. His trouble had started rather suddenly, in school; he became disruptive in the classroom and active in distributing pornographic material to his classmates. In his first arrest, for burglary, he had entered a shop and stolen phonographs and radios; he and a companion were caught filling several shopping bags with the "loot." Soon after his arrest he was caught burglarizing another shop. There followed charges of petty theft, burglary, and possession of lewd literature, wherein he had passed a nudist magazine to his girl classmates. At this point the authorities decided to look further into his problem. A psychiatrist found him monosyllabic in his answers, "egocentric and a sociopath." A study of the family revealed a stable home, a hard-working father, and no obvious reason for Carl's discontent and rebelliousness. He apparently had dedicated himself to destroying the world of adult values.

Carl's answers to questions regarding his depredations were of a uniform character: "I didn't do nothing." When pressed, he expressed the idea that it was all right to steal what he stole. The picture he presented was of a totally warped social attitude. The Catholic chaplain who interviewed Carl remarked that he "displayed an attitude of ridicule and defiance," whether the Father spoke to him about religion or other subjects. It was almost impossible to get Carl to admit that anything he did was wrong; when he was accused of taking sixty-five dollars from his parents' home he blurted out that he guessed some friend of his father's took it. His world lay external to authority. Admonitions and punishments made little impression. Psychiatric interviews were aimed at reaching behind his tough exterior to the basic dependence which, it was suspected, lay hidden there.

In order to break down his defenses, an aggressive approach was undertaken. In previous studies [16] it had been demonstrated that the depth at which an antisocial identification exists could be tested by firm handling, the adoption of an authoritarian attitude. In adopting this technique it was soon found that Carl was playing a game: to go as far as he could in misleading adults. The examiner, however, allowed Carl to sense that he would not permit himself to be "snowed." It was shown to the youth that his delinquencies were really techniques of testing adult reality. Thus it became easier for Carl to relate himself to the outside world as well as to his own interior world of bald aggression.

After considerable therapeutic contact, Carl's defensiveness softened, revealing not a psychopath but a misbehaving boy embarked on a career of reality testing, a psychological game from which he could not retreat. This maneuver may have had its base in his relatively low mental capacity (dull normal to low average). Whether his "dead conscience," as one worker described it, could be revived depended on how he was handled in the institution to which he was sent, and how he responded. It had become evident that Carl did not have primary sexual drives and that his interest in pornography was simply an undifferentiated piece of behavior aimed at mimicking adults.

The spirit of rebelliousness is so often noted in delinquent youth that it has come to be accepted as a constant accompaniment of crime. Displays of courage and flirtations with dangerous situations are highly charged with value among adolescents. Disdain of work and admiration of derring-do need not be based on any particular species of psychopathology among youth; they belong to the "subterranean tradition of youth" [17] that is so elusive of control but so real in the cosmogony of juvenile delinquency.

Still, the occasional physical factor in violent or aggressive behavior among youths should not be neglected, namely, the presence of brain-wave variations. These variations, not amounting to epilepsy or other organic brain disease, do signalize a basic irregularity in the activity of the brain. Some authorities feel that an organic dysrhythmia, or irregularity in brain waves as tested by the electroencephalograph, bear a causal relation to a "wide variety of violent behavior in childhood." [18]

Whether rebelliousness in association with violent behavior is organically conditioned or socially influenced, it remains a prime aspect of delinquency in youth and adolescents. The crimes of such youths may vary widely, but the emotional matrix behind the misbehavior turns upon the facets discussed above. So also with the psychic counterpart of destructive aggression: the sadistic fantasy.

SADISM IN THE YOUNG

Prepuberty sadistic fantasy plays a great part in child neurosis and in child delinquency. As has been noted elsewhere, the play of boys from eight to twelve (the so-called latency period) is replete with the most horrifying sadistic verbalisms and imaginings, most of them forgotten after the child has finished playing. Its extent among neurotic children has been amply documented by child psychiatrists. Among delinquent children these sadistic fantasies and urges eventuate in serious crime. Crude sadism, evidenced in actual wanton assault, has become disturbingly frequent during the last few decades.

Analysis of this facet of juvenile delinquency is rendered difficult by the strong defenses that adolescents raise against psychological probing of emotions. For this reason art techniques have been utilized to serve as a quick approach to the inner, nonverbalized psychologic lives of patients with mental conditions.

As with art symbolic representations of aggression of other types can be mirrored in actual cases seen in juvenile courts. Consider the case of Thomas Hicks,[20] arrested for assault with a deadly weapon.

Quietly watching television with his mother one evening, Tom suddenly, in his mother's words, "began to look strange. . . ." She noticed that his eyes bulged and that he was foaming at the mouth. Without a word he pulled a knife from his pocket and plunged it into his mother's chest. The knife-blade was deflected by a rib so that only a laceration of the chest wall occurred. The offense was doubly unexpected because there had been no previous delinquencies on Tom's part, no intrafamily tension, nothing but the history of a quiet, withdrawn, self-absorbed boy of fifteen.

A thorough social history provided little information beyond his parents' lack of perception of his indwelling character. The direct interview with the delinquent provided more: Tom claimed that he had "blacked out" at the time of the offense. He recalled nothing in the television presentation that had excited him—it was a musical comedy of the ordinary type—but in speaking of it he began to elucidate (with no insight into its significance) his daydreams and fantasies. They dealt with exaggerated accounts of body injury, of how to fight, and so on. This fifteen-year-old boy prattled on in a childish manner, making such statements as "If I fought with a fellow I would break his arm off and hit him over the head with it." When questioned further he said he would break the arm off at the shoulder to get a longer piece to use; this fantasy gave him a "good feeling." This material was given in a flat, matter-of-fact tone, in marked contradiction to what he actually did as a fighter. Tom admitted that when he actually was brought face to face with an opponent he would "grab him, not punch him, and rough him up," in obvious ignorance of the art of self-defense. The disparity between what he imagined he could do and his actual behavior with his peers was extraordinary. Tom had no perception of the reality meaning of the aggressive, sadistic fantasies he tossed off so glibly.

It was difficult to assess the so-called seizures that Tom's mother described. There had been no history of epilepsy. The knife used by Tom, a filed-down Japanese sword that Tom claimed he used as an all-purpose knife, was described with boyish enthusiasm, without that practiced coolness associated with those who relish the use of a weapon. But other indications of neurotic sadism appeared unexpectedly. Tom talked spontaneously about his fantasies when at his mother's request he washed her back when she bathed. He recognized that a few years earlier he had been aroused sexually by this practice, but now, he said, "it doesn't bother me any more." It is interesting that his mother, who was so alarmed and perplexed at the attack, said she treated sex rather casually in the home and "hid nothing" from her son.

The father, a career man in the Navy, away from home more than half of each year, was described as a heavily tattooed man of massive proportions. The mother herself was described by one observer as "a diminutive woman of nondescript features." It was evident that the mother had no notion of the florid sexual fantasies that filled Tom's mind. On the surface he appeared to be emotionally flat, almost barren; beneath the surface one could sense the seething emotion and sexual aggression. His ready talk about breaking arms off, a feat that he pictured with childish ease, undoubtedly was related to unconscious castration fantasies—a displacement from below upward. In this sense, the "black-out" can be regarded as due to a hysterical repression of sexual ideas that simultaneously warded off overwhelming sadistic fantasies threatening to flood his ego.

The sadism of the prepuberty and puberty aged boys has been amply explained as a dissociation and repression of sexual fantasies during the latency period, an aspect of the resolution of the Oedipus fantasy. Thus, on the surface, the ten-year-old boy displays open antagonism to girls and seemingly has little interest in the area of sex; sexuality itself consists mainly in use of a series of words acknowledged to carry an erotic connotation but, for them, little emotional charge. With prepuberty boys, even sex play tends to be mechanical. Actually, derision of love and its signs absorb their libidinously stimulated activities. The puberty boy is interested in motion, destruction, and fighting. Competitive sports serve as sublimations; the boy develops idols among professional athletes, adopts their manner, stance, indications of power, and so on.

The puberty girl, on the other hand, demonstrates a different manner of handling her latency period. She also represses sexuality, but she automatically, and sometimes consciously, projects herself into the adult situation. Thus, the puberty girl is interested in beauty, in clothes, in cosmetics and all the appurtenances of womanhood, including great preoccupation with children and infants.

SEXUAL AGGRESSION AND THE JUVENILE

When the sadistic aspects of puberty overflow their sublimated bounds among boys sexually aggressive or destructive, delinquency occurs. When the latency-period girl is unable to balance her impulses, sexual delinquency develops.

The predilections of girls for signs and activities of adult sexuality are well known among nondelinquents as well as among those who transgress sexual mores. Studies of large numbers of delinquents show that among girls sexual promiscuity represents an extension of the normal need for affection, security, and social status, while among boys sexual aggression is an extension of normal, developing sexual curiosity and the need to experiment. Atcheson and Williams [21] in examining 3,112 delinquents of both sexes encountered these "normal" reactions, in addition to those of mentally dull and emotionally disturbed youthful delinquents. There are, of course, many other factors influencing sexual behavior: family standards, environmental influences, interest of peers, and so on. An outstanding example of a sexually incorrigible girl is the case of Gloria Payne, a sixteen-year-old Negro girl charged with possession of drugs, prostitution, and incorrigibility.[22]

Gloria was unusually attractive; her dimpled cheeks and attractive figure matched her poise and sophistication. The interview was permeated with an air of seduction; Gloria expounded her life and her practices with no guilt, no remorse, in a matter-of-fact tone, and with an air of complete confidence. She was, as one examiner noted, "already committed." She explained with a suggestion of pride in her voice: "If I need money, I get out and hustle. After all," she said, with openness and good humored tolerance of the examiner, "I ought to know what it is to hustle—my mother hustled all her life."

Her mother and her grandmother wasted little time reprimanding Gloria for her irregularities. Indeed, the entire family accepted their professions with few qualms. Gloria had already indulged in the use of drugs. Her mother left her for as long as three weeks, with no provision for the girl's care. She had been assigned to various foster homes and finally to a convent school during the years of her antisocial conduct— apparently without success. Her youth and attractiveness made "beating my mother at her own game," a source of tremendous satisfaction. One could find no symptoms of neurosis here, merely an acceptance of a social standard so entrenched as to make it appear a natural tendency. In general, as has been noted in the case of Darlene Jackson, the unconscious aim of the adolescent girl is to displace her mother; Gloria strove to do this consciously and with spirit.

Even after she had been away from her mother's control, or lack of it, for months, Gloria spoke fervently of the "hustling" life. Although she complained that the grandmother had tried to set standards and had been a strict disciplinarian, Gloria seemed to be enamored of the adult position she had attained. So far as the father was concerned, she knew little about him, merely stating that her mother's infidelity had "killed her father." During the interviews she talked of pimps, knifings, robberies, homosexuality to such a degree that the examiner suspected she was confusing fantasy with reality.

What stood out in this case, aside from the sordid atmosphere in which Gloria lived, was the easy identification that this young colored girl had made with the world of antisociality and the firm consolidation of ego-ideal that had developed within her ego. Here was a "psychopathy" by benefit of environment.

The problem of sexual aggression among boys bears a different stamp. It is furtive, confused, often covering its neurotic layers by defensive maneuvers. The juvenile's explosive entrance into the world of sexuality comes to light when one examines children referred from school or home as behavior problems. In school and in play on the streets one encounters a world of sexual talk in games to which few adults are privy. The use of sexual terms comes out in the game called "ranking them out" or "topping them." It starts with exchanges of simple insults—such as, "You're a bum," "You're a rat"—and progresses to the point where incest is described in common obscene words, as, "mother-fucker." The object of the game is to ascertain how far words will replace fisticuffs. To hear boys, of what used to be called a tender age, spit out such phrases sounds ominous. However, when one examines these utterances carefully it turns out that neurotic sexual attitudes are entangled therein. It would be reasonable to speculate that this game of venturing verbally into dark waters is related to rape fantasies, if not incestuous fantasies.

The situation of Bert Schumer, a well-built, manly-looking boy of thirteen who was accused of assault and robbery of a woman,[23] illustrates these complexities. The details recited indicate that he impulsively assaulted a woman as if to rob her, but in fact, clasped her body, imitating the posture of coitus. Bert said that the robbery idea was simply an excuse for his impulse to grab the woman herself. His whole manner was so diffident, his boyishness so apparent, that one had difficulty thinking of him as a rapist.

Here was a youth whose structure approximated that of a man, but whose inner needs spoke more for dependence on women than for aggressive masculinity. Regarding the rape attempt, one had the intuitive feeling in this case that the boy's simple wish to have contact with a female body was of the same genre as the child seeking succor from the mother. This kind of "rape" is so specifically pubertal in form—it was almost a nonsexual rape—that it can be considered to fall into the area of fantasy enactment and reality testing.

These remarks, illustrated by Bert's case, relate more to the individual delinquent than to the member of a juvenile gang where actual rapes do occur. Parenthetically, the usual rapist is apt to be more than twenty-five years of age. In the gang rape, the gang indulges in the "line-up" on occasion, where one girl is subjected to the attentions of several youths. In the gang line-up (not to be confused with the police line-up), subtle psychologic elements are evident: the gang member cannot tolerate expressing his independence of, yet unconscious dependence on, women, so he joins his fellows in demanding intercourse from one female. Here, unconscious homosexual factors may also be present. To the victim and to society, the ruthless rape of a young woman or girl (even one who starts by agreeing to intercourse) by a group of hoodlums or a gang has nothing about it that suggests unconscious dependence, or even latent homosexuality. But a psychiatric scrutiny of these boys, away from the area of lateral emotional support within the gang, clearly indicates that there are elements involved other than the heterosexual drive. From another point of view, common sense would indicate that imitation within the group is an important factor in that type of group behavior. Viewed psychologically in this specific context, however, the lateral support of peers permits the sexual conflicts and defenses within the individual gang members to rise to the level of agreed-upon common behavior.

The defense against an inner sense of masculine inadequacy ordinarily takes the form of toughness, snarling defiance, and generalized hostility. It does not necessarily take a sexual form, although untoward sexual behavior in boys is very apt to be seized upon by sensitive adults and woven into a sexual delinquency charge. In fact, one would not be too far afield to suggest that the very frequency of boy sex play or child exhibitionism is a reflection, a sardonic one indeed, of the sensitivity of adults in our culture to sexual play among children. The following brief outline of a case will illustrate this point.

James,[24] a first-year high-school student, had a history of exposing himself to young girls, and, later, of grabbing women in the park with the intent to rape, and, still again, sexual exploration of younger children in a foster home. During the interview James was more willing to discuss his play with children than his clumsy attempts to rape women. Actually, there was little that was sexually precocious about him, but there was much rebelliousness toward society and an undercurrent of abiding dissatisfaction with the mores of society.

The problem of social misidentification of youths is further illustrated in the case of young Bobby,[25] who had been taken into custody for "glue sniffing" as part of his general social hostility. Bobby, of limited, but not defective, intelligence, had reached complete identification with the rough-and-tumble male image the Southwest often produces. Bobby explained that he was "a tough guy," by which he meant that to protect himself in life and achieve what he wanted, a snarling approach to the world was a prime requisite. When asked what he wished to do when he reached maturity, Bobby's answer was ready: "I want to be a Marine, a construction worker, or a locomotive engineer." The "glue sniffing" Bobby passed off with little comment: He admitted that he got "high" on it but remarked that the elation was only a crude imitation of the intoxication of alcohol. His surly attitude was a prized feature of his social image, an egosyntonic defense rather than an expression of far-reaching hostility toward society.

Juveniles need a role to play, a character to fill, until they reach a satisfactory social identification. Whether it be that of a tough guy, a hep cat or slick chick, or whatever comes next out of the lexicon of the future, accepted social forms form the model for the insecure young. In the first of the cases to be outlined, for example, Betty enacted a recognizable role, albeit not a desirable one, in her drive for social identification.

Betty Bianchi,[26] a young woman of twenty, picked up for waywardness and incorrigibility, displayed an unmistakable attitude toward the Youth Authority, and indeed toward all society. Speaking with the complete sophistication of the racketeer, Betty displayed her extensive knowledge of the underworld, showed in her forearms the "mainline" scars of the heroin addict, while discoursing learnedly on the business of pushing dope. Proudly she stated that she had been in the "life" since the age of sixteen, and could see little reason for changing. Her alliance with the underworld, which nurtured her self-esteem, was so intimate that any chance for therapy—in this case, a euphemism for "reform"—seemed quite remote.

The force of social identification with its inner reflections of pride, especially among neurotic and schizoid children, often impells them into delinquent behavior. To prove they "belong" somewhere, these children dare convention and flout the law. Their deeds, or misdeeds, speak for them, as in the case of Frank Koski.[27] He was thirteen when he attacked a girl of like age, as part of the initiation into a "club." The mother of the girl, assuming it to have been a sexual attack, called the authorities and Frank was arrested. Investigation showed the boy to have been a refugee from Germany, caught up in the Hitlerian expurgation of Polish Catholics. That he was a neurotic boy could not be doubted. Handicapped by the loss of his left eye at the age of five, self-conscious and ill at ease in his adopted country, Frank labored under difficulties that might have discouraged the average American youth. He was small for his age, but determined to ape at least the outward behavior of those American classmates whom he saw floating through a successful, fun-producing adolescence. Undoubtedly, little Frank longed to be a typical American boy, yearned to be masculine, aggressive, virile. Without doubt, he absorbed these attitudes not only from his schoolmates, but from the sum of life customs in the United States. The point to be made here is that Frank's aggressive sexual behavior, his inept acting out of the behavior he saw symbolized around him, was an uncoordinated attempt to fill out the ego-image that his anxieties and need for emotional security demanded.

THE DEMOGRAPHY OF JUVENILE AGGRESSION

Cases such as Frank's lead to generalizations regarding juvenile aggression. It has been indicated in earlier pages that adolescent and juvenile delinquency has spread its tentacles over a wider variety of crimes than was dreamed of a generation or two ago. A frequent interpretation of this phenomenon states either that "psychopathic" behavior, viewed as a psychiatric "disease," has achieved a near-epidemic state or that parental control has evaporated, leaving the young to follow the behavioral model of violence, sexual stimulation, and opportunism set before them by the mass media of our amoral culture. The diversity of crime among the young—from murder to rape, from robbery to mayhem—would, on the surface, give this view credence. But another interpretation is possible: that a wider distribution of behavioral models to which juveniles may react is available, communicated, and transmitted via the media of entertainment and the press.

What is meant is this: to be sexy, curvaceous and compliant is desirable for the female; to be knowledgeable, unable to be fooled, and alert is the desired model for males; to waste little time on sentiment, romanticizing, reflection, or thought is the approved life-model for all; to get things done, to be "with it," to eschew everything but success, is an expected goal. These unspoken attitudes are reflected in the wide panorama of sex crimes among youthful offenders, as well as in their interests in pornography. This discussion points far beyond the problem of statutory rape, a subject that will be discussed in Chapter X. Our present concern is in the influence of our current "sexy atmosphere" on what has been called the increased psychopathy of our young. The fact is that study of a long series of juvenile and adolescent offenders over a thirty-year span convinces one of the nonspecificity of adolescent sexual crime. It is not that the young in our culture are "sexual psychopaths," or sexually neurotic in greater numbers than before, but that their expression of juvenile and adolescent rebelliousness has widened in scope and intensity.

Since the inner life of man has been shorn of its mantle of privacy, the young are privy to many patterns of behavior that in older days were referred to as "secrets of the soul." The inner life has become public domain.

In assessing the social pathology or individual psychopathology of juvenile and adolescent delinquents, however, social factors—for instance, the factor of customary usage—must be carefully calibrated. Since the adolescent universe is committed to behavior expressing values opposite to those of the adult world, adolescent conduct and speech will, as adult behavior patterns change, similarly move into new areas. This generalization applies to crime also. Thus it is that the crimes described in these pages are on a level that may well be called "unspeakable" by one not in tune with the enterprising spirit of youth; the young seek, in ways always fresh and new, to deny their inner feelings of inadequacy before adult values that are both rejected and needed, scorned and respected.

A corollary of this generalization may be set forth here: this ever-moving adolescent subculture, in the area of crime as well as in slang, dress, dancing, manners, constitutes a necessary reality-testing maneuver. In scrutinizing the offenses of juvenile offenders, especially those of arrant boldness, one is struck by the fact that crime has less intrinsic meaning for the offender than it has in its relation to the adult world. Its effect on that world is a mainspring in the juvenile miscreant's motivation. The crime becomes an adventure in testing the limits of permissivity of the adult world, while simultaneously testing the limits of fantasy-enactment by the child or adolescent. The mechanisms outlined here, verifiable in the cases presented, are unsuspected by the juvenile himself. He is too involved in his emotional turmoil, too encased in the secure feeling of coordination with the "club" or gang from which the delinquent juvenile receives approval and moral support to recognize these anti-adult attitudes.

"GOOD NEIGHBORHOOD" DELINQUENCY

Criminal aggression in adolescent groups has been dealt with in this and earlier chapters in relation to cases of assault, homicide, and robbery. The group delinquencies among adolescents now to be discussed should be distinguished from those of the street gangs who engage in "rumbles" or gang fights, who range like wolf packs in search of excitement, who control and dominate a neighborhood and carry out carefully planned group larcenies. The kind of juvenile group under discussion does not live in underprivileged neighborhoods, its individual members do not have the aspirations typical of members of the true gangs found in big cities; their offenses are usually limited to a single series of such acts. The offense grows out of a sudden emergence of "gang" rebelliousness, an underlying mechanism that Fritz Redl has called "group intoxication."

The transitory adolescent group (*not* specifically motivated by the gang subculture common among underprivileged urban boys) is made up of adolescents in the 17- and 18-year-old group, coalescing around a high-school class, a neighborhood store, or even around a team of an athletic nature. They organize loosely, then divide and break up, with no continuity or special identifying insignia; they travel initially in pairs, trios, or in groups of four to six. They regard themselves as simply young fellows with like interests and tastes; their goals are chiefly fun and entertainment. Often these boys belong to respected families and are of better than average intelligence. There is only moderate evidence of aggression in school or at home; they are rarely considered to be "problems," and only occasionally show on examination signs of neurotic maladjustment through such minor difficulties as mild anxiety. Let an example serve to illustrate this group.[28]

In a small mountain town two well-grown, handsome athletes, fellow students in the last year of high school, equipped with the common interests of the community (cars, the goal of a college education and professional training, girl friends, fun, and youthful activity), appeared in school with large quantities of cash. They had mobilized a group, travelled to a neighboring town, and burglarized a haberdashery shop of clothing—shirts, slacks, sport jackets, and so on—to a value of $5,000.

One of the boys, Boris, a paradigm for the others, described this and other burglaries in straightforward terms:

There was nothing to do in Calville and no place for young people. We are not fighters, not gamblers, we drink a little and want to have fun—anything for a laugh. We drove to Blankville, broke into the store and besides the clothes, we took bottles of wine, cash, and in another place all the clothes we could find. We sold the stuff, trying to match up clothes sizes to the boys in our class. . . . we needed money, we didn't think we'd be caught. . . . the fellows in our group are live wires, some of their folks have money; my father is Justice of the Peace, and Jack's father is a dentist.

Examination disclosed nothing that could be considered in any degree neurotic or psychopathic in these youths. They were aware that what they had done showed a callous disregard for others; that they had burglarized several stores ruthlessly; that they gave away and sold the loot among their classmates without so much as a quaver of conscience. The episodes were carried out in a spirit of enterprise, fun, and derring-do. Their behavior approached the automatic and instinctive, although the law plainly called it burglary. When the parents became aware, as the boys had become aware, that their sons had committed a series of felonies, shock accompanied the knowledge. Both parents and boys were confronted with a new fact of social life.

EMOTIONAL IMMATURITY AND CRIME

What is the meaning of this outburst of egocentricity, disregard for others, and craftiness in a group of high-school boys no different than hundreds of others throughout the country? Was it a forerunner of criminal psychopathy? Did it fall into the class of that type of playful group-antisociality that crops out sporadically among college boys in such group behavior as the so-called panty raids on girls' dormitories? Was it emotional immaturity, or the beginning of criminal life? From the vignette presented, no one would state with certainty that these youths were destined for criminal careers.

Since the acts of Boris and his friends fall into the class of emotional immaturity, it is necessary to ask what it is and how it relates to crime. To begin with, emotional immaturity is a relative term. The definition of immaturity may vary greatly, depending on who gives the definition, the stage of life involved, the social and cultural values from which criteria are established. Perhaps the best definition of maturity has been given by Adolf Meyer in his oft quoted statement that maturity means

. . . dependability, a span of outlook and vision, i.e., insight, a capacity to accept illness, disappointment and frustration, an adjustment to emotional as well as sexual married life, a capacity to recognize limitations and an ability to appreciate and respect one's own place in the scale. . . . Maturity means also a philosophy of objectivity about the past, *i.e.*, a capacity to use the past.[29]

In everyday terms, maturity is measured by the rule of common sense: children and adolescents are immature, young men and women are attaining maturity, and persons over thirty are, by definition, mature personalities. The passage of time, with its myriad influences on social ideals, brings conformity to the ethos of the community and nation. The process of "settling down" involves the comprehension and observation of a long list of precise rules (rarely enumerated) governing sexual habits and practices, economic success and interests, family loyalties, educational, cultural, recreational pursuits, and so on. In spite of these unwritten rules, common sense also agrees that chronological age is not a reliable standard for measuring emotional and social maturity. Immature attitudes are tolerated in the young within the boundaries of socially tolerable mischief; beyond that, the law steps in. If behavior extends beyond that brashness and "fun seeking" that seems to be the *raison d'être* of the teenager's life, any injury to persons and/or property resulting from such behavior catapults the adolescent into the criminal arena. Thus it is a matter of importance whether this behavior persists, forming a pattern of chronic antisociality, or is merely a passing phase in the maturation process. Much hangs in the balance in such cases, since a diagnosis of psychopathic behavior, or an indication of its presence, often determines the issue for the offender: legal punishment or rehabilitation efforts.

So important is this problem that Eleanor and Sheldon Glueck devoted most of their lives to studying this factor among reformatory inmates and adolescent delinquents in Massachusetts. In the 1930's the Gluecks examined a group of offenders in great detail,[30] finding that this group of wrongdoers were abnormal in such important ways as (*a*) leaving the family roof at very early ages or for unusual reasons, (*b*) the widespread prevalence of various demoralizing habits and vices, (*c*) educational retardation, (*d*) early entry into industrial competition and the poor nature of their work habits, (*e*) delinquency and criminality beginning at very early ages, and (*f*) mental makeup.

The same group was reexamined ten years later and the finding was a steady decrease in offenses. The Gluecks came to this conclusion:

With the passing of years . . . steady diminution of youths who continued to be offenders; by the time delinquents reached the age of 29, 40% ceased to be criminals. Physical and mental changes that comprise the natural process of maturation offer the chief explanation of this improvement in conduct over the years.[31]

Further follow-up of the same group years later corroborated their earlier opinion.[32] Aside from the valuable predictive table that the Gluecks set up concerning the behavior of children who have not yet shown outward signs of delinquency, the most significant finding in their protracted study was that the cure for immaturity is the maturation process, with all its social and psychologic implications.

To these careful, sociopsychologic studies by the Gluecks should be added the result of much clinical work among immature offenders. From this accumulated material there has emerged the clinical axiom that there is a behavioral gradation, from immaturity in normal young people to that in immature adults and, finally, to that in psychopathic personalities. Emotional immaturity and psychopathic behavior form a behavioral continuum. Moreover, it must not be forgotten that an examination of normal life activity often brings to light examples of the reappearance—sometimes dramatic and unexpected—of remnants of immaturity in otherwise well-adjusted adults. Many of these immature fragments not only eventuate in criminal behavior, but are observable also in social life. The hallmarks of the immature, such as impracticality, impatience with the limitations of reality, reliance on fantasy aims and satisfaction, are reluctantly relinquished by all mankind and only under the continued pressure of reality. Immaturity is a pliable state, encompassing much that is awkward, embarrassing, disturbing, enlivening, uproarious, and impossible in life; it may also add that which is ingenious, entertaining, and sprightly.

To describe adolescents and youths as "immature emotionally" does not excuse those crimes, both casual and serious, in which they become involved. But such a characterization does illuminate the important possibility that training, education, and constructive social measures may in time increase or complete the maturation of individuals who might otherwise become sociopaths. The fact that many youths evaluated as sociopaths in clinics, educational and penal institutions, and hospitals lose within a few years the specific characteristics that called for this diagnosis suggests that our haste in so diagnosing them contained other aspects than clinical objectivity. The term "psychopathic personality" itself is an emotion-laden phrase, with its connotation of criminality, aggressiveness, and destructiveness. Perhaps society's own aggressive impulses find a scapegoat (and a justification) in the individual or group who is thus labelled, and so ostracized from law-abiding society. This subtle process occurred in the case of the "morally insane," the "moral imbecile," the "constitutional inadequate," and it occurs in the case of the "sociopath." It is more than likely that the terms themselves carry a charge of distrust and dislike, of reproof and reprobation, to which the individuals so named react. These are terms from which no reprieve seems possible. These are society's semantic weapons.

To this congealed, unconscious hostility, the psychopath, and to a lesser degree the immature delinquent, reacts by rebelliousness and aggression. The weapon of society, and of psychiatry, is converted to a defensive weapon by the psychopath and the immature (see Chapter V). The semantic cudgel thrown at the criminal acts as an invisible boomerang, curving back at society with redoubled force. When we view psychopathy and immaturity in the dynamic way suggested by this formulation—as the result of the interaction of society and the individual—the antisocial youth appears less formidable in his character structure, less fixated in his antisocial dedication. Moreover, this orientation gives those who try to help these offenders a toehold on the crags of juvenile delinquency.

REFERENCES

1. PECK, HARRIS, and BELLSMITH, VIRGINIA, *Treatment of the Delinquent Adolescent* (Family Service Association of America, New York, 3rd prtg., 1962), p. 3.

2. RUBIN, SOL, *Crime and Juvenile Delinquency* (Oceana Publications, New York, 2nd ed., 1961), p. 15.

3. WERTHAM, FREDRIC, *Seduction of the Innocent* (Rinehart & Co., Toronto and New York, 1954).

4. *Ibid.*, p. 199.

5. PECK and BELLSMITH, *op. cit.*, p. 18.

6. BENDER, LAURETTA, "Genesis of Hostility in Children," *American Journal of Psychiatry*, CV, No. 4 (1948), 242.

7. JOHNSON, ADELAIDE, and SZUREK, STANISLAUS, "The Genesis of Antisocial Acting Out in Children and Adults," *Psychoanalytic Quarterly*, XXL (1952), 323.

8. BLOCH, HERBERT A., and GEIS, GILBERT, *Man, Crime and Society* (Random House, New York, 1962), pp. 410, 412.

9. SACHER, EDWARD J., "Behavioral Science and Criminal Law," *Scientific American*, CCIX (November, 1963), 39.

10. WATTENBERG, WALTER, and FRANKLIN, JOHN, "Clinical Psychologic Study of Auto Thieves," *Journal of Clinical and Experimental Psychopathology*, IV (December, 1955), 289.

11. BROMBERG, WALTER, *Crime and the Mind* (J. B. Lippincott Co., Philadelphia, Pa., 1948), p. 125.

12. LARRY SILVER [*sic*], California Youth Authority Reception Center, Perkins, Calif., 1961.

13. DARLENE JACKSON [*sic*], C.Y.A. Rec. Center, Perkins, Calif., 1961.

14. DAVID PEEBLES [*sic*], C.Y.A. Rec. Center, Perkins, Calif., 1961.

15. CARL KUDE [*sic*], C.Y.A. Rec. Center, Perkins, Calif., 1961.

16. BROMBERG, WALTER, "Antagonism to Authority Among Young Offenders," *Handbook of Correctional Medicine* (Philosophical Library, New York, 1947), p. 452.

17. MATZA, DAVID, "Subterranean Traditions of Youth," *Annals of the American Academy of Political Science*, November, 1961, p. 102.

18. WOODS, SHERWYN M., "Adolescent Violence and Homicide," *Archives of General Psychiatry*, V (December, 1961), 528.

19. Case of M., California Youth Authority, 1963.

20. THOMAS HICKS [sic], C.Y.A. Rec. Center, Perkins, Calif., 1961.

21. ATCHESON, J. D., and WILLIAMS, D. C., "A Study of Juvenile Sex Offenders," *American Journal of Psychiatry* CXIV (November, 1954), 366.

22. GLORIA PAYNE [sic], C.Y.A. Rec. Center, Perkins, Calif., 1961.

23. BERT SCHUMER [sic], C.Y.A. Rec. Center, Perkins, Calif., 1961.

24. JAMES [sic], C.Y.A. Rec. Center, Perkins, Calif., 1961.

25. BOBBY [sic], C.Y.A. Rec. Center, Perkins, Calif., 1961.

26. BETTY BIANCHI [sic], C.Y.A. Rec. Center, Perkins, Calif., 1961.

27. FRANK KOSKI [sic], from author's personal files, 1958.

28. *People* vs. *Boris Papov* [sic], State of Calif., Sup. Ct., County of Nevada (sitting as Juvenile Court), 1961.

29. MEYER, ADOLF, in *Our Children: A Handbook for Parents*, Dorothy Canfield Fisher and Sidonie M. Gruenberg, eds. (Viking Press, New York, 1933), p. 155.

30. GLUECK, SHELDON and ELEANOR, *500 Criminal Careers* (Alfred A. Knopf, New York, 1930).

31. GLUECK, SHELDON and ELEANOR, *Juvenile Delinquents Grown Up* (Commonwealth Fund, New York, 1940), p. 264.

32. GLUECK, SHELDON and ELEANOR, *Law and Psychiatry* (Johns Hopkins Press, Baltimore, Md., 1960).

Crimes of Passive-Aggressive Nature

Passive–Aggressive is the designation applied to those criminal activities in which the aggression is veiled, silent, and unobtrusive, or the aggression manifested in the theft is of passive type. Burglary typifies this group. There is, of course, no sharp delimitation between crimes that are primarily aggressive and those whose aggression is passively manifested; for example, the safecracker works in the dark, but his activity is acquisitive, even destructive, in intent; the burglar deprives people of property, but his activity is silent and muffled. Both types of criminals utilize furtiveness in their aggression. Still, few crimes occur in pure culture. Recognizable psychological elements of stealth ('eluding of discovery or observation'–*Oxford English Dictionary*) provide characteristic coloring to such crimes as burglary, confidence games, embezzlement, conspiracy to defraud, forgery, larceny, and arson. For this reason they are classified in the passive-aggressive group.

BURGLARY—THE STEALTHY AGGRESSION

The contrast between burglary and robbery in their psychologic essence may further illustrate the practicality of the crime groupings suggested. Breaking and entering a house unobserved for the purpose of stealing is a stealthy act, whereas robbing a person of something is a direct action. The burglar is furtive in his movements, avoiding human contacts; the robber, on the other hand, must confront his victim. The robber uses a weapon to threaten or injure; the burglar commonly does not. The burglar enters a closed building or home to commit his crime; the robber encounters his victims in the open. The crime of breaking and entering (burglary) consists of gaining entrance into a building with "intent to commit a felony" [1]; in the crime of robbery, the act itself conveys the felonious intent. It is an interesting sidelight that the element of furtiveness in burglary was exemplified in the common law by the principle that burglary could only be committed at nighttime; if committed at a time of day when it was light enough "for one person to discern the features of another," the crime was larceny.[2] Modern statutes, however, have modified this element: breaking into a house, with or without material injury, in the daytime constitutes burglary if entry is made with felonious intent.[3]

The differing psychologic modalities underlying crimes of aggressive and passive-aggressive nature, respectively, rest on empirical findings in many cases. Psychiatric evaluation of burglars individually agrees with the formulation that burglary is essentially a passive crime. Behavior before and during the crime, especially in the adolescent or young adult group, confirmed this conclusion. This attitude of passivity is encased in the feeling that the objects taken were not really *stolen*. Many young burglars do not feel that taking an object from the home is important enough to be called a crime. Indeed, this attitude hides the symbolic nature of burglary: the unobserved acquisition of something to which the deprived child feels entitled. The aggression in burglary is subordinated to the stealthy appropriation of a "birthright."

As with burglary, petty thefts also illustrate the infantile derivation of this psychologic mechanism: for example, children's thefts from the neighborhood fruitstand, their mother's purse, the schoolroom, the teacher's desk, schoolmates, and so on. Among adults, it can be observed in the universal practice of "hotel stripping" ("lifting" minor articles—books, ashtrays, pencils, stationery) with little thought of its larcenous nature. This ubiquitous sort of minor burglary and petty larceny, easily justified by the thought "They'll never miss it," bespeaks a subliminal consciousness that what is taken "belongs" to the taker. The "they" most often encompasses large, impersonal institutions— schools, hotels, large business houses, libraries, government agencies. The euphemism "They'll never miss it" on analysis means "It really belongs to us (me)."

In criminologic practice one has no difficulty recognizing this attitude among adolescent shoplifters; during interrogations or interviews they express astonishment that objects taken by them were considered stolen. Even mature women who have practiced shoplifting for years as a livelihood assume a bland expression of childlike innocence during interrogations that is interpretable in this direction. Although it is recognized that among criminals denial is almost automatic, the attitude described here reflects the aura of injury one associates with children. Denial also earns an extra fraction of pleasure at the suppressed anger of irked investigators who, after all, possess proof of the thefts. The shoplifter thus exercises her passive aggression—the aggression of the dependent child who makes capital of his weakness. The soft approach of burglars is supported by this mechanism of aggression from a position of dependence.

If this assertion be granted—and further proof of its accuracy will be offered in these pages—it is difficult to explain the rarity of female burglars, whereas shoplifting is common among girls and women, whether they be occasional or professional offenders. To understand this disparity, attention is called to the fact that the technique of burglary, that of breaking into and entering a forbidden space, is a characteristically male activity, a symbolic phallic penetration. From this point of view shoplifting differs from burglary in that sexual symbolism is absent. This speculation—of an unconscious rape fantasy in the psychological matrix of burglary—receives added support from the fact that younger burglars often steal inexpensive or even worthless articles. The excitement of entering a locked area seems a greater stimulus for the burglary than the intrinsic value of the articles stolen.

It may be objected that these fine differentiations in the psychologic background of the various crime groups must be tempered by practical factors. It has been traditional, for example, to consider burglary as specifically a crime of the economically impoverished. This is still true, for burglaries by adolescents in economically disadvantaged areas (as, for instance, among the Puerto Ricans and Negroes in New York [4]) are still a major crime problem in this country. The traditional explanation is that hunger and economic pressure drive men to burglary. This may shed a dubious light on the psychodynamic explanation of burglary and shoplifting: that they are motivated by deeper, unconscious drives for revenge on the orally depriving mother [5] or the denying father. In our time, however, the romantic view that such crimes as burglary and shoplifting are responsive to reality needs is not justified.

Another consideration negates the "starvation" theory. In recent years burglary and shoplifting have been observed to be common among adolescents from economically comfortable, even wealthy, homes. It is safe to say that every criminal investigator in this country has encountered waves of complaints of shoplifting and burglary by adolescents in wealthy families. Because these cases rarely come to court, material for study of this type of offender is not readily available. Parents pay for the stolen goods quickly to keep the matter off the police records, or the victimized merchants (or families) do not report the crime to the police out of consideration for the parents and the status of the community whose social standards they share. A recent informal report [6] on adolescent crime in an "affluent community" (a New York State county reputed to be the wealthiest in the nation) called particular attention to the "hidden delinquency," shoplifting. The shopkeepers, it noted, did not complain, and pressed no charges for obvious reasons.

Questioning of the adolescents involved indicated that they considerd the shops "enemy territory" and that they stole for "kicks." The sociologists investigating this particular group of children of wealthy parents found that the "excitement and risk levels" of their thefts were high and that the economic value of the stolen objects was not considered. It seems difficult to deny, in view of this finding, that the game of "getting even" with adults in an indirect way rested on deep psychologic urges, of which the adolescents themselves were aware to some degree. It was asked why these children, who shared in the prestige of wealth that their parents prized, expressed their antagonism to adult standards so patently. The explanation advanced was that their extravagant behavior was an attempt to break out of "the jail of stratified wealth" in order to disrupt the "dullness" of a well-adjusted community. For the adolescent, the stable community is too staid, too blasé. If this be so, the psychologic explanation that burglary is an indirect, passive display of aggression is correct. The "kick" in the offense consists of the possibility of injuring, all at one time, the parents, their cherished society, and the parent-surrogate—in the case of shoplifting, the merchant—by the crime. The underprivileged youth also demonstrates this psychologic mechanism in crimes of burglary.

In view of the theory of furtiveness among burglars, it would be expected that all burglars would be inferior-feeling persons. The fact is many personality types engage in burglaries and larcenies since these crimes vary extensively in technique. Thus, the man who burglarizes medical offices for narcotics or prescription blanks differs in nature from the offender who "clouts" motorcars for clothes, bags, cameras, and so on, and from the sneak thief who seeks such objects as radios, watches, jewelry, in unguarded apartments and houses. Some offenders "work" alone, others operate in groups. The former may be unarmed, or equipped with gloves, flashlights, jimmies, occasionally a gun; the latter are organized gangs, "tooled," so to speak, for larger jobs, such as lofts, warehouses, stores, large commercial offices. Beyond this sketchy description of the varieties of burglary, it needs to be stated that in every business of any magnitude pilferage of supplies and merchandise goes on in a never-ending stream.

It is apparent, then, that a one-to-one relationship between types of personalities and the crime of burglary is not demonstrable. But that the quality of furtiveness is common to burglaries can be confirmed by clinical experience. An example of the introverted, emotionally flattened, inadequate-feeling burglary offender is Joey Kane.

Joey was the kind of man one could pick out as "born to trouble." He seemed always to be defending himself against some minor injustice. When arrested for burglary he claimed he had "covered up for his two brothers" who were on parole for burglary in another state and who had actually committed this crime. Convicted of his "brothers'" crime, Joey served eight months, was released, and, after three weeks of freedom, was picked up again for vagrancy. Within a few days after his subsequent release he was stopped by a policeman while driving. In the car were found a flashlight, gloves, screwdriver, and jimmy (tire-lug wrench). Burglar tools to the contrary, Joey complained, "The cop said I was burglarizing a house. . . . he suspicioned me, so he kicked me. . . . I was brokenhearted by the injustice of it all."

Again convicted of burglary,[7] Joey was sentenced to a road-camp for six months. The "injustice" of it was too much for him; he walked out of the camp the second day, but was soon apprehended. The psychiatric study followed Joey's arrest for escaping legal custody.

Records from another state indicated that Joey and his "brothers" were involved in seventy burglaries of homes in the better areas of town—which offenses ceased abruptly upon their arrest and incarceration. In the current offense, Joey conceded that he and one of his brothers climbed through the window of a home, found a purse on the table with fourteen dollars in it, and left through the front door.

The dogged, guilty air that suffused Joey led police officers to a constant interest in his activities. A depressive attitude seemed to have encompassed his whole life. Joey described his marriage of four years, which ended because of his wife's infidelity and his own loosely organized life of relative vagrancy. There didn't seem to be much use in trying to stabilize himself. Joey explained that neither his wife nor himself seemed to have much incentive for forging a better life. The police always seemed to appear when he was trying to work, urging him to leave town on a "floater." (This is a maneuver by the police to have an offender, usually a minor one, leave the area on pain of being arrested on sight.) Examination produced little material of dynamic import. What cannot be documented in Joey's psychic life can be interpolated; his shadowy existence could be summed up as that of a dullish young man, perennially rejected, living a marginal socioeconomic existence, ready to concede (if he thought of it) that the parabola of his life was destined to end nowhere.

The psychologic vignette of Joey and his brethren portrays emotional factors readily observed among minor burglars. This group, once known as "lead pipe" burglars, invades abandoned houses and buildings where few objects of great monetary value are to be found. Old water tanks, scrap metal, broken stoves, sections of lead or brass pipe, and so forth, are the prizes for their daring. Although less frequent now, such groups, formed almost uniformly of mentally dull boys and adults of low cultural level, typify the crude emotional pattern of theft. The low value of the objects taken, the abandoned house or building from which they steal, the clearly defined air of poverty surrounding the crime, merge with their own feelings of self-depreciation. Such an attitude psychologically signifies marked feelings of inferiority in the offenders.

Burglary among youths not necessary mentally dull demonstrates similar psychic mechanisms; for example, the common, school or store burglary seems on the surface to be motivated by the aggression, arrogance, and destructiveness of wayward boys. But study of these offenders shows that the underlying psychological mechanisms are reactive feelings of unworthiness and inferiority. In these cases burglary is an expression of aggression against the school or store—symbol of the parent. Significantly, the stores burglarized are often confectioners' shops, bars, or restaurants—symbolic repositories of nutriment. Such crimes represent a symbolic effort to participate in the community of family life, to share its common property. The individual's childhood deprivation (whether real or imagined) is the unconscious stimulus for theft from a barred or closed building. The burglary is an attempt to correct a historical situation in the emotional life of the offender, long since lost to memory.

THE "COMMON THIEF"

But what of the "common thief," the professional burglar, the sneak thief? Not regarded as neurotic in the clinical sense and generally recognized by criminologists as skilled professionals, relatively little psychological analysis is wasted on them.[8] Classifications have been set up to distinguish these offenders from amateur, or occasional, burglars. Thus, Gibbons and Garrity [9] differentiate property offenders as: (a) the professional thief, (b) the professional heavy criminal, (c) the quasi-professional property offender, and (d) the one-time-loser property offender. This sort of categorization, of course, sheds little light on the psychologic elements involved in this crime group.

The statement has been made that burglary is the court of first resort for the inadequate; it may also become a court of last resort. In such cases, burglary becomes a way of life, with its accepted routine of crime, arrests, imprisonments, parole, and rearrests. Still, it is undeniable that in many cases burglars make a good living at their trade [10] with a minimum of arrests and incarcerations, particularly when a "fixer" is employed to vitiate police vigilance or court convictions.[11]

While the psychology of burglary is of no particular importance to the police, the latter are alert to the characteristic techniques of the crime and knowledgeable of its practitioners. In a recent *New Yorker* article, Susan Black reported on the various types of burglars, the prowlers, or "hit-or-miss," operators who steal "on the blind," those who plan their jobs and use the research of their confederates or "fingers," the "good" burglar (an adjective that represents a "police judgment not a moral one"). Concentrating on the lucrative field of burglary in New York City, in her article, Miss Black gives the following information, drawn from the New York Police Department:

Police divide burglars into several technical categories—the jimmy burglar, the key burglar and the celluloid burglar. . . . those who use the jimmy commit forcible entry . . . the other technicians [attain] surreptitious entry because they get in quickly, quietly and without leaving any readily apparent marks.[12]

The police consider many burglars "competent" when they steal furs, jewelry, cash, or traveler's checks to the degree and with the success that occurs in large cities. It is this competence and that of their "fences," or disposers of the loot, that make apprehension so difficult and examination and study almost impossible. Nor is it always certain that the burglars who are apprehended belong to the professional class. In the experience of this writer, one is forced to interpolate the psychic pattern of these unapprehended offenders from experience with those who have been incarcerated and studied.

From this base line it can be said that the chronic burglar presents a sociopsychological profile as consistent in its contours as that, for example, of the schizophrenic, or inadequate, type of psychopath. The psychic profile contains the corner stone of suggestibility and a weak ego; it is molded by social examples close at hand, is nurtured by a few successful "jobs" and consequent rise in self-esteem, and consolidated by ego-gratification in the exercise of uncontested aggression. With unsuccessful burglars these mechanisms might not suffice. Burglary, for the chronic offender, may represent condensed episodes of success alternating with minor imprisonments or a tragedy of errors. The life story of John Micelli, the fourth of twelve children of immigrant parents, illustrates the latter denouement.

John's early life was typical of an economically marginal group. When he was able to leave school, having reached the fifth grade, John worked for brief periods as a truck driver's helper, a peddler of fruits and vegetables, and a laborer. For a period, John's family was on relief. One day, after a fist fight with his brother, John left home abruptly, rented a furnished room, and made the acquaintance of a man named "Joe." With Joe, he entered upon a series of burglaries of apartments, stealing suits, fountain pens, jewelry, and radios. John's serious entry into a life of alternating burglaries and arrests started at the age of twenty-three. Five years earlier, however, he had been placed on probation by a lower court for juvenile burglary.

It was recognized by the examiner that John was a dull youth of borderline intelligence, easily "led," handicapped for any employment requiring initiative, without much ethical tension in his personality structure. His explanation of the offense was pitched in a quiet, empty manner, factually correct, but without interest in the psychologic accompaniments of the crime. For example:

Q. How did this arrest occur?
A. I met this fellow Joe, and he talked me into it. We lived in the same house. We broke into an apartment and I broke in, the fellow next door. We got some clothes and we pawned it. We were caught together.
Q. How were you caught?
A. I live in the place and went back there. He was talking about the clothes, I was telling him I would take the clothes back, and he told the cop.[13]

For this burglary, John received a suspended sentence. Some time later, while on probation, he entered a building with another youth, stole some clothes, wrist watches, and cash.[14] Again his explanation to the examiners was pat, truthful to a degree, and quietly told.

A more thorough psychological test made at this time revealed an IQ of 67, which placed him in the Borderline Defective group, although it was noted that he showed a practical knowledge of life uninfluenced by learned material, for example, an ego-centered manner of living and conducting himself. The examiner noted that John was sensitive to his lack of concrete knowledge, portraying himself as a successful professional boxer—a more glamorous picture than could be supported objectively. He lived in an unformed realm of fantasy. John was inarticulate, his loose way of expressing himself making the production of clear ideas difficult. He was completely unable to read and capable only of writing his name and address.

Three years later, John was rearrested and sentenced to an institution for mental defectives.[15] During his three years as an inmate, John was subjected to industrial training and some elementary education. Apparently the training netted some gains, for the psychological examination repeated ten years after the first contact showed an increase in IQ to 84, in the dull normal range. In the meantime, John married, spawned a daughter, worked sporadically as a truck driver. Money seemed to come to him from nowhere, although his wife saw little of it; finally she haled him into court for nonsupport.

More than ten years after the original contact with the adult court, John was arrested on a charge of burglary, this time involving theft of cash and property valued at $1,400. By now John was recognized as well habituated to an antisocial career, with one state prison residence behind him as well as the several years spent in the institution for criminal defectives. The judge had no recourse but to sentence John to state prison for from two to three years.

A year after his release from prison John again fell into the hands of the law for burglary of an apartment involving about $350 worth of material.[16] Another examiner recognized the poor prognosis, the egocentric attitude, and so forth. The Court, on the basis of the record and the personality analysis submitted, sentenced John to another state prison term. By this time the psychiatric analysis reflected the presence of psychopathic traits and a diminished accent on the low intelligence which, fifteen years after the original estimate, was now found to be low average level.

Paroled from prison, John evidently worked steadily for a year as a general helper in a radio factory. His rehabilitation appeared to have begun. He was now forty-two years old, married but separated, without contact with his daughter or wife, and living quietly with a common-law wife. The parole officers were reasonably pleased until one day in Christmas week when John, celebrating at a tavern, drank more than he had expected to. With accustomed ease he found a partner in the bar; with him he broke into an apartment within a block of the tavern, stole a radio—and was again arrested.[17] The unnamed accomplice escaped, but John was again sentenced to state prison for two to five years.

Such is the prosaic profile of an unsuccessful professional burglar. That more efficient, better organized burglars would present a more on-going psychic silhouette is undoubted, but because of their proficiency they are lost to clinical scrutiny.

ARSON

The crime of arson attracts attention because of its serious nature and interesting underlying psychology. In older days, arson was a crime of great practical importance since the materials of which dwellings were built were especially susceptible to fire. It is interesting to note that arson derived legally from the crime of malicious mischief when burning barns or haystacks involved other problems than that of danger of life. From the earliest days, arson was a crime in the common law, provided it occurred to a dwelling and that intent, both willful and malicious, was evident. In some jurisdictions arson was punishable by death.[18] Statutory laws covering arson added these elements: burning a building, not necessarily a dwelling; burning to defraud an insurer; degrees of arson, depending on the seriousness of the offense.[19] In recent years, arson is less frequent because of improved fire prevention and fire control, but it may assume serious proportions because of the size of the buildings involved and the number of people exposed to danger.

Broadly speaking, arson is committed by two groups of persons: those with a financial motive, and those defective, mentally ill, or seriously neurotic offenders with personal motivations. Those in the first group, whom we may call the commercial arsonists, are difficult to investigate psychologically. Since relatively little material has been gathered on these offenders, interest has concentrated on the neurotic fire-setter, or pyromaniac. The classic monograph of Lewis and Yarnell [20] examines both groups in terms of psychological motivation. A psychological interpretation of arson leads to problems of psychosexuality, neurosis, and the specific condition of pyromania. The findings drawn by Lewis and Yarnell from their vast material was subsumed under several heads. They found the following motivations for fire-setting:

a) Primitive impulses—"immediate retribution or revenge as against an institution, an employer, a woman. . . ."
b) An irresistible impulse resting on "sensual satisfaction"—the "true pyromania(?)."
c) Mental defective reactions.
d) As sexual stimulant, considered as a substitute perversion.
e) Psychotic reactions, as organic brain disease, syphilis of the brain, "and so on."

Wilhelm Stekel, pioneer Viennese psychoanalyst,[21] also did much work among this group of offenders. Most authorities agree with Stekel that the "height of excitement" occurs in trying to assist the fire fighters and rescuers in their task after the fire has been set and the arsonist's crime is still undetected.

The present writer's experience indicates that the motives of revenge, passive aggression, and the fulfillment of sexual fantasies, especially among mentally defective or inadequate individuals and the mentally ill, are most significant. Aside from the subverted aggressive and destructive tendencies displayed, an interest in both fire-setting and fire-extinguishment were evident. It is corroborative of these opposing tendencies that fire marshals consider it almost axiomatic that the arsonist returns to the scene of the fire, as interested in the work of extinguishment as in his own earlier task of fire-setting. These opposing acts were difficult to explain until Freud offered an ingenious theory on masculine involvement with fire. Briefly stated, from his study of mythology and from the analysis of neurotic patients, Freud postulated that man's acquisition of power over fire arose from primitive man's discovery that he could conserve fire by repressing his infantile (urinary) power to extinguish it.[22] This inhibition represented the libidinous (sexual) drive associated with fire, as in such phrases as "the devouring fire of passion," "fiery lover," "flames of love," and many more. As a result of this long-since-solved instinctual conflict, only a symbolic interest in fire-setting and fire-extinguishment remains subliminally in man's unconscious.

The accepted relation between sexual excitement in arsonists and the fires they set, the fascination of fires for all men, the preconscious relation between power and urination in children, frequently observed in spontaneous play, all seem to lend credence to Freud's speculation. The present writer remembers an incident while examining a male infant in a dispensary years ago; he was the recipient of an unexpected stream of urine upon his immaculate white clinical coat. At this occurrence, the mother, of Old World background, who held the baby, said with vehemence and evident satisfaction, "Serves you right!" The psychologic imputation of aggressivity in this act was intuitively understood by the mother. The interpretation of aggression arising from its pregenital (urinary) source can also be made in arsonists who are carefully investigated.

To exemplify the arsonist, we turn to George, a young man of twenty-five who was enamored of the life of a fireman. He spent almost all his time in the firehouse, aping the work, mannerisms, and life of the professional fireman. Although suspected of being an arsonist, no charges could be brought until he was apprehended and convicted for impersonating a fire marshal.[23] The judge placed George on probation, with the injunction to stay away from the firehouse. George fought within himself to obey this proscription, but he could not resist his desire. He was rearrested for violation of probation when he persisted in visiting the firemen at the station. In George's case, association with fire equipment and those professionally interested in fires gratified his deeper impulses for mastery. However, anxiety developed in the probationer when he was restrained from the gratification of these neurotic impulses. He became tense, restless, and complained of what seemed to him unnecessary privation. He could see no relation between his offense and the restraint imposed by the court. The identification with the fire fighter was complete; in his fantasies George expressed his aggressive impulses through displacement of all his emotions to a position of mastery—that of fire marshal.

While arson is usually a male crime, women also are involved in this offense. One such case came to attention some years ago when a woman of thirty-seven, obviously distraught and neurotic, was accused of setting a fire in a hotel.[24] She had been addicted to barbiturate drugs and had had many emotional traumata in her life: her breast had been amputated for cancer fairly early in life; she had suffered a severe reaction to her childlessness, which produced a chronic depression and an unstable married life. At the time of her offense, her husband was forty-nine and she herself had become involved with a young man of twenty-seven, whom she had induced to propose marriage to her. Obviously distressed and frustrated, the patient had a strong drive to exercise control—one sign of which was her projected marriage to a younger man. However, this attempt to seek stability through another marriage had little substance to recommend it. It was felt that her fire-setting was a direct reaction to frustration and social hoplessness. Since no charge was brought against her, she was treated in a psychiatric hospital with some success.

LARCENY—THE HEART OF CRIME

Theft, with its various types and subdivisions, constitutes the largest group of felony offenses. In common and statutory law, the possession of the property of another with intent to keep it constitutes larceny. The law of larceny is complicated first by virtue of subclasses: those who appropriate what is not theirs; those who properly possess another's property but convert it to their own use; and so on.[25] Although the essential meaning of theft resides in the acquisition of material to which the offender has no rights, its psychological meaning varies with the techniques employed. Thus, an English author states: "The basic offence of dishonesty is theft. Theft, or larceny, . . . is to property what assault is to the person. . . . Larceny is an offence against possession." [26]

The law makes little distinction concerning the feeling behind various types of theft. From the standpoint of psychological analysis, however, the larcenous crime groups—swindling, forgery, embezzlement, car thefts, conspiracy to defraud, among others—do indicate differing psychological modalities operative within the offender.

Moreover, it cannot be questioned that larceny involves psychological elements common to all individuals, that is, the acquisitive wishes present in everyone. "Wanting" and "taking" represent residual cravings of the ego that have escaped complete repression normally developed during the period of early social training. "There is a little larceny in everyone" is a cliché that expresses this psychological truism. The machinery developed by governmental agencies and business organizations, the agreed-upon ethical codes of industries, the constant pressure of moral preachments, all seek to instill inner controls of universal predatory instincts. The forces exerted to control larcenous impulses in our work-a-day world are necessary and constant. Sutherland and other sociologists have drawn attention to a vital area of larcenous crime, the so-called "white-collar crime." [27] Although not necessarily resulting in legal punishment, infractions or violations of receivership committees, restraint of trade by monopoly, illegal rebates, violations of government regulations relating to labor, wages, hours, public contracts, patent infringements, and so on: all are criminal in intent. Clinard lists offenses by politicians and government employees as

direct misappropriation of funds, padded payrolls, monetary "kickbacks" . . . favors to business firms or criminal syndicates . . . illegal commissions on public contracts, issuance of licenses and certificates of building or fire inspection, tax exemptions or lowered tax valuations. . . . Labor union officials may . . . misappropriate or misapply funds, [enter into] collusion with employers, control their unions fraudulently. . . . Doctors may give illegal prescriptions, make fraudulent reports or give false testimony in accident cases, or split fees. . . . Lawyers may secure testimony from perjured witnesses, misappropriate funds in receiverships. . . .

In short, as Clinard points out,

The consideration of only conventional crimes gives an erroneous impression of the extent and effects of crimes on society as well as the nature of criminals.[28]

Sutherland, who brought this tremendous area to wide attention, stated: "White-collar crime is real crime . . . [though] not ordinarily called crime." [29] These considerations support the general conclusion that larceny is indigenous to the human heart; one should not neglect this human "weakness" in analyzing crime.

THE NEUROSIS OF LARCENY

It is an unpleasant, but validatable, fact that larcenies great or small occur almost hourly all over the world. An incident concerning Mark Twain will illustrate how we are prone to tolerate larcenous impulses within ourselves, almost without self-criticism. Having set out to write a story entitled "The First Melon I Ever Stole," Mark Twain, after he had "given out the title," stopped and asked himself, "*Was* it the first?"

In this discussion, of course, we speak of thefts of greater consequence. It is a truism that most larcenists are not apprehended. There are several reasons for this. Sometimes thieves are allied to "fixers" who have police connections or other ways to avoid arrest. Sometimes the victims do not press charges for various reasons, or the stolen objects are replaced (in fact or in value) by relatives, or the thefts are not discovered in time to apprehend the thief. Although monetary gain ostensibly lies behind thefts, there exists a psychologic "game" of larceny that cannot be mistaken even though it may evolve into a major life activity. Adolescents or young men, finding thefts easy to negotiate, continue their larcenies in the same or larger orbits, alone or in groups, until caught. The activity becomes a sort of psychologic contest, a piece of reality-testing of society and its agents. Reality-testing larcenies may be uncovered accidentally in the course of investigating another crime, or during therapy for a psychiatric problem other than criminality. The kleptomaniac (an overvalued term), or compulsive stealer, belongs to the group whose thefts serve no reality purpose, but are distinctly neurotic in character. Whether based on a symbolic unconscious need or analyzable as a contest of skill and finesse, the psychologic fact is this: success at larceny provides ego-gratification closely akin to those creative satisfactions postulated to underlie the impulse toward homicide.

The larcenist becomes immersed in the contest of hiding his aggression. Through the very form of his chosen crime activity, he outwits his victim, covers his tracks, or diverts suspicion. The game transcends the gain. Lagache,[30] a French psychoanalyst, reports an example of this form of satisfaction from larceny in his case of a "gangster" (we would probably use the term "psychopath" in this country) who freely stated to his psychiatrist:

Stealing is like a game: it was a pleasure, almost a voluptuous delight. The pleasure of stealing . . . you have to pay a high price for it, but it's worth it.

Sometimes the pleasure of larceny has deeper roots, buried from the offender's consciousness. He is only aware of his compulsive drive to steal and its accompanying "thrill"; whether he is apprehended or not makes litle psychologic difference to him.

Let us examine the situation of a man whose larcenous activity, revealed when he came for treatment for alcoholism, constituted one facet of a life spent in acting-out unconscious oral cravings, albeit represented in differing behavioral eventualities. His larcenies had been largely undiscovered. He did not recognize himself as a compulsive thief, but one for whom the game of larceny represented a way of life. The confirmed pattern of acting-out he recognized as "his way."

The patient, a trim, well-dressed man of thirty, came for consultation, confessing voluntarily to excessive drinking and other acts that made his life difficult. In spite of his complaints, Arthur exuded confidence as he talked. As a salesman he was an automatic success, whether he dealt with haberdashery or insurance policies, hardware or luggage. A "born" salesman, glibness infiltrated his social address; never at a loss for words, prevarication came easily to Arthur. His "line" was as effective with customers and employers as it was with girls he picked up in bars. Excuses and rationalizations were offered with ease; so also did he relate his history of alcoholism, promiscuity, and larceny. The story started at an early age:

Drinking killed my father. . . . I used to visit my father in jail and I was afraid when I went to see him: the other inmates used to call out to him and I was frightened at this. I wished my father dead and a week later, he did die and I became worried about that. My father was no good; he used to beat my mother.

Arthur was only eight when his father died, but he remembered vividly the latter's arrest for bootlegging; he remembered the scenes of heroic drinking in the backwoods bar.

There was something of the dandy in Arthur, a characteristic in sharp contrast to the prevailing attitude of the mountain logging community in which he grew up and to the life he witnessed there. Possibly his dandyism and his oral addiction were related. At all events, Arthur's addictive tendency came to light in an odd way:

Even when I was a small boy I had a craving for candy. . . . I've had it all my life; I used to eat five and six candy bars a day; when I couldn't get it I would write a note in my father's hand to the store to give me candy. I stole sacks of tobacco and pipes and would cache them away.

He stole money from his mother's purse, and when his mother remarried he started drinking beer surreptitiously. Arthur's technique was interesting: he would collect all the empty bottles in the bar, pour the dregs into one bottle, then go behind the tavern and drink it. One day he stole a pint of whiskey, drank it all, and became ill.

The family, in time, moved from the lumber camp into town. While in high school he worked delivering groceries and would steal liquor from the grocery orders. After school he amused himself when he got home by getting drunk. When it became difficult to obtain liquor, he would steal candy. Later, Arthur attended a junior college where he routinely cheated on examinations and work assignments.

By this time, stealing had become a way of life for Arthur. Living alone, he indulged himself in any direction he wished. It was apparent, also, that he had a way with the girls; he made it a rule never to sleep with the same girl more than twice. In this way, he accumulated about four hundred conquests in the twelve years between eighteen and thirty years of age—some of which could scarcely be dignified by the word "conquest." Known locally as a Lothario, he could not admit to himself that, in spite of his romantic success, an edge of sexual dissatisfaction kept pushing itself into his consciousness.

Arthur went to work for a department store. He sold well, but he also stole constantly. At first, a friend who worked for another men's shop would steal suits and Arthur would buy them for a fraction of their value. When he had accumulated enough, he sold some. He stole cash from his own customers by appropriating the receipts, neglecting to write up a sales check. Although he stole varied amounts of money several times a day—from five to fifty dollars—it was done so cleverly that he remained in one store for two years as a star salesman. Presently he got tired of this and got a job in another, larger store where his stealing continued. He always felt life was too easy for him.

His first arrest was for grand theft, but the charge was changed to intoxication in a public place, for which he served a day in city jail. During this period Arthur worked in a hardware store; he was fired from that job for drunkenness. He then got a job in a luggage shop, where, he said, he stole everything "I could lay my hands on . . . cash, luggage." Arthur used to have a contest with a friend to see who could report the greatest number of thefts in a day. Then, imperceptibly, he began asking himself, "Why am I stealing?"

Meanwhile, he had been married and divorced, continuing his dalliance with numerous girl friends. If he remained with one girl for more than a month he would steal money from her purse. A second marriage followed, this time to a rather masculine woman, whom he left because he suspected her of being a Lesbian. When the stealing faded, alcoholism increased. When the alcoholism decreased in response to treatment, he developed a new and disturbing symptom: the compulsive desire to strike the two-year-old son of his most recent enamorata. Frightened by this new evidence of his unconscious aggression, Arthur made one more attempt to be treated psychiatrically.[31]

One significant point in Arthur's case rests on his revelation of a world of petty thievery in the course of a psychiatric study of a serious character disorder. His story makes it appear plausible that much larceny of this type never comes to official attention. It may be that the victims of such depredations are unconsciously lulled into a parental position, permitting (in this case) Arthur to carry out his thefts without retribution, as they might an indulged child. As might be expected, on checking with his most recent employer (the haberdashery shop), it was discovered that Arthur had been well liked, and regarded as an excellent salesman—charming to customers and employees alike. In this connection, it would be well to remember the clinical axiom among psychiatric criminologists: the true psychopathic personality is the beguiling, charming fellow who stimulates our countertransference to protect and cherish him while he cleverly turns the unconscious "romance" into an opportunity to assert his passive-aggressive inclinations.

Aside from the neurosis indicated in Arthur's case—strong addictive tendencies based on strong oral cravings, the latter covered by acting-out mechanisms—his undetected larcenies may shed light on the general problem of "normal" acquisitive tendencies. Since he was not involved in criminal accusations, Arthur's larcenies resembled, in format at least, the myriad thefts that occur daily without a corresponding legal arrest or conviction. The patient's unsupported statements of his depredations may indeed have been, in reality, pure fantasy, but there was an air about Arthur that reminded one of the child sated with private gratifications, willing and anxious to give up secret oral satisfactions for social acceptance. Treated as reality, then, this case of a secret larcenist seems to support the view of Sutherland and his followers that the atmosphere of business, with its competitive struggles and ethos of success, permits the unconscious identification of many with universal larcenous tendencies, which identification sometimes eventuates in "white-collar crime."

The psychologic-criminologic problem, however, is to ascertain why in fact only a few of those exposed to the atmosphere of larceny succumb to punishable thefts. To this question there is no present answer. Although there are wide gaps in our knowledge of larcenists, since only those caught are studied, the only feasible technique by which to attempt to solve the problem is the tedious analysis of those cases that do come under clinical scrutiny. For this, we turn to a class of thefts that, though utilizing its own particular criminalistic modality, illustrates the essential psychologic paradigm of larcency—the type of thievery called swindling.

SWINDLING AND THE SWINDLER

The term "swindling" is loosely used to denote a specific type of criminal conspiracy: hence, in a strict sense, swindling is not a statutory crime. The actual language of the charge is usually larceny by trick (N.Y.), conspiracy to defraud, or cheating by false pretenses (Iowa), obtaining money by false pretenses (Mass.), false representation (Mont.), misrepresentation (Minn.), and so on.[32] The techniques employed in this type of larceny may range from swindling schemes in stock-market manipulations to bigamous marriages contracted with the hidden purpose of gaining control of money or property. The means by which the fraud is accomplished involves deception on the part of the swindler calculated to give an impression of legitimacy to the enterprises in which the victim becomes entangled. Technical perfection in swindling requires a mastery of trickery; hence, lying as an art must form an important element of the criminal's personality. The psychopathic swindler's use of fabrication is so skillful that the listener cannot distinguish the false statements presented from the true. The degree to which pathologic lying tendencies are integrated into the swindler's character determines the degree of his success in his fraudulent activities. Thus, the layman uses the word "swindling" loosely to include the prominent characteristics of the swindler's personality: specifically, an unctuousness of manner and a hypnotic fluency and facility of speech.

In considering the psychologic background of the swindler, an analogy between the pathologic lying of childhood and that of the adult swindler suggests itself. In the child, tendencies to fabricate are recognized as normal components of the active fantasies of childhood. Where they are exaggerated to the degree that every question is answered automatically by a lie, the child is regarded as a pathologic liar. However, the analogy between the child's development of pathologic lying and that which is a part of the technique of the adult swindler cannot be consistently maintained. Many swindlers prove on examination to have no history of pathologic lying in their early development. Nor do pathologic liars among children necessarily evolve into swindlers in their adult years.

The swindler was studied fairly early in the history of psychiatric criminology because he so patently wore his psychology on his sleeve. One of the early analysts, Karl Abraham,[33] found in analyzing the case of an imposter in the German Army that grandiosity developed from deprivation of love in childhood, indicating that the imposter was forced by his emotion-starved childhood to seek gratification in an imposing military title. Experience has confirmed the presence of deep emotional problems in the background of the swindler. Such persons fabricate their background, education, and family connections in order to convince themselves and others of the reality of their fantasies. For these men, being known as a financier, inventor, or scion of a noble family is sufficient recompense; their gratification resides in living the part they portray. One is reminded here of the universal fantasy, the "myth of royal birth."

The swindler, as has been noted, is a special type of larcenist, but his psychology is so intimately intertwined with his victim's that one must consider both the swindler and the swindled as a symbiotic pair in scrutinizing this type of crime reaction. For example, the self-elevating tendencies, disregard of the thinness of deception, and feelings of invincibility that characterize the swindler psychologically can only be successful if the victim identifies with this grandiosity. This is the bait that readily leads the victim to the slaughter. Greenacre goes further in saying: "Those on whom the fraudulence is imposed are not only victims but unconscious conspirators." [34] The feeling of infallibility in the swindler feeds upon his ability to understand and influence the victim's psychology. In many cases involving wildcat schemes promising high returns, the very audacity of the swindler and his implied invincibility are sufficient to dull the critical sense of the avaricious victim. In the same vein, study of the swindler's victims reveals the presence of similar unconscious tendencies within them, namely, the wish for unlimited bounty and the feeling of personal infallibility. The swindler, aware of these deep psychologic currents in his victim, uses in his technique elements of secrecy, mystery, or intricacy that befuddle the victim by blinding his judgment and allowing his repressed wishes to emerge. A nice example of the use of mystery to subdue the victim's judgment is provided in the common gypsy "switch" swindle.

The gypsy swindle, of hoary tradition, is allied to fortune-telling or, more accurately, is secondary to it. The gypsy's primitive family life, the swirl of skirts, the glitter of ornaments, the nomadic life exert a powerful force on the victim's unconscious sense of magic. Knowing that the fortune-teller trades on magic effects does not increase the critical functions. In fact, the more the gypsy is feared for her thieving tendencies, the more she attracts persons who are willing dupes of her swindlings. Rachel Adams, accused of grand larceny at the age of twenty-nine, is a case in point.[35]

The defendant, a gypsy to whom the complainant went to have her fortune told, had promised, for a fee, to "bless" the complainant's money. Placing the bundle of money to be blessed behind her back, she switched it with a bundle of paper produced from her voluminous skirts. The victim went her way with "blessed" money but soon discovered the fraud. In this way, Rachel secured the proceeds of a life insurance policy as well as the complainant's savings, totalling eight hundred dollars. An arrest for larceny by trick followed the victim's complaint.

As a native of Chicago, the youngest of nine children born to Serbian gypsies, Rachel claimed to have attended school in an ungraded class. She described her life as the ordinary lot of a gypsy girl, moving about the country in her parents' wagon with the rest of her tribe. At the age of eighteen, she claimed to have married in Florida—in a gypsy ceremony—Nick Adams, aged thirty-four. She admitted she earned funds by fortune-telling.

The examination of Rachel Adams proceeded on the basis of half-answers, unresponsive replies, and general vagueness. She claimed lack of knowledge of the illegality of what she was doing, even protesting illegality itself as a fact of life. Because of her limited schooling and obvious dullness, she was given a psychological examination. The report indicated a mental level of high-grade moron, but it was clear this was far from accurate. Analysis of the two subtest results had to be considered before a final classification was made. Thus, on verbal tests she scored an IQ of 64 (within the high-grade moron classification), whereas on the performance test her IQ of 74 placed her within the borderline level. She was purposely evasive on verbal tests, but showed her innate capacity on tests not requiring verbal ability. While this may have been due, in part, to a language handicap and limited schooling, the cultural pattern was the most significant feature of her limitations on the psychometric test. On the reading test, she scored up to her full educational capacity, showing that she was able to utilize her mentality if she so desired. The assumption of mental obtuseness was part of the net she wove around her victim, proof that she was far removed from the world of exactness, and hence the more mystical.

Incidentally, there is often present in the gypsy swindle a faint aura of sexual license, commonly attributed to gypsy women. Whether gypsies are or are not sexually immoral is not pertinent, but in generations past they were endowed with the projected images of free sexuality in the minds of the public. This sexual implication is found regularly in the swindle relation generally.

SOME DYNAMIC FACTORS IN SWINDLING

Sexual urges, particularly of a perverse or homosexual order, are often stimulated by the swindler in order to blind his victim's judgment prior to defrauding him. Sometimes the swindle is based on this principle directly. The victim may be lured to a hotel room, ostensibly to witness, or become a party to, some sexual irregularity. A card game is in progress on his arrival, in which he is eventually cheated. The swindler who builds up sexual tension in his victim astutely detects in the latter an interest in homosexuality or other sexual perversion.

This stress on sexuality in certain varieties of swindle games is not accidental. It is part of the complex relationship brought into being by the swindle. The criminal, with his knowledge of victim-psychology, expects to maintain his hold on the victim by appearing to socially debase himself. At the same time, unconscious elements in the offender's personality force him to adopt the submissive position, which he himself rationalizes by regarding it as only a maneuver in his skillful handling of the swindle.

As a matter of clinical fact, swindlers and pathologic liars do show deviations in their sexual life. In a routine examination of criminal psychopaths, it was found that more than half the swindlers under study recorded diminution of heterosexual impulses.[36] Sexual impotence, diminished libido accompanied by little psychosexual satisfaction, marriages of convenience, marriages for money, and frequent change of sexual partners were common findings. Some swindlers showed effeminate or homosexual tendencies in their dress and manner.

In the more brazen type of swindle, closely related to business larcenies and personal fraud by trick, the sexual implications are not so close to the surface. Here grandiosity is expressed through claims of financial greatness, powerful friends, and so on. The following case is an extreme example of this category.

The background of Jacob V. Stein was dramatic and glamorous. Jacob, thirty-six at the time of his first arrest for a stock swindle (for which he served three years in state prison), described his birth in Marseilles, France, of Jewish parents, his graduation from a Belgian university with a degree in engineering, a life of increasing successes— none of which could be verified. At another time, he claimed birth in Russia and education in a technical college in Russia.

Several years after his discharge from prison after an earlier conviction, Stein was indicted for grand larceny, second degree. The specific charge recited that he had obtained $300 from the complainant, for which he had promised to search the title of a building owned by the complainant, after which he was to obtain for the owner a loan of $16,000. Stein failed to make the search, and appropriated the complainant's money to his own uses. Another property owner stated that in a similar manner the defendant had obtained $750 from him.

Stein was known to the courts and had been examined on several occasions. His history as given on these occasions was garbled by claims of education in foreign universities, by statements of tremendous income, high living, and business connections that netted him fabulous returns. It was characteristic of Stein that he overexerted himself during the examinations in efforts to ingratiate himself. While being interviewed he would often make certain statements, then say he was telling the truth because he could prove every statement that he made. He showed correspondence that he had with him, making it clear before leaving the interview that he would be very much obliged if the examiner acted in his favor.

It was not too long after his latest release from a five-year sentence in state prison that Stein appeared in court again.[37] This time, an accomplice had, at Stein's behest, forged a check for $1,000 against the fictitious account of one A. L. Johnson "of Pennsylvania." The check, payable to the offender, was deposited and a check for $500 drawn against it, which Stein used as an impressive decoy for further "deals." As that of an "inveterate swindler," the diagnostic problem was reviewed, especially in view of Stein's flamboyance and persistent over-dramatization. Many of his statements bordered on delusions and a brain disorder (general paresis) was first suspected. This being ruled out, consideration was given to manic-depressive psychosis and pseudologia fantastica, or pathological lying—the inveterate, exuberant lying of the psychopath.

Sitting in dignity, his long, wavy gray hair fitting his expansive manner, Stein spoke fluently about his tremendous successes in business. He described two inventions that would win the war (World War II): one, a system to project electric current toward advancing enemy tanks, thus electrocuting the soldiers inside; another, a non-sinkable boat that would be impervious to torpedos. Both these ideas were presented to the Secretary of State; when they were consigned to a clerk in the Patent Office, Stein became infuriated. "Let them come to me," he said. His flood of self-confidence extended far beyond the world of finance: "I may save the world from chaos; I could stop this war in ninety days."

When reality difficulties pressed upon Stein, he tended to retreat to a position of childish omnipotence, as is well illustrated by the manner in which he conducted his own case in court. Insisting on a jury trial, he exploited the drama of the situation to the full. The press reported the event in semicomic style:

A suave, white-haired confidence man in silk-flowered tie and spats rounded out a career marked by uninterrupted audacity yesterday in General Session by dismissing his attorney and defending himself on a second-degree forgery charge. The jury of nine men and three women, for whose common sense he showed much marked contempt, replied by finding him guilty in three minutes.

When the defense was about to begin yesterday morning, a lawyer assigned by the Court to defend Stein announced that his client had discharged him. Stein, who is a graduate of the so-called Sing Sing Law School, having studied law while serving time at that prison for two grand larceny convictions and two violations of parole, said he would defend himself.

"I might remind you," said Judge Goldstein, "that, in the words of Voltaire, 'a lawyer who defends himself has a fool for a client.'" However, the confidence man was allowed to go ahead.

Virtually all the questions which he asked of witnesses were useless, as the Court sustained the D.A.'s objections to them. Stein summed up for forty-five minutes in a flood of oratory, contending that he didn't forge the check because his middle name was _____, and he had signed this name to the check. He also called upon God as his witness.[38]

In spite of his conviction, Stein continued to tell the examiners of such past activities as those in South America—buying gold mines there and selling arms to revolutionists. His fantasies would be dismissed as childish prattle had they not emanated from a corpulent, well-set man of fifty-one. It was significant that he minimized his sex life, evidently feeling above such mundane interests. When questioned about it, he stated that he had had heterosexual relations since the age of fifteen, that his first wife was frigid, that he had had several mistresses while living with her. He admitted perverted sex practices with women, including sodomy and fellatio. Actually, Stein's entire preoccupation was with business affairs and inventions. Frequently he dropped hints that he was of noble lineage. He even admitted that he used a title, Count, while living in a smart New York apartment house, some of whose tenants were listed in the Social Register. On that occasion, he had subleased a fourteen-room apartment, hired a butler, and ordered a tremendous stock of liquor—which he paid for with a forged check. And a cabdriver in the neighborhood reported that he received a bad check for a one dollar cab fare. (It requires a stouthearted man to try to cheat a New York cabdriver!)

The dynamic elements that nourished this tremendous defense of grandiosity undoubtedly related to feelings of inferiority about his racial origin (he was born a Russian Jew). The frequent aliases adopted by Stein, his grandiose reaction to an impoverished background, his important undertakings and world-saving inventions represented the hysterical means by which he won relief from oppressive feelings of smallness and insignificance. Stein's case, as presented, forms a caricature of the swindler, but many of the elements described in this offender can be seen in less grotesque and less nearly psychotic offenders.

FORGERY AND KINDRED CRIMES

The crime of forgery differs in its psychologic essence from theft by swindling. It lies closest to extortion in its usurpation of authority. Legally, forgery consists in any writing—whether on a check, legal document, or letter—which may "prejudice another's rights," having the effect of defrauding someone. As in the crime of extortion, the assumed authority that permits the forger to utter checks without funds, or utilize another man's name to issue checks, seems basically to arise from an intense need to expand the forger's ego to fit a self-image, distant from the actual self. For this reason, forgeries are frequently uttered during drinking sprees. The offender, feeling expansive and euphoric under the influence of alcohol, flows, by his acts, into that image that is his ego-ideal: a successful, omnipotent figure distributing largesse to his suddenly expanded circle of "friends." It is a matter of criminologic experience that forgers do not always need the money their forged checks produce. The powerful urge to transcend their mediocre position in life, to fill in for a brief moment the expanded ideal of themselves, is a strong motivating factor.

Less obviously neurotic forgers, it is true, live on the money illegally obtained. Their techniques are carefully considered: These forgers study the signatures they are to forge, steal blank checks that will make their signatures plausible, and proceed in general in a workmanlike manner to appropriate another's money or property through forgery. In these cases, the feeling of omniscience is buried under the larcenous plan, although pride in a clever forgery does betray the psychologic usurpation of authority already pointed to.

On a more intricate technical level, but using the same psychologic modality, one finds counterfeiters enacting the drama of borrowed grandeur. The counterfeiter pits his wit and skill against that of the government. Although the gains are great in successful counterfeiting, it seems reasonable to infer that the operators are motivated by feelings of borrowed omniscience in their technical perfection of minting money. A story of a notorious counterfeiter in the federal penitentiary in Atlanta humorously illustrates this point. A counterfeit bill, printed by a competitor, was shown to this inmate. Holding the bill slantwise to the light, the prisoner said, with infinite scorn for an inferior product, "I could have split it three ways."

A case that combines the elements of forgery and larceny by trick with the magic appropriation of a revered name is that of a mother and son who variously assumed the names and credit ratings of nationally known millionaires. Terence, a youth of seventeen, was brought up as a little Lord Fauntleroy by his mother. The father was a weak, submissive character who played a secondary role in the household. As a child, Terence is alleged to have attracted the attention of a wealthy woman, Mrs. R., who befriended him, and at her death left him a cash bequest of $15,000, in addition to valuable gifts of jewels. On the basis of this reported fortune, mother and son lived in opulence on a credit level. In the exclusive clubs which they frequented, the mother was introduced by the son as his aunt, the Duchess; while Terence himself adopted the name William J. K. Vanderbilt. The pair, living on credit, continued this gay deception for several years. In retrospect, exhaustive inquiry by the court officers did not yield any clues as to the gift of $15,000 to Terence or to the existence of a Mrs. R. At the time of his current arrest for larceny, Terence, stating that he "wanted something halfway decent for Mother," had purchased an expensive ring for her from a fashionable jewelry establishment, using a worthless check signed "William J. K. Vanderbilt." The ring, valued at thousands of dollars, had been pawned immediately upon its receipt.[39] Monetary gains from the ring were important to Terence, but for emotional reasons the theft required a setting of grandeur.

The psychologic implications of forgery and the kindred crimes mentioned here bring to the foreground those elements in jewel larcenies that share a similar psychologic basis. It is admitted that jewels have a high monetary value, but it must also be pointed out that jewels have always been endowed, as folklore indicates, with magical properties; this added psychologic value strikes a responsive chord in the jewel thief. The concentration of great value in a tiny precious stone acts as a magnet to those whose fantasy of magic plays a strong role in their eventual behavior.

Forgers, whether of the careful, calculating type or catapulted into forgeries during a drinking spree, illustrate a significant aspect of forging psychology through their behavior before the authorities. Forgers, like alcoholics, are filled with genuine, if transient, remorse after apprehension. One hears regrets and repeated promises of reform; denials of the offense are rare among forgers. There appears to be an acceptance of their failure, a mildly depressive affect in the setting of a relatively simple personality structure. Under the superficial remorse can be glimpsed a steadfast but passive rebelliousness to the restrictions of social and economic rules. It is axiomatic among workers in criminology that check forgery constitutes a type of addiction that is rarely cured. Occasionally the alcoholic forger who utters checks on a spree changes his practices, but professional forgers seldom modify their behavior, in spite of punishment by imprisonment.

The simplicity of the forger's psychological structure may be visualized in the basic emotional dependence displayed. While the forger usurps the authority of the person or business organization whose name he forges, he feels that the injured person or institution will (like a father surrogate) forgive and protect him. This mechanism can be seen among embezzlers also; similarly, it is frequent in income-tax evasion cases. To verbalize this rather universal feeling, one might say: "The bank is so wealthy, the government owns so much, the industrial empire is so powerful, a small amount would not be missed. . . . The benevolent father will understand and forgive." This fantasy of benevolence rides past the conscience with surprising ease in many persons. The forger, counterfeiter, and embezzler, however, become virtually hypnotized by this fantasy, lulled by its soft voice, immunized to reality considerations. The forger in particular accepts his dependence without a struggle; consciously he is aware only of being impatient to share the world's wealth while riding on another's back.

A clinical picture of a chronic forger is provided in the history of a man of thirty-nine, arrested, in the present instance, for uttering a batch of worthless checks.[40]

Disregard for reality was the outstanding characteristic of Jules DeMarcot. One could perceive it in his breathless speech, his ready answers, which, like prayers memorized in childhood, gave the impression of having been learned verbatim. Even before he described his state hospital admissions in Pennsylvania, his brief admissions to California state hospitals, his record, starting at the age of eighteen, of larcenies, auto thefts, burglaries, and fictitious checks, one had a clear picture of an individual without a goal. His employers, during the brief, semiskilled jobs he had held, described him as being stable; industrious for a short time, then erratic.

By the time he was thirty-six, Jules had contracted five marriages, the first four having been annulled after liaisons not exceeding six months. His Army record ended with an inevitable dishonorable discharge because of a civil conviction for larceny. From the age of twenty there was a succession of arrests, convictions, incarcerations, and parole violations in his criminal record, to the number of eighteen. His current wife of three years' duration reported that Jules was a good husband and a good father; she passed lightly over his drinking and gambling, preferring to venture no opinion as to why the frequent job changes and the appearance in Jules of constant internal pressure.

The offense for which he was being examined was forging a signature on a bank credit card that he used as the basis for signing fifteen checks amounting to $570. The purchases made on the basis of the forged bank credit card were in small amounts and covered a period of less than a month. On previous occasions Jules had forged signatures on regular checks; the hidden persuasion of the credit system determined his choice of technique in the current offense.

In the psychological testing, the offender showed good mental capacity. He was fluent and cooperative, with little perception of his total pattern. Beyond his show of remorse over the forgeries, a general air of depression and contrition acted as a veneer for his inadequate personality. Words came readily: "I turned to cashing fictitious checks to put food on the table and to keep from drinking. I fully realize that my problems cannot be solved by drinking."

This readiness to verbalize has been described by Cleckley as a sort of semantic dementia, characteristic of true psychopaths. There is, he states, a misalliance between the verbal expression of words and their inner meaning:

The mechanics of speech are available to him [the psychopathic personality] but he has lost the true use of language, its assigned function and symbolism.[41]

Cleckley thus puts into a concise statement the striking fluency of the psychopath, noted by many; the excuses and explanations that bear so little meaning in the relation between words and subsequent behavior.

With this psychopathic characteristic outstanding in Jules, it was difficult to elicit crucial material in his life history; attempts to probe met only further verbalizations and defensive orations. It was obvious, too, that punishment by incarceration had left no mark on him. The offender remarked easily, "My life has been wasted," and, as glibly, related details of seven suicidal attempts, by slashing his wrists, use of gas, sleeping pills, and so on.

Since introspection was foreign to Jules, his remorse and contrition representing no more than verbalisms, one had to rely on symbolic interpretations to find meaning in his acts of forgery. From this standpoint it could be concluded that writing a fictitious name on a check, or using somebody else's name on a credit card, represented the succor by a magical force that would permit his unstable ego to ward off ego-disintegration. In a sense, this is the problem of all psychopaths, but forgery comes closest to illustrating the use of magic in their unconscious and preconscious mental life.

VARIETIES OF EMBEZZLERS

A variant of the magical use of another's name is evident in the crime of embezzlement. Clearly, the magic spell of names denoting wealth or power is a normal aspect of our social psychology: the prevalence of the "name dropper," who shares by association the glory of those in the public eye, attests to our inner need for ego-support through symbols of wealth, of power, and glamour. So it is with the embezzler.

That such acts are unconsciously, or at least emotionally, motivated is indicated in the finding that the majority of embezzlers give every appearance of sobriety and social adjustment. Their stability remains apparent until an offense comes to light that proves to have been a disastrous attempt to solve an insoluble psychological problem in a superficially adjusted person.

The emotional problems of embezzlers are not always so patent as in the case of Mrs. Button, a matron of fifty-six, who worked as a clerk in a municipal court. Mrs. Button was known to her fellow workers as a rather dowdy woman, slow-moving, but thorough in her work. The quizzical expression on her face was usually attributed to her near-sightedness. On the whole, they considered Mrs. Button to be polite and reliable, apparently accepting her place in the world—a small cog in the machinery of justice. She wrote out the traffic fines in a large, round hand, kept the records meticulously, collected the fines with a smile. But over these years of service to her community she managed to embezzle several thousand dollars, appropriating small amounts each day from the fines received in the traffic court.

For ten years, the state examiner was unable to pin down the cause of dwindling court receipts. Then one day, when suspicion fastened its improbable hold on Mrs. Button, the misappropriations were solved. She confessed readily.[42] The dam broken, a tearful Mrs. Button described in detail her life of emotional starvation, how she dwelt in a world of fantasy, receiving psychic gratification from writing love letters to movie stars. As she talked, she poured out her carefully guarded secrets: her husband's rapid weakening from leukemia, her son's homo-sexuality, and her own worsening diabetes. She told of her strange "sugar addiction," pursued in spite of the diabetes. Even the piddling embezzlements—five dollars today, ten dollars tomorrow—represented a kind of addiction from which she could not free herself. With forlorn tears and heavy sighs, Mrs. Button told how she had gradually become aware of the emotional thinness of her home life. She recognized that each of her secret vices was a nibble at the magic of fantasy, a desper-ate attempt to allay the bitter sense of life slowly disintegrating.

Embezzlement does not always represent so clear a transliteration of conflict into larceny. More often the embezzler is unable to arrive at a precise pinpointing of his dissatisfactions in life. Generalized irrita-tions replace the specific emotional starvation seen in the case of Mrs. Button. This is evident in the case of Neil Farley.

Neil Farley's life could have served as a textbook description of an unstable psychopath. Born to a family where bickering, outbursts of temper, and mutual recriminations spurred on by an abusive father were daily fare, Neil showed early evidences of emotional instability. From the age of fourteen, he was in constant trouble with the police for petty thefts, burglary, and truancy. During his stormy adolescence and early youth, Neil was observed to be suspicious and unnecessarily belligerent. When finally committed to a reformatory in an Eastern state,[43] Neil was clearly diagnosable as a prepsychotic personality. He accused his parents of "railroading" him, was hostile, derisive, and un-cooperative. On the fifth day of his observation period, Neil barricaded himself in his room behind the bed and other furniture, threatening to kill anyone who tried to get in. But this startling earlier behavior somehow managed to neutralize itself; some years later he joined the armed forces, earned an honorable discharge, and settled down to married life. By the time Farley was thirty-two, a broad-shouldered, handsome, not unintelligent man, he had risen to a responsible job in a large corporation and was living with his sophisticated, fashion-conscious wife in relative comfort.

But suspicion gnawed at Neil. His wife, also successful in business, seemed to him to be dressing too sexily. He sensed, without reason, that she had other interests. He became belligerent, ugly, chronically unhappy. Finally, after months of gnawing uncertainty, he accused his wife of infidelity. It was during the months preceding this marital explosion that Neil had been steadily embezzling funds amounting to $4,000 from his employers in amounts varying from $50 to $300. The money was appropriated by altering the deposit slip each time he banked the firm's money and was used in gambling, with the inevitable losses.

The Court,[44] aware of the offender's psychiatric background, placed Farley on probation with the injunction that he was to seek psychiatric treatment. For several months Neil faithfully kept his appointments, working conscientiously to understand his sensitivity, to restrain his tendency to violence, and to agree that his unreasoning suspicion of his wife was based on some emotion deep within him. He could not understand why he could not tolerate his wife or other women indulging their natural love of beautiful clothes. It went against his grain, the grain of his unconscious homosexuality. Of this, nothing was mentioned.

In time, a reconciliation was affected and Farley started on the long road to recouping his financial losses. As psychiatric study proceeded, it became evident that this embezzler was more a psychopath than a neurotic. His aggressivity was almost impossible to throttle. On several occasions he related dreams bearing this general format: "I have killed some person or animal and buried it under concrete. I wake up in a fright, drenched with sweat."

The probationer was a bright man, disturbed inwardly by his evident lack of emotional control, and outwardly by hints of his wife's disinterest and fear. The presiding judge, still unwilling to imprison Neil for the larceny, agreed to a state hospital admission. Farley was soon released and, chronically dissatisfied with his life, resumed a tenuous life at home. Finally, divorce seemed the only recourse to his wife. This added "insult" so infuriated Neil that he assaulted and kidnapped his wife—an unusual occurrence in the life-pattern of an embezzler.

To return to the more usual type of embezzler, crimes of this nature occur with regularity throughout this country, seldom noticed in the public press when the amounts misappropriated are small. When, however, they involve large companies and large sums of money, they do reach public attention. It is this more usual type of case that reveals the embezzler to have been a reliable and honest worker, whose very façade of honesty shunts off suspicion until thousands of dollars prove on audit to be unaccounted for. Indeed, the offender's very trustworthiness in a large corporation *is* the defensive structure behind which is hidden his drive for participation in what appears to be the unlimited wealth of the company. Study will show in these instances that the offender's infantile conception of sharing in unlimited wealth has grown, unsuspected, to the point where it blinds the judgment of the embezzler-to-be. If the money appropriated is frittered away in gambling or high living, this becomes the offender's rationalization of his crime, but it is difficult to mistake the neurotic nature of embezzlement. Nor does there seem reason to disagree with the psychoanalytic formulation that this yearning for unlimited wealth means, symbolically, unlimited parental love. An individual under this unconscious influence longs, without being aware of it, for paternalistic affection from his employers more eagerly than he wishes for monetary recompense.

If there was ever a really reliable employee, it was Christopher Paige. As a bookkeeper for the corporation he was an ideal worker. Everybody liked Chris, so it was natural when the employees decided to form their own credit union that Chris should be chosen to run it. He was genial, he was on the job, he had few pretensions or affectations. When a worker had trouble with a hospital bill he could always count on Chris to lend him five or fifty dollars. He was humane, kind, and understanding; his home life was quiet and normal; he was one of the rank and file. Besides, his four years in the Army, spent overseas, had given Chris a solid appreciation of how this country was built, and his parents' origin in Central Europe had led them to teach him the virtues of thrift, of hard work, and of steadiness.

The credit union started auspiciously with $85. The system was simple at first: Chris would lend out a total of $100 and take in perhaps $115 in small amounts. The records were not complicated at first; they could be handled out of his desk drawer. His didn't mind this extra labor: he made transactions with his fellow workers on the street, in the yards, or at home. He kept the records in his desk drawer, made loans out of cash, took in the payments, entered a quick record, and everyone seemed happy—there was always money available. No one questioned Chris's loyalty or his work.

Presently, the officers of the union decided, as its capital grew to several thousand dollars, to set up a little office to handle the paper work. By this time Chris had fallen into the habit of taking small amounts out of the drawer and using them for living expenses and to repay loans, but always he put back the proper amount—he thought.

His accounts were in disorder; acceptance of payment from union members without crediting them properly, in some cases converting them to his own use, had reached the level of one or two thousand dollars. After his eventual apprehension, Chris summed up the situation thus:

The credit union was my life, but the amounts of money began to mount. First there was several thousand dollars which had to be covered, and when the accountants went over the books I was shocked to find it ran way up.

The indictment [45] detailed false entries to cover his conversion of monies that had increased in the last years of the credit union's eight years of life to levels of $100,000 and beyond. To put it in the offender's words, "I knew something was wrong, I was so mixed up."

The offender's confusion was real: the borrowings, lendings, misappropriations of the past few years left tangled records for the auditors to unravel; they also left a mental tangle in Christopher's mind. The sheer overtaxing of his mental capacities, hidden by affability and the desire to help his fellow unionists, was mingled with apprehension and guilt feelings. His astonishment at the happenings within the inner recesses of his psyche was genuine. Chris had no perception of the mechanisms at work within him.

When the credit fund was small, early in the organization's history, Chris's good intentions and fantasy of magnanimity formed one psychologic unit; his ability to distribute largesse to his fellow workers satisfied a strong emotional need. As the amounts to be balanced increased beyond his capacity to disentangle the accounts, his intrapsychic homeostasis (balance) began to wobble. As the transactions grew in size, his psychologic identification with the credit union grew more tenuous. With this subtle change, Chris's depression and confusion increased. Money used for emotional sustenance became money stolen; fantasy was replaced by the reality of crime.

The mental mechanisms displayed in this case can be duplicated in the study of many embezzlers. The lure of wealth acquired suddenly involves a peculiarly neurotic attitude toward money. Since gambling and embezzlement, in this respect, bear a close internal relationship, the neurotic meaning of the desire to acquire large amounts of money will be pursued into our examination of the practice and crime of gambling.

GAMBLING AND THE GAMBLER

Gambling may be recreation, addiction, or crime; in each of these forms it has always been colored by attitudes carrying a high moral

charge. It is difficult to discover why gambling has suffered from the
moral obloquy which attends it; why, since it is part and parcel of the
very human tendency toward prediction, it is condemned by ethics
and decried by law. Why is gambling a sin? Is it because it constitutes
an affront to the Supreme Ruler who alone directs the outcome of
human probabilities? A recent writer, aware of this connotation, and
commenting on widespread gambling in England,[46] found nothing in
the Scriptures that specifically made gambling a sin.

Obviously, gaming is weighted with a heavy load of opprobrium,
but in spite of this gambling has been indigenous to civilized and
primitive peoples alike for centuries. As long ago as A.D. 60, Tacitus,
the Roman historian, is reported to have commented:

The old Germans, after losing everything they possess at a dice game, then
stake their freedom and even their life on the last throw. [Another historian]
gives a whole series of illustrations showing when the Germans' gambling
mania was roused to its highest pitch they would literally stake their freedom, their wife and child, the limbs of their body, even their very life.[47]

Of itself, gambling is a misdemeanor when carried out in public.
Dice games, blackjack, betting on horse races through "bookies," the
numbers (policy) game, slot machines, roulette or other gambling
"implements," animal races (greyhounds), cockfights, and so on—these
forms of gambling are contrary to statutes or local ordinance in accordance with the jurisdiction involved. On the other hand, wagering
in any sort of game or contest, when practiced in private, is countenanced. Apparently the crucial issue in most states and counties is the
use of gambling equipment by those whose income is derived from
proceeds of these games. In most states, the "common gambler" is
defined as one who derives a substantial portion of his living from
operating games of any type including the policy racket. According to
the New York Penal Code, the "owner or agent of a place for gambling
where money or property is dependent on the result . . . is a common
gambler and guilty of a misdemeanor."[48] As a matter of public policy,
it has been stated by a New York judge that the "people have a legal
right to gamble until the legislature expressly decrees otherwise,"[49]
but a gambling house is considered a public nuisance; hence its operators are indictable.

There are many other areas of gambling that may or may not be
involved with the law; for example, "playing" the stock market on
margin was considered legal. (Now, of course, the Securities and Exchange Act[50] has removed much of the hazard from this area; see
Chapter XII.) In spite of ethical proscription, gambling is handled
lightly in everyday life. It appears in a criminal light chiefly when
associated with antisocial persons, as in gambling syndicates, whose

members are often involved in other illegal activities. These others may be extortion, compulsory prostitution, narcotic traffic, usury ("loan sharks"), union racketeering, conspiracy to defraud, assault, mayhem, and homicide. Although gambling is a minor crime in most jurisdictions, its criminal ramifications may be significant. Addictive gambling often comes to light in association with embezzling and larceny, but only tangentially, in accounting for misappropriated funds. The professional gambler does not often run afoul of the law unless he is involved in criminal conspiracy.

From a clinical viewpoint, gamblers may be classified in three broad groups: social; compulsive, or addictive; professional. The *social* gambler, which includes the average person, rarely becomes involved with the law. The *compulsive*, or *addictive*, gambler may become secondarily subject to criminal prosecution because of forgeries, embezzlements, or burglaries undertaken to cover excessive or ruinous losses. The *professional*, if associated with other criminal rackets, may be arrested on local ordinance violation or on a disorderly conduct charge. When the professional operates in areas where gambling is legalized, as in the state of Nevada, he is no gambler at all, but a practical psychologist who *permits* the player to pay for the privilege of indulging his neurotic gambling urge. This is likewise true where the professional uses cheating methods, calculated to insure him an "angle," or fixed advantage.

This brief summary would seem to indicate that the psychological accent in gambling takes precedence over the criminologic aspect of this activity. It may be significant of human self-indulgence that of the various compulsions, the gambling addiction has been subjected to psychologic study by only a handful of workers. It has received literary attention from world-famous authors, from Dostoyevsky to Ian Fleming (*Casino Royale*), from Hemingway to Richard Jessup (*The Cincinnati Kid*), but its source in man's irrational depths has been plumbed mainly since the advent of psychoanalysis. Freud himself, intrigued by Dostoyevsky's passion for gambling, advanced the speculation that masturbation and gambling present startling psychologic similarities: namely, use of the hands, self-punishment tendencies, self-castigation, ethical struggle with restraint and indulgence, the addictive aspect of both activities. In his classic paper on the Russian novelist, Freud wrote:

The "vice" of masturbation is replaced by the mania for gambling: and the emphasis laid upon the passionate activity of the hands betrays this derivation.[51]

But it was Bergler, one of the early students of the subject, who more realistically used the insights of psychoanalysis to understand this compulsive neurosis. The compulsive gambler, Bergler noted, takes "bigger and bigger chances . . . never stopping when he has won": the energy invested in the "pleasure-painful tension" of gaming betrays its irrational source. The compulsive gambler, Bergler stated, "is a neurotic with the unconscious wish to lose." Rather than a symbolic sexual act, gambling is an expression of a childish "fiction of omnipotence," a latent rebellion against the reality-principle.[52]

The few writers on the psychology of gambling have based their conclusions on the analysis of a relatively few cases of neurotic gamblers. Greenson,[53] for example, traced the attitude of the gambler toward luck as "determined by the Oedipus constellation of the specific gambler." This writer noted in the various patients' studied that playing against other players held different meanings in each case: for example, "participation in forbidden and exciting activities (*i.e.*, sexual) . . . attempts to bribe the powerful father figure. . . ." Lindner,[54] who wrote on the basis of analysis of one case of "pure" gambling neurosis, concluded, among other things, that the "gambler . . . is strongly aggressive . . . with huge reservoirs of unconscious hostility . . . and [gamblers are] chronic masturbators to boot." These writers agree that the compulsive gambler is permeated with a masochistic urge to suffer and atone for his aggression by bitter self-incriminations after having sustained losses.

It may be of interest to note here parenthetically that gamblers are loath to be treated for their addiction, and when forced into treatment by distraught relatives rarely stay in it. Even professional gamblers who are themselves trapped in a gambling addiction, referred for treatment by anxious spouses, may retreat after the first therapeutic hour.[55] Hence the observations here set down are of gamblers treated and untreated, in many areas, including Nevada. The psychologic observations that follow, although directed toward the compulsive gambler, are esentially valid for the social gambler as well.

THE BASIC PSYCHOLOGY OF GAMBLING

In general, the neurotic aspects of gambling involve the activity itself, without respect to the atmosphere of gaming. In Nevada, where gambling is legal, the same emotional conflicts erupt as are observed in areas where gambling is illegal. This generalized statement brings us immediately to the essence of the gambling neurosis. Whereas neuroses and psychoses represent conflicts within the ego with its various functions, the gambling neurosis revolves around a conflict between the ego and implacable Fate. The gambler sets himself in opposition to this magical power, which he may call Lady Luck,

Chance, the law of averages, and so on. The compulsive gambler, within himself, begs "Chance" to become humanized, when in fact he enters the game knowing that chance is impersonal, extrahuman, and completely intangible. He therefore institutes a series of rationalizations and defense mechanisms to hide from himself the obvious fact that he has no power whatsoever over luck, or Fate. The most common of these defenses is a series of superstitions that hide magic wishes in the form of little technical tricks. Like the compulsive neurotic, the gambler wards off by formulas and incantations the inner anxieties caused by fear of loss. The numerous protective devices that gamblers use against the unequal match with Fate are well known: the rabbit's foot, peculiar gestures, rhythmic phrases, proscription of women at the gambling table, obscene words in repetitive phrases, methods of skipping a certain number, and so on. Even the vaunted "intuition" relied on by the gambler is a defense mechanism, a rationalization that he can beat that which cannot be beaten.

The ultimate defense of the gambler, however, is that most rational of rationalizations, the law of probability or chance. Because of the average person's familiarity with prediction and probabilities, he feels at home with the assumption that if he is losing his "luck must change." It is common knowledge that in a series of events that depend on chance, say, tosses of a coin, the appearance of heads or tails will be in the ratio of one-half, respectively; that is, first heads, then tails, and so on. However, there is no certainty that if the first five tosses in a series of ten bring heads, the next five tosses will bring tails. It is true that in a long series of plays—say, one hundred or a thousand— the distribution of heads and tails tends to be equal, but this cannot be foretold *at any given* toss. Thus, the gambler who depends on the inevitability of the one-half ratio (i.e., alternate heads and tails) occurring at a *given* toss, is simply invoking a heartfelt wish that chance will act the way he wishes it to act.

The question of probabilities touches on complicated mathematical and philosophical problems beyond our concern. For our discussion of gambling, it is enough to say that logicians [56] consider probability a hypothesis that needs to be tested empirically. Hence, to test the probability of luck changing for the gambler requires an infinite amount of money. This situation has been encompassed in Bernoulli's theorem, which states in effect: The frequency of a given number (or point, or card) that is wished for coming up, will approach its probability (p) as the number (n) of trials or plays increases indefinitely. And in the case of the gambler, the indefinite increase in plays depends on an infinite supply of money. Bernoulli's theorem is called the law of large numbers; to assume that it will lead to the law of averages is, as James R. Newman expresses it, "[an] odd opinion [that] derives apparently from the conviction that in the long run nature is bound to imitate man." [57]

It is clear, then, that the law of chance is no law at all; when the gambler insists that the "law of chance" favors him, he is evoking the magic of childhood to grant his wishes for an infinity of money, power, and egocentric good will. As Bertrand, the French mathematician, is quoted as saying, "How dare we speak of the law of chance? Is not chance the antithesis of all law?" [58]

Beyond these mathematical principles lies the usual arrangement of the "house" to make sure its odds are greater than mere probability. Against the obvious conclusion that the player "can't win" lie some interesting psychologic elements that push the compulsive gambler into his hopeless cul-de-sac. The addictive gambler sooner or later, becomes involved with an obsessive interest in "beating the house," "breaking the bank," or "wiping out" his opponent. At this point, ordinary competitiveness is replaced by hostility, welling up from a buried hatred of some overweening authority (father, God, Fate). The social gambler soon retreats from this position of incipient rage against the house, bank, opponent and quits his gambling. The compulsive gambler, angry at having lost but having entered the lists, cannot quit until he has surrendered to ruin and thus satisfy his masochistic urge to be vanquished. His rage is submerged in his vanity. From the infantile fantasy of "having all the money in the world," to the fantasy of forcing luck to obey one's magic wish and command, to the ensuing rage (and masochistic satisfaction) at losing, runs the whole psychologic gamut of the gambling neurosis.

All gamblers will agree that a time arrives in a given game when the gambler goes "wild" if he is in a winning streak and large amounts are involved. This may be rationalized by saying that one must "plunge," that one must "go for broke," that the time comes to "take a chance." It is at this point that the compulsive gambler's excitement is suggestive of the excitement of orgasm, that signs of physiological excitation (flushed face, perspiration, rapid breathing) are present, concentration becomes intense, and reality-considerations fade. Checks are signed, motorcars are consigned to cover loans, even houses have been mortgaged in the supreme excitement. Guilt vanishes; no one exists except the players and the game. Money loses its value as money; it becomes sheafs of paper or bits of metal. The compulsive gambler becomes obsessed with the idea that it is "my day," the moment he has sought all his life, the ineffable moment of union with Lilith, mother of the world—his world. Money, which is always a narcissistic reality partaking of a "mine" and "not mine" character, merges into a stream of commonality. Ego boundaries loosen and money is "deindividualized," no longer an intimate aspect of the ego. Its reality significance is lost.

At this stage the compulsive gambler can easily write checks with abandon. This curious dissociation arising at the height of the game was described by a member of Gamblers Anonymous (a group fashioned along the plan of Alcoholics Anonymous):

You act like you really want to win, and consciously you keep telling yourself you're going to hit the big score. But the funny thing is . . . maybe you're winning . . . yet you find yourself thinking of tomorrow's game.[59]

The phenomenon of loosened ego boundaries, for this is what happens in the "far-out" land of the excited gambler, touches a deep level in the developing ego. Psychoanalysts demonstrate that the child learns what is "mine" and "not mine" by the tortuous process of differentiating its body from the outside world. Fenichel notes that for the child "loss of feces, to him a precious substance, a part of his body" is replaced by other possessions that attain the meaning of "things that do not belong to me . . . but ought to. . . ." Hence the peculiar symbolic meaning of money as a precious aspect of one's body; it may suddenly change from an intimate possession to a despised external object. The significance in this explanation for the gambler's excitement is indicated by Fenichel:

What money and feces have in common is the fact that they are de-individualized possessions: and de-individualized means necessarily losable. Thus money, in the same way as was feces previously, is watched over as a possession which is in constant danger of losing its ego quality. Both substances, in spite of their high evaluation, are regarded with contempt. . . .[60]

One may well conclude that the gambler's excitement at winning (or losing) plunges deeply into unconscious layers of his psychic structure, thus far transcending the importance of what started as a game.

One may ask whether the social player, the "little player," necessarily passes through this Dantesque psychological inferno. The answer is, the little player does pass through the same unconscious conflict that assails the compulsive, neurotic player, but he provides the rationalization that he has not succumbed to the debacle, that he has been able to control himself. The little player takes his anxiety in small doses lest a greater anxiety impel him into the maelstrom of masochism. The kibitzer who seeks vicarious enjoyment outside the game is even more fearful to test his luck than the little player. His fun, too, has a twin function: it protects him from the wild onslaught of infantile frenzy that could overtake him if he allowed himself to enter the game fully; it channels off his aggression through exercising his wit and "playing at playing." He thus undergoes in miniature the player's anxiety, excitement, and guilt, but without the loosening of ego boundaries that besets the addictive gambler at the height of his excitement.

What of the man who does win, whose wishes for magic have been granted by the turn of the wheel? If he is a social gambler he accepts his beneficence, leaving the game elated. Even so, he is conscious of a craving to return and make the "big killing." In the compulsive gambler, no gain will satisfy him because his unconscious compulsion drives him to play on until a level of depression, self-degradation, and rage has been reached through eventual losses.

Nothing has been said up to this point about the psychology of an increasing number of women who engage in gambling at bridge clubs, race tracks, stock market, bingo rooms, and casinos in areas of legalized gambling. The observations noted concerning men pertain to women also, with the observable difference that the sexual implications in speech and thought do not apply. In general, women face the fact of gain or loss more directly. Addictive gamblers exist among women also. In these situations—as observed in Nevada casinos, for example—the same childlike expectation of outwitting Fate and the same intensity of anger at losing are present, with perhaps a less powerful drive toward "desperation betting." As a point of theoretical interest, the use by obsessive women gamblers of scatological, rather than sexual, expletives when losing may indicate that with them anal, rather than phallic, areas of the unconscious psyche are involved.

Where gambling has been legalized, the professional gambler is, as has been indicated, a practical psychologist, extracting his fee from the total "handle" in exchange for permitting the player freedom to indulge his masochistic urges. It would be supposed, then, that the professional is not burdened with guilt or anxiety since, in theory, he is performing a sociopsychological service. Experience shows, however, that a man who has been associated with gambling during his entire adult lifetime is not able to escape the all-pervading feelings of infantile magic and omnipotence that invest the compulsive gambler. According to a recent book by Ray Smith, owner of Harold's Club in Reno, and a highly successful games operator, these feelings, hiding under reliance on intuition and experience, are recognizable:

Gambling in any of its forms creates thrills. It is wired with tension. The sex act itself can never be as thrilling to some people as the sensation of winning, of making the right decision. . . . There's another time when you better get out of the game. That's when you feel anger. . . . Oh, I guarantee you can get angry in a crap game. When you're playing big money and the dice seven out, you feel the fury explode.[61]

When the hardheaded operator shifts his role to that of player, the total panorama of the gambler's unequal struggle with Fate appears in its full display of excitement, anxiety, anger, and reliance on the evanescent law of probabilities:

Lady Luck comes and goes. She tries to hit most of us. . . . She does, however, seem to admire the confident person who has brought himself to her table with a clear and win-conditioned mind. . . . The expert gambler believes implicitly in the supernatural and develops his extrasensory perception to its ultimate keenness. . . . Hunches and ESP are closely intertwined, and good hunches are worth money in the bank.[62]

In areas where gambling is illegal and cheating and increasing the "angle" is prevalent, the professional is more apt to be a clearly psychopathic personality of the swindler type; these are men who are psychologically impelled to larcenous enterprises of one kind or another.

It is not fortuitous that gambling has been included in a chapter devoted to forms of larceny. For in the last analysis the accretion of money is the basic purpose of both activities. No matter what the underlying psychology of these acts may be, both the gambler and the larcenist entertain the intent of acquisitive aggression. Since in both cases the activities are prohibited, the intent can be said to lie on criminal substrata. What is said here, in effect, is that gambling provides a channel for the exercise of normal larcenous impulses. This may explain why gambling carries a lighter legal sanction than does theft, although it still bears a quasi-criminal connotation. In the common view, gambling lies between a vice and a crime. But the technique and atmosphere of gambling are that of "play"; for this reason the voice of conscience, echoing from the long ago, translates the larcenous intent inherent in the play to that of winning the game. Gambling thus detoxifies and humanizes criminal intent masquerading as greed. In doing this, it is assisted by a minimum of legal sanctions.

BIGAMY—LARCENY OF LOVE

The psychologic characteristics of bigamists remind one of the subverted (passive) aggression of the psychopathic personality. It is not meant that sexual deviation lies behind the crime of bigamy; rather, a subtle destructiveness is the basic hidden motivation.

Fitzgerald, an English lawyer, comments, "Bigamy is in reality an offense against the marriage ceremony"[63]—not against the sexual mores of the area in which the bigamy occurs. The motive for bigamy is that of subverted aggression, hiding under sexual or romantic allure. Whether he is aware of it or not, the male bigamist has an unconscious interest in injuring both wives; the cream of the jest is that neither wife is aware of the bigamy until the offense comes to light. Bigamy in most cases rests upon an incomplete resolution of a neurotic problem in the perpetrator, or is in the service of a fraudulent plan to control legacies, gain capital for investments, or, in a foreigner, to secure citizen status. The sexual aspect of bigamy is a convenience, more closely representing normal than perverted sexuality.

Study of male bigamists reveals them to be either emotionally immature individuals, or swindlers for whom multiple marriages are merely techniques for appropriating money from women. Hence, bigamy is less a result of excessive sexual passion than it is an unconscious search for the ideal wife who represents a mother-figure to the neurotic bigamist. The characteristic history of a bigamist is that of a man who, while separated from his wife because of emotional disharmony or sexual incompatibility, meets and marries another girl in whom he sees the embodiment of all the characteristics he cherishes in a woman; or he may rationalize his impulsive action by declaring that he was answering his second wife's crying need for a protector, or he may marry during an alcoholic orgy. The psychological motive behind this apparently romantic behavior is that of emotional dependence. The one woman is overvalued, the other undervalued by the offender according to the strength of his dependency needs and the degree of his marital frustration.

The man who contracts a bigamous marriage through deceit displays an interesting variation of the psychological mechanisms outlined above. This type of offense is initiated by a claim of position or wealth. Here the bigamous marriage has as its aim the acquisition of control of the second wife's money. This form of bigamy (see discussion of swindling) involves unconscious hostility toward both women. The money gained is one source of ego gratification in the swindler-bigamy; another is the witnessing of pain and humiliation in both wives. The case of Francis P., convicted of grand larceny on six counts, illustrates in part the psychodynamic elements in the swindler-bigamist.

At the age of twenty-six a successful securities salesman, Francis joined a group who operated an international money-pool subscribed to by German-Americans, and calculated to effect a devaluation of the French franc. The appeal to the patriotic bias of the subscribers received impetus from the rising tide of National Socialism in Germany at that time (1930s). Writing to influential German-Americans all over the country, the operators of the pool promised a high rate of interest to subscribers. Within a short time funds for the purchase of French francs poured in. People literally begged the backers of the pool to take their money. Over a period of two years the syndicate widened its lure from the promise of a monthly rate of interest of 8 per cent to plans for marketing a machine that would transmute base metals into gold.

A few years before the offense for which he was now being examined, Francis had been arrested for bigamy,[64] having married a radio singer, Althea, without legally terminating a marriage of ten years. He had neglected his first wife since he became engaged in the stock swindle. After he promised marriage to Althea, he produced spurious divorce papers, which erased any doubts she may have had. During the period preceding their marriage he caused Althea considerable inconvenience by ordering house furnishings paid for with worthless checks. Following the marriage, a charge of bigamy was brought. He was given a sentence of five years but was placed on probation.

The average bigamist does not usually show such an intensity of criminal mechanisms; he is apt to be a heedless, careless individual, either psychopathic or enmeshed in an insoluble neurotic conflict. A grotesque example to illustrate the union of neurotic and psychopathic behavior operative in bigamy is that of a young woman who married eight times and lived with several paramours.[65]

At the age of thirteen, Iris, fair-haired and blue-eyed, became acquainted with a gypsy near her home in Massachusetts. With the consent of her mother, she married him. For two weeks, they lived together; there was no sexual life and she left him promptly. At sixteen years of age, Iris bigamously married her second husband, Jim, who became the father of her four children. She was very happy for the first several years, but brooded over her first marriage. Married life with Jim became tiresome, a constant round of drudgery and care of the children. Her husband earned only a small salary and she had a yearning for pretty clothes and travel.

The doctor who delivered one of her children talked to Iris of his regret that " a girl of her age" should be so harassed. By this time, she and her husband were very much in debt; they talked it over and decided to separate. The home was broken up, and Iris went out with the sympathetic doctor on several occasions. Presently she ran off to New York. There she met Joseph E. in a hotel and speedily married him. After six weeks she left him precipitately and returned to her husband, telling him nothing of her escapade. Their marital life was resumed, a fifth child was born, and a normal life course was pursued for a year and a half. Then Iris suddenly left home with a former schoolmate, Claude, whom she married. After a few weeks she left him. By now, Iris had contracted marriage with four men. When she again came home to Jim, he accepted her without question. Soon she fell into intimate relations with Thomas. "It was just an affair, but I couldn't get rid of him. . . . I went away again, with Thomas." "Going away" meant to Iris being married. Disheartened, she soon went back to Jim, who, still unaware of her interim marriages, took her in again.

(The children had meanwhile been sent to a foster home.) Iris presently met a William H., an Englishman, and a Mr. C., both of whom she married in due succession.

On her next return home, Iris, at the age of twenty-five, had been married six or seven times. She was arrested on the charge of polyandry. After serving fourteen months of her fifteen-month sentence, Iris ran away from the reformatory to the city, where she met a Fred N. and promptly married him. In the building where they lived was another roomer, William W.; during her second month of marriage to Fred, William "forced her to marry him," although he knew she was already married. Aside from the eight marriages (it was difficult to rely on Iris's account), there were other liaisons, such as the one with Charles G., with whom she lived for a time in a common-law relationship.

The offender's life story indicated significant factors in the development of her neurotic behavior. She was an only child of parents who themselves were in constant emotional difficulties. The rejection of the child by both parents was an outstanding feature of Iris's early life. Her training ran along unusual, almost unnatural, lines that reflected her mother's indifference. The latter was particular about having the child immaculately dressed on all occasions, keeping her from natural and spontaneous association with other children. But this attention was superficial and concerned mostly with externals. The father was distant and never showed her any affection. The parents were divorced when Iris was twenty-two years old.

From Iris's account of her polyandry, one received the definite impression that she looked on her liaisons as play-marriages. Sexual attraction was a secondary factor in these relationships. For example, in speaking of Claude, she said: "Claude was good to me; he treated me like a little girl, bought me candy and presents, and finally asked if I wanted to marry him. I agreed. It was the only church wedding I had. I had a beautiful white dress, a great big bunch of orchids." Throughout the marriage history there runs a note of emotional emptiness; no one man was satisfactory because no one marriage was real. She spoke of sexual satisfaction only in connection with Jim; in the other marriages, sexual feelings played little part in the relationship. Her husbands were men who "took care of her"; the images of the men as husbands were confused and shadowy. Each marriage seemed to mirror the childlike atmosphere of her first marriage to the gypsy, which her mother did nothing to prevent or disrupt, even approved. The psychological significance of her plural marriages had more to do with her mother than with her husbands. This caricature of obedience to her mother's wishes, *i.e.*, that she marry the gypsy (the first husband), was an illusory mode of securing a mother's love that was never available. Iris's marriages were continuing efforts in her search for approving, protecting, loving parents.

REFERENCES

1. *Penal Code, State of California, West's Annotated Code,* Sec. 459 (Burglary defined) (West Publishing Co., St. Paul, Minn.).

2. BLACKSTONE, SIR WILLIAM, *Commentaries on the Laws of England,* George Chose, ed., 3rd ed. (Banks and Brothers, Albany, N.Y., 1890), p. 224.

3. CLARK, WILLIAM L., and MARSHALL, WILLIAM L., *A Treatise on the Law of Crimes,* Melvin F. Wingersky, ed., 6th ed. (Callaghan & Co., Chicago, Ill., 1958), p. 892.

4. *Annual Report,* Psychiatric Clinic, Supreme Court, Criminal Division, County of New York, 1962.

5. BERGLER, EDMUND, *Basic Neurosis* (Grune & Stratton, New York, 1949), pp. 304 ff.

6. WITHERS, SAMUEL, "Putting the Label on Stealing," *The New York Times Magazine,* July 21, 1963, p. 49.

7. *People* vs. *Kane* [sic], State of Calif., Sup. Ct., County of Sacramento, Cr., 1959.

8. BLOCH, HERBERT A., and GEIS, GILBERT, *Man, Crime and Society* (Random House, New York, 1962), p. 320.

9. GIBBONS, DON C., and GARRITY, DONALD L., "Some Suggestions for the Definition of Etiological and Treatment Theory in Criminology," quoted in Bloch and Geis, *ibid.,* p. 321.

10. Personal communication to the author, Court of General Sessions, New York, 1935–41.

11. Anonymous, *A Professional Thief,* Edwin Sutherland, ed. (University of Chicago Press, Chicago, 1937).

12. BLACK, SUSAN, "Burglary," in "A Reporter at Large," *The New Yorker,* December 7, 14, 1963, vol. 39, p. 63.

13. *People* vs. *John Micelli* [sic], County of New York, Court of General Sessions, N.Y., Ind. #17025, 1938.

14. *Ibid.,* Ind. #226460, 1941.

15. *Ibid.,* Ind. #280648, 1948.

16. *Ibid.,* Ind. #3425–52, 1952.

17. *Ibid.,* Ind. #5–58, 1958.

18. PERKINS, ROLLIN M., *Criminal Law* (Foundation Press, Brooklyn, N.Y., 1957), p. 173.

19. CLARK and MARSHALL, *op. cit.,* p. 900.

20. LEWIS, NOLAN D. C., and YARNELL, HELEN, *Pathological Firesetting,* Monograph #82 (Nervous and Mental Disease Publishing Co., Washington, D.C., 1951).

21. STEKEL, WILHELM, *Peculiarities of Behavior: Dipsomania, Cleptomania. . . . ,* Vol. 21 (Liveright Publishing Co., New York, 1924).

22. FREUD, SIGMUND, *The Acquisition of Power of Fire,* in *Collected Works,* Vol. 5 (Hogarth Press, London, 1950), p. 289.

23. *People* vs. *George* [sic], State of New York, County of New York, Court of General Sessions, 1938.

24. Personal files, 1955.

25. MICHAEL, JEROME, and WECHSLER, HERBERT, *Criminal Law and Its Administration* (Foundation Press, Brooklyn, N.Y., 1940), pp. 401 ff.

26. FITZGERALD, F. J., *Criminal Law and Punishment* (Clarendon Press, Oxford, 1962), pp. 37, 39.

27. SUTHERLAND, EDWIN H., *White-Collar Crime* (Dryden Press, New York, 1949).

28. CLINARD, MARSHALL B., *Sociology of Deviant Behavior* (Rinehart & Co., New York, 1958), p. 158.

29. SUTHERLAND, EDWIN H., "White-Collar Criminality," *American Sociological Review*, V, No. 1 (February, 1940).

30. LAGACHE, DANIEL, "The Psychoanalysis of a Gangster," *Archives of Criminal Psychodynamics*, I (1955), 833.

31. Personal files, 1962.

32. MICHAEL and WECHSLER, *op. cit.*, pp. 415 ff.

33. ABRAHAM, KARL, "The History of an Imposter in the Light of Psychoanalytic Knowledge," trans. by A. Strachey, *Psychoanalytic Quarterly*, IV (1935), 570.

34. GREENACRE, PHYLLIS, "The Imposter," *Psychoanalytic Quarterly*, XXVII (1958), 359.

35. *People* vs. *Rachel Adams* [sic], State of New York, County of New York, Court of General Sessions, 1941.

36. BROMBERG, WALTER, and KEISER, SYLVAN, "A Psychological Study of The Swindler," *American Journal of Psychiatry*, XCIV, No. 6 (1938), 1441.

37. *People* vs. *Stein* [sic], State of New York, County of New York, Court of General Sessions, 1941.

38. New York *Herald Tribune*, October 17, 1941.

39. *People* vs. *Terence* [sic], State of New York, County of New York, Court of General Sessions, 1938.

40. *People* vs. *DeMarcot* [sic], State of California, County of Sacramento, Superior Court, 1960.

41. CLECKLEY, HERVEY, *The Mask of Sanity* (C. V. Mosby Co., St. Louis, Mo., 1950), p. 407.

42. *People* vs. *Button* [sic], State of California, County of Yolo, Superior Court, 1955.

43. Juvenile Court, State of Michigan, Probation Department, the Department of Corrections, 1947.

44. *People* vs. *Neil Farley* [sic], State of California, County of Nevada, Superior Court, 1962.

45. *People* vs. *Christopher Paige* [sic], U.S. District Court for N. Calif., CN 13178, 1961.

46. GORER, GEOFFREY, "British Life—It's a Gamble," *The New York Times Magazine*, September 1, 1963, p. 10.

47. Quoted from Wilhelm Stekel, *Peculiarities of Behavior*, trans. by J. S. Van Teslaar, (Liveright Publishing Co., New York, 1924), p. 233.

48. *Penal Law, McKinney's Consolidated Laws of New York, Annotated* (Edward Thompson Co., Brooklyn, N.Y., 1944), Book 39, Sec. 970.

49. *People* vs. *Revolta,* 162 Misc. 555, 295, New York, 102 (1937).

50. Securities and Exchange Act, enacted June 6, 1934, U.S. Congress.

51. FREUD, SIGMUND, *Dostoyevsky and Parricide,* in *Collected Papers,* Vol. V (Hogarth Press, London, 1950), p. 240.

52. BERGLER, EDMUND, "The Gambler: a Misunderstood Neurotic," *Journal of Criminal Psychopathology,* IV (1943), 370.

53. GREENSON, RALPH, "On Gambling," *American Imago,* IV, No. 2 (1948), 3.

54. LINDNER, ROBERT M., "The Psychodynamics of Gambling," *Annals of the American Academy of Political and Social Science* (May, 1950), p. 93.

55. Personal files, 1949.

56. NAGEL, ERNEST, *Probabilities,* in *The World of Mathematics,* Vol. II, James R. Newman, ed. (Simon & Schuster, New York, 1956), p. 1410.

57. NEWMAN, JAMES R., Introduction to *The World of Mathematics,* Vol. III, *ibid.,* p. 1448.

58. POINCARÉ, HENRI, "The Laws of Chance," in *The World of Mathematics,* Vol. III, *ibid.,* p. 1380.

59. Personal communication to the author, 1961.

60. FENICHEL, OTTO, *Psychoanalytic Theory of Neurosis* (W. W. Norton & Co., New York, 1945), p. 281.

61. SMITH, RAY, with JOHN W. NOBLE, *I Want To Quit Winners* (Prentice-Hall, Englewood Cliffs, N.J., 1960), pp. 77, 248.

62. *Ibid.,* pp. 253, 269.

63. FITZGERALD, P. J., *op cit.,* p. 77.

64. *People* vs. *Francis P.* [*sic*], State of New York, County of New York, Court of General Sessions, 1936.

65. *People* vs. *Iris* [*sic*], State of New York, County of New York, Court of General Sessions, 1935.

Homosexuality and Sexual Crime

The Crime–as–Behavior classification suggested in Chapter IV includes as a third group offenses arising from psychophysiological stresses of various types. Criminal behavior within this behavioral category lies in close relation to body needs. This means that the impulse and motivation for the crimes arise not from aggressive or furtive-aggressive modalities, but from the needs and instinctual cravings of the body. It might be repeated here that within the three behavioral groups—(1) *aggressive in motivation;* (2) *passive-aggressive in motivation;* (3) *related to psychophysiological stresses*—overlapping occurs. For example, murders have been described in which sexual tensions (stresses) are basic to the crime in question; sex crimes have demonstrated the form of passive aggression; and drug addicts, impelled by physiological craving for drugs, have (in rare instances) shown naked aggression in their crimes. Nevertheless, these three crime-as-behavior groupings represent a practical approach to a discussion of the panorama of criminal phenomenology.

In embarking on a scrutiny of the third group, it can scarcely be questioned that sexual crimes constitute the largest subgroup of psychophysiologic crime, others being crimes related to narcotic drugs. The problem of sex crime, besides being interwoven with aspects of "normal" sexuality, is intimately concerned with the field of sexual psychopathology. This intimate relationship, however, is subject to calibration, for all sexual psychopathology is not necessarily criminal in intent, and not all sexual crime depends on sexual pathology. In this section, sexual psychopathology will be discussed principally in relation to sexual crime.

Preliminarily, as a matter of orientation, the field of sexual aberration will be surveyed, with its social implications. It is significant that social attitudes toward sexuality—aberrant and normal alike—already fixed in the social "mind" more than five thousand years ago, have become firmly encased in the criminal law.

There shall be no whore of the daughters of Israel, nor a sodomite of the sons of Israel. (Deut. 23:18)

As a consequence, the varieties and phenomenology of sexual crime were rarely discussed, being virtually sealed into the law until the pioneer sexologists, Krafft-Ebing, Havelock Ellis, and others, opened the field to medical purview in the 1890's. The early material was thin, obscurely stated behind Latinisms, and, in Karpman's words, "almost sterile." [1] The literature on sex crimes was similarly thin and purely descriptive until the 1920's when, under the impact of Freudianism, discussion of sexual crime and sexual deviation became dynamic in orientation. This new field of sexual psychopathology [2] was to exert far-reaching influences on public attitudes, and on judicial and penologic handling of sexual "degenerates," but in Freud's time the idea of probing into the loathsome depths of perverse sexuality shocked psychiatric and legal experts alike. Pierre Janet, the leading French psychologist of the period, complained of Freud's methods:

It [psychoanalysis] is a criminal investigation which aims at the discovery of a culprit in the unearthing of past happenings. . . . it is more the work of a detective than a psychiatrist.[3]

The law itself regarded sexual crime with disdain, having little interest in its ramifications within the soul of man. This disinterest in, and passive dislike of, sexual crime has been indicated by a legal scholar (Wingersky) in a passage of judicial majesty written in 1958:

Planted by superstition and watered by ignorance the taproots of our criminal law concerning sex offenders and offenses lie deeply embedded in a compost of religious notions of sin and legal ideas of crime.[4]

SEX CRIME AND SEXUAL DEVIATION

It might be pertinent here to summarize briefly what is meant by the term sexual deviate and what its criminal reflections may be. A deviate, strictly speaking, is one who has come to the attention of law-enforcement authorities for sexual misbehavior. Until he is apprehended—either charged or convicted of a sexual crime—his deviation is unknown to society, except in the case of those homosexuals who blatantly exhibit their predilections in public.

"Sexual deviate" is the modern equivalent of "sexual pervert" and of the older and unnecessarily harsh term "sexual degenerate." In general, it refers to anyone whose sexual satisfaction is obtained from practices other than heterosexual intercourse. Even this general definition is not all-inclusive because masturbation, which confers sexual gratification, is not classified as a sexual deviation if it occurs in the absence of adequate and available sexual objects.

The most prevalent and important deviation is *homosexuality*: this refers to sexual relations between two adults of the same sex. Sexual contact between male adolescents is not properly classified as homosexual because they may not be followed by adult homosexual relations. There are many synonyms for homosexuals: "inverts" "gay" (the one preferred by homosexuals themselves), "queers," "fairies," and so on. Among women homosexuals, the term "Lesbian," or "lesbo," is most common, while the term "dyke," or "bull dyker," is in vulgar usage. The actual activities of homosexuals consist of pederasty (anal intercourse), oral copulation, and mutual masturbation. In legal phraseology, the term *sodomy* usually covers fellatio, cunnilingus, and anal intercourse, whether performed on male or female.

Child molesters, or *pedophiles* (literally child-lovers), represent the next most significant class of sexual deviates. These are male persons who obtain sexual gratification by palpating, or sexually playing, with minor female children, or having children palpate them; male persons who perform homosexual acts on male children also fall into this class. Peeping Toms (*voyeurs*) are also classed as sexual deviates if their gratification is obtained by witnessing a woman disrobing or by observing sexual activity by others; masturbation may accompany the viewing of these acts. This deviation is, as might be expected, more frequent (but not exclusively so) among young men, as is *exhibitionism*, which consists of presenting the sexual organ to an unsuspecting female without contact. This activity also may be accompanied by masturbation at the time or soon after.

Sadists and *masochists* are also classed as deviates. The former are more apt to come to attention as a result of criminal activity; the latter, during the treatment of neurotics for other nervous problems. The enjoyment of sexual satisfaction through sadistic activity is generally found in psychopaths, whereas masochistic satisfaction is more common in neurotics. *Flagellation* is an aspect of masochism. *Fetishism* is a type of deviation in which a male obtains sexual gratification from an object worn by a woman, as, shoes, underwear, stockings, and the like.

Transvestism, dressing in clothes of the opposite sex, is accounted a deviation whether worn on festive occasions at a homosexual "drag" (party) or in private. *Frottage,* which consists of obtaining gratification from rubbing against clothed women, as in a subway crowd, is a type of deviation not seriously considered by the law, as is *goosing* which, incidentally, may release an uncontrollable compulsion in the victim to shout obscene words at the moment of the attack (coprolalia).

The rarer types of deviation—*bestiality,* sexual relations with animals; *necrophilia,* sexual relations with a corpse—are encountered occasionally, as are various types of *self-flagellation,* such as whippings, bindings, and crushings that are inflicted for their capacity to provide sexual gratification. *Pornography,* in writing or in the graphic arts, may be classified as a sexual deviation if it serves more than the usual sexual curiosity, *i.e.,* is an end in itself. These deviations may or may not be considered criminal acts; their criminal reflections will be discussed in detail later.

There are, moreover, aspects of normal sexuality that involve crime: *incest* and *rape* are such practices. It has been customary to include *bigamy* among sexual crimes, but with little justification. Essentially, bigamy is a violation of a civil contract and a religious covenant; hence, it would seem to have little to do with sexual deviation (see Chapter VIII). Finally, *fornication,* still prohibited by statute in a few states (as, Massachusetts),[5] and *adultery,* regarded in New York [6] and in most other states as a misdemeanor, complete the sexual crimes, the latter two being obviously related to normal heterosexuality.

In a discussion of sexual deviation, it is of interest that historical-social attitudes toward sexual expression have had much to do with the construction of laws governing sexual offenses. Ploscowe, who has traced the evolution of the law of sexual crimes, notes that the common law in England took a "comparatively liberal attitude toward sex expression. . . . Fornication was no crime. . . . Adultery was not a punishable offense [but] the sanctions of the common law were invoked when sex activity created public scandal . . . [or] outraged decency. . . ." Until about 1650, Ploscowe adds, "incest, fellatio, cunnilingus, adultery, fornication, and mutual masturbation could be brought before the Ecclesiastical Court of the Church of England"; [7] after this date these acts were made capital (statutory) offenses. Judging by the sanctions applied, the seriousness of these offenses remains imbedded in the law, but modern attitudes toward sex expression have removed some of their sinful connotation. For example, the present attitude toward partial impulses, including touching, rubbing, sucking, kissing—normal elements in sexual forepleasure—has given these activities a nondeviate connotation. Otherwise, sexual maneuvers that tend to excite and stimulate intercourse might be viewed, apart from the act, as deviations. Nevertheless, though regarded tolerantly by the population, such activities may still be subject to criminal investigation if charged by an outraged partner or exposed to public view. As a matter of fact, the total panorama of sexual activity is far from codified in the law with any particularity or precision.

The range of deviation that comes into conflict with the law must be viewed in terms of the tremendous social changes that have affected sexual mores and morals since early in the century. Starting with Krafft-Ebing and Freud, and continuing through Kinsey, varieties of sexual behavior have become matters for psychologists and sociologists to investigate with the same freedom accorded other problems of biology. The present age of sexual freedom for both sexes, since World War II, itself merits a large chapter to describe its extent adequately. Yet, in spite of this revolutionary social change, even Kinsey,[8] the intrepid investigator of sexuality, found it expedient to defend his "right to investigate" male and female sexual behavior because of the tremendous resistance by a public steeped in Western culture to opening any investigation of these "forbidden" areas. Until recent years, the Judaeo-Christian code of moral conduct has had so strong a repressive influence on thought devoted to sexual deviation that an objective view of these psychobiologic phenomena is an emotionally trying experience for society.

There is another complicating factor in this area: the relationship between specific sexual deviation and specific crimes. Homosexuals who engage youths as partners are criminally liable for a felony, whereas if they engage in homosexual acts with persons over twenty-one they are potential misdemeanants; if discreet, they remain unrecognized or unapprehended. Homosexuality in a public place is a crime, whereas if it is carried out in private, without witnesses, it carries no legal penalty.

Legally, homosexual offenses fall into several ill-defined categories: (a) adult homosexual relations, a misdemeanor in many jurisdictions, as, indecency or vagrancy in New York;[9] (b) homosexual relations with a minor, a felony, termed sodomy or impairing morals of a minor, also crimes against nature;[10] (c) male prostitution, a misdemeanor, listed as vagrancy in New York, California, and other areas. In California, a general charge of vagrancy may be made against any type of sexual misconduct not amounting to a felony.[11] ("Every idle, or lewd or dissolute person . . . is a vagrant and punishable by a fine . . . or imprisonment in the county jail. . . .") As noted, the difficulties in relating sexual deviations to specific sexual crimes are compounded by a generally hazy concept of the technical term "sexual psychopath." It would be clarifying, therefore, before embarking on the description of specific cases, to elucidate the meaning of the phrase.

WHAT IS A SEXUAL PSYCHOPATH?

From a medical point of view, the sexual psychopath forms one sub-type of the diagnostic classification "psychopathic personality" or, as more recently stated, "sociopathic personality." The sexual deviate falls into the clinical class of psychopaths *if* his deviation is fixed in his personality structure, even though fixity of deviation within the personality is itself a debatable question.

Many states have passed laws aimed at isolating sexual cases from the general criminal population in their institutions; to eventuate this, a delimiting definition is required. The State of California (whose laws in the main correspond to those of New York State and are similar to those of other states) defines a sexual psychopath as one

. . . who is affected in a form predisposing to the commission of sexual offenses and in a degree constituting him a menace to the health or safety of others.

Further characteristics set forth in this legal definition are that he has involved

. . . a child under the age of fourteen in a sexual act . . . or has had a previous sexual offense . . . or [as listed in codes of other states, as Wisconsin, Illinois, etc.] has uncontrollable impulses towards abnormal sexual acts.[12]

A report from the Group for the Advancement of Psychiatry, a commitee that made a thorough study of the subject, offers this definition:

A sexual psychopath . . . is guilty of repetitive, compulsive acts . . . carried out to the point of community intolerance . . . manifesting a heedless disregard of consequences . . . seeking to attain ultimate expression even if momentary obstacles are encountered.[13]

The term sexual psychopath, then, legally circumscribes certain behavioral characteristics and attitudes; the diagnosis is determined by psychiatrists interpreting emotional reactions within the terms of the legal definition. In most jurisdictions, after a petition or complaint concerning the sexual psychopathy of an offender is filed, a provisional diagnosis is made by two or three psychiatrists appointed by the court. In addition, reports of probation officers and social workers are presented to the court, which makes the final pronouncement of the presence or absence of sexual psychopathy in a given offender. The right of commitment to a specified institution lies solely in the hands of a judge of a court of record. Some statutes prescribe that the superintendent of the state hospital to which the offender is committed is responsible to the judge for a final opinion of the sexual psychopathy of the subject-offender. From this brief sketch of the legal process, it can be seen how the courts and psychiatrists establish the medicolegal fact that a given sexual deviate is by legal definition a "sexual psychopath."

The chief purpose of thus designating an offender a "sexual psychopath" (after examination has established this) is to undertake his treatment and rehabilitation, to segregate him from society at large and from the main body of offenders in a penal institution or state hospital, and to prevent further sexual crime. There is another reason to establish the psychopathy of certain offenders, namely, their availability thereafter for interrogation in unsolved sex crimes. The State Criminal Identification and Investigation Bureau in California, for example, maintains a file to enable law-enforcement officers to recognize diagnosed sexual psychopaths who are at large and available for questioning when a sexual crime has been committed.[14]

There have been varied reports as to the success of programs for treatment of these offenders. Later in this chapter, an extended discussion will be given of a treatment program initiated by the present writer in a California State Hospital. Since laws relating to the sexual psychopath have a relatively brief history (about 25 years), categorical statements as to results cannot be made. In 1958, Dr. Karl Bowman and Bernice Engle [15] (the former influential in implementing California's Sex Psychopath law) reported on cases treated in 1956 from Atascadero State Hospital (Calif.). Of those released from treatment, about 7.4 per cent repeated their sex offenses within a year; 6.5 per cent were also recidivistic, but in other than sexual offenses. The survey of the results of treatment in another state (Colorado) indicated that the same percentage, 7 per cent, of discharged patient-deviates were returned to prison or hospital. This degree of control of sexual deviation as reflected in arrests for sexual crime, although not extended over a long period, indicated the relative success of such treatment programs. Bowman and Engle made the comment that "with the rise of more and better treatment facilities (1958) has gone the trend against singling out the sexual psychopath" for rehabilitation. The California Legislature reacted to this trend by altering the law to change the designation "sex psychopath" to "mentally disordered sex offender." [16] This change in accent from relative indifference and hopelessness to a cautious optimism in the treatment of homosexuals and other deviates is reflected in the recent comment (1963) by a director of a state department of mental hygiene that

[Since] 1939, when the original sex psychopath law was enacted . . . we have gained considerable experience which indicates that certain individuals are helped by hospital treatment and others are not.[17]

As might be expected, sexual psychopath laws have been attacked on grounds of their constitutionality. An appeal was brought in New Hampshire in 1945 contending that that state's act was too ambiguous, too general in wording, and that consequently "the policy and purpose of the act could be abused and severely applied to minor sex deviations." It was further contended that measures to "provide for indeterminate segregation and treatment" were unconstitutional. On review (1950), the Appeals Court held that although the "validity of the definition of a sexual psychopath" would not be passed on, the constitionality of the act was upheld. The reason set forth was:

The act seeks to benefit society as well as the person involved within the framework of a special statutory method which is civil rather than criminal and which attempts to cure and prevent rather than to punish.[18]

Growing psychiatric interest in sexual deviation during the past three decades has reduced some of the contumely to which society has subjected this group of offenders. This has been reflected in the courts, which have been agreeable to entertaining the notion that sexual offenders are suitable material for psychotherapy and psychiatric study. For example, the attitude of the Criminal Court Bench in Baltimore, as reported by Guttmacher,[19] reflects the present attitude of most enlightened judges. The conclusions reached by Guttmacher agree in the main with those of this author and his associates at the Supreme Court, Criminal Division, New York County, and in the Superior Courts in California regarding judicial attitudes toward sex offenders. Guttmacher's comments on the attitude of the Criminal Court in Baltimore toward sexual offenses during the twenty-five years preceding 1955 may be summarized as follows:

Sexual offenders are individuals who should be referred for a psychiatric report.

Sexual offenses entered into willingly by two adults are viewed benignly, unless public affront is involved or unless one of the individuals is aggressive.

Sexual offenses by adults with children are viewed rather benignly if the adults are beyond fifty-five years; they are treated more harshly if the offender is younger. . . .

Sexual crimes of violence are treated as very serious offenses.

Incest is considered one of the more grievous sex offenses.

Exhibitionism is considered of minor importance.

The initial aims of this newer orientation toward sexual offenders included the segregation of dangerous sexual deviates. As psychiatric studies illuminated these little-understood persons, the notion of treatment gained acceptance by society. Of the entire group of deviates, the homosexual appeared to represent the least danger to society and treatment possibilities opened up readily. Admission for therapy of the "degenerate" who preyed on minors (for example, the pedophile) met with greater resistance. It would be fair to state that in the sexual revolution, of which tolerance to deviates formed but one aspect, the homosexual, forming the most significant sector of deviancy, was the first to find reluctant social acceptance.

CLINICAL PROFILE OF THE HOMOSEXUAL

Clinical types of homosexuals vary widely. Dr. Karpman [20] makes a distinction between homosexuals with respect to oral or anal predilections, but this is not a true clinical distinction. Actually, a classification based on technique, predilections, and so on is of little moment. From a social point of view, there are conservative and promiscuous homosexuals, the former seeking and maintaining lifelong relationships with a given man or woman, as the case may be, the latter choosing one partner after another.

The technique of male homosexuality consists of kissing, sucking the penis (oral activities), and pederasty (anal intercourse). There are many variations in this activity: for example, some homosexuals are fixated on the feet or buttocks of their partners; some perform intracrural or axillary intercourse (the groin or armpit). Among female homosexuals, the techniques are similar, with obvious biological differences. Here, as Havelock Ellis pointed out long ago, embracing and passionate kissing provide much sexual excitement among female homosexuals. In both male and female groups, mutual masturbation is a frequent practice.

In this country, the apparent increase in homosexuality in recent years has motivated the "educated guess" by many involved with these persons that 2 per cent of the male population are, or have been, homosexual in their activity, whereas fewer than 1 per cent of the female population have been so involved. A 1957 report by Cambridge University's Department of Criminal Science [21] indicated that 15 per cent of all homosexual offenders in England were undetected, the total homosexual population being estimated at half a million (approximately 1.5 per cent). In England there was a visible increase in homosexuals during and immediately after World War II, because they were more blatant in their activity. This aroused English law-enforcement officers to attempt further control, which, in turn, led to an estimation of their numbers.

As stated above, one can only guess at the undetected number of homosexual offenders in this country. Kinsey has reported (1953) that 4 per cent of American adult white males are "exclusively homosexual throughout their lives after the onset of adolescence," [22] a figure much higher than earlier estimates. According to Kinsey, between 30 and 45 per cent of American males have engaged in homosexual activity on occasion. However, it must be borne in mind that a high proportion of youths engaging in homosexual acts relinquish the practice in their late twenties. Of these, a small number function as male prostitutes for purely mercenary ends; others engage in homosexual practices for the novelty experienced and still others because of neurotic fears of girls and women, or during a period of enforced abstinence (as in prison or reformatories or in military installations). In regard to penal institutions, most authorities agree that as many as 85 per cent of prison inmates [23] engage in "one form or other of homoerotic activity"— this, of course, in a population under emotional privation. In general, the figure of 2 per cent would constitute a more conservative estimate of the number of active homosexuals in the United States. In this discussion, it should be noted that a practicing homosexual (according to police records) may be either a confirmed, a casual, or even a once-in-a-lifetime deviate. He becomes an offender only when he is caught *flagrante delicto*, or in a compromising position.

A few comments concerning the psychology and life practices of homosexuals may make their position as criminals more understandable. The homosexual, or "gay" person, lives in an esoteric environment of his own making. He may live in that environment without interference for years, or leave his group and pick up youths for sexual purposes and thus become involved with the law. Further, there are bisexual persons who maintain a home and a wife, but whose latent homosexual feeling seeks extramarital expression from time to time with male partners. The life pattern of the bisexual individual varies widely: he may have given up a life of homosexuality and adopted marriage under social pressure; he may find satisfaction with both men and women; or he may derive greater gratification (as, stronger potency) with a homosexual partner than with a wife. Hence, bisexual persons often resort to the former when under stress or anxiety, or merely as an occasional secret "fling." Karpman has pointed out that the bisexual person, under constant social pressure to adopt heterosexuality, carries in his psyche a deep, pervasive inner need for homosexual indulgence. Conversely, Fenichel states that "most homosexuals cannot so easily free themselves of their normal biological longing for women." [24] Or, as Bieber, a recent student of the subject, has put it: "In our view, every homosexual is in reality a 'latent' heterosexual." [25] Fenichel, in justification of this formula, explains that when the homosexual is attracted to boys or fair youths he is succumbing to his interest in femininity, albeit femininity in an organism equipped with a penis. This subtle psychologic situation appears to underlie the excitement that the transvestite arouses in the homosexual—the combination of female clothing outside and, concealed beneath it, the male organ. In this situation, sexual excitement derives from two unconscious sources simultaneously.

The ever-present conflict within the homosexual, one which continues subterraneously in spite of his protests about being a "born" homosexual, is best depicted in his spontaneous drawings. The drawing of Jacob L. S. (Plate IV), a seaman sentenced to a naval prison during World War II for homosexual activities, plainly bespeaks this conflict, the passivity, the sacrifical suffering through identification with the Christ. In a blind analysis of these plates, made under the direction of Tarmo Pasto (by J.F.M.), the following comments were made:

The hundreds of short, thin, ink-lines whose vertical rhythms are constantly crossing over the horizontal lines state the crux of his conflict. In the figure itself it is confirmed that the "eyes" of the man on the bench refuse to accept his tell-tale hands, the hands suggesting masochism, sacrifice, blood. But the latent meaning belies such a statement for the "blood" is, probably, a substitution for the real identity of human semen which drips from the long, boneless, fingers.

The arrangement of the legs suggests an attempted denial, protection, or hiding of the male genitalia; the knees are contracted in much the way a man contracts his knees, involuntarily, when some kind of potential harm approaches the reproductive organs.

The drawing has been sustained, completely, on an unconscious level of creativity. A conscious, deliberate effort, on the part of the artist, to accentuate that which his unconscious divulged, would have proven an intolerable intrusion upon the privacy of his psychic structure. The body is "cut" by a pillar in such a way that the upper torso and the legs, in a different spatial relationship, are not related and enough room has not been allowed for the pelvic sexual area. Resistance to and a blocking out of the threat is indicated by the darkly emphasized outline given the figure.[26]

It is a fascinating commentary on the neurotic homosexual, who "wears his guilt on his sleeve," so to speak, that an artist trained in psychologic interpretation is able to read the neurotic problem from a drawing without having seen or known the history of the prisoner.

On a grander scale is the drawing by J. M., a Navy lieutenant con-

victed of scandalous conduct (the court martial board's term for homosexual behavior). In Plate V can be seen the psychic conflict of the
prisoner projected to include the total prison population. Here, the
figures are the symbols of anonymity, and the expression of helpless
fear on their faces suggests an infantile position of rejection. The nude
prisoners reentering the womb emerge as demasculinized characters.
They are truly infants whose sexuality has not yet been established
who have been ground to anonymity by the military organization and
their imprisonment. Under these pressures, basic elements that presumably underlie the homosexual pattern come to light. This drawing
also was submitted to the same, distant artist-psychologist, who offered
the following interpretation:

The picture could very well be titled "Ascent to Heaven," or "Saint Peter
at the Pearly Gates." It seems to represent a young man's guilt as he is being
judged by a punishing father-image or super-ego in the figure of St. Peter.
The inner and outer manifestations of his conflict are represented by a line
of faceless men penetrating the lower chamber of the Tower of Babel. Above
the men (re-incarnated?) appear on the outside ramp in endless procession.
A ray of hope is forecast by the curving walkway (ladder?) which circles
to the right and reaches the Gothic (vaginal) entrance above. This entrance,
however, is rather weak, half cut in that only the upper half is showing,
making its appearance merely as an echo of the anal maw below into which
the men are being forced by the "St. Peter" image of a punishing super-ego.

The patient, in the toils of his crisis, has sought revenge on St. Peter (and
the mother) by shearing St. Peter's wings, thus cutting down his divine
power. Yet, in conflict, he has made the wings like raised epaulets, symbols
of authority; thus the avenging image still remains the victor.

The phallic towers are angular and masculine rather than curvilinear and
effeminate. It would therefore appear that the patient is active and aggressive rather than passive and effeminate in his homosexual attitudes.

The inner conflict tends to drive him into circular compulsive patterns of
behavior. Even the sky is blocked out so that no vista of hope appears. The
figures reflect acceptance and hopelessness.

On another symbolic level one could say that the purification by fire is
required by passing through the anal maw to reach the female, half-hidden
up "high on a pedestal." She is untouchable so the patient needs to turn to
anal pursuits as a symbolic act of atonement for having the desires of pos-
sessing the female (mother).

The problem of bisexuality is specifically portrayed in Plate VI
drawn by prisoner J. M. The evil aspect of the male figure who, in the
manner of Janus, has engrafted upon his head the more comely female
face, pays through blood sacrifice for his lust. The female half of the
bisexual is youthful, noble, uplifted and supported by strong male
figures, the male half is primitive, aged, satanic, and sadistic.

The anxiety exhibited in these free drawings by homosexuals and bisexuals is an eloquent statement of the psychologic situation of many deviates. Behind the trends portrayed lies the unconscious fear of the female genitals. "The homosexual," writes Bergler, "is a frantic fugitive from women; unconsciously he is mortally afraid of them." [27] The reason for this fear leads directly into the complicated theme of castration fears. For the homosexual to have a partner without a penis (a woman) is to arouse unconscious anxiety and conscious disinterest. "We know," wrote Freud, "to what a degree depreciation of women, loathing of women and a disposition to homosexuality are derived from a final conviction of women's lack of a penis." [28] The presence of the trial of feelings that the homosexual entertains for the female, and of which he is not aware—fear, anger and hostility, the wish to injure—can be gleaned in those cases of bisexuals who become involved in crime. These mechanisms will appear in the cases to be cited in this chapter. The excitement and manifest pleasure of homosexuals in each other's company is clearly a reaction to the unconscious trends discussed above. All this, however, is not only buried from perception but also denied by homosexuals.

The practicing homosexual would be the first to find loopholes in the formulation given above; he would point out that the orgastic excitement of the homosexual act is as intense and poignant as that in heterosexual relations; he would indicate the relative lack of hostility between men in a homosexual relation, the esthetic appreciation common to both parties, the historical example of Greek youths and their philosopher admirers, and so on. The homosexual admits no fear of women, only disinterest; no yearning when he beholds the female form, only sensual neutrality. But simultaneously the homosexual speaks of his partner's phallus in terms of admiration, seeking only the largest (as in the case of an intelligent homosexual who came for analytic treatment because of his social and economic decline.) He was without recognition of the unconscious meaning of his phallic admiration.

This rapid survey of homosexuality as a predominant type of sexual deviation serves as a backdrop upon which to project the panorama of sexual crime that follows. Not only is homosexuality predominant among such offenses, it is crucial for sexual deviations. Karpman's statement probably summed up the situation most accurately when he summarized his vast experience: "Homosexuality and perversions . . . appear as brothers under the skin for they stem from the same sources and roots . . . namely, neurosis." [29]

The relation between the homosexual, his personality, his deviation, and the crime with which he is charged will be traced through several clinical examples. We start with the case of a young clergyman whose homosexuality enmeshed him in the tentacles of the law.

EROS IN CONFLICT

As a young minister, Hugo Feldharr was warmly applauded for his interest in youth groups. Indeed, Hugo's devotion to his church work, especially among the youth, was a welcome change from the conservatism of his predecessor. Intelligent, highly verbal, and personable, Hugo ministered to his small-town congregation, advising, counselling, intensely interested in the personal lives of his young parishioners. His patience and restraint were remarked by grateful parents; members of the community depended on him. On his drives beyond the town, around the semirural area that he served, Hugo was not so easily able to restrain himself. He would pick up hitchhiking youths, "proposition" them for homosexual activity, indulge himself, pay them moderately well, and go his way. Certainly the offense for which he was arrested was not his first.[30] Overwhelmed by contrition, he immediately pleaded guilty, secretly relieved that he would finally receive some psychiatric help to rid him of his burdensome, yet exciting, interest in young men.

An educated man, yearning to find the truth, Hugo became one of those satisfactory patients that psychiatrists welcome. He was prepared to bare his soul in the therapeutic situation: somehow he had always considered himself unworthy of women; he believed he was a born introvert; he was convinced that his homosexual urge was a "sick delusion" allied to feelings of guilt and inferiority; he longed to view himself objectively. Indeed, Hugo's "delusion," as he later came to call it, of being a "born homosexual" was so overpowering that he had planned to write an autobiography to show how his life had been damned by this infirmity. Struggling through his boyhood and adolescence, he was able to complete his college and seminary studies and to become an active and even effective minister. But his struggles continued; his homosexual feelings and early feelings of inferiority and inadequacy remained with him. "If I am a born homosexual," he thought, before he recognized his "delusion," "I can only live with the aid of religion and turn my affliction into a source of aid for others. After all, what peculiar relation subsisted between Christ and John, the disciple who lay on Jesus' breast?"

But the urges for young men strangled his resolution to submerge such feelings. The yearning to be liked and taken in by men, to be liked by a father- or brother-image so as to lighten the terrible weight of inferiority all but crushed him psychologically. His early life was punctuated by struggles with masturbation. Girls rejected him, or so he thought, and he became "male-conscious." He envied men who he thought had better physiques or were handsomer than he. Eventually he met a young man who seemed to embody the virility and good looks for which he himself yearned. Hugo describes his introduction to homosexual life:

I found my companion was also struggling with the block to his masculinity. . . . This handsome male has gone through the same pattern I have . . . for the first time I experienced the ecstasy of sex and I felt my pattern now definitely established. One clandestine experience followed another. I was introduced to the "gay life"—I was "coming out," as the homosexuals say. Promiscuity seemed a normal result. Other homosexuals agreed we were all different. It was our birthright. . . . My natural interest in girls which I attempted to repress, but which could not be extinguished, began to manifest itself in unexpected ways. I began to adopt feminine mannerisms and voice inflections. I was welcomed into the company of musicians, artists and teachers . . . but I was a minister now. . . . what a tragedy I was involved in!

His special position in society brought him up short, illuminating the abyss into which he was slipping. The "gay life," at first an entertaining diversion, became a nightmare. It was about this time that his arrest, conviction, hospitalization, and treatment took place. Through many hours of discussion in the hospital, Hugo recognized the "gay" life as a mass delusion, a commentary on the participants' need for peer approbation. For more than a year, therapy continued and with help Hugo began to lose his fear of women. His struggles were not over, but it was the beginning of insight. He could now speak of his "psychopathic malady and homosexual fixation." The pressure of the deviate nature of his conduct, which he had once regarded simply as his "intensive affection and worship of men," had taken on a slightly different coloring.

After his release from the hospital, followed by his resignation from the ministry, Hugo worked at the plebeian job of driving a truck while studying for his master's degree, hoping eventually to enter the teaching profession. Over a five-year period during which the patient was followed up through correspondence, Hugo communicated sporadically. He wrote of his struggles with homosexual impulses, of his "slow progress" and his "changed attitude." At one time he entered into a relationship with a divorced woman. As he described it: "I drifted naturally into a bed-partner relationship that was very natural and very satisfying. . . . Still, I was unwilling to be married." He continued to work, aware after he broke up with his female paramour that he still had homosexual yearnings. Periods of anxiety persisted, alternating with periods of optimism: Five years after treatment, Hugo recognized that he was "still predominately homosexual." But several positive features had also been noted: he was able to talk about sexual problems freely; he was able to enter into at least temporary (and satisfactory) liaisons with women.

Hugo Feldharr had been treated by the group-therapy method in a special setting [31] for about a year; for four years he had been under a type of guidance or, more accurately stated, a type of psychiatrically colored paternalism. This treatment program, although it did not produce a cure, made life tolerable for Hugo. Coincidentally, it taught the therapist that which the patient already knew well—that the psychology of the sexual deviate is interlarded with social and cultural attitudes that must be understood, if not solved, to make therapy for deviates a practical endeavor. Therapy for this group of offenders, therefore, must encompass the reciprocal feelings which he and his society entertain for each other.

PSYCHOTHERAPY OF HOMOSEXUALS AND SEXUAL DEVIATES

The therapy of sexual deviates involves many sociopsychologic factors that transcend, while in part encompassing, technical aspects of psychotherapy. Of these factors, the primary one is the patient's fear of society and its legal agencies. Experience shows that no patient seeks private psychiatric aid for his alleged, or actual, sexual deviation except through fear of possible future arrest, as a condition of probation or parole, or through pressure from a close relative. Similarly, treatment within an institution is sought by deviates (who have been arrested and confined) through fear of future arrest. Institutional regulations may also demand exposure to a therapeutic program. Such offender-patients in an institution begin to recognize the mental and emotional difficulties within themselves—neurosis or psychopathy—under the influence of a persuasive therapeutic atmosphere. It cannot be easily said that deviates start treatment with an initial enthusiasm to change their sexual aims. The perception of the need to change often represents merely lip service to therapeutic efforts on the part of the administration of the institution. In fact, the generalization seems warranted that the sexual offender, whether pedophile, homosexual, voyeur, or exhibitionist, comes to accept himself as a patient chiefly through the operation of fear of society and its agencies.

This conclusion leads to another generalization: that for the deviate sexual perversity is an egosyntonic condition. The perceptive sexual offender may be aware of pressure from his conscience, he may decry his compulsion toward sexual abnormality within himself, but he is also aware of the congenial nature of his deviation. It is *his* major source of satisfaction. These two clinical propositions make it obvious that strong resistance faces those who seek to modify sexual deviation through treatment.

Resistance toward change in these cases is further increased by a general cultural attitude and the social value given sex expression. The sexual impulse and its expression (or repression) occupies the core of the average male's self-perception. In the Western world, and especially in America because of the heightened values given sexuality, the genital organs have become the central focus of the body-image for males. The high biologic value of sexual virility and its symbols has given way to psychologic values. The devotee of Pan has become a psychic Casanova. Sexuality has achieved the level of a social force. We need not be reminded that pictures, photographs, advertisements, movies, and illustrations utilize sexually stimulating themes to advance the business of marketing objects as far removed from sex as spark plugs, soft drinks, cigarettes, and motorcars. The cultural *conserve* of sex has become the symbol of man's aliveness to the world around him. Muscular development—that is, physical fitness—is still important, but more vital is sexual potency and susceptibility to feminine sexual attraction. It is not that sexual fantasy has reared its ugly head, but that sex *is* the head—the five senses of social "belongingness."

It is necessary to recognize the present-day cultural accent on sexuality, especially in its scoptophilic direction, to conjure with the psychologic conditions surrounding therapy in sexual cases. The resistance that the individual sex deviate encounters on entering therapy is both society-backed and individually derived. He must combat the negative value that society has placed on his abnormal sex adjustment while he combats his own private compromise adjustment.

As a corollary, the therapist and the hospital staff are naturally involved, through identification, with society's accent on sex as a value-symbol. Given this circumstance it can be expected that counter-resistances will develop within the therapists, thus complicating the therapeutic process further. Such unconscious elements can be, and are, minimized within themselves by the therapists through constant self-analysis and a striving toward objectivity.

The thorny task of attempting therapy on sexual offenders is further complicated by the legal requirement that they be incarcerated in a hospital or prison, since a prime objective of the sexual psychopath laws in several states was the offender's removal from society. The necessity of treating such persons in an institution introduces a slightly artificial element into the situation.

The various difficulties arising from these resistances presented themselves in irregular fashion during the group-therapy process. Initially, the sexual deviates studied consisted of seventy-five patients, whose varied crimes included incest, lewd and lascivious conduct, rape, exhibitionism, pedophilia, and homosexual behavior toward younger males. Before a patient-offender was brought into the group, detailed interviews and psychological studies of the cases (including the Draw-a-Person, Rorschach, and Bellevue-Wechsler tests) were completed.

Group therapy introduced at the Mendocino State Hospital (Calif.) as part of the Sex Psychopath Treatment Project (1950–51) utilized a rather free design: it followed the needs and emotional movements of the patients. The interreaction between patients and staff was studied, and almost as much attention was paid to the staff's inner feelings as to that of the patients. The treatment could best be called *group experience* with psychodrama as a frame of reference. At the same time, play techniques, acting, and acting-out, were freely allowed so that catharsis, ego-support, kinetic release through acting-out, and increasing maturity through staff identifications (including transference reactions) were experienced. Permissivity and empathy were admittedly a generalized therapeutic attitude.

RESULTS OF SEXUAL DEVIATE TREATMENT

The immediate result of a year of intensive group therapy was not apparent. The California law required that a sexual deviate who had been committed as a sexual psychopath (and all these patients were so adjudged) was to be certified as having "recovered to the extent that he is no longer a menace to the health and safety of others . . . or would not benefit by care and treatment and was no longer a menace to the health and safety of others." [32] Following this recommendation (if it was made) the offender was returned to the court for disposition. Because of the standard phrase in the code that the offender was or was not a "menace to society," one could not speak in terms of clinical "cure" or "improvement." However, many of the original seventy-five offenders had reached home (after four to six years in hospitals or prisons), were working, had married, and were adjusted to their respective social levels. From reports of these men and a follow-up study of seventeen of the seventy-five originally treated, a general conclusion might be drawn; namely, that the basic deviation itself was unaltered, but the so-called "reasonable" ego's reaction to the deviation had become profoundly modified. Quite as important was the recognition by these persons of their formerly unsuspected neurotic symptoms: sexual, physical, and social feelings of inadequacy, strong passive-dependence needs, confusion of sexual roles, and infantile aggressive impulses turned predominately toward female-figures.

In terms of social behavior, the homosexuals retained their drives but made their homosexual contacts without becoming involved with the law, pedophiles removed themselves from children, exhibitionists resisted their urges to exhibit themselves, and so on.

The question of whether dynamic interpretations made during this group-therapy experience were effective in altering the patients' insights was given special attention during the follow-up study. Patients reported their reactions and insights in such terms as the following: "I have a greater feeling of confidence and security" . . . "I find myself analyzing my feelings before I act" . . . "I count my changed attitude as a mark of progress" . . . "I feel more stable and more controlled" —and, in relation to interpretations: "Even a person like me was usually shocked at the wonder and meaning of your deductitory remarks (deductions)." One can see clearly in the responses of these patients the idealization of the therapist, "shock" reactions with development of insights, perceptions of the neurotic, immature nature of their previous sexual responses, and so on.

To put the results of group therapy of sexual deviates in general terms, reported improvements may be summarized as follows:

a) Decrease in feelings of sexual and physical inadequacy.

b) Awareness of confusion of sexual aim and frequently feminine identifications.

c) Perception of projection of hostility to females.

d) Improvement in interpersonal relationships with decreased self-consciousness or timidity.

e) Relief of guilt and anxiety concerning sexual impulses.

f) Decreased dependency needs.

In general, the intensity of the perverse drive had been reduced and ego-control of aberrant impulses supervened. Before a measure of control was achieved, however, almost as a rule, the patients under therapy committed at least one or two more deviated acts as a delayed, final rebellious act against society. This after-act, incidentally, is a common occurrence among psychopaths under therapy.

This follow-up experience was contrasted with a cross-section study of sex patients under treatment a few years later (1955) at another California state hospital.[33] In this second and more recent group, the program had been enlarged. Intensive psychotherapy by the hospital staff, to which was added a rehabilitation program, was carried on, with this additional factor: the total atmosphere of the hospital was therapeutically oriented. In general, the patients were more active in the program. Patient government was instituted and the treated patients determined the therapeutic atmosphere in the wards. In terms of patient-perceptions it may be concluded, in contrasting the early group treated in 1950–51 with the later one under treatment in 1955, that the inner changes arrived at under treatment were identical. Improvement or freedom from relapse in deviate behavior resulted from strengthening of ego-control rather than from resolution of basic, unconscious conflicts.

From such continued efforts, a new and significant development arose. The offender-patients' perception of their emotional needs led in the years that followed to a movement known as the Emotional

Security Program.[34] With the guidance of psychiatrists, psychologists, and staff social workers, deviated patients worked through their sexual immaturity in relation to society's demands, while the doctors and therapists acted as catalysts in the process. In the lateral support these deviate-patients gained from each other, in their perception of society's involvement in the sexual-deviate problem, can be glimpsed an attitude, self-seeking perhaps, but one that looks beyond punishment to a more stable future through therapy. The Preamble to the Emotional Security Program states:

We are not advocating any sort of paternalism, for we have conceived an organization similar to the Northern California Service League, which works with the men in and out of the San Francisco Jail, and like the famous Osborne Association in New York City in its aid to ex-prisoners, or like the Alcoholics Anonymous.

The body of their credo, titled "Eight Steps from Chaos to Control," sets forth such self-revelatory statements as these:

We must admit to ourselves that we have come to a point in our lives when we are no longer the masters of our emotions, and are in need of assistance.

We must admit that according to the legal interpretation of the term, we are sexual psychopaths, and as such are a menace to society and to ourselves.

We must admit that as sane individuals, capable of determining right from wrong, we *alone* are responsible for the act that led to our apprehension and/or confinement, regardless of how great the outside pressure or contributing factors.

We must realize that since we are sexual psychopaths we are also potential repeaters of sexual offenses, and must be continually on guard against temptation to revert.

It would be difficult to underline more forcibly the sociopsychological problems and therapeutic obstacles encountered in dealing with sexual deviation than by quoting this self-imposed program. The passage from group therapy to self-help, from resistance to treatment to an unabashed self-examination of the complicated psychophysiological behavior of sexual crime, represents, in effect, a leap over five thousand years of moral admonition, social obloquy, and rigorous punishment. Whether stoned or beheaded, legally maimed, or imprisoned for life, sexual criminals were the last to be considered fit subjects for treatment. It might be accounted an oddity of human history that of all the crime groups from which society has suffered, and to which it has reacted with anger and retaliatory measures, those who have committed the most repugnant crimes have been among the first to perceive their need and communicate their desire to be dealt with therapeutically.

It has only been in recent time—particularly since the advent of Freudian psychoanalysis—that the notion of treating sexual deviates has been countenanced. It is true that the early analysts (Stekel, for example,[35] and one of his students in particular, Karpman) attempted analytic treatment of homosexuals and sexual deviates. In recent years, the orthodox type of analysis has been less astringently applied, and intensive psychotherapy, as in the hands of Bergler,[36] has been reported successful. Whereas most workers have dealt with homosexuals specifically, treatment reports of cases of exhibitionism and other types of sexual deviation do not present as favorable results. Psychotherapy of individual types has been modified by many workers, notably Jacob Conn,[37] and group therapy has been used extensively by Cruvant and associates [38] at St. Elizabeth's Hospital (Washington, D.C.).

It is worth noting at this point that more cases would actually have been treated had not the accent in reporting results of psychotherapy of sexual deviates been on elucidation of psychodynamic mechanisms.[39] Perhaps the scientific criteria for "cure" of sexual deviates are too rigid; a more eclectic frame-work is needed. The strong initial need for a theoretical framework involving ego-psychology within the therapist's mind seems to have overshadowed the need for an undirected description of how and why the sex deviate improved, if he did. Judging from the cases reported or discussed in the literature, attempts to trace an individual deviate's life history back to the point of fixations at various pregenital levels in the interest of explaining particular persistent deviations, almost replaced searching out and identifying those therapeutic factors that have actively relieved such patients.

The psychiatric literature contains many scattered reports of psychoanalytic treatment of homosexuals. Perhaps the most careful work has been that of Bieber and his associates,[40] who undertook to analyze 106 homosexuals and to compare them with a control group of 100 heterosexual men under treatment by psychoanalysts. The material for the heterosexual group was gathered from 77 recognized psychoanalysts who had worked with their patients over a nine-year period. The homosexuals who came for treatment were under no legal or other compulsion to do so. The technique employed was psychoanalytic and the patients were worked with for periods varying from 150 hours (roughly, ten months) to 350 hours (two or three years). One clinical finding was that the complaints and psychologic dynamics of the heterosexual patients were similar to the complaints and dynamics of the homosexual group. Although not all of these homosexuals changed their sexual patterns after treatment (27 per cent successfully adjusted to exclusive heterosexuality), almost half of the 106 patients experienced "improvement in certain non-sexual areas of behavior." [41] Bieber concluded that a "heterosexual shift was a possibility for all homosexuals strongly motivated to change." This finding is of great interest therapeutically in view of the careful study by Evelyn Hooker,[42] who, by studying their Rorschach responses, compared a male group of thirty homosexuals with thirty heterosexuals. The two groups were matched carefully for age, education, economic status, and so on, and the test results were studied by judges who had no knowledge of the life stories of the subjects examined. The significant finding by Hooker and her fellow psychologists was that *no difference* could be discerned in the personality structure of the two groups, except for the sexual patterns displayed. In other words, homosexuality cannot be considered "a clinical entity." This new view states that homosexuality is potentially reversible—in spite of the remonstrances and rationalizations of homosexuals, "a man's a man for a' that"!

It should be mentioned that there have been attempts to treat homosexuals by other methods than psychotherapy. For example, castration by surgical or hormonal means has been recommended on the naïve theory that if "the eye offend thee, pluck it out." Advocated years ago when sexual disorders were considered to be essentially physiological in nature, castration had a few proponents [43] in this country and Europe. In 1929, Denmark passed a law permitting sexual offenders to give consent to castration if they felt impelled toward dangerous crimes. Sturup, who has had extensive experience with this group in an institution near Copenhagen, reported [44] that in a few cases castration, in addition to psychotherapy, helped patients to adjust outside an institution. Main reliance today, however, is placed on the slow, persistent efforts of intensive psychotherapy in group or individual sessions.

When the homosexual lives a life of bisexuality, he may be forced into treatment through committing a criminal offense or on pain of divorce or exposure. Let us resume the survey of homosexuals as offenders by examining the case of a youngish teacher who lived an indifferently successful bisexual life until his seduction of his pupils catapulted him into arrest, conviction, and, finally, treatment.

SEDUCTION IN THE CLASSROOM

The mountain community was stirred; a stranger could sense an uneasy, ugly mood in the town. The parents of students at the local high school met in indignation, comparing notes. There had been rumors for weeks that one of their best teachers, the swimming coach, had been guilty of behavior that was alarming to the parents and frightening to the more alert students. Committees were formed, the superintendent of schools approached, material accumulated, and the wife of the suspected teacher questioned.

The couple, recent arrivals in that school district, seemed on the surface to be an average young couple, educated, personable, adjusted. But the wife, Ida, complained to no one that after two years of marriage she never felt secure in her "man." He seemed so boyish, so sexually disinterested in Ida, with none of the impetuousness that a vigorous young college graduate should have. Everett, the product of a good family, had served in the Air Force as a captain, had seen real action; her friends envied Ida. But married life had no savor, no romance. "Am I to blame?" she wondered as she lay awake in the early-morning hours.

With complaints from the parents threatening his job, Everett confessed his homosexual leanings to his wife. She, having known there was "something wrong with my man," sat down to face the issue with him. If he wanted boys, that was none of her concern, but life for her could not go on in this way. Ida insisted on an immediate separation. Stunned, but not unprepared for this denouement, Everett agreed. But he wanted to talk it over first, discuss his feelings; maybe something could be worked out. He proceeded to unburden himself to Ida.

He had always mistrusted marriage itself. While she (Ida) complained about his outstanding childishness, he himself considered her too demanding. He acknowledged a certain degree of emotional flatness, evident in his inability to be relaxed among his fellow teachers, but he expressed an open dislike of adult company. He explained that for him, the real warmth of friendship found expression in associating with his students; perhaps Ida did not know that from early childhood he had been aware of a strong sexual interest in boys. In school, in the world of boys, he felt at ease; he touched them unnecessarily, he palpated their legs and thighs—he played with their genitals. When Ida in amazement saw the complexion of things, Everett readily admitted his preoccupation with day-long sexual fantasies of playing with boys. In answer to her questions about his previous sex life he glibly rehearsed for her his fleeting fantasies of playing with women's breasts and a few cool friendships with girls in college. Gradually it dawned on Ida that where emotional comfort or satisfaction was concerned, Everett was totally immersed in his—boys.

Discussion, cogitation, questioning, self-revelation—all were soon ended. Everett was arrested on the charge of impairing the morals of a minor (12 counts).[45] When a diagnosis of sexual psychopathy with pedophilic and homosexual tendencies had been made, the Court agreed to Everett's treatment while on probation. The announcement from the bench of this therapeutic experiment aroused public indignation. The local parent-teacher association objected strenuously to the Court's substitution of treatment for punishment. Parents were horrified at an educational system that permitted sexual deviates to teach their sons; they demanded a prison sentence for Everett. The State Department of Education was castigated for not forthwith imprisoning all teachers involved in similar actions with minors. The Court, too, came in for public criticism for granting probation, as did the program that aimed at rehabilitating "moral criminals," whom everyone knew to be incurable by definition. Letters in the local press mirrored this feeling:

Enough of this stupid democratic method . . . any group of parents is better able to pass on what is a moral offense than any ordinary judge or jury. . . .[46]

It was against this background of outraged feelings against moral turpitude among teachers, and indignation against treatment of such offenders, that the therapeutic program went forward.

Intensive psychotherapy was initiated: Everett was faithful in coming regularly. Early in the treatment his fear of adult society showed through his comments and jokes deriding women generally and heterosexual intercourse in particular. His infantile sexual attitude was obvious in his description of his feelings during sex relations with his wife—"It felt like a pea in a glass," he joked.

For months he alternately giggled and writhed as he poured out the details of his life. At times his attitude toward the therapist was that of passive obedience punctuated by outbursts of childish aggression and spiteful denial: "No one will ever know what is inside of me," he often said. Gradually, Everett was able guardedly to express some of his fantasies: one was a striking fear of anal pregnancy. The patient soon was able to indicate his terror of women, as witness the following dream: "I am sitting opposite a woman; we both have double rows of teeth like a shark and as we laugh I pull out the front teeth." He laughed as he related the dream—a cover for his inner fear.

This dream amused Everett; his associations remained on a superficial level. He could not know that his dream fear of the sharklike teeth was a symbol of the *vagina dentata*, the vagina with teeth to rend the cherished male phallus, a derivative of the castration complex as old as man, buried in primitive layers of the unconscious. Analysts have found that this age-old fear in neurotic patients stretches back to the early days of the male infant's life when it feared revenge for its own oral-sadistic impulses. Anthropologists have discovered this fear among the myths of primitive people. The Paiute Indians (also, the Plains Indians, Wolf tribe [47]) of California and Nevada have wound it into their legends of Coyote, mythical father of the Paiutes.[48]

According to one such legend, Father Coyote vanquished a woman sent to trick him by throwing faggots under the table, thus foiling the woman of evil. He then had the satisfaction of hearing the "teeth of the vagina" (*vagina dentata*) crunch against the clublike bundle of sticks; thus Father Coyote saved future generations of Paiute braves from the curse of eternal castration.

Of all this, Everett knew nothing; he spoke only of his dislike for women. "They can't be trusted," said Everett with considerable heat. "They want everything for themselves, they stab you in the back, they're mean, critical, want to be placed on a pedestal. I hate them." Then, after a pause, he began to speak of his dislike for his own appearance, his jaw structure, his irregular teeth, the pimples on his face. For months the patient-offender's confidences alternated between complaints about his broad buttocks and protruding stomach and fury at the alleged advantages women are given, which, he said, they use for their own "nefarious" purposes.

As the transference relation developed, resistances of a different type appeared; they assumed the form of excessive anger at his parents, belligerence toward the therapist, and disappointment with the latter. He felt he was known as a "loser"; nobody cared for him. During this period, life was lonely for Everett. Now living in a neighboring city, he struggled to adjust to a new economic field. As months of analysis went by, Everett experienced less interest in boys, evidencing his psychosexual growth by being able to masturbate without guilt. However, his growth toward maturity brought new problems in its train.

There are long periods during which Everett insisted that he was unable to understand female anatomy: he could not understand the structure of the vagina and uterus or the mechanism of birth, even in the simplest terms. During this period Everett expressed copious anxiety, centering about fears of being enveloped by an octopus while swimming (he had been an excellent swimmer), fears of attacks from the rear by sharks. Repression of both sexual curiosity and sexual knowledge in his childhood stood out in bold relief. The patient began to see that he had automatically blocked out all common knowledge in the entire sexual area, especially concerning the female sex.

In this period of beginning awareness of Everett's confusion of sexual roles, in order to lessen resistances, several treatments were undertaken with lysergic acid (L.S.D. 25). The patient's reactions to this drug were marked disorganization, sexual regression, and a nauseating playfulness.

After several experimental sessions, a larger dose was administered; its effects were accompanied by typical hallucinatory experiences, a loosening of speech, and a lack of restraint that the patient had not exhibited during the two years of analytic sessions that preceded use of the drug. For several hours, actual intellectual dissociation appeared in his productions and behavior—an experience that Everett enjoyed hugely, in contrast to the anxiety displayed by many patients under the influence of lysergic acid. During later sessions with the same drug, he was able to speak of women in matter-of-fact terms, able to address the therapist as a friend, and enjoying his newfound freedom hugely. In the months that followed the use of this hallucinogenic drug, Everett's analysis progressed rapidly. From a boyish, often boring, man of thirty, he grew able to speak maturely, entering actively into the business of interpreting his reactions and productions. Following a long period of regression into infantile sexual talk and preoccupations, he began to probe the world of sexuality, first as an adolescent, then as a young man. During this time, much sexual energy and interest was released. Along with a confused outpouring of a masturbatory interest in older men and coincident feelings of independence, Everett talked and thought of women. At one point during this period he spoke of changing his name.

His economic situation improved: having taken the requisite schooling, he developed a new profession. He became interested in folk dancing, became acquainted with several women, and within five years of his original offense made a successful remarriage to a divorced woman with two young children.

THE COMPULSIVE, AGGRESSIVE HOMOSEXUAL

In Everett's case, the picture of a homosexual convicted of impairing morals of a minor is more specifically that of a pedophile, although homosexual techniques were used. Fear of the female genitalia was an unconscious determinant in Everett's choice of sexual objects. Therapy over a period of two-and-a-half years succeeded in opening this "forbidden" area to his consciousness, while his behavior crystallized around a more acceptable masculine image. But all homosexuals and pedophiles do not react to treatment so readily. Fortunately, the impulses within Everett were pitched on a rather immature scale, with a minimum of aggressive display. There are other cases, encountered by the hundreds in courts throughout the land, where homosexual demands for sexual release are aggressively expressed. These are the blatant type of accosters who freely admit their obsessive drive for homosexual contacts, no matter the cost. Among these men, an intense need for genital-viewing and genital-touching drives them in search of sexual quarry.

The obsessive urge for contact parallels the compulsion that invades most homosexuals, to talk and think sex to a degree intolerable to the average person. The present writer has dealt therapeutically with a number of homosexuals who freely admit this preoccupation. As one verbal, compulsive homosexual put it: "After *all,* after sex what *is* there?" This patient, whose heedlessness in public exposed him to probable arrest, spent all his leisure hours in coffeehouses and at parties where the conversation, pleasurable to him, dealt entirely with sexual adventures of the past and similar adventures-to-come. Bieber, out of his careful study of homosexuals, concluded that the compulsive preoccupation with sexuality, besides providing gratification, "serves to fulfill a range of irrational defensive and reparative needs." [49]

The type of compulsive homosexual now to be described differs from his fellows in that he does not hide behind the mask of the "gay" life; nor does he enjoy its flippancy around bar or coffee table. His aggressive need for sexual contact forces him into the public market; this "contact-need," if one may coin an expression, demands of him a constant supply of new conquests. His compulsiveness brings him eventually into the courts. This type of deviate is genital-oriented rather than man-oriented; his friendships are few; his life perforce lonely. But let the case of Wilton Lebal speak for these. [50]

Wilton was arrested on the complaints of several young men whom he picked up on the highway and actively induced into homosexual activity. A characteristic of Wilton's approach was the direct engagement of his victims in frank sexual talk and activity. The first youthful complainant stated that Wilton, after he picked the boy up in his car, turned and inquired of the victim if he "had ten inches." He then drove the car a little farther down the road; while doing so, he "grabbed" the boy's penis, palpating him as they drove. No force was used, but the immediacy of his need can be gauged by the victim's report that Wilton also masturbated as they drove along. Another young man complained that Wilton picked him up while he was hitchhiking, subjecting him to homosexual overtures almost immediately; his conversation was limited to a clear statement of his interest in the male genitals. Wilton's arrest cleared up dozens of complaints entered in the police records.

The examination proceeded with Wilton's cooperation; he was interested in the strange compulsion that drove him. He stated that his relationships with women were satisfactory—he had been married for many years and had also made numerous heterosexual contacts at bars—but nothing, he said, gave him the thrill of a homosexual relation: "It's something different and exciting." He confessed that he was not at all interested in love relations with men or boys, although he did on occasion "caress them and kiss them enough to make me hot." Despite Wilton's slightly effeminate manner, he disclaimed any interest in the "gay" life. His preoccupation with the hope of encountering a large penis in his search for new victims betrayed the neurotic nature of his homosexuality. Although as an attractive male he never lacked for women, his anxiety drove him to hunt for and pick up young men and initiate sexual advances without even modest preliminaries. His compulsion proved his undoing. It is noteworthy that Wilton, who had been a lieutenant in the United States Navy in World War II, serving with distinction, had only became aware of his compulsive homosexuality during the last ten years of his life (he was forty-two when examined).

The variety of homosexual behavior is extensive. The fact that the law, except for the distinction between adult homosexual relations and those with minors, lumps deviates into one class is due perhaps to a general distaste, during the long evolution of the law, for the details of sexual psychopathology. In truth, from the standpoint of legal punishment, details of sexual dynamics have been unimportant, but from the viewpoint of attempts at treatment—since imprisonment is conceded to make not the slightest dent in the homosexual pattern—the clinical varieties of homosexuals, with their varying dynamic meanings to the individuals, are significant.

The psychopathology of the homosexual invades the ego to the degree that paranoid or other psychotic elements occur among homosexuals, as in any other group of persons. Particularly are paranoid defenses found; these derive from the same deep unconscious conflicts that occur among bisexual individuals. Criminal actions may thus arise from this mental mechanism, as in the occasional latent homosexual who attacks women rather than men.

THE FEMALE INVERT

As with the male deviate, the female homosexual demonstrates the varieties of behavioral reactions, whether neurotic, psychopathic, or psychotic, noted in these pages. The Lesbian is less apt to find herself before the courts because of criminal action, yet she too harbors the aggressive tendencies noted in the cases cited. Charges of assault or disturbing the peace are brought against female homosexuals when they become embroiled in fights arising from flare-ups of jealousy, often tinctured with alcoholism. While the quiet, law-abiding Lesbian is in the majority, cases have been observed of young women whose homosexual affiliations form part of a general pattern of aggressive antisociality. Homosexuality to these girls may represent a path leading to a formless, rebellious life, rather than arising from a passionate drive toward love inversion. One finds, also, instances of bisexuality, either in marriage or in prostitution, among women of this group. A brief outline of Billie Page and her offense will illustrate one type of female homosexual involved in criminal behavior.

Billie was the kind of girl who belonged to no one. Breezy, glib, worldly-wise, she was equally at home in bars, among her friends, and in the examiner's consulting room. Poised and unashamed of her sexual allure, Billie described her family history as if it were a footnote to her current life: She never saw her father; her mother had been married "many times"—a euphemism for a life of promiscuity. Billie herself had married a sailor at the age of seventeen, soon lost track of him, and divorced him—at the insistence of the sailor's mother. By the time Billie was eighteen she was living alone, having moved from Texas to the West Coast. Here she had entered a life of prostitution, finding time to be arrested for contributing to the delinquency of a minor and for shoplifting. She associated with male criminals for a while and "worked" in hotels as a call girl for a brief period; she then left the prostitution "racket" because she was too independent to be controlled by any one man. The antisocial life was her life. Her account of the various aspects of illegitimate life in cities in which she had lived gave clear indication of her identification with the demimonde. As Billie put it, "I know I am attractive and I can write my own ticket." With refreshing candor she said, "My mother was a professional, I am a professional . . . and I like the life."

The current offense [53] involved a charge of assault and battery for stabbing another young woman in the buttock. Billie, spending two days at a house party of girls in a friend's apartment, enjoyed the freedom and company of girls. Under the influence of considerable drinking, the party had advanced to the level of a mild orgy. One of the girls, of whom Billie was enamored, took another girl into a bedroom, engaging her in an act of cunnilingus. Inflamed by jealousy, Billie waited, knife in hand, until the pair reentered the living room; she then stabbed her rival to the accompaniment of shrieked obscenities.

The group had been active homosexuals for a long period of time, although Billie averred that her relation with them was more opportunistic than habitual: she had been simply seeking an interim of relief from men. Since Billie frankly stated that she was "oversexed," she offered little information concerning her perceptions, inner feelings, or emotional attitudes. Dynamic explanations of her behavior or rationalizations for her life of bisexuality were pointless. She took her arrest and forthcoming imprisonment in stride, as she took her pleasures. Billie's case provides a glimpse into the social setting of the aggressive Lesbian, the opportunistic world of youthful Sapphos, and the acceptance of "vice" as normal.

Among males, the procedure for meeting new sex objects, the technique of making conquests and maintaining old ones with a minimum of legal interference, has burgeoned into a total social enterprise. This enterprise of deviated sexuality encompasses stereotyped attitudes and behavior, sets of values, and methods of approaches that can best be described as a species of "sexual sociology." A scrutiny of this corner of the homosexual universe may help us understand the peculiarities of homosexual crime.

THE SOCIOLOGY OF HOMOSEXUALITY

The criminologic aspect of homosexuality is not limited to the benign seduction of schoolboys, or to peripatetic youths, or to the jealousies of youthful Lesbians. Nor is it encompassed by "drags," parties where "gay" people gather for alcoholic sociality, flaunting their assumed femininity in "swish" clothes, accenting their mincing steps, or reconnoitering for future conquests. Homosexuality becomes a serious problem in crime when aggression joins with sexual appetite. The nightly "cruising," now the hallmark of the invert, has become the matrix for crime on our highways. In areas of the country where the climate permits spending much time in the open, the motorcar, like the roadside motel, has become virtually a travelling house of assignation for homosexual activity. It is significant that "occasional" homosexual contacts have grown in number; however, the circumstances under which these contacts occur may require elucidation.

Since homosexuals are in the main disinterested in permanent liaisons, preferring occasional contacts, it has become an accepted, even admired, pattern to seek sex objects in the bars, on the streets, and on the highways. As a matter of sociological interest, it should be noted that not only the motorcar and the public parks, but the motion-pictures houses and public rest rooms, have become game preserves for the predatory male homosexual. Some of the places where arrests are frequently made by vice-squad officers are the public toilets in the subways of the nation's largest city, the rest rooms in small-town plazas, the comfort stations in or adjoining parks. Here casual contacts may be made under or through breaks in stall walls, so that the homosexual knows nothing about his sexual partner. Less publicly blatant situations are likely to come about in such places as Turkish baths or health clubs, where the "gay" habitué, protected by anonymity, feels safe to flush out and enjoy his quarry in harmonious surroundings. The institution of the homosexual steam-bath—where, surprisingly, men of "high moral character and otherwise dependable and upright" [54] spend an occasional night—extends from coast to coast. Criminal activity does not commonly occur here, for the aggressive, sadistic homosexual prefers the anonymity of the highway and the darkness and privacy of the parked motorcar. To complete the picture of the environs of homosexual crime, it should be added that prisons, military facilities, and college dormitories may be sites of homosexual activities, but the possibility of criminal activity is small here, except for use of such occasions for blackmail purposes.

The increase among young persons and adolescents of overt sexual activity, including homosexuality, requires special consideration. In seeking reasons for this phenomenon, the social disarrangements of World War II and its aftermath are often cited. Separation of servicemen from their families, relocation of wives and children, the impact of other cultures on young American men overseas, and increased national mobility were all indirect factors in increased sexual activity. Coincident with this there occurred a reassessment of the sexual urge as an aspect of the fulfilled life. Referred to in some quarters as a "loosening of American moral fiber," this phenomenon appears to be due in part to a democratization of psychologic and sexual information and to a general growth in sophistication. The blinders placed on sexual knowledge, either normal or pathologic, loosened. The "family newspaper" of another age, which had protected its readers in touching on venereal diseases by referring to them as "social diseases," now spoke of syphilis and gonorrhea; magazines that once ran articles about "unfortunate girls" now discussed illegitimacy openly; problems of sexual rhythm, impotence, premature ejaculation, vaginal orgasm, and frigidity are written about with familiar ease.

This spirit of openness regarding sexual topics of all kinds became the hallmark of the 1950's. With the numerical superiority of women over men, an increased divorce rate, working wives, and discussion of sexual problems relating to the population explosion, sexuality attained a normative position in our national life. The social atmosphere in the 1960's tended to provide equal sexual prerogatives for both men and women; further, it touched lower age-groups than ever before. College students and even high-school groups entered into sexual life with little guilt and with a sense of realistic accomplishment of that which had hitherto been denied. It is often stated that the Kinsey reports of the 1950's were responsible for the increase in sexual freedom in this country. Careful analysis will show, however, that the great expansion in sexual outlets via promiscuity, premarital intercourse, masturbation, and homosexuality among the "normal" population simply represents an awareness of the place of sexuality in life. Those close to the common man—medical men who deal with vagaries of emotional life among a grass-roots population that rarely reach the dignity of a psychiatric diagnosis; novelists who search under the surface of polite society; social workers and clergymen—all know that abnormal sexuality was not invented in the 1950's; it was merely given a public hearing. That which was designated as psychopathic and neurotic during the first two decades of this half-century became illicit conduct during the second fifteen-year span and outspoken behavior during the current period.

This barest outline of a sexual sociology could be buttressed by quotations from literature—novels, plays, motion pictures—from studies of the sexual preoccupation of children and adolescents in their games, fantasies, and speech, and through analyses of the daily jokes, conversations, and interests of the adult population. There is as much sexual preoccupation outside the clinic, physician's office, and/or penal institution as in them. The materials and opinions set down here are drawn from years of observation and study among criminal and noncriminal cross sections of our society.

For the purposes of this discussion, the significance of a burgeoning preoccupation with sex among our youth is its direct bearing on homosexuality and sexual crime. The spurring of this universal drive to experience sexual pleasure earlier in life than was the custom during the first half of the present century has undoubtedly stimulated the practice of homosexuality. In spite of the assertions of homosexuals that their ranks are increased by those who recognize that they are "born" with this tendency, there are other factors operating. One is the ease of sexual satisfaction obtained with men; a second, the lightening of the responsibility and cost that attends heterosexual relations: these have influenced the rise of homosexuality. The sexual revolution that began in the second decade of the twentieth century has progressed to the point where romantic sublimation has given way to sexual freedom and the legitimacy of forepleasure. Permissible forepleasure has given way to the primacy of the orgasm, and the primacy of the easily achieved orgasm is a strong factor in homosexual indulgence. "D. H. Lawrence," states a writer [55] in *Time*, "sentimentalized the orgasm"—today's practicing homosexual has idealized it.

The purpose of this digression into the sociology of homosexuality is to place in its natural setting the significant crime of *homosexual assault*. For in the tangled matrix of sexual crime no situational or psychological factor can be neglected in the effort to understand this peculiarly modern crime. Although homosexuality is an ancient practice, even an accepted one in older and some current cultures, the homosexual *physical assault* appears to be a new phenomenon. The case now to be presented demonstrates an assault by a professed homosexual —one whose sadistic fantasies bordered, if they did not invade, the psychotic process—on a youthful victim picked up in the course of the attacker's regular forays.

THE CHASE AND THE QUARRY

The sheriff brought his big fist down on the table: "Men," he said, "we've got to find him. This is the sixth boy that's been found strangled, sexually molested, hit from behind. You've got to find the—"

The other men moved uneasily in their chairs; they glanced at the official photographs of the nude bodies stretched among the weeds along the waterway. While the sheriff looked down at the table, his big fingers working slowly, he thought of his own son, boyish yet manly, daring yet relatively innocent—a pleasant kid who thought he knew everything. The sheriff bit his lip, unclenched his hand. There was nothing in the world of crime that he hadn't encountered—dope addicts, peddlers, hustlers, con men, pimps—it was his professional world. But this—

"Let's go over it again," he said. Bit by bit he and his deputies went over the unsolved killings of the past few years: the first victim was a man of thirty-nine who disappeared from his home and was found strangled in the brush two weeks later; the second was a youth of eighteen, found nude, floating in the river, less than a month after the first murder; the third was a boy aged seventeen, his head nearly severed from his torso, whose body had been stumbled on in a ditch a month and a half later. The next three were all young, similarly mistreated, their bodies left in the same locality, a few miles apart. The last youth survived—survived, that is, with a deep gash across his neck, blood gushing from the wound, just able to stumble to the highway and flag down an approaching car. Although in critical condition, he remembered enough details of that night of horror to help the harried detectives identify the assailant's car, break down the owner's alibi, identify objects belonging to the victim in the assailant's room, and obtain a confession. It was a story rivaling anything ever dreamed of by the Marquis de Sade.

The suspect [56] was a man of thirty, solidly built, muscular but not excessively powerful. He might have been called handsome: a soft smile curving over his lips, his voice quiet, his manner calm, he answered the questions of the police with the gentle patience of a tired teacher. It was not until later, when the details of his fantastic psychosexual life came to light, that his smile became more twisted than gentle. Then a distant air enveloped the prisoner; he withdrew into himself, speaking as if he were disinclined to pay out the full flood of his psychopathology before the examiners. Always polite, the prisoner's attitude gradually changed as acceptance of his confession was succeeded by requests for details of his sexual life. He became increasingly excited as he moved into his own world of sexual fantasies. Calm left him and a hardness creased his face. With little persuasion he launched into a minute description of the crime:

I quit work at 10:30 that night and went to my cabin, but I couldn't stay there. I got restless—I wanted a boy to spend the night with me. I got into my pick-up to cruise the freeway. About midnight I picked up a young man; he was a doll. I took him in the car, asked him if he wanted to make a little money. "Do what I tell you; I won't hurt you"—it was a lie, of course, but he went along. When I got to my place I got a little excited. I told him to bend his head down and I tied his hands behind his back.

I made him take off his clothes with a knife in my hand. He got a little frightened and said, "Don't hurt me." He was a good-looking kid, muscular, not too big. I got undressed, and took a shower with him. By this time I was aroused. I put him on the sofa and started to dry him with a towel and play around. I made him go down on me. He became a little frightened, so I said, "Let's do some exercises," and made him do some knee bends in front of me. This excited me more. I had the knife against his neck and I caressed his hair. A strong feeling was moving inside of me, a feeling of love. I'd do anything for him. I kissed him—I had intercourse with him in the rectum—I just loved him. Then I took his wallet; I helped him dress and got him back in the car.

We drove back to the freeway; I kept his hands tied behind his back and once more I got excited. I loved him, do you understand? I wanted to keep him—he was mine. I held my face against his. Then I cut the rope behind his back—somehow his neck got cut and there was blood all over my hands. I didn't want to hurt him . . . he fell limp in my arms.

I heard the boy had his throat slashed. I couldn't believe it because I don't remember cutting him; I did crack him with a belt at home, but he fell and I held him up. . . .

His recital of the crime finished, the prisoner sat back. After a few questions, he etched in further details of his life. He had been adopted as an infant and regarded his mother and father as good parents. About the age of sixteen he suffered a compound fracture of one of his legs in a car accident that kept him from school for almost a year. A graft in the bone delayed his resuming activity with other boys for two more years; he was on crutches for another year, then braces for four months; finally he was well enough to enter the Navy. He was then twenty-three. During his Navy experience the offender was arrested once for vagrancy and was convicted of a sexual offense, for which he served a three-year sentence. His Navy experience earned him an undesirable discharge.

Good rapport having been established, the prisoner traced his sexual life without reserve and in full detail. His homosexuality started in the Navy when he found himself in a "gay" crowd, which, he said, was "all new to me." He became a part of the "gay" life almost instinctively:

I suddenly found women didn't interest me. I had one girl in the Navy. I didn't love her, but she was okay. There was no particular "bang" with her—besides, she said, "You've got bedroom eyes, kissable lips."

When he slipped into the circle of "gay" men, he forgot about women and the Navy, wallowing in his new-found admiration and desirability. A large cash settlement from the accident that had injured his leg came into his hands at this time. He now was transformed into "Mr. Big"; he spent the money lavishly in the Los Angeles clubs—on men, clothes, and on boys.

For a while I lived the life I had dreamt, and then when the money gave out (after I did time in prison) I dreamt the life I wanted to live.

Out of prison, the offender found himself. He dedicated himself to one aim in life—sexual excitement. Deserting his good-time friends, he embarked on the chase, picking up youths who would satisfy his not inconsiderable lust; he described how he would masturbate, perform fellatio on these boys; he talked glowingly about the details of his swallowing their semen, the feeling of eternal vigor and life, the excitement of living for only one pleasure and one goal. Although he managed to work rather steadily and maintain himself in his own apartment, his life focused only on freedom for sexual contacts.

By now he had deserted the high-flying "gay" set, maneuvering his own pickups. New fantasies that went beyond his actual sex relations flooded his mind: cutting, slashing, mayhem. He carried a knife now on his nightly cruising—once he assaulted a boy and held a loaded rifle to his head. The idea of a knife emerged from a fantasy that he would cut the testicles off the boy with whom he was having intercourse. Then he recalled that in the current offense he had said to the victim: "If it slips out, I'll cut your nuts off!" "It was an idea—it was half a joke," he told the examiner, "but I was going to do it!"

During these years, before he was arrested for the final assault, he used to amuse himself in his lonely room with florid fantasies of trips he would make. "Tripping" was his way of daydreaming:

I remember I used to imagine I would cut the boys to pieces after I have sex with them and feed the parts to my dog. He is a big German shepherd. Or I cut them, they fall down and I leave them to go do something else. Once in a while also, I bring flowers and lay them on the body as if they were dead.

He was asked if this happened in the current case. The prisoner, by now ecstatic in the recital of his fantasies, smiled:

I cut his neck on the side, there was a lot of blood, it felt good, it was real holy, as if he gave the blood to me. Young blood is better than old blood. I had fantasies of the Romans who used to take young boys with them in battle, have sex and then throw them away. Sometimes, I am one of the German S.S. squads; we torture young men to get information from them or we chain them up on the rack, tie their feet and arms, extended, then pull them apart until their arms come off at the shoulders. In that case, we are working on people who are against the government.

Sometimes I invent ingenious torture methods: I take them out in the sun or I drop acid on their body drop by drop or I drive them crazy and let them loose. Sometimes I bend their fingers back until they break or cut off their testicles.

The recital was stopped by the examiner: "Did this actually happen with your pickups?"

The one that I had sex with at rifle point—I had that feeling with him. He was mine and nobody else's. It was like having a slave. I had the feeling that I could do what I wanted with him.

As the study continued, the reports of the "trippings" became more florid, more sybaritic. Out of the rich storehouse of his reveries he invented "trips" for the examiner:

What would I do if I had money?—I would get a Japanese houseboy and a big house on the beach. If I wanted something I would send the houseboy out for a man. I would burn him on the chest with cigarettes. I would have sex and go to sleep.

His favorite fantasies, however, had to do with blood:

Blood gives you a holy feeling. It is real pure, not exposed to air, not dirty. It never gets out like semen. It's a feeling you can look at it and it's real pure. I've thought of drinking it—more strength and more holy feeling—would add more to what they already had. . . . It is okay to have slaves if you treat them right, like the Germans and the Russians—the weak belong to the strong.

As the study progressed, the prisoner became more realistic and a little less ecstatic. On the psychological test he showed up as being no better than dull normal in intelligence. With the subsiding of his excited state, a certain basic emotional flatness appeared. This was demonstrated when his flights of fantasy were restricted, as in the psychological test, and tension developed. The prisoner became perceptibly distraught; to him the world could be viewed only as a place where blood, corpses, and mangled flesh filled the foreground. The

range of his interests proved to be quite narrow. Schizophrenic thinking was recognized in the Rorschach and Thematic Apperception tests.
Gradually during the numerous psychiatric interviews, the prisoner
became morose and self-conscious. When the examiners showed him
a colored photograph of his victim, his response to the sight was: "He
isn't very pretty now." The edge seemed to have gone from his sexual
fantasies. In a letter to the present writer, he said:

I am glad you were willing to listen to me, as most people would shy away
from me.

A tone of depression crept into the prisoner's manner: he talked of
his parents' suffering because of his crime and the social repercussions;
long, sober letters to the examiner replaced the ecstatic fantasies of his
spoken words. Sadly he agreed that to be a confirmed homosexual was
a painful thing; he hoped the "law" would give "correct treatment" to
similar offenders:

A person driven by an overpowering sex drive . . . should be sent to a
mental sanitarium, and not a prison . . . how can the American people
condemn a man to death or prison when he can't control himself.

At this point, a note was intercepted by the prison authorities in
which the prisoner-patient outlined a plan to escape from court when
brought in for trial. A fellow prisoner was to be hired to kill the victim
as he sat in the witness-box testifying. The long note, written in his
cell, was composed the day before the trial was to commence. Intercepted by an alert deputy sheriff, the note was found to contain a full-
blown story of a jailbreak, a killing of the victim, a rendezvous in Las
Vegas—all colored by fantasy and set down in florid and immature
terms.

Preparations for a spectacular court trial went ahead. The night
before the trial was to begin the prisoner was busy writing long letters
to the press and to law-enforcement officers. He thanked his attorneys,
concluding,

My life ends now after thirty years and I hope some good will come from
these pages.

At 1:00 A.M. he was found unconscious in his cell, the belt around his
throat revealing a quiet suicide attempt. The belt had broken and he
had fallen against the concrete floor. He was taken to the hospital but
never responded to treatment. Death came from brain damage caused
by a skull fracture.

The florid psychopathology of this prisoner, half-revealed in his expressed fantasies, was unique in the sense that it stemmed from a not unusual homosexual life. The prisoner's ego cracked under the flood of actual and fancied sexual indulgences, which, reaching the realm of horror in bloodcurdling sadism, produced as if by its own weight a split in his ego. The fantasies, having run their grizzly course, made way for reality. A rush of conscience poured into the breach, burying his ego in the debris of remorse. There was no way out but suicide. The ecstasy flowed, ebbed, and extinguished itself. It was the end of the chase.

REFERENCES

1. KARPMAN, BENJAMIN, *The Sexual Offender and His Offenses* (Julian Press, New York, 1954), p. viii.

2. FREUD, SIGMUND, *Three Contributions to the Theory of Sex*, Monograph No. 7 (Nervous and Mental Disease Publishing Co., Washington, D.C., 1930).

3. JANET, PIERRE M. F., *Psychological Healing*, trans. by E. and C. Paul (The Macmillan Company, New York, 1925), p. 610.

4. CLARK, WILLIAM L., and MARSHALL, WILLIAM L., *A Treatise on the Law of Crimes*, rev. by Melvin F. Wingersky (Callaghan & Co., Chicago, Ill., 1958), p. 669.

5. *Laws of Massachusetts, annotated by G. Mottla and F. Hitchins*, (Michie Co., Charlottesville, Va., 1956), Vol. 9a, C-272, Sec. 18.

6. *Penal Law, McKinney's Consolidated Laws of New York* (Edward Thompson Co., Brooklyn, N.Y., 1944), Part 1, Sec. 100, p. 56.

7. PLOSCOWE, MORRIS, *Sex and the Law* (Prentice-Hall, Englewood Cliffs, N.J., 1951), p. 138.

8. KINSEY, A. C., MARTIN, C. E., POMEROY, W. B., and GEBHARD, P. H., *Sexual Behavior in the Human Male* (W. B. Saunders Co., Philadelphia, Pa., 1953).

9. *Penal Law, McKinney's Consolidated Laws of New York, ibid.*, Part 3, Sec. 887, p. 250.

10. *Ibid.*, Sec. 690, Art. 66.

11. *Penal Code, State of California*, ed. by Francis R. Deering (Bancroft-Whitney Co., San Francisco, Calif., 1957), Part I, Title 15, Chapter II.

12. *Welfare and Institutions Code, State of California* (State Printing Office, Sacramento, Calif., 1955), Chap. 4, Sec. 5500.

13. Group for the Advancement of Psychiatry, *Psychiatrically Deviated Sex Offenders*, Report No. 9, May, 1949 (Topeka, Kansas).

14. *Penal Code, State of California, ibid.*, 290 (1947), Amended 1949 and 1950.

15. BOWMAN, KARL M., and ENGLE, BERNICE, "Certain Aspects of Sex Psychopath Laws," *American Journal of Psychiatry*, CXIV (February, 1958), 690.

16. State of California, Senate Bill 1040, Chapter 4, Welfare and Institutions Code, approved July, 1963.

17. State of California, Department of Mental Hygiene, Letter #2329, Dr. D. Lieberman, Director, September, 1963.

18. *In re Moulton,* 96 New Hampshire, 370, 77, A 2nd, 26 (1950).

19. GUTTMACHER, MANFRED S., "The Homosexual in Court," *American Journal of Psychiatry,* CXII, No. 8 (February, 1956), 591.

20. KARPMAN, *op. cit.,* p. 303.

21. RADZINOWICZ, L., *Sexual Offences: English Studies in Criminal Science.* Report of the Cambridge Dept. of Criminal Science (The Macmillan Company, London, 1957), p. 26.

22. KINSEY, MARTIN, POMEROY, and GEBHARD, *op. cit.,* p. 651.

23. LINDNER, ROBERT M., *Sex Habits of American Men,* Albert Deutsch, ed. (Prentice-Hall, Englewood Cliffs, N.J., 1948), p. 203.

24. FENICHEL, OTTO, *The Psychoanalytic Theory of Neurosis* (W. W. Norton & Co., New York, 1945), pp. 328 ff.

25. BIEBER, IRVING, *et al.* (Harvey J. Dain, Paul R. Dince, Marvin G. Drelich, Henry G. Grand, Ralph H. Gundlach, Malvina W. Kremer, Alfred H. Rifkin, Cornelia B. Wilber, Toby B. Bieber), *Homosexuality, A Psychoanalytic Study of Male Homosexuals* (Basic Books, New York, 1962), p. 220.

26. PASTO, TARMO, and RUNKEL, PETER, National Institute of Mental Health Project #1278–1, Ars Gratia Hominis, Sacramento State College, California.

27. BERGLER, EDMUND, *Homosexuality, Disease or Way of Life?* (Hill & Wang, New York, 1956), p. 17.

28. FREUD, SIGMUND, *The Infantile Genital Organization of the Libido* (1923), in *Collected Papers,* Vol. 2 (Hogarth Press, London, 1950), p. 247.

29. KARPMAN, BENJAMIN, "The Structure of Neurosis," *Archives of Criminal Psychodynamics,* IV (1961), 599.

30. *People* vs. *Feldharr* [*sic*], State of California, County of Fresno, Superior Court, 1951.

31. BROMBERG, W., and FRANKLIN, G., "Treatment of Sexual Deviates with Group Psychotherapy," *Group Psychotherapy,* IV, No. 4 (March, 1952), 274.

32. *Welfare and Institutions Code, State of California, ibid.,* Sec. 5517, 1955; amended to read: Mentally Disordered Sex Offenders, Chap. 4.

33. Department of Mental Hygiene, State of California, Walter Rapaport, M.D., Director, and R. S. Rood, Superintendent, Atascadero State Hospital, Atascadero, California, 1955.

34. Emotional Security Program, Auspices of Department of Mental Hygiene, State of California, Los Angeles, 1954.

35. STEKEL, WILHELM, *Peculiarities of Behavior,* Vol. 2 (Liveright Publishing Corp., New York, 1924).

36. BERGLER, *op. cit.*

37. CONN, JACOB, "Brief Psychotherapy of the Sex Offender," *Journal of Clinical Psychopathology* (October, 1949), p. 347.

38. CRUVANT, BERNARD, MELTZER, M., and TARTAGLINO, F., "An Institu-

tional Program for Committed Sex Deviants," *American Journal of Psychiatry*, CVII, No. 3 (September, 1950), 190.

39. GILLESPIE, W. M., "Contribution to the Study of Fetishism," *International Journal of Psychoanalysis*, XXII (October, 1940), 401.

40. BIEBER and others, *op. cit.*, pp. 220 ff.

41. *Ibid.*, p. 277.

42. HOOKER, EVELYN, *The Adjustment of the Male Overt Homosexual*, in *Problems of Homosexuality in Modern Society*, M. Ruitenbeek, ed. (E. P. Dutton & Co., New York, 1963), p. 141.

43. KOPP, MARIE, "Surgical Treatment as Sex Prevention," *Journal of Criminal Law and Criminology*, XXVIII (1938), 692.

44. STURUP, GEORG K., *Sex Offenders: The Scandinavian Experience*, in *Law and Contemporary Problems* (Duke University Press, Durham, N.C., 1960).

45. *People* vs. *Everett* [*sic*], State of California, County of Mendocino, Superior Court, 1952.

46. *Sacramento Bee*, news columns and letters to the Editor, June, 1952.

47. DEVEREAUX, GEORGE, *Reality and Dream, Psychotherapy of a Plains Indian* (International Universities Press, New York, 1951), pp. 174, 340.

48. STEWARD, J. H., *Ethnography of the Owens Valley Paiute* (University of California Press, Berkeley, Calif., 1934); also *Myths of the Owens Valley Paiute* (University of California Press, Berkeley, Calif., 1934).

49. BIEBER and others, *op. cit.*, p. 252.

50. *People* vs. *Wilton Lebal* [*sic*], State of California, County of Sacramento, 1958.

51. Case of J. F., courtesy of Dr. G. Lee Sandritter, Superintendent, and Paul Johnson, Supervisor, Rehabilitation Service, Atascadero State Hospital, Atascadero, California.

52. PASTO and RUNKEL, *op. cit.*

53. *People* vs. *Page* [*sic*], State of California, Sacramento, Municipal Court, 1963.

54. KARPMAN, *op. cit.*, p. 319.

55. *Time*, "Art, Morals and Second Sexual Revolution," January 14, 1964.

56. *People* vs. *Prisoner* [*sic*], State of California, County of Sacramento, Superior Court, 1962.

CHAPTER X

Crimes of the Sexual Deviate

THE PEDOPHILE / CLINICAL TYPES OF
PEDOPHILES / INCEST / EXHIBITIONISM, OR
INDECENT EXPOSURE / VOYEURISM /
TRANSSEXUALISM AND TRANSVESTISM /
SADISM, DISMEMBERMENT, AND RAPE /
MASOCHISM IN CRIME / FETISHISM /
PORNOGRAPHY AND ITS CRIMINAL REFLECTIONS /
THE LEGAL STATUS OF PORNOGRAPHY / THE
CRIME OF OBSCENE CALLS / INDECENCY AND
KINDRED OFFENSES / PROSTITUTION / CRIMES
OF "NORMAL" SEXUALITY / REFERENCES

The classification of sexual crimes is no longer considered specific, since overlapping of clinical types is found among actual cases. The term "deviation" covers most of the aberrant forms of sexual expression, including homosexuality. One may also use the term "paraphilia," popularized by Karpman,[1] to indicate all those sexual activities "characterized by the absence of a biological aim." Sexual activity by adults with children, technically called pedophilia—translated literally as "love for children"—constitutes a large area of sexual crimes of the deviate.

THE PEDOPHILE

The discussion of homosexuality in crime in Chapter IX passed over, on more than one occasion, into the area of pedophilia. This term is more precisely a psychiatric descriptive designation than a legal one. Pedophiles brought before the court may have indulged in homosexual acts with boys, attempted intercourse with female children, exposed their genitals to children, fondled, palpated, or performed masturbatory acts or any form of erotic activity with a child. Although the term encompasses "love" for children, the emphasis is on the sexual expression of such "love." The legal offenses covering pedophilic behavior may be designated "sodomy," "carnally abusing a minor," "impairing the morals of a minor," "lewd and lascivious conduct," and so on, depending on the statutes of a particular jurisdiction.

The large number of pedophiles who pass through the courts may be separated into broad groups in relation to the underlying pathology of the offender, as: (a) offenders motivated by pansexual drives, *i.e.*, excessive sexual impulses gratified by any sex object, (b) cases of sexual neurosis and psychopathy, (c) men afflicted with organic brain disease (senile psychosis, cerebral arteriosclerosis, mental deficiency) or functional mental illnesses (as, schizophrenia), where lack of inhibitions permits them to attempt sex relations with children. The majority of pedophiles belong in the middle-aged population group, although not necessarily so. Before citing specific cases, some general impressions gained from examining a long series of pedophiles over many years may be of orientative value.

In contrast to the homosexual, who is often handsome, colorful, even charming in social address, the middle-aged pedophile gives the clinical impression of being a failure and a social bore. This is partly because of a semisanctimonious attitude this offender adopts, which arises from his recognition of his deviated sexual cravings and his struggle to deny these impulses. It is as if the pedophile agrees with the voice of conscience as easily as he accepts the stimulation of his pansexual impulses. As might be predicted, the middle-aged pedophile is particularly afflicted with anxiety concerning his sexual potency. A large number give histories of impotence or partial impotence. It is evident that the pedophile's inferiority feelings lead him to search for younger and less formidable love objects, whose ignorance would prevent his deficiencies from becoming obvious. The child sexual object, replacing the unattainable adult female, saves the offender's ego from psychic traumata that might prove destructive to his mental equilibrium. The fact that pedophilia develops out of a background of neurosis is partly demonstrated by its occurrence as an "occasional" crime in an apparently adjusted individual. Such an offender may have a satisfactory relationship with his wife and live with a family to whom he is devoted. When the wife is pregnant or ill, ungratified infantile tendencies emerge, often as a startling phenomenon to the criminal himself, in the form of sexual play with a child.

The mainspring of this abnormal sex drive proves to be the wish to be a child again, a regression to an earlier period when the sexual instinct was expressed in partial impulses of playing, seeing, smelling, touching, and so on. Disappointment with the spouse for one reason or another stimulates infantile yearnings. What appeared to be satisfactory, in the tedium of marriage, now appears in its true light. The yearning for ineffable satisfaction passes beyond the wife to the loving, permissive mother of old who, in retrospect, seemed to have allowed the boy-child full play for his sexual fantasies. Thus, when the spouse passes her sexual prime or loses interest in her husband, his infantile needs reassert themselves. This regression to an infantile psychosexual position occurs silently; the pedophile knows only that he has become aware that gratification of the wished-for kind is possible only with the child love-object. To the older pedophile the switch in sexual object seems natural and unremarkable. To society and the parents of the child-victim it is an unspeakable and unnatural crime.

The offender rationalizes his crime by pointing to the need to be released from a lifelong sexual suppression occasioned by a Victorian, aloof, or disinterested wife. Such an offender states that his emotional life has been without real gratification for years. The abandon he longs for in sexual play and forepleasure, denied him by adult partners, can only be found among children. This offender is often law-abiding in other respects; he may be a father or grandfather of a representative family, rarely mentioning his inner desire to revel in voluptuous gratification. Sometimes the history of such an offender, apprehended in middle life, indicates that his libidinous desires were secretly gratified for years. More often, the pedophile denies the alleged offense, or openly describes the stimulation offered by children as an adult would express pleasure in the allure of innocent childhood. Often the pedophile justifies his acts by virtue of the privileges that age confers, or projects the blame to his child-victim. Rarely does he reveal inner feelings that touch on the sexual excitement stimulated in him by children.

The claim made by older pedophiles that the children they offend against are, under cover of innocence, unduly enticing has been the subject of studies in recent years. The analysis of the criminal-victim relation, first intensively studied by Von Hentig,[2] has been borne out in a number of sexual offenses. Von Hentig postulated that the potential victim often attracts his or her attacker out of a "mutuality" existing between them. This mutuality can be recognized as an unconscious seduction on the part of the victim on one hand and a reading of this trend that coincides with the pedophile's desires on the other. We have met what Von Hentig has called the "latent" victim among the swindler victims in an earlier chapter; it is a valid hypothesis that they occur to a degree in some cases of rape and among those who are repeatedly robbed of jewelry, or burglarized and are generally "attack-prone."[3] In the specific case of the sexual victim of the pedophile, it can be said without indicting the vast number of innocent victims of these offenders that the unconscious wish of the victim to be fondled and loved undoubtedly plays a role in these cases.

CLINICAL TYPES OF PEDOPHILES

From these generalizations, we may proceed to examine the three clinical groupings of pedophiles:

(a) The offenders motivated by pansexual drives are more polysexual than deviated, hedonistic and uninhibited rather than perverted in the usual sense. They do not cavil at any mode of sex experience. Perhaps the phrase "over-sexed," a term that has no precise clinical meaning, can be applied to this group of men. The case that follows will serve as an example.

Arthur Marin, strongly built and voluble, with only a modest respect for the king's English, was a hard-working operating engineer of fifty-seven. Married for years, his life had been spent in labor camps and with construction gangs. Rugged and weatherbeaten, Arthur's life had been dedicated to work; he liked to call himself a "construction stiff." He had always been a law-abiding citizen. It was only when he spoke about the background of the offense for which he was arrested [4] that one could sense his sexual intensity, his pride in his animalism. For Arthur, masculinity and the phallic function were inseparable: "I was always sexy," he said, recalling the advent of erections at the age of ten, his visits to brothels with the "men," and his acquisition of gonorrhea at an early age. He said that in both his first and second marriages, his sex life was "okay" until four years before his arrest, when his wife became cold. Speaking in naturalistic terms, he stated that he wouldn't cheat on her; but he began to regard boys with an eager eye. There was no attempt either to evade or minimize his sexual life. More a John Bunyan of sex than a Don Juan, Arthur concentrated on orgastic activity, its instrument, function, and execution. For him, sexuality was genital exclusively; his attitude was an embodiment of the unconscious fantasy of megalopenis, the magic fantasy of a gargantuan penile endowment.

The offender described the events leading to his arrest in a pleasant tone, with the air of a man describing a fact beyond his control. "It started three years ago in a cabin in the mountains where I had been mining for gold," he said. A boy had wandered up to the cabin and they had begun "playing around." The group soon grew to three men, who would indulge in sexual play together. Warming to his recital, Arthur told of his "ten-inch erection," describing oral intercourse with the boy guest and mutual anal intercourse in the group. His recital finished in a matter-of-fact tone, saying he "believed that I could get along without it now," but expressing no regrets for his crime.

Of his previous pedophilic episodes he was equally free in description. His sexual acts with boys were to him simply expressions of naturalistic impulses:

There was an immoral act with a boy of fifteen, who was the nephew of my first wife, just playing around—screw him in the rear end and sucked him. I never saw a peter as big as that. I liked to see it and handle it. My uncle and I played—we sucked each other. When I was in Canadian harvest and logging camps I had no girl friend. I had to fight for "intercourse" with my wife when she would say I ought to forget it.

Arthur did not recognize perversions as more than just another aspect of sex. Even his homosexual contacts with fellow workers were described by this man-of-the-woods as opportunities for dealing with normal sexual needs. The court seemed to have sensed the *ur-mensch* (primitive man) in Arthur, for his state prison sentence was suspended; he was placed on probation for ten years.

(b) Experience with criminologic material demonstrates that the greater number of pedophiles suffer from sexual neurosis or latent sexual psychopathy. A man in his forties, whom we shall call Horace the pound master, illustrates this second group, albeit with more evidence of sexual psychopathy than of sexual neurosis.

The pound master occupied a position that made him a singularly attractive figure to the boys and girls of the neighborhood. Surrounded by yelping dogs, the rescuer of frightened little girls, a savior to the small boy who had lost his pet, Horace reached into the place in the hearts of the city's residents wherein their canine pets were enshrined. Here was a pound master who understood the emotional implications of his position; he took his job seriously. He spoke kindly to the children who, with streaming tears, reclaimed their pets; he spoke professionally to young parents who timorously picked out a mongrel to the delight of their children; he spoke sweetly to old ladies who had lost a favorite cat. An ideal pound master, he fed his charges, silenced them, petted them. The city fathers were especially pleased, since Horace never asked for a raise in pay, never complained about the quarters to which he was assigned. No one dreamed that he wanted more than the niche that compassion had carved for him at the city pound.

But Horace had other fish to fry. At forty-three, slightly obese, slow-moving, and with a twinkle in his eye, he played host to the children of the neighborhood, who were attracted, first, by his clamoring charges and, second, by the freedom he allowed them. One by one, girls and boys would come to his quarters to while away the hours with their idol. Horace petted them, played with them, and introduced them to sexual games—a Santa Claus in the never-never land of sexuality. It was not known that he had a record of sodomy with a girl of fifteen some years before, that he had homosexual contacts with boys, and that he had introduced children to oral intercourse. The afternoons were especially exciting when Horace held a "circus": he and his play-mates invented new games; one was called "spin the top" with sexual activity to match.

Thus the Idyl of the Pound continued until a series of complaints were filed and Horace was convicted of lewd and lascivious conduct on four counts.[5] After a thorough examination by court psychiatrists he was adjudged a sexual psychopath and remanded to a state hospital. There, as one in a group of sexual psychopaths taking special treatment, he was studied and treated intensively by individual and group-therapy techniques.

During the long treatment process that ensued (not to be detailed here) Horace gradually lost the pariahlike feelings that beset most of his fellow sexual psychopaths. A sense of realism replaced the opportunistic heaven in which he had lived; he lost his look of cupidity and sublimated his interest in children by becoming a leader of his fellow patients. When the time came for Horace to be released, the issue of whether he would still be a menace to society in the sense of the Penal Code provision came up for consideration. Because of his arrant behavior the Court was very loath to release him, even after several years of treatment. The attempt to treat such a man at all was questioned by the Court. Several examiners felt that ingrained in the offender was a persistent drive toward children almost constitutional in its fixity. Others saw in Horace's sex-play a regression developing from a delayed immaturity. The prosecutor pointed out that pedophilia exists *in potentia* in many men of mature age; therefore why free a man who had already demonstrated this type of sexual release? How many pedophiles would prey on the public if the suppressive power of the law was vitiated by "treatment" procedures instead of supported by punishment? So ran the arguments on the feasibility of treatment of the confirmed middle-aged deviate. Finally, after four years in an institution devoted to therapeutic handling of psychopathic individuals, Horace's original state prison sentence was suspended and he was placed on ten years' probation. These ten years have now elapsed without any further convictions.

(c) Sexual crime with children is frequently attributed to reduction in ego control due to cerebral arteriosclerosis, early senility, or other deteriorating brain conditions. There is truth in this assertion, although it is more common to find men with minimal organic conditions involved in this crime. Under cover of loneliness, the organic symptoms, which are relatively innocuous, come to the fore in the sexual activity. In this pedophilic subgroup, the sex relationship may be with a child closely related—a daughter or stepdaughter or child of a close friend. In this sense, their crimes are related to incest. The closeness of this type of pedophile to that of the incest offender suggests a comparison of these frequent types of sexual miscreants.

Initially, it is noteworthy that the psychological atmosphere in which incest is perpetrated differs from that surrounding child-molesting. The personalities of incest offenders do not contain the neurotic reflection observed among other sexual criminals. One surface indication of this finding is that the examination responses of incest prisoners are much less clouded by evasion or complete denial than are the responses of sexual deviates in general. These offenders appear to sense the connotation that incest, being essentially a normal type of sexual activity, albeit misdirected, is less reprehensible than is perverted sexuality. The forthrightness observed in incest offenders suggests that incest, although taboo, conveys a spirit of adult sexuality, whereas pedophilia contains within it many infantile reflections.

INCEST

The subject of incest lies on the edge of sexual psychopathy, being considered as either an extension of normal sexuality in certain foci or as sexual psychopathy of a milder type. Experience with inbred communities, or those isolated from social interchange, often reveals cases of incest between the father and his eldest daughter, or, more commonly, a stepdaughter. A primitive family organization, with the father in the role of patriarch, lends itself to incest. Here, the father (and this occurs especially in large families) is emotionally removed as an integral part of the family whole. He is its titular head, and as such considers all his children subject to his rule and sexual sovereignty. As may easily be imagined, this type of offense occurs where the mother is burdened with many children, is physically ill, or has lost her attractiveness. Unquestionably, more cases of incestuous relations occur than are brought before the courts.

The victims of incest are usually girls in the adolescent group. Whether the offense is simply that of palpating the breasts or body of the girl, or sleeping with her in a protective, yet suggestive, position, or actual intercourse is of less psychologic moment than criminologic significance. Even fatherly discussions of menstruation, of courtship practices, of wifely duties in preparation for a young woman's life may have incestuous reflections. Every experienced psychiatrist and psychoanalyst has heard accounts of parental sexual interest in, or preoccupation with, a daughter, concealed under a blanket of fatherly solicitude. In a recent case, a father of forty-three, obsessed with the obesity of his puberty-aged daughter, insisted that she weigh herself, nude, in his presence nightly. His solicitude extended to long discussions of orgastic experiences to come in the girl's life, of their health import, the effect of sexual excesses, and so on.[6] There is usually in these cases a corresponding preoccupation with incestuous fantasies on the part of the daughter (related to competitive struggles with the mother over femininity), which lie deeply buried in the unconscious layers of her mind. As a matter of clinical experience, cases of incest come to light that are claimed to be single instances; on investigation these prove to have followed years of intimacy between the father and a cherished daughter. The crime of incest is related to episodes of alcoholism in the offender, who, though otherwise well controlled, then suffers a lowering of inhibitions that permits not-too-deeply buried sexual impulses to appear.

The incest tendency has been studied intensively, but more from an anthropological than a criminal point of view. Indeed, the crime is so close to normal sexual fantasies in the male that little wonder is excited as to the mechanisms operating in the offender. For when King David was old and striken in years,

. . . his servants said unto him, Let there be sought for my lord the king a young virgin; and let her stand before the king, and let her cherish him, and let her lie in thy bosom, that my lord the king may get heat. (I Kings 1:2)

Whether the usual incest offender rationalizes his act by biblical reference is impossible to establish, but the following case is not too unusual in court practice.

Born in the rural Midwest, of less than average intelligence, DeWitt Dawson had spent his life working at semiskilled labor. During his twenty-one years of married life he raised two girls without the help of his wife, who was for the most part confined to a state hospital for a chronic mental illness. These last twelve years saw DeWitt "too busy raising the kids" to bother about his wife. On the surface, he lived within the limits of his busy life. He had occasional sexual contacts with women he encountered at bars, but in recent years seemed to have devoted himself, all too assiduously, to his youngest daughter. By the time the eldest daughter joined the military service, DeWitt, living alone with the fifteen-year-old daughter, made it a practice to sleep with her, especially after drinking. The case came to light when his landlady observed him in bed with his daughter in a suggestive position.[7] Examination disclosed nothing of a distinctly psychopathic nature in the offender, but an opportunistic attitude toward his daughter and a disregard for social mores. His heavy weekend drinking was clearly a release factor in his behavior.

EXHIBITIONISM, OR INDECENT EXPOSURE

More arresting than incest, from the standpoint of public concern, is the crime of exhibitionism, or indecent exposure. For reasons that dip into society's antiprurient attitude toward viewing the male genitals, exhibitionism has aroused interest in psychiatric investigators. Exhibitionism is a common sexual offense as criminologic experience indicates. The actual technique of indecent exposure has been modified since the automobile has become an important part of our national life; the motorcar symbolizes the fleeting character of the exposure that the exhibitionist wishes to enact. The most common type of exhibitionism is that of a young man in a motorcar who drives alongside girls and women, presents his penis to them in a moment of their unawareness, and either drives off and masturbates later, or masturbates at that time.

As has been indicated, the psychologic meaning of exhibitionism has been debated, and there are several theories that seek to explain it. Rickles,[8] for example, imputes early psychologic traumata due to a dominating mother as the effective factor in a high proportion of exhibitionists. Others consider the act a wish to arouse the female sexually; more sophisticated investigators feel it is to reassure the exhibitionist of his own masculinity. From the considerable number of cases studied by this author, a somewhat different view was developed. The exhibitionist, when studied on a phenomenologic level, presents an attitude that demonstrates aggression, rather than seduction, toward women. One must recognize, of course, a degree of sexual excitement in the offender, but the exhibitionist asserts his male prowess only to deny the female and express his contempt for her: he symbolically shakes his penis at women as he might shake his fist. The reaction of the woman is as important to the exhibitor as are his own sexual feelings: women must be shocked or dismayed, or there is no pleasure in the act. That shock or dismay is a sign of their perception of his contempt or resentment. When an occasional woman victim smiles indulgently or with amusement at such a youth or man, the latter usually runs off in confusion and embarrassment. The aggression-toward-women of men who indulge in exhibitionism is covered by passivity. Their flight from the scene is a better indication of their libidinous interest in women than is the exhibition itself. Exhibitionism is seduction without a finale, an invitation to pleasure that is immediately denied, a supreme symbolic act of sexual independence—which eventually miscarries the offender into court.

The exhibitionist, accounted more of a public nuisance than a dangerous psychopath, displays several characteristic patterns. One such was young Radley, an exhibitionist since his 'teens, arrested on this charge at the age of twenty-four.

Pincus Radley insisted on exercising his penchant for early morning drives, which was beyond his wife's understanding. But he was so dutiful a young husband that his wife scarcely questioned this oddity of behavior. After he dutifully deposited her at her place of work each morning, he would spin through the suburbs before he reported to his own job. He would regularly drive up to the gates of the local high school, or near a group of women standing or talking in a residential area, and exhibit himself. These morning tours proved to be his undoing. He was finally brought to court, and in due time was put under examination.[9]

Pincus lived in eternal conflict with his mother and his wife: he was the very paradigm of the browbeaten husband and passive son. Pincus never had a fight in his life; he walked away from trouble. His mother, intent on bringing up her children according to her principle of vigorous individualism, was severe in his upbringing. She felt she had outdistanced her husband, acknowledged to be a quiet man but ineffective, by reading, study, and planning for her son.

Pincus acted as if he had been destined to live outside the world of men and women. "I would always hesitate to say anything to express my opinion. . . . it would not be acceptable to others," he said. Early during the therapy Pincus moved as if in a "temporary" atmosphere, not quite ready to join in discussions or even to listen with full attention; he lived *en passant*, as it were. Even under therapy two years later, he was unable to speak about his actual feelings during his exhibitionistic sorties. The ventilation of strongly suppressed feelings about his mother and women in general consumed considerable time, but a period did come when he was able to recognize and express deep feelings of resentment. This period signalized a decrease in the urge to expose himself. But, as with many psychopathic persons, his hard-won freedom from neurotic blocking was interrupted by a last fling at exhibitionism.

One morning, instead of driving to work, Pincus drove up before a school, stepped out of the car, stripped to his shoes, and masturbated before two female students. Quick arrest followed and at the hearing a knowledgeable judge, perceiving that this was a last act of defiance as a piece of reality-testing, accepted the therapist's explanation of the psychological basis for the offense. The judge released Pincus once more for further therapy. In the years that followed, no further offenses occurred until, in the eleventh year after therapy, the impulse returned and he was rearrested. The urge was not eradicated.

In the course of an active psychiatric practice, it is often difficult to fill out the detailed psychodynamics in a given case, whereas a behavioral vignette will often demonstrate psychic mechanisms as clearly as if they had been analyzed minutely. In this way, the rich material of multitudinous cross sections of criminal psychopathology approaches an intensively studied longitudinal section of a criminal. In the area of exhibitionism, the mechanism advanced above—that of symbolic sexual denial combined with aggressive feelings against women—can be seen with clarity in the occasional case and in outline, or symbolically, in most cases.

Joseph Ricca started exhibitionism at the age of twenty-eight, almost explosively, out of anger at his wife's coldness. Joseph met his wife while in Europe in the armed forces; under the illusion that European women are more "sexy" than American women, he married her and brought her to America. Mrs. Ricca, still shattered by her destructive experiences during the war—she was born in Poland, living in Germany under Communist rule—could not forget her past sorrows and spoke of little else. For this, Joseph had little tolerance. He expressed his frustration openly; his wife "responded" by becoming pregnant, as if to justify, by a physical obstacle, his constant complaints against her coldness. She readily admitted that her feelings "froze when I got married." Her heart lay with the eight siblings she had left in Europe.

Suffused by a feeling of having been cheated, Joseph could not resign himself to this turn of events. He was seized by a desire to be seen by all women, to deny all women—to revenge himself against all women. Daily for a month, Joseph walked through an alley, exposing himself each time; nothing happened, nor was his anger appeased. Finally, one day, as Joseph retold it with disdain: "I opened my pants in the alley, a girl saw my penis. I walked away, walked back, and they arrested me." [10] One can visualize in diagrammatic clarity, Joseph's pantomimic rejection of women in the sexual role; it was obvious in his manner and behind his words.

The explanation of aggressiveness adduced for the pattern of exhibitionism as illustrated by Joseph's case seems to run counter to other, more dependent, exhibitionists. Here the offenders act in a more childlike way; their motivation for indecent exposure seems to rest on dependence on mother-figures, to whom they exhibit themselves. It is as if these offenders pleaded with the women to admire them with approving warmth. Behind this plea for phallic admiration in the dependent exhibitionist lies the aggression noted above. In fact, in the case of Pincus, there is more than a hint of mixed feelings displayed and interpretable. There is a mixture of yearning for love and approval and derision for the women toward whom Pincus (through his exposures) pointed his phallus. In short, exhibitionism represents a public exposure of ambivalent feelings toward women—a phallic representation of a sexual neurosis unappreciated by the offender himself.

VOYEURISM

It is a psychiatric truism that exhibitionism and voyeurism are two sides of the same coin. The peeping tendency, or scoptophilia, as it is technically termed, has been analyzed minutely where it has cropped out in the analysis of neuroses. Most analysts find scoptophilia to be a defense against castration anxiety. As Fenichel puts it, "Voyeurs are fixated on experiences that arouse castration anxiety, either the primal scene or the sight of adult genitals." [11] This theory, based on analysis of unconscious material from neurotic patients, indicates that the peeper derives his fear (which he covers over by seeking to witness current sexual scenes) from early images, perhaps of observing parental love-making in childhood. Hence, the voyeur acts as if to say "I did not do it, I only watched the other fellow do it." Although this psychoanalytic statement by Fenichel of the unconscious basis for peeping is true, one does not always find material to substantiate the theory in criminologic cases. In actual offenders brought before the court, exhibitionism and voyeurism occur in combination in the same person. Hence, the peeper is more willing to expound on his exhibitionism than on the other tendency. Further, there are cultural reasons for minimizing the peeping tendency.

In our social world, conscious peeping (or its unconscious analogue, scoptophilia) is so much a partly normal activity, so aided by the picturing of alluringly draped females—on television and in photographs in many media of girls in sports clothes, swimming and vacation togs, and so on—that it becomes neutralized by humor and minimized by acceptance. Further, the primal motivation of such "peeping," sexual curiosity, is clearly part of the maturation process, in that it subtly involves all sorts of cravings, inhibitions, guilt feelings, and so on. It is only when the peeping is done knowing that the person or persons being observed would object to such viewing, or as an insatiable inner drive, that voyeurism becomes a public nuisance, and hence a misdemeanor. Scoptophilia may lead to serious criminal charges when it extends to photographing acts of intercourse, publishing and/or selling these pictures, using them for blackmail, and the like (see later section on Indecency). It is strange how wide a disparity exists between the social acceptance of female partial-nudity in today's fashionable clothing, and the anger aroused when a partially nude woman is spied on without her knowledge in the privacy of her boudoir. It seems almost superfluous to analyze voyeurism as a tendency unless it carries a neurotic or criminal stamp, since the tendency is so egosyntonic, although resisted, in the average male. Cases of voyeurism do not often come to the criminologic psychiatrist for this reason; however, an exception to this generalization is found in the case of Lloyd Kinzel.

Lloyd was a man of gentle breeding and cultivated tastes. Graduate of a large university where he had earned a master's degree, he taught school for years, rising to the level of principal. The essentials of his early life can be summed by saying that his family was very religious, his mother as strict as his father easygoing. Brought up in an environment where talk of sex was eschewed, Lloyd at forty-four (when he undertook treatment) had the air of a strait-laced, school-teacherish person, a conscientious worker devoted to his profession.

At about the age of eighteen, he had impulsively exhibited himself to women on the street and had continued this behavior until his arrest.[12] The current charge arose from complaints of his teen-age girl students that he showed undue familiarity with them: there were specific complaints of his self-exposure, but none of peeping. Investigation disclosed that his sexual life was clearly inhibited: his first heterosexual contact occurred at the age of twenty-nine while overseas in the military service. Soon after, he married a widow with two grown children, living a life of regularity and unexceptional behavior with her.

Because he had been ejected from the teaching profession after his arrest for exhibitionism, he was taken on for therapy. Pleased to be the subject of treatment, Lloyd talked in a rather desiccated way, giving his history in the manner of an obedient student—aware of his position as patient. Soon it became apparent that his sexual feelings had become automatically repressed. Considerable effort was required for him to admit to an obsession since childhood to "see" the sexual parts, especially those of girls. He would castigate himself in an effort to subdue such urges by telling himself that his attitude was "unnatural," but this drive toward voyeurism ran like a thread through his life.

As therapy proceeded, his sexuality remained strongly suppressed. In discussing his dreams, he would say, "I have no sexual dreams, only job dreams." In spite of the absence of interpretable material, the therapy released some of the aggression that had been buried in Lloyd and he was able to relate, later on, that his temper—quite out of keeping with his gentlemanly demeanor—was violent, almost murderous. He recalled one childhood incident: he threw his sister on the ground so forcibly that she sustained a back injury. It is possible that his dedication to school children represented a reaction-formation against a wish not to have children. To want to "see" female children sexually meant that he unconsciously denied the wish—and denied children in toto. The impression obtained throughout the contact was that Lloyd's outburst of temper at his sister had borrowed emotion from a deeper level. Whether this reaction was related to memories of witnessing a "primal scene," as hypothesized in the literature, can only be speculative. Although a thorough working-through of Lloyd's sexual preoccupation was not possible, he lost much of his rigidity during therapy. In time, his teaching license was restored and he returned to part-time work in a local high school with apparent success.

TRANSSEXUALISM AND TRANSVESTISM

Transsexualism is the term given to the wish to change sexes through medical or surgical means. In this sense, transsexualism is an extension of the transvestite urge—the urge to dress in the garments of the opposite sex. In the transsexualist, the patient (if a man) desires to be emasculated, to have a vagina formed surgically and to receive hormonal injections that might result in female breast formation. Here, the desire for transformation into a woman is a reality-wish, contrary to that of the transvesite, who wishes to produce the *illusion* of being female by the vesture, manner and gait, speech, and other aspects of femininity. With female transsexualists, the wish is to reduce breast tissue, promote hairy growth by means of hormones, deepen the voice, wear masculine clothes, and adopt the attitudes and habits of the male. The female transvestite aspires to the *illusion* of masculinity through clothes and manners, whereas the female transsexualist wishes to accomplish this feat in reality. It is obvious in the latter case that the surgery required (that is, the plastic construction of a penis) is a highly impractical surgical feat. In the case of either a male or female seeking sexual transformation, the urge at the base of this deviation is emotional in nature, although sexual activity of an appropriate kind is sometimes desired. Finally, it should be noted that this problem is intertwined to a degree with the rare condition of hermaphroditism, wherein the glands of both sexes are represented in the person's body.

In the case of female transsexualism to be recounted, the glandular problem was of little importance, as is so in most cases. An emotional identification with the opposite sex was the basic reason for the desire for change. From a criminologic point of view, this condition is of little consequence except for the legal problem of obtaining judicial permission to change sex, an eventuality that is practically impossible in the United States. Such persons suffer intensely from inner conflict and social obloquy as they struggle in a world of clearly defined sexuality to maintain what they consider their proper sphere. Rare though these cases are, an example is included here for the sake of completeness.

Teddy Thurston [13] when first seen appeared to be a muscular person, hair clipped and combed in mannish fashion, dressed in slacks, jacket, and a man's shirt, talking crisply but with evident agitation. Life had become intolerable for her: dressed as a man, walking down the street with swinging stride, passersby and children at play gazed at her curiously, or a child might stop her, asking in innocent arrogance, "What are you?" Only at home was she comfortable, able to lounge about, smoke her pipe, work at the carpentry she loved. Her ménage included a "wife," a homosexual partner who maintained her feminine role. The immediate cause for consultation was the imminent withdrawal of the "wife," who had decided to marry, giving up this pleasant, but abnormal life. Although Teddy had been dedicated to her transvestite life for as long as she could remember, Gladys, the "wife," who acted in a slightly scolding, slightly patronizing manner to the patient, had been interested in this deviated situation for only a short time. Teddy's depression was real and acute—a major problem in her life.

Counsellors of many types had advised Teddy to give up her dream of becoming a man. Already jilted in two "love affairs" with women, Teddy was now despondent, despairing of ever finding even comparative emotional comfort in her transvestite condition. She had determined to seek medical help for the longed-for final transformation: surgical amputation of her breasts, hormonal treatment to reduce her rounded abdomen, increase the body-hair growth, deepen her voice, and reduce or halt menstruation. As a basically well-developed female of normal contour, the wisest counsel seemed to be to persuade Teddy to resume the life that her genes had decreed for her. This advice was of no avail; her determination to have her sex changed could not be shaken. She told how close she had been to her father, a carpenter; how she had entered the life-pattern of a boy with complete ease and without conflict; how the usual satisfactions of femininity left her cold. The immediate problem was treatment for the depression and, at the patient's insistence, a legal change of name and sexual habitus if this could be secured. An endocrinologist had already treated her over several years with glandular preparations, which had accomplished some of the aims desired in voice, structure, hairiness, menses. If Teddy dressed as a woman, she was constantly embarrassed: clad in a bathing suit, her muscular legs and arms, masculine body-hair, and manner of moving were greeted by curious glances and whispered comment. If she dressed as a man and used her natural speaking voice she was looked at in disbelief. Once a policeman stopped her while driving, asking for her license, and could scarcely be convinced that she owned the car, registered in her female name.

Consultation with legal authorities as to statutory provisions for changing her "official sex" resulted in the finding that nothing in the law permitted a judge to grant her this transformation. It was obvious that no attorney would or could represent her in her bizarre request. Although the right of a woman to wear men's clothes and to "register" as a man (or the reverse) was given legal sanction in Germany before World War I, and in Denmark later [14] when voluntary castration was approved if the patient's sexuality made "him prone to commit crimes, thereby making him a danger to society or when it involves mental disturbance, to a considerable degree, or social deterioration," no such law was found in any jurisdiction in the United States. Turning to Denmark, the present writer engaged in correspondence with Dr. Georg K. Sturup, whose work with sexual psychopaths had been outstanding in Copenhagen. With no help for her problem in this country, Teddy insisted on visiting Denmark to see what aid could be obtained there. The Danish Ministry of Justice (1955) had meanwhile become chary of legally handling cases from other lands, in view of the publicity given cases like that of Christine Jorgensen. They regretfully refused to invite the patient to Denmark. Further searching revealed neither surgical nor legal help for the patient. She remained in a state of dissatisfaction, rendered acute from time to time by her insistence on dressing as a man, despondent over the social-legal impossibility of being "registered" as a man, unable to accept a psychological identification with women.

The feeling of utter futility and frustration experienced by such rare individuals in our culture as Teddy is best described in the words of Dr. Hamburger, who, writing with Drs. Sturup and Dahl-Iversen from Copenhagen, states:

It has been an exceedingly depressing experience to learn the degree to which these persons feel they have been let down by the medical profession and by their fellow men. In loneliness and misery they fight their own tragic fate.[15]

Among transsexualists, males are in the majority [16] and for this reason suffer more social obloquy than does the rarer female transsexualists.

The transvestite, however, is not so deeply afflicted as the transsexualist; his problem is somewhat different. Like the exhibitionist, the transvestite exposes himself symbolically. Whereas the exhibitionist contrives, via his phallus, to make public his inner feelings, the transvestite utilizes the covering of the entire body to express his sexual neurosis. The act of dressing in clothes of the opposite sex is not in itself a crime. The transvestite when arrested is charged with disorderly conduct, or perhaps lewd and lascivious conduct, of a homosexual nature. The transvestite, usually a male, wears feminine clothes and high heels, adopts a female hairdo and falsies, uses cosmetics, perfume, and so forth, all to a degree that caricatures the female. Ordinarily, such appearances are at "gay" parties or in theater presentations by female impersonators. The woman who affects men's clothes is also found in homosexual gatherings, although she may be so attired in public. Bowman and Engle [17] point out that with a good many transvestites the whole force of the sexual impulse seems to be concentrated on cross-dressing with little genuine sexual desire. Significant psychologically is a group of neurotic individuals who dress in women's clothing privately, indulging in self-play before a mirror—a situation that usually comes to light in the psychiatric treatment of sexual neurotics.

The psychology of the male transvestite who yearns to take on the appearance of a female is that of denial of his masculinity. The homosexual characteristically equipped with female accoutrements, from high heels to coiffure, from shoulderless gowns to bra, is acting the part of a seductress to his fellows. He revels in the arts of womanhood, inviting his associates to look on him as a genitalless creature.

From a psychologic point of view, however, we are most concerned with men and boys who wear female clothing in private. It is not uncommon for boys to experiment at home with the bras and panties of mother or sister, wearing them in a private orgy of female identification. After the initial shock, parents often overlook this behavior, understanding intuitively the passing phase of basic bisexual interests in puberty-aged boys. Such behavior rarely reaches the courts; however, workers with juveniles are often confronted with such cases as that of Harold, a fourteen-year-old who was brought to the authorities for continued disobedience and insubordination in school.[18] It was found that since the age of twelve Harold had been appropriating his mother's underwear and that of a neighbor (which he stole from the clothesline) in which he paraded before a mirror. In a sense, this appropriation of women's underclothing, especially of silken materials, has a fetishistic quality, although considered a species of sexual neurosis.

More important from a criminal point of view is the youth who expresses his transvestite craving in sadistic ways. In such a case, the articles of underclothing are ripped or cut, in symbolic mayhem, after they have been used. The cutting represents a savage attack on the chief symbol of womanhood—the breast. The extremes of sadism, adumbrated among juveniles by symbolic destruction of female anatomy, come to light in mutilation murders of young women, beat-

ings and slashings of the female body, and the revolting crime of dismemberment.

SADISM, DISMEMBERMENT, AND RAPE

It is not always easy in these cases of actual mayhem to isolate the
lust-feelings that spill over into sexual destruction. As a matter of
fact, the forceful rapist and despoiler of women is not often subjected
to psychiatric study beyond inquiry into the question of legal insanity.
This type of crime is so universally abhorred that rehabilitation is
rarely thought of, and examinations to this end are infrequently made.
The position of the psychiatric criminologist in these cases is anomalous
because the extremely primitive techniques of sexual satisfaction
utilized in cases of this repugnant nature arouse defenses that are
reflected in a disinclination to study such deviations further. One finds
this reaction also in the occasional case of necrophilia (sexual relations
with a dead female). Finally, there is cannibalism, rarest of this type
of perversion occurring among psychotic persons. Impulses toward dismemberment of the human body and cannibalism in fact are more frequent in the fantasies and delusions of melancholic patients, and in the
dreams of neurotic individuals, than in actuality. A tangential approach
to these inhuman impulses can be made, therefore, by analysis of the
delusions and hallucinations of psychotic egos, as in cases of alcoholic
deliria (delirium tremens).

It has long been known that in such cases and in alcoholic hallucinosis a specific effect of alcohol is demonstrable on the psychosexual elements of the human personality. It is known from common experience that alcoholism stimulates heterosexual desires initially, but
that in the deeper levels of alcoholic intoxication sexual drives decrease
markedly. When, however, hallucinations and delusions develop later
in the psychotic stage, they demonstrate unequivocally the presence
of latent homosexual and perverted sexual elements. These deviated
trends, arising from subliminal layers of the personality, are projected
by the alcoholic victim to his imaginary persecutors. Thus, his delusions
deal with fears of being cut, mutilated, murdered, castrated, dismem-
bered. Cases of alcoholic hallucinosis frequently express, with every
appearance of vivid terror, such real and symbolic castration fears. For
example, a young man suffering from alcoholic delirium, admitted to
the hospital in a state of extreme agitation, said that people

were whispering about him . . . a girl wants my private parts . . . they
want to take them off by operation . . . they want to smash my body.[19]

Another patient studied in this series of alcoholic psychosis cases said
in great fear: "One fellow said to cut off my legs at the knees, cut my

head off and throw the parts into the river. . . ." Since this study of dismemberment motives prominent in the thoughts of psychotic alcoholics was made (1933), attention has turned to its meaning in the total psychology of the patient. It appears that the fear of dismemberment is related to the unconscious fear of femininity in men. To be killed piecemeal is the extreme of passivity, an extension of being deprived by castration of the sexual parts of a man. Thus the deepest expression of fear of human destruction is voiced in alcoholic hallucinosis.

The significance of this analysis can be tied to such brutal murders of women and, rarely, of men as feature dismemberment, sadistic mutilation, and so on. Might not these fears-turned-delusions, as were exemplified by alcoholic psychopathology, account for murders of women by young men in which savage sexual attacks are gruesome features? Experience with perpetrators of brutal murders of women involving mutilation leaves the impression that criminal viciousness passes through sadism to that intimate layer of organic fear within the murderer himself that rests on an unrecognized fear of feminization. For this completely unconscious fear, the female victim has to suffer. It is therefore of great practical importance in criminology to understand mutilating aggression and its background in the pathologic world of the criminal's mind.

A fertile field for exploration of aggressive sexual fantasies of a sadistic nature lies in the psychic netherworld of boys and youths of immature or psychopathic tendencies. It should not be supposed that in the majority of these situations the musings of juveniles actually do eventuate in criminal acts of the horrendous proportions that are foreshadowed in examining their psychic lives. Still, it should not be mistakenly assumed that the reservoir of sadism that seems so characteristic of the prepuberty- and puberty-aged boy, as seen in their play, dreams, language, and daydreams, evaporates completely when they achieve adulthood. As puberty moves into adolescence, this basic sadism is sublimated in contact sports, racing cars, social causes, exciting entertainment, or in the beginning of the sexual life, or it is converted into wit, as witness "sick" jokes. During the next decade of life, the grind of daily living and the economic-social struggle nullify or neutralize such feelings except among psychopathic or severely neurotic persons; here, sadism may emerge from the unconscious with savage vigor, as the frequent reports of brutal murders of women and young men will attest. The surprising fact is that among juveniles one may find the *anlage*, the rudiments, of slashings and mayhem—associated or not with rape—that in later life may occur in savage completion (cf. case of Horton, Chapter V).

The patient, introduced by a sweet-faced youngish mother, sat quietly in his chair, a thin smile fixed permanently on his lips. A tall boy at twelve, he towered above his parents. There was little to sug‹ gest his extremely high intelligence beyond a quizzical manner that the examiner ascribed to an Oriental stolidity. Hugh Lee Wong's family history indicated a true integration into the American scene. Competent professionals in many fields adorned the family tree; a college education was the rule and westernization the ideal. There had been no hint of antisociality in the behavior of any member of the family. The Wongs were a well-regulated, adjusted family, living with ease and dignity the accepted life of prosperous American suburbanites. The ground from which Hugh's delinquencies had sprung was innocent of sexual or antisocial taint, untouched by any known neurotic or psychopathic behavior.

One evening, a neighbor of the Wongs reported that on his arrival home there was evidence that his house had been broken into, and fifteen bras, five girdles, two pairs of panties, and some sanitary pads, all belonging to a single daughter, had been taken. A portrait-photograph of the girl was also missing. The parents and their daughter were equally mystified. Several days later, the underthings were found strewn over their garage roof, the nipples of the bras neatly removed with scissors and each bra slashed down the mid-line. It was as if, said the alarmed parents, "a sadist cut the nipples and contemplated stabbing the girl between the breasts." Within the next few weeks more of the missing undergarments were found; some were slashed in the crotch; some were smeared with dark paint in this area; a note was attached to one, on which was written in crude letters: "Sue—go rape your pussy. . . . You titless prostitute. . . . signed, the Red Raper."

The parents and the young lady, racked by terror, enlisted the aid of the police. After a fruitless search for a presumably dangerous sadist, the police, through a coincidence, turned up as the culprit the son of the Wongs.[20] A confession was readily obtained. Astonished rather than angered, the presiding judge agreed to place the boy under therapy with the proviso that he remain away from the neighborhood where his sexual fantasies had materialized in such disturbing form.

The psychological test (Wechsler-Bellevue Intelligence Scale), administered early in the therapeutic contact, indicated the boy's very superior intelligence, but noted also a tendency toward mental inflexibility and a weakness in social intelligence. Hugh's attitude was cooperative but his conversation with the therapist was never free. One could easily interpret the formality of the relation as arising from Oriental impassivity; the lack of any hint of hostility or rebelliousness could be interpreted as politeness toward parent-figures. As the interviews progressed, Hugh still showed a compulsive interest in women and their clothes; at times he was seen loitering about the ladies' rest rooms in the office building where the therapy was conducted. His curiosity concerning women seemed to be greater than his sexual drive, judging from associations observed in his conversation. Because Hugh spent much time alone reading and had few friends among his schoolmates, it was recommended that he be placed in a situation where he would meet boys of a more predominantly American cultural background.

This proposed program evoked a reaction from the boy: he said that his family had ordained certain goals for him; he was to learn the tongue of his forebears; he was to become a lawyer; he was to become rich. Slowly, the boy was able to express rebelliousness at this ingrained program. Still, little anxiety developed and he assumed the Americanization program recommended for him with small enthusiasm. It was clear that the clash of cultures, Oriental and Caucasian, giving Hugh little chance to identify with his American schoolboy peers, had resulted in a poorly organized personality. It was felt that his experimentation with female underclothes (it had been discovered during the therapy that Hugh had worn the bras and panties in private before cutting them) represented more a clumsy attempt to find a sexual identification than a true perversion. But the vigor and brutality with which he handled the garments betrayed the strength of his hostility toward females. The salacious words, the cutting of the underwear, and the rape in effigy carried more hatred and aggression than sexual lust. The rigid cultural code in which his life had been encased had apparently stifled his developing sexual fantasies, allowing little freedom for their exercise and subsequent sublimation.

It will serve no purpose to detail cases of brutal murders illustrating sexual sadism; the case cited above represents, in symbolic form, the emotional display seen in cases of lust-murder, mayhem, and despoliation of women. Dismemberment of the body, slashings—often of the breasts, the thighs, and pelvic area—defacing of the features by acid, burnings, and other types of mutilation, all illustrate the basic hostility toward females that has absorbed the sexual impulse. As noted in an earlier chapter, sadism is also expressed against homosexuals by male assailants. It needs to be added that sadistic homicides or assaults are not infrequently committed by psychotic individuals, usually schizophrenics or incipient schizophrenics.

MASOCHISM IN CRIME

The counterpart of sadism, masochism, has received more attention from psychiatrists and psychotherapists than has its opposite condition.

Among criminals, the reverse is true, for sadism is a grave problem in aggressive crime. Masochists are rarely involved in criminal offenses except as complainants. In victims of sexual assault the presence of inductive, or "seductive," influences, unconsciously provoking the attack, can often be identified. Among homosexuals, instances of beatings or savage anal intercourse [21] have been encountered where the assault, although unsolicited on a conscious level, resulted in intense satisfaction on the part of the victim. In such cases, for obvious reasons, criminal charges are rarely brought by the victim.

A distinction between two types of masochism has been made that aids in understanding the position of masochism in crime. It has been noted that sadism is expressed directly in the assailant while masochism is indirectly represented in the person of the victim. This can be understood when the distinction between sexual and moral masochism is noted: Freud [22] recognized the tendency to suffer humiliation, defeat, and rejection as a form of masochism (moral masochism) to be differentiated from the form that derives sexual pleasure from injury and humiliation. Neurotics often display the first form, the unconscious need to suffer—"The moral masochist loves the person who mistreats him" [23]—or, to put it in a social frame of reference: certain neurotics require their "daily dose of injustice." [24] The significance of moral masochism in criminology is its direct relation to the victims of criminal attacks. The "potential" victim, the "latent" victim, identified by Hans Von Hentig, may carry within his unconscious a strong tendency toward "injustice collecting" that emerges in his or her proneness to be attacked or injured.

To return to the masochistic offender, if one may use this paradoxical term, the case now to be reported is that of a female patient in a state hospital whose masochistic perversion almost amounted to an infringement of "public decency," although no charge was placed against her. In presenting the case of Marie, it should be borne in mind that a masochistic component is regularly present in the female at the height of sexual passion. But, as Helene Deutsch, in her exhaustive study on the psychology of women, states, normal feminine masochism is "activity directed inwards . . . parallel to man's intensified activity directed outward." [25] It lacks the "cruelty, destructive drive, suffering and pain" that is present in the perversion of sexual masochism. When pain becomes pleasure, the deviation enters. Such was the behavior pattern of Marie,[26] who was hospitalized because of behavior she could not control.

Since the age of nine, Marie had been aware of strong wishes to be punished by a man, either spanked across her buttocks or struck on her back with a belt or wet towel. As she entered into sexual life during adolescence, it became apparent to Marie that her desire for physical injury preceded sexual feelings. She would discuss preliminarily with her male partner whether or not he would cooperate in giving her, as she said, "what I want." Her confession that a beating permitted her to experience an orgasm frightened her sex partners (and her husband); it puzzled the patient herself as she strove to understand her peculiarity. Marie had analyzed, with psychiatric help and on her own, what she considered significant elements in her development. She related two traumatic periods in her life: one with her father at the age of four, when he apparently had her masturbate him, on the promise of a doll as a reward; and, second, in her 'teens with her stepfather, who would alternately punish her and caress her.

As Marie attained maturity she recognized that the granting of her wish to be beaten or punched was a prerequisite for sexual gratification. When men partners were not available, she would nick her own legs with a razor in an effort to achieve satisfaction. Marie's description of the vaginal orgasm achieved when she had been beaten sufficiently was detailed and vivid. Her life, since an early marriage followed by divorce and promiscuity, had settled into a search for punishing male partners. Even her open avowal of sexual masochism before the psychiatric examiners seemed in itself to produce emotional gratification.

The succession of events described by Marie, in each of which she was beaten, became faint, experienced orgasm, and then, feeling "mentally befuddled," was able to permit penetration by the male partner who had beaten her, hinted at the functioning of specific unconscious mechanisms. Reconstructing the psychologic meaning of Marie's masochism, the "befuddlement" she described clearly constituted an ego defense, allowing Marie to deny the unconscious origin of her wish to be penetrated. This wish, it was hypothecated, was based on an unconscious incest fantasy. In her sex ritual, Marie was child and woman simultaneously: she had to be a bewildered child suffering a masochistic beating before she could become a sensual, accepting woman.

The theoretical reconstruction advanced above followed a lengthy interview in the setting of a hospital staff conference. It was illuminating that her behavior during the conference mirrored the unconscious mechanisms described above. The patient's manner toward the predominantly male group of physicians was clearly seductive as she freely described her masochistic ritual, inviting their criticism and discussion of her difficulty. Nevertheless, there was also a directing, manipulative aspect in her manner of conducting the interview. It was as if she wished to reproduce her incest fantasy toward every man she met by inviting an open scrutiny of orgastic details—quite in contrast to the behavior of the usual female patient at a staff conference.

FETISHISM

In delineating the various perversions encountered among sexual criminals there are found, often intermingled with clear-cut deviations, elements of partial sexual impulses themselves not responsible for crime. Thus, the fetishist may be apprehended for offenses of homosexuality, pedophilia, or voyeurism, but it may be correctly surmised that fetishism is not of itself a major problem in sexual crime. Isolated cases of fetishism were more commonly seen in the past than at present. In the older literature (Krafft-Ebing), fetishists were described as primarily cases of perversion: [27] here the fetish was related to shoes, the feet, underclothes, handkerchiefs of mother or nurses, odorous items, and so on. Stekel, who assayed to treat fetishes and other sexual peculiarities, related the fetish to a stimulus to masturbation, as in the case of a man who "took his sister's old underclothes to bed . . . the odor arousing him so tremendously as to induce orgasm." [28] Later, fetishism, studied in the psychoanalysis of sexual neurosis, was encountered more frequently as a childhood neurosis. Freud [29] and his followers were able to extract a psychological principle from their study of fetishists; namely, that the object, whether shoe, handkerchief, foot, or the like, was a symbolic denial of their castration fears. Although fetishism is of great theoretical interest in psychoanalysis, as has been noted before, one rarely sees it in pure culture in our time. Indeed, in the case to be described, one competent psychiatrist who studied it felt that the shoe fetish had been deliberately cultivated as a red herring, "to detract attention from the main interest of the offender; namely, his homosexual desires for men and children."

Randolph's secret was never carefully guarded. Possessed of a master's degree in English literature, he taught at a large university where his interest overflowed the bounds of literature and entered the psychology of fetishism and the "new" science of psychosexuality. He talked of his newly acquired knowledge to many; his boot fetish which, through self-analysis, he easily related to a vigorous, domineering father, became campus gossip. Gathering all the psychiatric material available to him, Randolph's major preoccupation was the effort to prove that he had been a fetishist from childhood. Even after he had been committed as a sexual psychopath, Randolph's energies were bent on proving that he was a sick man, and that any accusation of pedophilia was beside the point, and furthermore, highly unscientific!

The offender's criminal history started nine years earlier when he had been arrested and committed to a state hospital for oral copulation on two boys. Now, three years later, he had been rearrested for a new pedophilic offense; it was during this second period of incarceration [30] that the complications of fetishism came to light. Being a highly articulate person, Randolph developed a long brief in an attempt to have his case retried from the standpoint of his study of psychopathology. The brief that the prisoner presented to the court was a defense against the original charge of homosexual contacts with boys; in it, he called attention to his cache of eighty pairs of boots and shoes and to his dreams (in which he equated the boot and the breast) as evidence that he was being misdiagnosed as a homosexual when in truth he should be classified as a fetishist. It was true that Randolph had collected many pairs of boots at home, all highly polished and of various sizes, many of the cowboy boot type; it was also true that he collected these with pride and fondness.

So vigorous was his defense of his fetish that there appeared to be a paucity of sexual connotation and a predominance of narcissistic gratification. The satisfaction of manipulating the fetish, exposing it to analysis, seemed to take precedence over the actual excitement the fetish itself induced.

As the legal struggle went on, on his writ of habeas corpus, the offender sought to expunge the diagnosis of sexual psychopath, insisting more and more that he had lifted his boot fetish to a breast fetish level, with the implication that thus he was beginning to approach a normal attitude toward women. As time went on, a certain emotional flatness intervened; the prisoner's extreme preoccupation with the subject of fetishism indicated to his examiners an intellectual deterioration. Paranoid elements obtruded themselves and the total picture receded more and more into a schizophrenic frame.

This case illustrates the indirect way in which a deviation of the more obscure type finds itself in conflict with the law. The problem that Randolph lived out in his semipsychotic utterances and behavior revolved around an originally valid sexual deviation, fetishism. Nevertheless, it was his pedophilic (homosexual) activities that attracted official attention to his psychopathy. This case is analogous to other situations in which the sexual problems that are aired obscure other elements of deviation; for example, cases of obscene telephone calls, possession or sale of pornographic literature or photographs. In these situations, public misbehavior brings the criminal aspect of the deviation to the fore.

PORNOGRAPHY AND ITS CRIMINAL REFLECTIONS

The psychologic significance of pornography has become so encrusted with debatable elements that delineation of the criminal aspects of this problem is difficult. Public morals, changing attitudes toward public decency, the content of literature and motion pictures, the question of constitutional rights and freedom of speech are all involved. The exact extent of pornography in this country is at best conjectural, and its influence on behavior and/or crime is almost impossible to gauge with any degree of certainty. Because our reactions to pornography pass through the filter of our conscious and unconscious feelings and prejudices, the greatest care should be taken to objectify this highly subjective area.

At the outset it may be observed that the dictionary definition of pornography differs significantly from its current meaning. The *Oxford English Dictionary* defines pornography thus: 'description of the life, manners, etc. of prostitutes and their patrons; hence, the expression or suggestion of obscene or unchaste subjects in literature or art.' The Funk & Wagnalls *New Practical Standard Dictionary* (1955) gives the first meaning of pornography as 'the expression or suggestion of the obscene in speaking, writing, etc.' and, as a second meaning, 'description of prostitutes and prostitution as related to public hygiene.' The word derives from the Greek *porne*, meaning harlot. Prior to relatively recent times the word "harlot," meaning camp follower, was substituted for the biblical term "whore." [31]

From the connotation of the definitions quoted, it can be assumed that prostitutes were lascivious individuals, given to obscenity. But there has been a change in this accent: eroticism has moved away from professional women in the literature. It is probable that the taint of obscenity in the literature concerning prostitutes started with John Cleland's *Memoirs of a Woman of Pleasure* (*Fanny Hill*), published in England about 1749, for the book was censored in Massachusetts in 1821 when republished by a reputable American publisher.[32] In any event, prostitution and obscenity were joined in the minds of readers under the general term "pornography." That there has been a movement away from the original definition of pornography, from prostitutes to the general area of eroticism, is shown by the attitude of such writers as D. H. Lawrence:

And probably most harlots had somewhere a streak of womanly generosity. Why be so cut and dried? The law is a dreary thing, and its judgments have nothing to do with life.[33]

Clinical surveys of prostitutes convicted of various criminal charges, exclusive of soliciting, made in the Psychiatric Clinic of the Criminal Court of New York County over a period of years gave the impression that the libidinal quotient of prostitutes is low rather than high.[34] The clinical experience of Sir Norwood East, an English authority, confirms these findings: "The literature affords examples of hypersexuality, hyposexuality and homosexuality among prostitutes as well as among nonpromiscuous women." Perhaps, as East suggests, prostitutes were credited with more sexual drive "when sexuality of women was less understood." [35] In examining stories about prostitutes, with the exception of *Fanny Hill*,[36] which is replete with vivid descriptions of sexual excitement and libidinous drives, one finds little of a sexually stimulating nature. A recent example is *The Revolt of Mamie Stover*,[37] a description of a prostitute's activity in Hawaii, written in a racy style, yet sober and factual in detail, especially those involving the commercial end of prostitution. Indecency is an integral part of the story, which, however, is not indecently told. The writing avoids four-letter words; the writer appears to focus on, and admire, the prostitute's business methods. Another recent story, *Street Walker*,[38] the story of a London prostitute, describes sexual scenes blandly, in terms far removed from sexual excitement or lasciviousness.

In considering erotic novels not involving prostitutes, the writings become more lusty, more obviously sexual in tone. A random selection, *Pleasure Girl* [39] provides graphic descriptions of sexual preparation, adequate accounts of mounting sexual passion, details of the orgasm, and so on. In these works, which feature actual libidinous expression, one finds an absence of four-letter words. However, in more classic works—that is, more in the literary tradition—as Lawrence's *Lady Chatterley's Lover* or Miller's *Tropic of Cancer*, the text is liberally sprinkled with four-letter words, as are many novels dealing with military life in wartime, modern psychological novels, and so on. The point of this brief statement on literature that stresses sexual themes is whether the use of four-letter words is the essence of literary pornography or whether the sexually exciting character of the scenes portrayed carries the illegal connotation of pornography. This point deserves further analysis before the legal position and its criminal implications are discussed.

The strong taboo on four-letter words of Anglo-Saxon derivation has prevailed in written literature since pre-Elizabethan times, when objection to such outright terms was first voiced. In contrast to words of classical derivation describing sexual activity, Anglo-Saxon words are shocking and indecent. Leo Stone, who has written a well-documented and penetrating study of the psychologic impact of the "Principal Obscene Word of the English Language," [40] has shown that the word *fuck* developed its emotional impact from its rhythmic association with the word *suck*. The former word first appeared in a lexicon in 1598 but was soon repressed in literature; deriving from the French *foutre* and the German *ficken*, the Anglo-Saxon term was replaced by the word *fornicate* (from the Latin *fornix*, meaning a brothel, vault, or arch).

Eric Partridge [41] comments that polite English frowned on the simpler word *fuck* while the vulgar continued its use in speech, it being accounted standard English, neither slang nor dialect. Compare the emotional impact of *copulate* or *fornicate* with that of the four-letter word—the Latin term for "sexual congress" with the Anglo-Saxon—or, for that matter, the socially distasteful connotation of the word *spit* with *expectorate*. In all such cases, the closeness of the word to the mother tongue (*Muttersprache,*) which betrays its closeness to infantile experiences, has much to do with its exclusion from polite English. Examples could be multiplied: the word *vulva* is accepted, whereas *cunt* (Middle English, from Latin *cunnus, cuneus,* 'a wedge') is decried:

. . . because of its powerful sexuality the term has, since the 15th Century, been avoided in written and in polite English . . . it is the most notable of all vulgarisms (Partridge).

So strong is this taboo that occasionally when printed the words are rendered *c*nt* and *f*ck*, whereas *coitus, sexual congress, copulation* require no such modification. Even the word *pudendum*, a medical term for the vulval area derived directly from the Latin, is noted in the *Oxford English Dictionary* as "that of which one ought to be ashamed"— evidence for the theory that emotions surrounding the mother, as well as the mother tongue, are strongly repressed.

In the paper referred to above, Stone points out that "the oral receptive attitude of sucking," which is emotionally and linguistically associated with the term *fucking* as "an unconscious rhyme relation," represents "predominant oral aggression." Thus, the closeness to infantile experiences and to the mother-bond arouses anxieties against which we defend ourselves by outlawing Anglo-Saxon terms. Four-letter words when written provide an open advertisement of these deep tendencies and emotions; they are pornographic because they represent too strong an emotional investment. Indeed, decency in social intercourse depends on our combined renunciation of infantile emotions and thought processes. Hence pornography and obscenity are illegal.

The shift in emphasis from prostitution to eroticism that arose when psychological insights were turned on the problem of obscenity and pornography came to light in the attempts of the courts to lay down rules for judgment of pornographic publications. The essential legal point of culpable pornography (its publication and distribution to the general public) does not apparently depend on whether four-letter words themselves, or the scenes depicted, constitute the essential elements, but on their effect on the auditor or viewer.

THE LEGAL STATUS OF PORNOGRAPHY

Statutes and decisions in cases involving pornographic publications have followed the "immoral influence" theory laid down by Chief Justice Cockburn in 1868 in the case of *Regina* vs. *Hicklin*.[42] Thus, the New York Penal Code forbids the dissemination to children under eighteen of material that "consists of pictures of nude or partially denuded figures, posed or presented in a manner to provoke or arouse lust or passion." [43] That which tends to "corrupt public morals" or shock decency standards is indictable under the New York Code (and most states of the Union have similar statutes), including immoral shows or exhibitions, obscene prints or writing "where exposure is willfully or lewdly made." [44] In a recent case (1963) the court defined a pornographic book as "one where all other incidents and qualities are mere accessories to the primary purpose of stimulating immoral thoughts." [45] The current test, if one *can* be made in view of changing attitudes toward sexuality—"the courts must recognize that they are rendering decisions in a dynamic field" [46]—was stated by the United States Court of Appeals:

[Obscene material] tends to promote lust and impure thoughts. . . . The correct test is the effect on sexual thoughts and desires, not of the "young" or "immature" but on the average, normal adult person.[47]

An interesting aspect of this problem, which touches on the subtle influence of pornographic material on potential sexual offenders, is the point at which sexual "thoughts and desires" are stimulated. How can we know whether pornography stimulates normal or perverted feelings or whether it motivates actions? Perhaps the test devised by the Court of Appeals, noted above, may be rendered into psychological language by saying that when such writings or presentations invade the inner, private thoughts and images of the persons exposed to them, to the degree of forcing the reality of sexual excitement upon them, the material is pornographic.

A conviction in a recent case [48] of the exhibition of a lewd motion picture film points up the significance of this invasion of the "private" sexual feelings of the viewer. The film in question showed women models undressing and lying on a couch nude in various postures. These involved exposure of the breasts and buttocks, pointing the buttocks toward the camera, exposure of the pubic region, and suggestive movements, including moving the "body and private parts" in circular fashion, and so on. At the trial, the defense argument revolved around the point that the models in permitting their pubic hair to be photographed did not become implicated in obscenity. The defense counsel quoted the following from an established decision:

. . . sex and obscenity are not synonymous. Obscene material is material which deals with sex in a manner appealing to prurient interest. The portrayal of sex in art, literature and scientific works, is not itself sufficient reason to deny material the constitutional protection of freedom of Speech and Press.[49]

On the other hand, the prosecution argued that any *movement* of the pelvis that was suggestive was legally obscene. The crucial point in this case, as in others, was whether the material in question tended to deprave or corrupt an average, normal person by inciting lascivious thoughts or arousing lustful desire. It was pointed out that while many people may find a picture of a nude man with his genitalia in view to be in bad taste or vulgar, ". . . as a matter of law if a picture of a nude is not otherwise obscene . . . it does not become obscene merely because the male genitalia are visible." The issue, then, concerned the "invasion of unsolicited obscenity" on the psychologic privacy of the viewer. It becomes a public matter—that is, subject to review for unlawful obscenity—when the seal of personal psychologic privacy is broken by the communication of sexual ideas that stimulate lasciviousness.

The invasion of private fantasy, protected by the law in the case of pornographic publications, has, over recent decades, yielded to the arguments and attitudes of literary men as well as psychologists. D. H. Lawrence, in defense of his writings, wrote: "pornography is an attempt to insult sex, to do dirt on it," [50] and Margaret Mead, the eminent social anthropologist, has stated that

pornography does not lead to laughter, it leads to deadly serious pursuit of sexual satisfaction divorced from personality and every other meaning.[51]

And Ben Ray Redman, as early as the 1930's, commented:

Obscenity does not reside in the stimulating object, but in the determined-to-be-stimulated subject; . . . obscenity assumes all forms, it is created by every individual for himself, from whatever materials may be available, according to the current dictates of his individual desires.[52]

The fact is that obscene words in everyday speech, if not in literary writings, are in the service of anger, contempt, and aggression as much as in that of sexual stimulation. An obscene word used for aggressive purposes loses its lascivious quality almost automatically. Into the arsenal of obscene words that would be pornographic in print enters an element of magic: an indecent expletive conveys more aggressivity, a greater sense of destructive power, and a deeper satisfaction to the utterer, than does a milder, more appropriate word. Hence the "current dictates of individual desires" may move the obscene term out of its original sexual context.

Pornography and obscenity are, then, not absolute: each has "many variables," [53] a major one being the use to which it is put by the individual who is reading or viewing it. The widespread publication of obscenity and pornography and the free use of forbidden words in the conversation of adults and even children might be considered a sign of moral deterioration in our times. In one sense, this general reaction and freedom of speech might be characterized as a diffuse, universal, sociopsychologic movement toward verbal aggression. Let us glance at a parallel situation in the social psychopathology of another time period—the Middle Ages.

If we may take the Church's position during the Middle Ages as one championing morality, we must consider its report of lascivious conduct on the part of witches as an accurate statement of the obscenity and pornography of the times. In Great Britain and on the Continent such accounts in original documents are too uniform to be ignored. The legendary institution of the witches' Sabbath represented a conglomerate reservoir of obscene interest in witches and devils in an anti-Christ setting. A description of the witches' Sabbath, the "Covenant of Witches" (the pornography of the time, paraphrased from several older sources) points up the relation between pagan aggression and obscenity:

To this general meeting. Satan would come in the form of a sheep, goat, bull or enormous black man. Sometimes he appeared as a thick fog. When the ugly vapor had cleared, there stood revealed the Master himself. With this, the ceremony of reception began. . . . The devil embraced his subjects individually and they "kissed him in such filthy parts that it is altogether shameful merely to recount." The witches by this time had been stimulated by these attentions. Now each outdid the other in plotting horrible crimes against mankind. The crowd applauded, the devil encouraged, the cold wind blew. Suddenly an altar rose from the ground and in a glare of lurid light, the figure of Christ appeared. The grisly crowd flew into a frenzy of hate. Led by the devil, they stamped upon Him, spat upon His face. In one wave of revelry, the devil urinated into a dish prepared for the final ritual of contempt for God and His Hosts. This done, pandemonium broke loose and madness passed all limits. God was eaten, cut, beaten, trampled, while the icy wind blew and the "wine" whose "odor and taste was insupportable" was passed around to the company. With the drink, they were served dishes of excrement, flesh of hangmen and unbaptized children. Drink and the victuals whipped them to the last fraction of frenzied excitement. The sexual orgy broke loose in reckless abandon. The devil, besieged by palpitating, quivering witches, seized them to satisfy his carnal lust. The throbbing mass of witches stood waving their bellies in a most sensuous dance, writhing in sexual torment and delight, while the fever grew to intense proportions. . . .[54]

Whether this reconstructed saturnalia is fact or fantasy, it parallels today's pornography in its combination of sexual excitement and rebellious, aggressive intent, that of defying and desecrating the authority of God and of His surrogate, Christ.

This digression into the obscenity of another era suggests yet another psychological implication of indecent language. The four-letter word when used as an aggressive epithet implies belittlement of the one addressed, a reduction of his sexual prowess, and a blow to his self-esteem. This use of sexual expletives, though coarse and insulting, is considered within the area of normality. But there is one type of criminal offender connected with foul words; this is the obscene telephone caller, who uses lewd words and phrases inviting women to sexual acts by combining belittlement with seduction. In recent years, the obscene call has been related to violent crimes—even murders—sufficiently distant from the offense of the call itself to warrant psychologic scrutiny.

THE CRIME OF OBSCENE CALLS

Many cases of obscene calls have been traced to adolescents, whose calling has the function of voyeurism. Such persons, often under the influence of alcohol, indulge their peeping tendencies vicariously by anonymously telephoning the home of a man and wife and inquiring whether intercourse is being, or has been, performed. Other types of obscene calls are addressed to single women, or women who, though married, are alone at the time of the call. When the call is obviously directed toward a home situation, the drive within the offender is of a scoptophilic type; when the call invites the female victim to sexual acts, the motivation in the caller is that of the rapist with sadistic fantasies. In general, the adolescent or youthful caller who furtively indulges his fantasies in this manner is less significant criminologically than the older offender, whose sadistic tendencies have been known on occasion to result in assault or homicide. Of the many cases of obscene calls that come to the attention of the police, few are considered of any magnitude criminologically: the charges generally fall within the purview of disorderly conduct, disturbing the peace, and the like. A case of this sort is illustrated by a youth whom we may call Henry.[55]

A young woman, annoyed by repeated obscene calls, agreed to meet her pursuer at a telephone booth. When the police arrived by prearrangement they found a boyish young man, timid and frightened, who had developed the idea of calling from a newspaper advertisement asking for a travelling companion. Henry had answered the ad, and hearing a young woman's voice made many lewd remarks, such as inviting her to "fornicate." Successful in obtaining a brief hearing, Henry then called other girls and, like the exhibitionist, masturbated while calling, or soon afterward.

On examination Henry was found to be a bland, slightly obese youth. His first experience with sexuality had been with a professional woman in Tokyo while in the service. Back in this country he had thought of marrying but "couldn't find the right girl." The examination disclosed more timidity than aggression, secret yearning without the forthrightness needed to make sexual contacts, and marked inferiority feelings. He was well behaved and, according to his parents, a model boy. To the examiner, his shyness bespoke a personality rigidity with little obvious aggression.

An instance of obscene calls in which the motivation proved to be that of definitely deviated sexuality followed reports that had been circulating in a certain area that a telephone repairman had made unsolicited calls to women subscribers. The conversations, jocular at first, became salacious, and finally lewd. Since the caller spoke in a voice of simulated tenderness and playfulness, and was a member of the telephone company's staff, the women were loath to complain. Whereas the initial calls were only mildly indecent—"I'll make the [telephone] bell soft and sexy for you, baby"—they gradually developed an air of lewdness—"My wife has a bad back, honey; I'd like to get into your pants. . . ." Finally, one subscriber overheard remarks, of obvious indecency addressed to her maid: "You're good enough to eat, honey—to eat pussy, I mean. . . ." The repairman was tracked down and an arrest made, but no charge was brought. The telephone company discharged the worker, with a strong recommendation that he undergo psychiatric treatment.[56]

The patient had been considered a competent, trustworthy worker with an exemplary home life. Nothing in his marriage or sexual life pointed toward deviation. A handsome man, trimly and powerfully built, his wife spoke of him as restrained and tender in sexual feelings; his friends knew him as suave, personable, and witty. During the early interviews, the patient was evaluated as a masculine type, describable as an *Urmensch* ('primitive man'), a designation applied by Freud to the man endowed with an animalistic, primitive sexual organization.

Psychological projective tests (as, the Rorschach), however, developed signs of hostile, aggressive attitudes toward women, poor emotional controls, and a confusion of male and female identification: this, in contradistinction to his apparently strong drive toward women. Because of his flair for adornment with striking clothes and his unctuous (seductive) talkativeness, the suspicion of a latent homosexual component arose as the interviews progressed. This could not be substantiated until suddenly, some three months after treatment had begun, his wife reported coming upon her husband in an act of oral copulation with an adolescent relative in their home. The displacement of oral aggression toward women (via the phone calls) by homosexual acts shed new light on the patient's obscene calls. They could now be seen as representing a furtive means of expressing, through his pseudo-sexuality, an unconscious projection beyond the woman on the phone to the invisible man of the home. The jocularity for which the patient was noted among his fellow workers and his seductive, playful manner with women proved to be unconscious defenses against latent homosexual impulses.

The situation outlined above was repeated in the case of a female obscene caller—itself a rarity—who was charged with disturbing the peace.[57] The offender, Joyce Penner, a slim, wiry woman of forty-two, had been known in her neighborhood as an unpleasant, verbose woman. In recognition of her masculine manner, she had been nicknamed "Tommy." Her family history suggested an antisocial background: one son had been a twice-convicted felon; Joyce herself had been accused of child-beating, although the charge was dropped; a brother had been convicted of child-molesting. The neighbors, independently of each other, considered her a "trouble-maker": she accused women of "tapping her wire," intercepting her phone calls, implicating her with the sheriff, and so on. The criminal situation came to light when Joyce poured out her venom over the telephone beyond toleration. What started as seductive conversation (Joyce disguised her voice to appear to be an intoxicated man) became bitter invective. She accused her women friends of sexual perversions of an oral type (cunnilingus) and insisted on telling them smutty stories over the phone, particularly ones featuring this perversion. When the women hung up on her, she called them again and again, to the discomfiture of her victims and her own evident satisfaction. Finally, she was brought to court. The resulting psychiatric examination revealed a primitive, aggressive person, whose instability, perseveration, paranoid attitudes, and restricted mental content suggested an organic brain condition.

The rather senseless obscenity expressed repeatedly by Joyce in her phone calls seems to confirm the theory that the telephone serves such an offender as a magic means of influencing people at a distance. The tendency to communicate excitement about sexual matters, whether normal or perverse, is far greater than might be imagined. Many cases of obscene calls that appear before the courts on signed complaints do not reach the stage of conviction; the majority never are reported to the police. Allied to obscene calls are indecent exhibitions and offensive sexual behavior of various kinds, which attest the surprising universality of preoccupation with sexual perversion in our population.

INDECENCY AND KINDRED OFFENSES

The variety of indecent acts that do not merit criminal charges, excluding the occasional acts of neurotics uncovered during psychiatric treatment, is surprisingly great. Such activities as "wife-swapping," social parties that evolve into orgies stimulated by alcoholism, obscene photographs, cases of troilism (sex relations involving two men and a woman, or the converse) are not uncommon. Some individuals involved in these varied acts are bisexual, sublimating their latent homosexuality through deviations practiced on women. Some are psychopathic individuals openly espousing their pansexuality in shady practices. Among wife-swappers, the majority of situations are initiated by men; in such cases, it has been found that the women acceding to indecent proposals and acts present a flat emotionality, which may hide their own unconscious interest in deviation. On the surface, the women involved appear bewildered by their spouses' actions, striving to satisfy the bizarre desires presented to them. Two random cases will illustrate this type of behavior.

An attractive, matronly woman referred for counselling because of a state of chronic anxiety unfolded a history of this type of behavior in her husband.[58] Although she had been advised to file for a divorce, she demurred because of her loyalty to her children. Several years after they were married, the wife was astonished to hear her husband insist that they perform the sex act in a motorcar on a busy thoroughfare, or at home before an open window, with the intent to be observed. She became increasingly aware that he had peeping tendencies, that he lurked around ladies' rest rooms, and that he spoke wildly about being observed in various sexual maneuvers. Pornographic pictures of other couples appeared about the house and the husband insisted that he and his wife be photographed in sexual embrace. Finally, he threatened to force his wife to ride in their car nude from the waist down. Rather than bring the case to court, both individuals came for psychiatric counselling. Thorough ventilation of the situation with the couple reduced the tension and anxiety experienced by the wife, opening the way for later therapeutic consideration of the husband's bisexuality.

The second case came to light in a divorce situation, when the wife related a vivid picture of sexual psychopathy in the case of Frank Held.[59] Mrs. Held was referred for counselling by an attorney, who was preparing to defend her in a divorce action charging her with alcoholism and mental illness. The examination disclosed a flattened individual, curiously placid for one accused of sexual enormities by a husband who was himself evidently sexually psychopathic. In questioning the wife as to her compliance with Frank's perverted sexual demands, she replied with a passivity that was difficult to believe, "I'm Mary the maid." Admitting the accusation of drinking, Mrs. Held unfolded a history of sexual actions by her husband, corroborated by good evidence, that mirrored a chapter from Krafft-Ebing.

Early in their marriage, Frank displayed strong sexual urges: he required intercourse nightly and often insisted that his wife masturbate him, explaining that this was required to stimulate her own sexual appetite. Within a year, Frank insisted that she perform fellatio on him during her menstrual periods, and then arranged to have them both photographed in the act of oral copulation. Other sexual maneuvers were demanded: Frank requested that she swallow the semen to "build her up and make her sexy." As her compliance continued under the rationalization that "that was his way," Frank's perverted requests increased: he demanded that she urinate on his face, he drinking the urine as it splattered over him; insisted on witnessing her urinating; had her sit astride him after intercourse so the ejaculate would smear over his face, and so forth and so on. Finally, Frank, who had always been interested in photography, purchased a motion-picture camera and arranged to have a friend photograph him and his wife during intercourse.

Although the husband refused to attend the counselling session, his wife's recital was so detailed that only a knowledgeful sexologist would have known enough to retail these happenings. Her explanation for submitting to these indignities was that she had vaguely heard of these activities, but considered them part of some men's world. No criminal charge had been brought, but investigation proved the truth of the wife's assertions, as well as confirming her own emotionally inadequate, schizoid mental state. The mixture of scoptophilic, exhibitionistic, urolagnic, and autoerotic elements contained within Frank's activities very plausibly found a congenial element within the wife's unconscious fantasies.

PROSTITUTION

Prostitution as a subject of criminologic inquiry does not specifically belong in a section on sexual deviation. Since it is the "world's oldest profession," chivalry, no less than professional respect, should dictate its examination on the same objective level as other offenses. Aside from the moral obloquy attending it, the subject of prostitution should be studied as to its codes and practices, inducements, and hazards and the psychologic and social status of its practitioners to evaluate it as a sexual perversion. In a broad approach of this kind, sexual deviation would enter these considerations perforce, yet prostitutes may be mentally retarded persons, neurotically frigid women, psychopathic characters, schizoid personalities, or simply unethical persons. They may be allied to the world of crime or to the world of culture and refinement; they may be shrewd business women or persons unable to survive in a competitive society because of inadequacy or mental deterioration. Indeed, the psychopathology of the prostitute may be that of every woman: the psychology of the prostitute may touch on the psychology of every woman: to witness, the prostitute fantasy that has been encountered by psychoanalysts among masochistic women and in women patients struggling with conflicts surrounding enjoyment of sexuality.[60]

From the standpoint of criminality, however, prostitution is a misdemeanor, coming under the head of public nuisance, disorderly conduct, or vagrancy.[61] Vagrancy as a charge covers soliciting, living without visible means of support (except that of prostitution), keeping a bawdyhouse, or house of ill fame, and so on. The act of prostitution itself is a misdemeanor, a prostitute being defined in New York law, for example, as: "A person who offers to commit prostitution for hire." [62] Indirectly, prostitutes may become involved in the felonies of compulsory prostitution (white slavery), extortion, and larceny, whether committed by their male associates (pimps) or themselves. The ramifications of prostitution as an organized racket—involving the services of legal counsel, bail-bonding, medical inspection, supply and distribution of women on a regular "route" by booking agents, protection from police and possible extortion or robberies by rival groups—brings the prostitute into a group of crimes associated with gangsters. Disregard for law and an identification with an antisocial viewpoint, as well as addiction to alcohol or narcotics, stamp this type of prostitute as akin to the aggressive type of criminal offender. Parenthetically, it may be noted that in male prostitution, a relatively new field of antisociality, the question of economics and organized protection is secondary to questions of individual deviation. Here, the male prostitute is a homosexual or a youth not yet confirmed in his perversion, whose acts are sporadic, neither organized as a business nor considered a profession—the fees being more in the nature of an honorarium. Male prostitutes, like courtesans, are often "kept" by men as a private convenience and hence rarely come into contact with the law.

The experience of most criminologists would coincide with the opinion of Guttmacher and Weihofen, who stated: [63] "Prostitution is primarily a socio-economic rather than a psychiatric problem." Yet the periphery of prostitution does impinge on sexual deviation, especially among women of psychopathic make-up. The use of prostitutes by male patrons includes every type of deviation: flagellation of the man, swallowing the secretions and excretions of the partner, dressing in a fetishistic manner, oral (cunnilingus and fellatio) and anal copulation, intercourse in the axilla, between the breasts or other semiclosed areas, and sadistic and masochistic acts of infinite variety. The acts described are usually dictated by extra remuneration; sexual deviation begins to lose its meaning in the world of permissible pansexuality for pay. The statutes make little provisions for the varieties of "unnatural" sexual acts among prostitutes. They are included under such general headings as sodomy, crimes against nature or "infamous crimes against nature," assault, and so on, as in the New York Penal Law,[64] since they rarely come to courts.

CRIMES OF "NORMAL" SEXUALITY

Of the crimes involving psychophysiological drives of a sexual type, those employing "normal" (nondeviate) sexual drives—adultery, fornication, rape, and (to a degree) bestiality—remain to be discussed. The last-named offense, in law uniformly considered a felony (sodomy), is not commonly prosecuted and has significance chiefly with mentally deficient or mentally ill persons, or those living in isolated areas.

In the main, this section deals with sexual activities that bear legal and psychological stigmas. The acts of adultery and fornication are so bound up with social attitudes and sexual mores that they reflect the social psychology of permissible sex in a given community more than they reflect sexual deviation in the individual. For example, several states, according to Guttmacher,[65] still carry laws on their books "punishing those who entice or lure others to masturbate." Adultery is a crime in most jurisdictions, although the tendency has been to shut legal eyes to the offense; similarly, fornication is rarely prosecuted unless it constitutes "open lewdness or notorious acts of public indecency," as in New Jersey, where it may be charged as a misdemeanor.[66] Because of a more realistic view of sexual life in recent years, many leading jurists have advocated removing adultery and fornication from the list of crimes. Ploscowe, in his definitive work *Sex and the Law*, states:

Few branches of the law have shown such a wide divergence between actual human behavior and stated legal norms. Sexuality simply cannot realistically be confined within present legal bounds.[67]

The American Law Institute has taken cognizance of this need for reorientation in its tentative draft of a Model Penal Code wherein it takes its stand "against punishing Illicit Sex Relations except when open and notorious. . . ." [68] The reasoned conclusion set forth states:

In sum, the major issue of policy in this field is whether to abandon criminal law altogether as a device for regulating voluntary heterosexual behavior or to attempt to restrict the liability to certain behavior involving secular evils . . . controllable by penal law.[69]

The crime of rape has varied significance, depending on whether it is forceful or statutory; the former, when there is no consent by the woman or girl, where force, duress, or threats are used; the latter, when the act involves a girl under the age of consent where consent is given. Forceful rape may occur in a variety of situations, some of which have been outlined in earlier sections discusing sex and aggressive crime (see Chapters V and VI). In these cases, various psychopathic or neurotic situations are present in the male, varying from inferiority reactions, stimulation by alcohol and drugs, sadistic reactions among psychopaths, psychotic states (both functional and organic), rage reactions in frustrated men.

In statutory rape, the age of eighteen (New York) [70] marks a sexual act as criminal even though consent and willing cooperation were present. In some jurisdictions the legal age of consent is sixteen, and, in the distant past, intercourse with a child over ten was not indictable as rape [71] if consent was obtained. In present-day juvenile and adult practice, the problem of statutory rape is a constant one, especially when pregnancy is the issue and marriage is inadvisable or not agreed to by the male. The only generalization possible in statutory rape is that the broadening of sexual interest in young persons and early maturation have reduced the necessity of regarding statutory rape as a sexual crime in the sense described in these pages. Cases by the score have been examined by psychiatrists and psychologists, hundreds have been handled by social workers and children's courts, with the finding that the sexual values and ideals of adolescents, both male and female, differ little from those held by the adult population.

REFERENCES

1. KARPMAN, BENJAMIN, The Sexual Offender and His Offenses (Julian Press, New York, 1954), p. 343.

2. VON HENTIG, HANS, The Criminal and His Victim (Yale University Press, New Haven, Conn., 1948).

3. ELLENBERGER, HENRI, "Psychological Relationships Between Criminal and Victim," Archives of Criminal Psychodynamics, I (Spring, 1955), 257.

4. *People* vs. *Arthur Marin* [*sic*], State of California, County of Sacramento, Superior Court, 1961.

5. *People* vs. *Horace* [*sic*], State of California, County of Sacramento, Superior Court, 1950.

6. Personal files, 1963.

7. *People* vs. *DeWitt Dawson* [*sic*], State of California, County of Sacramento, Superior Court, 1959.

8. RICKLES, NATHAN, *Exhibitionism* (J. B. Lippincott Co., Philadelphia, Pa., 1950).

9. *People* vs. *Pincus Radley* [*sic*], State of California, County of Sacramento, Superior Court, 1951.

10. *People* vs. *Joseph Ricca* [*sic*], State of California, County of Sacramento, Superior Court, 1957.

11. FENICHEL, OTTO, *The Psychoanalytic Theory of Neurosis* (W. W. Norton & Co., New York, 1945), p. 347.

12. *People* vs. *Lloyd Kinzel* [*sic*], Probation Department, State of Oregon, Counties of Marion and Polk, 1960.

13. Personal files, 1954.

14. Danish Sterilization and Castration Act, No. 176, May, 1935; also Act No. 130, June, 1929.

15. HAMBURGER, CHRISTIAN, STURUP, GEORG K., and DAHL-IVERSEN, E., "Transvestism: Hormonal, Psychiatric and Surgical Treatment," *Journal of the American Medical Association*, CLII (May 30, 1953), 391.

16. GREENBERG, N. H., ROSENWALD, A. K., and NIELSON, P. E., "A Study in Transsexualism," *Psychiatric Quarterly*, XXXIV (April, 1960), 203.

17. BOWMAN, KARL M., and ENGLE, BERNICE, "Medico-Legal Aspects of Transvestism," *American Journal of Psychiatry*, CXIII (January, 1957), 583.

18. Personal files, 1959.

19. BROMBERG, WALTER, and SCHILDER, PAUL, "Psychologic Considerations in Alcoholic Hallucinosis—Castration and Dismemberment Motives (*Zerstückelungmotiv*)," *International Journal of Psychoanalysis* (April, 1933), 206.

20. *Hugh Lee Wong* [*sic*], State of California, County of Sacramento, Juvenile Court, 1963.

21. Personal files, 1954.

22. FREUD, SIGMUND, *The Economic Problem in Masochism*, in *Collected Papers*, Vol. 2 (Hogarth Press, London, 1950), p. 255.

23. BERLINER, BERNHARD, "On Some Psychodynamics of Masochism," *Psychoanalytic Quarterly*, XVI (October, 1947), 459.

24. BERGLER, EDMUND, *Basic Neurosis* (Grune & Stratton, New York, 1949), p. 14.

25. DEUTSCH, HELENE, *The Psychology of Women* (Grune & Stratton, New York, 1944), p. 191.

26. *Marie* [*sic*], Stockton State Hospital, Stockton, California, 1962.

27. KRAFFT-EBING, RICHARD VON, *Psychopathia Sexualis*, 12th German ed., introduction by Victor Robinson (Pioneer Publications, New York, 1947).

28. STEKEL, WILHELM, *Peculiarities of Behavior, Wandering Mania,*

Dipsomania, Cleptomania, and Allied Impulsive Acts, trans. by J. Van Teslaar, Vol. 2 (Liveright Publishing Co., New York, 1924), p. 253.

29. FREUD, SIGMUND, *Fetishism,* in *Collected Papers,* Vol. 5 (Hogarth Press, London, 1927), p. 198.

30. *People* vs. *Randolph* [*sic*], State of California, County of Solano, Superior Court, 1955.

31. MENCKEN, H. L., *The American Language* (Alfred A. Knopf, New York, 1936), Vol. 1, p. 300: Appendix, p. 639.

32. GERBER, ALBERT B., "A Suggested Solution to the Riddle of Obscenity," *University of Pennsylvania Law Review,* CXII, No. 6 (April, 1964), 843 *n.*

33. LAWRENCE, D. H., "Pornography and Obscenity," in *The First Freedom,* Robert B. Downs, ed. (American Library Association, Chicago, Ill., 1960), p. 171.

34. Court of General Sessions, State of New York, County of New York, files of the Psychiatric Clinic, 1932–1941.

35. EAST, SIR NORWOOD, *Society and the Criminal* (Charles C Thomas, Springfield, Ill., 1951), p. 349.

36. CLELAND, JOHN, *Memoirs of a Woman of Pleasure (Fanny Hill),* introduction by Peter Quennell (G. P. Putnam's Sons, New York, 1963).

37. HUIE, W. B., *The Revolt of Mamie Stover* (Signet Books, New American Library of World Literature, New York, 1952).

38. Anonymous, *Street Walker* (Dell Publishing Co., New York, 1961).

39. ELLIS, JOAN, *Pleasure Girl* (Midwood [Tower] Publications, New York, 1961).

40. STONE, LEO, "On the Principal Obscene Word of the English Language, An Inquiry, with Hypothesis, Regarding its Origin and Persistence," *The International Journal of Psychoanalysis,* XXXV, 1954, Part 1, p. 1.

41. PARTRIDGE, ERIC, *A Dictionary of Slang and Unconventional English* (Manhattan Co., New York, 1951).

42. DOWNS, ROBERT B., "The Court Looks at Books," in *The First Freedom, op. cit.,* p. 50.

43. *Penal Law, McKinney's Consolidated Laws of New York, Annotated* (Edward Thompson, Brooklyn, N.Y., 1958), Secs. 484, 484 H.

44. *Ibid.,* Sec. 1140 a.

45. *People* vs. *Fritch,* 38 Misc. 2nd, 333, New York State, 2nd, 706 (1963).

46. GERBER, *op. cit.,* p. 847.

47. *U.S.* vs. *Roth,* 237 F 2nd, 796 (2nd Cir. 1956); U.S. 476, 1 L. Ed. 2nd, 1498 (1957).

48. *People* vs. *Pugnacci and Williams,* State of California, City of Sacramento, Municipal Court, 1960.

49. *People* vs. *Alberts,* State of California, Appellate Dept., Supreme Court, 138 CAZ, Supp. 909.

50. LAWRENCE, *op. cit.,* p. 171.

51. MEAD, MARGARET, quoted in Gerber, *op. cit.,* p. 842.

52. REDMAN, BEN RAY, "Is Censorship Possible?" in *The First Freedom, op. cit.,* p. 213.

53. GERBER, *op. cit.*, p. 847.

54. GARCON, M., and VINCHON, J., *The Devil: An Historical, Critical and Medical Study*, trans. by S. H. Guest (Victor Gollancz Ltd., London, 1929).

55. *People* vs. *Henry* [*sic*], State of California, City of Sacramento, Municipal Court, 1957.

56. Personal files, 1961.

57. *People* vs. *Penner* [*sic*], State of California, City of Sacramento, Municipal Court, 1957.

58. Personal files, 1959.

59. Personal files, 1957.

60. DEUTSCH, *op. cit.*, p. 260.

61. *Code of Criminal Procedure, McKinney's Consolidated Laws of New York, op. cit.*, Book 66, Sec. 887, p. 250.

62. *Penal Law, ibid.*, Sec. 722.

63. GUTTMACHER, MANFRED S., and WEIHOFEN, HENRY, *Psychiatry and the Law* (W. W. Norton & Co., New York, 1952), p. 113.

64. *Penal Law, McKinney's Consolidated Laws of New York, op. cit.*, Part I, Art. 66, Sec. 609, p. 374.

65. GUTTMACHER and WEIHOFEN, *op. cit.*, p. 112.

66. PLOSCOWE, MORRIS, *Sex and the Law* (Prentice-Hall, Englewood Cliffs, N.J., 1951), p. 158.

67. PLOSCOWE, MORRIS, *Sex Offenses: The American Context*, in *Law and Contemporary Problems*, Vol. 25 (Duke University Press, Durham, N.C., 1960), p. 217.

68. American Law Institute, *Model Penal Code*, Tentative Draft 4, April 25, 1955, H. Wechsler, Chief Reporter (American Law Institute, Philadelphia, Pa.)

69. *Ibid.*, p. 204.

70. *Penal Law, McKinney's Consolidated Laws of New York, op. cit.*, Part II, Art. 180.

71. CLARK, WILLIAM L., and MARSHALL, WILLIAM L., *A Treatise on the Law of Crimes*, rev. by Melvin F. Wingersky (Callaghan & Co., Chicago, Ill., 1958), p. 675.

CHAPTER XI

Crimes of Drug Addiction

EVOLUTION OF THE ADDICTION PROBLEM /
CRIME AND ADDICTION / THE PSYCHIATRIC
VIEW OF ADDICTION / THE MEDICALLY INDUCED
ADDICT / THE PRESENT PICTURE / SEDUCTION
OF THE ADOLESCENT / THE MICROCOSM OF
ADDICTION / REFERENCES

Narcotic addiction and the crimes arising therefrom belong to that behavior group that is intimately related to psychophysiological needs and cravings. A disordered body chemistry, a poorly integrated ego, specific subcultural patterns of pleasure, and the impelling force of suggestion are inextricably mixed in the syndrome of drug addiction.

EVOLUTION OF THE ADDICTION PROBLEM

Drug addiction has been known as a medical entity for only two centuries, since John Lettsom, a Quaker and founder of the Medical Society of London, wrote the first paper on the drug habit in 1789.[1] For at least seventy-five years drug addiction has been a medico-criminologic problem and a social evil—an albatross around the neck of society—although opium, as everyone is aware, has been used for centuries in medicine. When morphine was chemically separated out from opium in 1806, cocaine was introduced about 1880, and heroin synthetically developed in 1898, their illegal use first focused attention on the eventual need for control.

Increase in the exportation of opium from China during the nineteenth century and the insidious increase in illicit use of opium by the public aroused the governments of Europe and the United States to the point where an International Commission on Opium met in Shanghai in 1909. By 1912, at the Hague Opium Convention, sixty-nine nations had recommended restricting morphine and cocaine to medical use; restriction on the import of raw opium from the Orient was also recommended. In the United States, the Harrison Narcotic Act, passed in 1914 "partly to carry out a treaty obligation,"[2] made the nonmedical use and possession of narcotic drugs a federal offense. At the time of the Harrison Narcotic Act's passage, the term "addict" had not come into general use, but by the 1920's, under the stimulus of the Narcotics Division (later the Bureau of Narcotics) of the Treasury Department, the "dope menace" became a national neurosis. In 1923, the Treasury Department reported that there were one million drug addicts, mainly under the age of twenty, in the United States. The drug user now became a "dope fiend." [3] Due to the efforts of the Narcotics Division the estimate of drug users dropped to 100,000 during the 1930's. Although the public hysteria surrounding the dope menace faded, the problem itself remained.

Since the 1930's, the illicit manufacturer, the smuggler, distributor, pusher, peddler, and racketeer have entered the picture to the point where narcotic addiction has become entangled with a complicated financial universe absorbing millions of dollars.

That drug addiction is not a local problem is readily seen from the fact that the World Health Organization of the United Nations has since 1948 maintained an entire section devoted to the study of the world problem of drug addiction.

Not only opium and its derivatives and the new substitutes for morphine—Demerol, methadone, Dilaudid—but sedative drugs of the barbiturate group have induced addictions that have concerned physicians and police officers. Benzedrine and the present group of energizers and tranquillizers, as well as older analgesics (aspirin, phenacetin, codeine), have entered the lists of habit-forming drugs through their use in obesity pills, headache-relievers, anxiety-reducing medications, and stimulating drugs. Marihuana and peyote similarly have joined the ranks of drugs that may exert an addictive effect on the user in the same sense that the hallucinogenic drugs (Lysergic Acid, or L.S.D. 25) alter the consciousness, and affect the psychological physiology of the user to a degree where socially dangerous habits might develop. The persistence of illicit traffic in drugs, its relation to professional criminals, its propagation by the demimonde, have kept the supply of users constant. Efforts to stem this tide through legal means have been vigorously prosecuted. The Uniform Drug Law is, with slight modifications, the law in forty-six states, Puerto Rico, and the District of Columbia; the remaining four states have their own narcotic laws.[4] One of these states, California, has made the fact of addiction a criminal offense (misdemeanor) under its Health and Safety Code[5] (cf. infra).

The original wording of the Harrison Narcotic Act, it is to be noted, has been interpreted to mean that addiction could be regarded as a disease; however, the Treasury Department has interpreted the Act to mean that any use of narcotics for the "purpose of satisfying the demands of the addiction itself"[6] is illegal. The fine line between addiction as a medical disease and as a state of lawlessness has been redrawn by the United States Supreme Court in a recent decision.[7] The case concerned one Robinson, whose attorney maintained that "California's effort to impose criminal disability merely for the [*status*] . . . of narcotic addition was cruel and unusual punishment prohibited by the 8th Amendment to the Constitution. . . ." The Supreme Court, in a 6 to 2 decision, held for the defendant, stating that "even one day in prison would be a cruel and unusual punishment for the crime" of having a medical illness. Justice Douglas pointed out that the statute appealed against "is penalizing an illness," but the Court left unimpaired the power of the state of California to provide for "compulsory treatment or quarantine of addicts." The situation can be summed up by saying that addiction is not a crime per se, but the illegal satisfaction of that condition by purchasing drugs illicitly is criminal.

It seems pertinent at this point to draw a distinction between narcotic and addictive drugs. Addictive drugs (as, cocaine) are not necessarily narcotic, although most narcotic drugs are, or can be, addictive. A satisfactory definition of addiction has been given by the Committee on Morphine and Heroin Addiction in Great Britain:

[The drug addict is] a person, who, not requiring the continued use of a drug for the relief of the symptoms of organic disease, has acquired, as a result of repeated administration, an overpowering desire for its continuance, and in whom withdrawal of the drug leads to definite symptoms of mental or physical distress or disorder.[8]

Under the state laws in America, however (as in New York State[9]), the word "narcotic" has come to mean "addictive": marihuana, as well as opium derivatives and cocaine, has been included in the New York penal law although it is agreed that marihuana confers chiefly a "sensual addiction" in the service of the hedonistic elements of the personality.[10]

The distinction between true drug addiction and "hedonistic" reliance on a drug, also known as "drug habituation," centers on presence of withdrawal symptoms in the former and their absence in the case of drug habituation.[11] Even here, some clinicians have seen withdrawal effects in users of marihuana, which is not generally accredited as an addictive drug.

CRIME AND ADDICTION

The question of the relation of criminal activity to drug addiction is a moot one. Most experts agree that the acquisition of the drug habit itself induces such criminal acts as burglary, petty thievery, and prostitution to obtain money for the expensive habit, but that the usual addict himself is not essentially criminal in propensity.[12] Dr. M. J. Pescor, of the United States Public Health Service, reported in a study of one thousand cases that 75 per cent of the addicts had no criminal records before their entrance into addiction.[13] Others, including Commissioner H. J. Anslinger, of the Bureau of Narcotics, disagree that most addicts were formerly innocent of crime. According to a statement by Anslinger they have "already established a criminal pattern before becoming addicted." [14]

Undoubtedly, underworld associations weigh the scale heavily in favor of the criminality of many users: unless they are plentifully supplied with money, those who have no criminal history fall into the ranks of pushers and peddlers, thus running afoul of the law sooner or later. The large group of users whose entrance into the world of drugs was through curiosity or the example or persuasion of friends fall into that subcultural group that sociologists have dubbed the "addict culture." From that level it may be a short, easy step to criminality. Beyond this group lies an army of smugglers, peddlers, and dealers who have no connection with the habit per se, but who are immersed in illicit drug trade for profit. With the exception of marihuana (which may or may not lead to the use of heroin), seasoned opinion leans to the view that drug addicts are not criminals *au fond,* except insofar as their possession or usage of the drug is contrary to specific statutes—a conclusion that Lawrence Kolb stated thirty years ago in his early classic studies.[15]

As to the criminal propensities induced in their users by marihuana and cocaine (now a rarity), opinions differ slightly from the findings stated above. Some authors feel that cocaine stimulates and marihuana disinhibits the aggressive impulses that lead to crimes of murder and assault, while others find that cocaine simply is used by aggressive persons and marihuana is not possessed of any mysterious hypnotic power to force its users to commit acts that they would not otherwise have performed. The present author agrees with this latter formulation, having concluded after study of many offenders in both civilian and Navy life (with Dr. Terry Rodgers) that "no positive (causal) relationship between aggressive crime and marihuana usage exists." [16, 17]

Nevertheless, it must be said that, although drug addiction per se is technically not a crime, the commerce of users with the criminal world does confer a degree of criminal intent on its continued use. Actually, the psychological and physiological thralldom in which addictive drugs hold their habitués practically forces them, unless they can be cured or self-cured of the habit, to break the law in efforts to obtain money. The superstructure of antisociality that hangs over addiction—the smuggling, adulteration, watering, peddling, and distribution control of illicit drugs, which lead to assault, hijacking, murder, and extortion—

lie beyond drug addiction itself. The true criminality surrounding addictive drugs is the criminality of larceny, gangsterism, and viciously organized illicit business. The sociology of this type of crime leads to avenues only fractionally visible to law-enforcing agents. It is in the production and distribution of morphine and heroin that crime lies, and many responsible police officials feel that were the herculean task of controlling the smuggling of drugs at all possible, drug addiction would fade as a problem in criminology.

The society of drug habitués is a complex one, intertwining professional gangsters, members of the demimonde, drifters, beatniks, hustlers, petty thieves, and prostitutes with otherwise law-abiding persons—actors, physicians, nurses, artists, housewives, writers, and that formless, disenfranchised group that lies on the periphery of society. Of the young persons involved in drug usage, a considerable number outgrow both their socially disenfranchised state and their addiction. Contrary to popular opinion, many outgrow the drug habit when the particular depersonalized state called "way out" ceases to exert an allure. On the other hand, if the user does not "kick" the habit within a few years he, or she, does become almost incurable. Of the total number of addicts generally quoted as a quasi-official figure—60,000—the confirmed addicts are in the older age-group. (Parenthetically, this figure is undoubtedly too small.)

THE PSYCHIATRIC VIEW OF ADDICTION

That drug addiction has been known to physicians for a century is shown by the fact that the invention of the hypodermic needle in 1855 by Alexander Wood, and its introduction into this country by Lleweyllen Barker in 1856,[18] popularized the use of morphine for painful conditions. During the Civil War, the injection of morphine to deaden the agony of gunshot wounds was so gratefully received by Union troops that addiction to morphine became known as the "Army Disease." [19] It soon became evident to physicians that the habit could constitute a danger to health. Early in this century, nerve specialists had already classified drug users as sick emotionally: "The victims of drug habits," wrote Dr. Charles L. Dana, eminent New York neurologist, in 1905, "belong as a rule to the more degenerate types of phrenasthenias [neurotics]." [20]

Since physicians refused to encourage the growing habit, drastically reducing the prescription of narcotics, illicit sources came into being and illegal trading in narcotics began its long subterranean development. Although the medical profession still insists that drug addiction is a medical condition,[21] the alliance of users with illegal suppliers has raised drug usage far beyond the modest level of its ancient progenitor, opium. As Dr. Marie Nyswander put it, "Once a respectable member of the community, the . . . [addict] has become a criminal." [22]

A substantial number of persons enter upon the drug habit innocently as the result of treatment for painful, long-lasting medical conditions. Many persons, however, use this as a rationalization when their psychologic dependence on a drug outlasts its use as an analgesic. Such persons, exhausting their prescribed medical supply, reach out to illegal suppliers. The medically induced addict, although in the minority, still poses a criminologic problem. As the cases to be reviewed below attest, they become as firmly fixed in the narcotic habit as if their introduction to drugs had come about for other reasons.

Consideration of the medically induced addict brings the discussion immediately to the important problem of the psychologic reasons for addiction. Many investigators emphasize the personality deviation of the user as an index to his susceptibility. In fact, in psychiatric nomenclature the addict is regularly classed as a variant of the group of "psychopathic personalities." Thus, in a standard psychiatric text Noyes opens his discussion by stating: "Drug addiction is usually symptomatic of a personality disorder, i.e., Sociopathic Personality." [23] It has been routine to diagnose addicts under this rubric, assuming addiction in itself to be proof of inadequacy, dependency, and emotional instability of character. The results of addiction—a slothful, disorganized way of life, adoption of the "addict culture" ideology with its emphasis on sensations and the state of other-worldliness, the need to be close to antisocial, even criminal, persons in order to insure an adequate supply of the drug—all combine to suggest the psychopathic pattern. Beyond this, the clinical finding that drugs diminish the sexual drive and that sexual pleasure becomes transposed to the needle, injection of the "stuff," the "kick," finds support in the psychoanalytic contention that drugs satisfy sexual and pregenital (oral) cravings of which the users are not consciously aware.[24] In short, clinical as well as dynamic considerations justify the diagnosis of psychopath for the drug addict.

In this connection, the 1957 *Report* of the Council on Mental Health states: "There is a general agreement among all students of addiction that addicts have personality aberrations and that these psychiatric conditions preceded and played an important role in the genesis of addiction. . . ." [25] The distortion of personality that *precedes* drug addiction, and may be enhanced and modified by it, is that which the pyschiatrist envisions when he places drug addiction among the psychopathies in the classifications used in psychiatric court clinics.[26] The United States Public Health Service sums up the problem of "the kinds of people who become addicted" by stating: "It takes three things to make an addict—a psychologically maladjusted individual, an available drug and a mechanism for bringing them together." [27]

Criticism of this accepted position among psychiatrists has been forthcoming from sociologists who have worked in the area of drug addiction. For example, A. R. Lindesmith notes that the opinion advanced above stems from the particular bias of the mental scientist. The latter, states Lindesmith,

> actually studied addicts only after addiction. . . . They do not tell us how those traits which were the result of addiction were separated from those that were the causes of addiction. . . . The unspoken assumption is that any trait which distinguishes addicts from non-addicts is ipso facto a criterion of abnormality. . . .[28]

Pointing to drug addicts of earlier generations, as well as those now medically induced, Lindesmith asserts that psychopathic and normal persons behave in uniform ways with respect to drugs—that is, to withdrawal symptoms, dependence, and so on—and hence are not distinguishable from each other. Addicts themselves, in describing the phenomenology of drug usage, use terms that a poetic person would (or might) use; they describe the retreat from daily cares, a philosophic attitude toward existence that demonstrates their satisfaction with the "drug way of life." "With the help of heroin," wrote Alexander Trocchi in his novel on addicts, "one is no longer grotesquely involved in becoming. One simply is." [29] The borderline between psychopathy and the esoteric is thin indeed.

The question of psychopathy among addicts is important clinically and from a therapeutic point of view. Some investigators have refined the psychopathic concept to more accurately encompass the distinctions discussed above. Felix [30] used the term "psychopathic diathesis or predisposition" to describe persons not falling into the usual category of psychopathic personality, yet showing at least borderline maladjustment.

In spite of these criticisms and amendments, experience shows that one whose personality requires drugs to attain an existence satisfactory to himself embodies that unevenness of character structure that fits the diagnostic category of "psychopathy." In large urban centers, such as New York City, where the number of drug addicts is great, long-term studies of such cases point to the pertinence of the psychopathic diagnosis for this group. Dr. Emanuel Messinger, present Director of the Psychiatric Clinic of the Court of General Sessions (now Supreme Court, Criminal Division) of New York County, has noted, [31] in comparing addicts with nonaddicts, a high proportion of psychopaths among addicts as compared with a control group. (In considering his analysis of this material, it must be remembered that New York is perhaps the world center of the drug trade and an area of intense concentration of drug addicts.)

Messinger makes the further point that these addicts who were examined, each after conviction of a felony, in a psychiatric clinic by a competent staff, had already "passed through the stage of withdrawal symptoms. In other words, they have been able to function (albeit on a criminal and ambulatory level) in the community and have not required hospitalization at the time of their arrest." This group, then, was not strictly comparable to others, such as those seen in United States Public Health Service hospitals, or in prisons or clinics during and after treatment. In the New York group of addicts neither hospitalized nor exposed to stresses of prolonged incarceration, a lower incidence of functional nervous disorders might be anticipated.

In the analysis reported in Table 7, (taken directly from Messinger's paper), the entire gamut of psychiatric and personality diagnoses for both groups was scrutinized. Of the 6,039 drug-addicted offenders, all had been convicted of felonies (murder, assault, larceny, burglary), in addition to possession and selling of drugs. The 16,236 nonaddict offenders (the control group) had also been convicted of the entire range of offenses, excluding, of course, drug addiction.

Table 7 also demonstrates several interesting findings: (1) not a single case of overt psychosis was seen in the large number of addicts; (2) the incidence of mental deficiency was lower among addicts than among nonaddicts; (3) the number of clinically diagnosed psychoneurotics was quite low among the addicts; (4) the incidence of psychopathic personalities among the drug group was high; (5) personality analyses predominated in the Inadequate and Adynamic-Dull categories.

In a later study (1964), Dr. Messinger analyzed the crime representation in comparative groups of addicts and nonaddicts during the latter half of 1960—the cases being studied serially as they passed through the courts during that period. The type of crime (aggressive, passive-aggressive, or other type of crime-behavior) was contrasted in the two groups (see Table 8).

Dr. Messinger's conclusions, culled from his vast experience with drug addicts in New York County, are:

When we consider the drug addict group as *distinct* from felons of many crime-types, we find that the incidence of psychosis and psychoneurosis has shrunk to almost infinitesimal proportions, while the percentage of psychopaths has approximately trebled (14.4% to 45%) and that aggressive criminal behavior is distinctly lower proportionately among addicts.[32]

Thus, in the addict group, 17 per cent of all felony crimes involved aggressive behavior; among the nonaddict group, crimes involving aggressive behavior constituted 53 per cent. This breakdown of 1,650

TABLE 7 *

Diagnosis	6,039 Examinations of Felony Offenders Drug Addicts	16,236 Examinations of Felony Offenders Nonaddicts
	percentage	percentage
Psychosis	0.	2.5
Psychoneurosis	.03	.7
Mental Defectives	.2	2.8
Psychopathic Personality		
Antisocial Type	26.6	6.1
Inadequate and Emotionally Unstable	16.	4.1
Schizoid	1.6	2.8
Cyclothymic	.03	.025
Paranoid	.1	.3
Sex Deviant	.2	.8
Asocial	.2	.3
Personality Disorders †		
Aggressive	10.4	26.4
Inadequate	30.2	10.
Emotionally Unstable	.1	6.4
Immature and Maladjusted Adolescent	1.1	8.
Immature Adult	1.7	4.6
Unethical	2.5	3.5
Egocentric	.4	2.
Suggestible-Passive	3.5	1.4
Adynamic-Dull	4.8	6.6
Primitive	.2	2.
Adjusted to Low Cultural Level	.6	4.7
Adjusted	.05	2.7

* Courtesy of Dr. Emanuel Messinger, Director, Psychiatric Clinic, Supreme Court, Criminal Division, New York County, N.Y.

† See Chapter IV, pages 42 through 44, for detailed criteria of personality classification.

felonies clearly establishes the qualitative difference in the aggressivity of addicts and nonaddicts.

In a setting such as New York County, the recidivism rate is extremely high among drug addicts. This is expected, since a metropolitan center such as New York attracts a mobile population, many with histories of instability and inadequacy or with criminal associations. There are several corollary findings to be noted from Messinger's studies. For example, the drug traffic in an international port such as New York,

TABLE 8 *

Comparison of Felonies Committed by Male Drug Addicts and Nonaddicts (Supreme Court, Criminal Division, County of New York, July to December inclusive, 1960)		
	Drug Addicts	*Nonaddicts*
Crimes against the Person (murder, manslaughter, assault, rape, etc.)	70	655
Crimes against Property (burglary, robbery, etc.)	145	490
Crimes involving Drugs (selling, possession, etc.)	194	66
Crimes against Statutes (perjury, gambling, forgery, violation of probation, etc.)	2	24
	411	1,239

* Courtesy of Dr. Emanuel Messinger, Director, Psychiatric Clinic, Supreme Court Criminal Division, New York County, N.Y.

or in a metropolis such as Los Angeles or New Orleans, attracts those attuned to drug usage or seeking association with the drug subculture.

THE MEDICALLY INDUCED ADDICT

While the dynamic psychological basis for a propensity toward drug addiction has been satisfactorily established by those working with actual case material, its chemical basis is still obscure. Since addiction is partly a chemicophysiological and partly a psychological dependence reaction, it might be concluded that anyone can build up an addiction if the appropriate drug is used persistently enough. This, of course, cannot be confirmed clinically, but the number of nurses and doctors who develop an addiction suggests that accessibility to narcotic drugs is an important factor. When one considers the high incidence of drug addiction among medical personnel, several factors come to mind: the aura of secrecy concerning usage of drugs, which can be maintained for long periods by nurses and doctors, an identification with sacrosanct medical authority, and so forth. Although many variables must be conjured with in considering the evolution of addiction, self-medication among those practicing the healing arts does seem to predispose to its development. Whatever the cause, the individual doctor or nurse who is swept into the habit becomes a criminal offender when he or she falsifies records, forges prescriptions, or appropriates narcotics from hospital or office cabinets. The case of Elsie Gordon,[33] a nurse with a long background of devoted work in hospitals, illustrates this type of addict.

Mrs. Gordon's situation came to attention when the morphine supply in the surgery of the large hospital in which she worked dwindled too rapidly. A check of the narcotic records revealed that Mrs. Gordon had consistently altered the hospital records of drugs. Fellow workers remembered that they had seen her walk into the rest room with a syringe in hand as if intending to use it on a patient. A physical examination of Mrs. Gordon showed injection marks on the upper arms and thighs, with characteristic discoloration of the skin. A charge of theft and use of addictive drugs was brought against the nurse. Examination developed a history that pointed toward medical induction of the habit.

Several years before her arrest, Elsie had developed a medical condition, with a subsequent cerebral hemorrhage. Examination disclosed some residual signs of an early paralysis that she had been able to cover up fairly adequately in her work. But insomnia, which had always been troublesome to Elsie, plagued her until she yielded to the temptation to prescribe morphine for herself. Thus, Mrs. Gordon drifted into addiction, moving from hospital to hospital as the possibility of detection became more probable. Even more significant than the residual paralysis were indications of brain deterioration, evident in her mental sluggishness and vague, preoccupied manner. At the age of forty, Elsie Gordon was not the woman she had been during her four years of duty as a Navy nurse, a lieutenant in the Medical Corps. Elsie Gordon, R.N., was by definition a criminal; she was also a sick individual, keeping an organically impaired ego afloat on the wings of morphine.

Acquaintance with the ease-producing effects of morphine can very soon develop into an attachment that overthrows judgment and flies in the face of rationality. The person who slips into the habit of increasing his drug-taking may manipulate his physician to prescribe drugs in excess of his needs, go to a number of physicians, steal prescriptions, which are then forged, trick pharmacists into delivering telephone orders, and so on. Thus, such persons live their addictive lives in the respectability of a medical environment, remaining out of the hands of peddlers or pushers. It has become a clinical axiom to suspect that such a person shields more than a hint of psychopathic deviation in her, or his, personality. The case of Sibyl Jacobson,[34] arrested for falsifying prescriptions for Percodan, a narcotic drug chemically allied to codeine, supports the truth of this general statement.

As a girl, Sibyl demonstrated nothing that could have foreshadowed her later psychopathic predilection. Her mother, it is true, was a strict, almost severe taskmaster, constantly concerned with Sibyl's moral life. The atmosphere in the home was pervaded with a religious influence that the offender appeared to accept naturally. Upon graduation from high school, Sibyl worked as a telephone operator, leaving after a short time to marry a stable young man. Just prior to her marriage, Sibyl, operated on for appendicitis, discovered the euphoria produced by the codeine prescribed by her physicians for postoperative pain.

Life went on: Sibyl married, suffered a miscarriage, a second pregnancy resulted in a child who died of a brain injury, another infant was born with a tumor. During this trying period Sibyl, working as a practical nurse for a bedridden woman, helped herself to the patient's codeine to give herself a "lift" from her troubles. The drug seemed to give her energy, so she visited various doctors complaining of many vague pains in order to obtain more codeine. When one physician demurred she called others, using false names to obtain prescriptions for drugs over the telephone. By presenting new symptoms to succeeding doctors Sibyl was able to continue on medically prescribed narcotics for several years. Finally, the state narcotic inspectors checked her trail of prescriptions throughout the city, eventually confronting her with twenty counts of falsifying drug requests.

Further observation indicated that Sibyl's personality had shown early signs of deterioration. She spoke constantly of illnesses and drugs; her daily life became disorganized; her husband found her stories inconsistent to the point of pathological lying. Tests of the projective type (as, Rorschach) demonstrated infantile emotional expression with oral dependent cravings; much anxiety was also present in the face of a basic personality aloofness and an inability to give and receive emotion. As a matter of experiment, Sibyl was placed on mild tranquillizer drugs and denied the use of narcotics. The reaction to this maneuver was complaints of nausea; usage of another mild drug was followed by the development of migraine symptoms. When this condition was treated without narcotics it was learned that the patient had been able to obtain Percodan in spite of all prohibitions. Eventually, a recommendation that she be committed to a state hospital was made and concurred in by the presiding judge. Meanwhile, Sibyl's mental confusion and personality deterioration had progressed to the point of psychosis. Two years were spent in the hospital with apparently good results: Sibyl had developed sufficient insight to warrant discharge. Six months later she was readmitted in a state of alcoholism; her problems had multiplied—a new pregnancy, an increasingly critical husband, the discomfort of a neglected home. Within four months Sibyl was again discharged to return home, there to await whatever new crises life held for her. A final diagnosis, that of sociopathic personality, after four years of contact, was unavoidable. Whether emotional rigidity, physical disabilities, or a combination of these had engendered in the patient an unstable, psychopathic pattern, or whether it was there originally may be questioned. In any event, the ease-producing effect of narcotics met some compelling need within her. The product of all these factors propelled her into addiction.

Another common type of addiction development occurs among physicians who treat themselves for insomnia, advancing then to addiction with the barbiturates, Demerol, or morphine. It is not difficult to find specific psychological problems in these men that can be said to have influenced or stimulated the development of addiction. Often they are competent, busy practitioners, frequently overworked, whose fatigue leads to a dose or two of a stimulant, followed by insomnia, which can lead ultimately to narcotics. Many institutions, and particularly the federal hospitals for narcotic treatment at Lexington, Kentucky, and Fort Worth, Texas, have reported experiences of the type to be described briefly below. The rate of recidivism among these doctor-addicts is not as high as it is among those whose drug habit springs from hedonistic sources. The typical doctor-patient, unless he has an incurable and painful disease, such as cancer or Buerger's disease, is often able to conquer the habit with the aid of psychotherapy.

Dr. X was the kind of man patients instinctively trust. He was conscientious to a fault, worrying over his charges, distressed over serious conditions that confronted him, working long hours to bring comfort. His practice grew, his hours were never-ending. Fatigue gathered around him like a heavy cloak; he carried his responsibilities into sleepless nights. Alcohol seemed to help him only minimally, so he experimented with drugs—to get a little sleep and start him on his rounds in the morning. The stimulants worked well but they required sedatives to control the consequent wakefulness. From sedatives he found it necessary to move to narcotics. Alarmed, he tried to do without his medications; the struggle was useless; he was enmeshed in the habit. Fortunately, before his excessive use of drugs attracted the attention of the state narcotic officials through the drug reporting system, the doctor was induced to enter a federal hospital. A brief treatment sufficed to clear up his condition, but his basic problems were not resolved without considerable psychotherapeutic work. Elements of inferiority, a masochistic tendency to overidentify with his suffering patients, unconscious fears of body injury, needed to be uncovered and worked through before this doctor's tendency to seek relief through drugs could be withstood.[35]

THE PRESENT PICTURE

Examples of medical initiation of addiction could be multiplied endlessly. Through proper advice by physicians or lawyers, such addicts are seldom incarcerated in penal institutions. The type of case that usually commands police attention belongs to areas other than those indicated in the medical group. Youth and semicriminal associations form the matrix, economic disadvantage and association with low-culture groups act together as a stimulus and a goad. The hedonistic user starts with marihuana, from which he travels on to the addictive drugs, or he may flirt with heroin "as long as you don't get hooked." That the influence of rebelliousness, with its concretization in group antisociality among adolescents and young adults, is strong in youthful drug addiction is shown by the fact that the majority of users of "pot" (marihuana) after a period of experiment with "H" or "horse" (heroin) drop both habits. This is true partly because heroin as received by the buyer has been watered down, or cut, to the point where the addiction to it is milder than the user suspects, partly because the subculture associations lose their attractions and partly because of the maturation process. The fraction of addicts that do remain with the habit, however, constitute a real problem to police officials and to medical specialists. Dr. Abraham Wikler, whose experience at the United States Public Health Hospital in Lexington, Kentucky, is great, points to the changing social and medicopsychological picture of the addict in the 1960's. Commenting on an earlier composite picture described by Pescor at the same institution in 1936, Wikler states:

There have been changes in the "typical addict" from 1936 to 1955. . . . He isn't a "white male" prisoner 38 years of age given a 2-year sentence for illegal sale . . . he is a Negro male voluntary patient in his 20s. . . . He didn't have a parental home intact to the age of 18 . . . he probably can't remember seeing his father; he didn't become a morphine addict at 27, . . . he started heroin at the age of 20; he was not arrested on a criminal charge . . . he would be a volunteer patient whose F.B.I. record could not be requested by the hospital; he would not suffer from asthma, lung trouble . . . he would be free of medical afflictions. . . .[36]

The worldly-wise addict with his comparative youth spells out another type of sociopsychological problem among addicts. It is this addict who mainly engages the attention of those who deal with present-day addiction.

SEDUCTION OF THE ADOLESCENT

To understand the adolescent addict, one must first understand the small segment of society from which he springs. This subculture varies, but the practice of marihuana usage and recently of heroin experimentations, which starts the chain of addiction, often involves the high-school years. The sociology of this group may be summarized briefly as follows: The "society" of the high-school user is not demonstrated in the classroom; it is to be found in the groupings that automatically, and with almost scientific precision, gather about the polarities of clothes, habits, aspirations, and recreations—it is a society that lives and breathes between classes, during lunch periods and before and after school. It thrives in its favorite haunts: the drive-in, the coffee-stand, the poolroom, the "club." The type of student who experiments with drugs may or may not belong to the "hoods," a group whose members are dedicated to a token-display of antisocial spirit and who engage in burglaries, petty thievery, or the operations of gambling combines, or in motorcycle or hot-rod "gang" activities. Nor is the marihuana user a "square"—the boy or girl who attends school in a dumb, driven way, submerged in the ideal of education for its own sake, or that of future advancement. Nor does he belong to the "frats," the sons and daughters of wealthier parents or of those belonging to the professional class, their aspirations turned toward college and elements of social status dear to the hearts of their parents.

The drug-using group is formless, cutting across all these subcultural lines. Its antisociality results in a slightly different attitude than that found in those whose behavior eventuates in crime. The youthful drug user is passively disobedient. The acme of his, or her, aggressiveness is contained in a sneer, and in an irritating aloofness toward the pusillanimous efforts of teachers and parents to get him to "act right," of social workers and psychiatrists to get him to "adjust." He has no interest in giving up his antisocial attitudes, except insofar as using "pot" is against the law. Efforts devoted to study, to learning—to anything the world prizes—are not worthy of his attention. He or she lives on a tight little island with its own shibboleths, special phraseology, meaningful smiles, and (to them) rich, shared pleasures. Translated into the behavioral terms used by teachers and parents, he is a truant, an educational misfit, a drop-out, a "person-in-need-of-supervision." The realities of the scholastic world, its marks, courses, social activities, even its athletics, are of no significance to him. In the larger city, he joins his fellow users, drifting along aimlessly "with a mattress on his back," as the saying goes. In smaller towns or suburban areas, the members of such private groups number from two to four. With studied passivity he, or she, drifts into marihuana smoking and a life of indolence.

This is not, however, a final portrait: within two or three years many of these young people drop this dreamlike existence, emerging into life as moderately successful young adults. But all show somewhere along the line traces of inferiority, shadings of sensitivity, anxiety-reactions of varying degrees, or schizoid characteristics. This group of hedonistic addicts is less structuralized in their personality reactions than those described under the psychopathic personality and are less likely to slip into another shadowy world of homosexual associations. It is, nevertheless, a loosely woven group whose members can be singled out and dealt with therapeutically. Brad Winkelman was one such youth when he appeared before the judge of a juvenile court [37] at the age of seventeen.

A tall, wavy-haired youth, quietly arrogant, and becomingly aloof, Brad was never any trouble to his parents until he entered junior high school. It seemed that something very mysterious occurred as he rounded his twelfth year. Study lost its interest for him; he seemed quieter than most boys of his age, dreamy and distant. Laziness was compounded by indifference. In the hope that he would "grow out of it," his parents, who had carefully guarded from him the secret of his adoption at the age of six weeks, watched his behavior silently. One day, the school attendance officer sent home the astounding news that Brad had been found smoking the "weed." What was worse, it had gone on for two years under their very noses. Lamentation, threats, and the offering of rewards were the immediate reactions; strong talk followed. Brad promised to do better. He stopped smoking "pot." He returned to school, but the same passivity seemed to color all his movements; his grades dropped precipitately, his attendance decreased, his teachers were concerned and issued warnings. His mother, meanwhile, now alert to the dangers involved, watched Brad with greater care and more intense supervision. The result was the discovery that Brad was again smoking marihuana.

This time the boy was taken to a psychiatrist at the suggestion of the court and the probation department of the juvenile court. Brad's seeming dullness was tested by a psychometric examination. The results were surprising: he rated close to superior intelligence, but a lack of drive, a general apathy, characterized his attitude during the examinations. Placed in group therapy in company with boys of his age and type, Brad demonstrated a passive disobedience and an easy indifference to things valued by the adult world. He endured the therapist and his fellow group-members with the studied aloofness that had frustrated his teachers so often. Gradually, under treatment, he showed beginning signs of identifying with the therapist and the values his parents prized. But this did not come suddenly: two months after being entered in therapy he had relapsed into marihuana smoking and a return to his own social group. Conferences were held with his parents, the probation worker, and the patient himself; plans were outlined, but Brad consistently vetoed them with a fine show of disrespect for all adults concerned. Returned to Juvenile Hall, the youth spent his time in kitchen work with not the slightest show of interest in the schooling provided by the institution. He struggled with his defiance, but signs of identification, of maturing, appeared nevertheless.

Several months later, he ceased smoking marihuana and agreed to the conditions laid down by the parole officer: curfew, new associations, and regular periods of therapy. Within two months Brad inveigled his parents into sending him to another state for "another chance on my own." A year later, away from his old group, he had stabilized somewhat, was working, and also preparing for a forthcoming marriage at the age of seventeen! The drug habit had been fogotten in this impulsive start at a "regular" life. His new identification with a comparatively stable society of law-abiding people was, if not complete, definitely begun.

THE MICROCOSM OF ADDICTION

The world of addiction is not limited to the adolescent or the "voluntary patient in his twenties" who eventually finds himself in a hospital or institution. Not all addicts are catapulted into criminal arenas. An unfailing source of income to support the habit, a constant supply of drugs, a standard of living that permits no suspicion of low associations allows many men and women addicts to "live the life of a respectable, honored citizen in his home community." [38] But most commonly, courts and law-enforcement agencies are forced to deal with the recidivists, the hardened addicts, who go through the courts and jails as one goes through a revolving door. These are the users (who also may be pushers), who live on the proceeds of drug selling or prostitution or shoplifting, if women, and on drug selling or pimping or robbery and burglary, if men. They live in city areas where they are "known," where their buyers can always find them, and where their distributors can maintain contact.

The drug-selling world is a vast hierarchy, each member known only to a few and all beholden to the men "on top," who, like characters in Kafka's *Castle*, are shrouded in anonymity. The pusher is an agent of the distributor; the latter receives his "goods" from the lieutenant, the lieutenant from the "connection," the "connection" from some innonimate Mr. Big, and the latter from some unknown source out of the country. The pusher, or peddler, may be an addict, although members of the upper echelon do not often use their own product. All contacts are made in strict secrecy; the world of the seller is one of constant worry. There is concern over friends who cannot be trusted, fear of undercover federal narcotic agents (the "feds") who may be purchasers of the drug, worry over adulterated or watered heroin and marked money. All pushers assert that they sell only to "friends" and that their chief function is to relieve "sick" users; they assume no responsibility for inducing the habit in their customers. These persons have little traffic with marihuana, cocaine, or the lesser drugs (as, barbiturates). Their customers may be businessmen, professionals, prostitutes, or men and women who have no visible means of support beyond petty thievery, shoplifting (an activity known to the initiated as "boosting"), and possibly check forgery and drug selling.

The sociology of these underworld characters can be gleaned from a description of one Gwen Hollis, an attractive Negro girl facing a felony charge [39] for selling heroin in the center of Manhattan's infamous "Hell's Kitchen." Gwen, who had had eight prior arrests for drug peddling and one federal conviction, gave the information to be outlined in the next paragraphs with charm, verve, conviction, and devotion. The fact that she was "hooked," a "junkie" with no way out, gave validity to her story. Her account was documented—a clinical, sociological report by a willing victim of *the* life.

The seller, as in the case of Gwen, often has a job, such as waitress or domestic, as a cover for her activity. She lives in an apartment with a friend or husband, perhaps a child, and is generally pleased with her existence. The code of the seller includes certain inviolable rules: never sell to a novice, handle only cash, check your own merchandise, help your sick friends. The risks of arrest and incarceration, of infections and clogged veins, even of disease and death, are accepted with outward equanimity and inner masochistic pleasure. The confirmed addict may rail against his fate, hate his misfortune, but the pusher accepts, even loves, his or her life. The psychologic elements in this inbred community of drug users and sellers are the need for interdependence, participation in the network of antisociality, and the satisfaction of being "in the know." The workaday news of life in the drug community is absorbed and retailed eagerly—who has been "pinched"; who made a "score" in shoplifting, robbery, or theft; who went to the "joint" (penitentiary or state prison); who is a "hustler" in confidence games or is "turning tricks" (prostitution); where the big money is and where it goes, and so forth. Beneath the surface silence ("I mind my business, they mind theirs") is a seething world of associations, cross-associations, information-gathering and information-disseminating, the protection of friends and the exposure of "rats." It is a universe whose central core is constructed around the principle of antisociality, not viciously but benignly, not derisively but out of an inner conviction and need for a sociopsychologic world of their own. Dependence on the drug brings in its train dependence on this antisocial world. The libido of the user and the seller has been ceded as much to the ethos that surrounds the distribution, sale, and use of drugs as to the drug itself.

There are numerous other drugs to which persons become habituated. These medications may be purchased with or without medical prescription in any quantity one wishes in many places. Every psychiatric hospital unit has had daily experiences with addicted users of amphetamine, the barbiturates, tranquillizers, and other sedatives of many chemical derivations. Occasionally, medical men working in the West and Southwest have encountered intoxication with peyote, or the mescal button. In the case of peyote, for which a federal regulation exists interdicting its transportation across state lines, users of this drug are rarely before the courts. Its use is intimately connected with the American Christian Church and its ritual, a church subscribed to by the Indians of the Southwest, combining Christian principles and primitive rites.[40] As noted, the criminological significance of peyote is almost nonexistent.

Finally, to complete the account of addiction, mention should be made of alcoholism, which constitutes a tremendous problem both psychiatrically and criminologically. Alcoholic addiction is discussed as it is encountered in the various crime groups under study in this book.

REFERENCES

1. GARRISON, FIELDING H., *History of Medicine* (W. B. Saunders Co., Philadelphia, Pa., 3rd ed., 1921), p. 372.

2. KING, RUFUS G., "The Narcotic Bureau and the Narcotics Act: Jailing the Healers and the Sick," *Yale Law Journal*, LXII (1952), 736.

3. *Ibid.*, p. 738.

4. CANTOR, DONALD, "Criminal Law and the Narcotics Problem," *Journal of Criminal Law and Criminology*, LI (1951), 512.

5. Health and Safety Code, State of California, Sec. 11721.

6. United States Treasury Department Regulation No. 5, Art. 167 (1957).

7. *Robinson* vs. *California*, 370, U.S. 660 (1962).

8. Report of the Committee on Morphine and Heroin Addiction, Ministry of Health, United Kingdom, London, 1926.

9. *Penal Code, State of New York, McKinney's Consolidated Laws* (Edward Thompson Co., Brooklyn, N.Y., 1944) Book 39, Part 2, Sec. 1751–1753.

10. BROMBERG, WALTER, "Marihuana, a Psychiatric Study," *Journal of the American Medical Association*, CXII (July 1, 1939), 4.

11. World Health Organization, *Expert Committee on Addiction-Producing Drugs*, 7th Report, WHO, Technical Report Series 116, (1957).

12. MAURER, D. W., and VOGEL, V. H., *Narcotics and Narcotic Addiction* (Charles C Thomas, Springfield, Ill., 1954) pp. 214 ff.

13. PESCOR, M. J., *Statistical Analysis of Clinical Records of Hospitalized Drug Addicts*, Public Health Reports, U.S. Public Health Service, Supp'l. Report #143 (U.S. Government Printing Office, Washington, D.C., 1943).

14. ANSLINGER, H. J., quoted in Maurer and Vogel, *op. cit.*, p. 213.

15. KOLB, LAWRENCE, "Drug Addiction and Its Relation to Crime," *Mental Hygiene*, IX (January, 1935), 74.

16. BROMBERG, WALTER, and RODGERS, TERRY C., "Marihuana and Aggressive Crime," *American Journal of Psychiatry*, CII (May, 1946), 825.

17. BOWMAN, KARL M., and ALLENTUCK, S., "Psychiatric Aspects of Marihuana Intoxication," *American Journal of Psychiatry*, XCIX (September, 1942), 250.

18. GARRISON, *op. cit.*, p. 708.

19. *Narcotic Drug Addiction*, Mental Health Monograph #2 (U.S. Department of Health, Education, and Welfare, Bethesda, Md., 1963), p. 1.

20. DANA, CHARLES L., *Textbook of Nervous Diseases* (William Wood Co., New York, 7th ed., 1908), p. 741.

21. Editorial, *Journal of the American Medical Association*, CLXXXIX (September 21, 1963), 962.

22. NYSWANDER, MARIE, *History of a Nightmare* in *The Addict*, Dan Wakefield, ed. (Fawcett Publications, Greenwich, Conn., 1963), p. 31.

23. NOYES, ARTHUR, *Modern Clinical Psychiatry* (W. B. Saunders Co., Philadelphia, Pa., 4th ed., 1955), p. 513.

24. RADO, SANDOR, "The Psychoanalysis of Pharmacothymia, *Psychoanalytic Quarterly*, II (1933), 1.

25. Council on Mental Health, *Report, Journal of the American Medical Association* (September 21, 1963), p. 977.

26. BROMBERG, WALTER, and THOMPSON, CHARLES B., "The Relation of Psychosis, Mental Defect and Personality Types to Crime," *Journal of Criminal Law and Criminology*, XXVII, (May, 1937), 13.

27. *Narcotic Drug Addiction, op. cit.*, p. 5.

28. LINDESMITH, A. R., "Dope Fiend Mythology," *Journal of Criminal Law and Criminology*, XXXI (July–August 1940), 199.

29. TROCCHI, ALEXANDER, *Inside the Cave* in *The Addict, op. cit.*, p. 98.

30. FELIX, ROBERT H., "An Appraisal of the Personality Types of the Addict," *American Journal of Psychiatry*, C (1944), 462.

31. MESSINGER, EMANUEL, "Psychosis, Psychoneurosis, and Mental Deficiency and Personality Types in Criminal Drug Addicts," *Crime and Delinquency* (National Council on Crime and Delinquency, New York, to be published, 1965).

32. MESSINGER, "The Relation Between Crimes of Addicts and Non-addicts," *ibid.*

33. *People* vs. *Elsie Gordon* [*sic*], State of California, County of Yolo, 1961.

34. *People* vs. *Sibyl Jacobson,* [*sic*], State of California, County of Sacramento: DeWitt State Hospital, Auburn, California. Courtesy of Dr. John Mitchell, Superintendent, 1957.

35. Personal files, 1957.

36. WIKLER, ABRAHAM, *Drug Addiction,* in *Tice's Practice of Medicine,* Vol. 8 (W. F. Pryor Co., Hagerstown, Md., 1953).

37. *People* vs. *Brad Winkelman,* [*sic*], State of California, County of Sacramento, Juvenile Court, 1957.

38. PESCOR, MICHAEL, *Drug Addiction* in *Encyclopedia of Criminology,* Vernon C. Branham and Samuel B. Kutasch, eds. (Philosophical Library, New York, 1949), p. 132.

39. *People* vs. *Gwen Hollis* [*sic*], State of New York, County of New York, Supreme Court, Criminal Division, July, 1963.

40. BROMBERG, WALTER, and TRANTER, CHARLES L., "Peyote Intoxication, Some Psychological Aspects of the Peyote Rite," *Journal of Nervous and Mental Diseases,* XCVII, No. 5 (May, 1943), 518.

Business Crimes and the Business of Crime

Business crimes, although contrary to the criminal law, bring another aspect of the offender's psychology into view. In this discussion a somewhat different accent will be noted. Here, the intensely individual motives and emotions of the criminal offender broaden to include the permissible motive of financial success. The social matrix, or process, that sociologists insist is a vital aspect of criminality [1]—in this situation, the ethos, or ethical "tone," of business and commerce—becomes important in beginning this survey, for there is a thin line indeed between successful business enterprise and some business crimes. Sutherland, who isolated the "white-collar" criminal, showed how intimate the relation is between accepted commercial practices and shrewd, if not "good," business practices. In business, the "social process" of which these sociologists write permits all manner of thinly veiled misrepresentations, exaggerated claims, shady "deals," use of shoddy materials, and so on. Sometimes it seems as though the feverish drive to make money, to vanquish competitors, to climb to the top of the economic ladder, demand such activities. Sutherland, and those who followed him, found in this vast field of opportunism and "gimmicks" that the social process suggested, fostered, and even stimulated the sharp practices that lie on the periphery of crime.

ETHICS AND BUSINESS CRIME

In business crimes, individual and psychologic motivations necessarily invade cultural and social modes, economic ideologies, and elements of our national ethos. Hence, when the social process is involved, philosophic and legal realities—ethics and justice—arise to confound the primacy claimed by psychiatric investigators for mental dynamics in a given offender. Sociologists have been right in bringing the whole area of the social matrix to the attention of dynamically oriented psychiatrists and psychologists. Nevertheless, the relation between personality function and the social process is intimate, intricate, and reciprocal. Let us take the social influence of ethics as an example of how a philosophic notion bears on the individual psychologic dynamics of the perpetrators of business crimes. Why do not ethical principles act as a brake on business crime?

We start this inquiry by again pointing out that a formidable sociopsychologic force, to be reckoned with, is society's bristling arsenal of ethical sanctions: Crime is "bad," punishment is "good," abiding by the law is "good," avoiding punishment is "bad" (a man must face the music), and so on. (See Chapter I). For, if crime and punishment have been equivalences in the social consciousness for thousands of years, so also is the crime = punishment equation inextricably joined with ethical principles. Ethics pervades the criminal law, acting as an interstitial substance to bind justice to the fabric of statutes, decisions, and legal judgments. But, more importantly, in the area of punishment ethical considerations form the basic rationale of legal punishment for crime. Indeed, general satisfaction with the ethical basis of criminal jurisprudence has, as the discussion of the history of punishment indicated (Chapter II), left little room until recent times for an objective, behavioral viewing of those activities called criminal. The satisfaction of applying ethical sanctions in retaliation became, and still is, an end in itself; this preoccupation with punishment effectively precluded a penetrating scrutiny of criminal psychology. The "why" of crime was neglected in the need to punish and remove the criminal from the social scene.

There are other impediments to efforts to analyze psychologic motivations in crime, lying chiefly in the area of business crimes. Here, financial maneuverings involve corporations blameless in themselves, but headed by directors who manipulate and exploit both money and power by methods they would disdain in their personal lives. The original description of "white-collar crime" by Sutherland includes business crimes that arise out of the very process of carrying on business:

White-collar crime may be defined approximately as a crime committed by a person of respectability and high social status in the course of his occupation.[2]

In the area of business crimes, ethics are not so neatly applicable: here the zone of gray, lying between the black and white of right and wrong, becomes significant. Sharp business practices, chiefly by large corporations or cartels, once considered ethical in the larger frame of private enterprise began, on scrutiny (about 1900–1910), to appear suspiciously like criminal actions. Manipulations arising out of cartels, subsidiaries, and monopolies, overemphasis or omissions of vital facts in economic competition, short cuts, circumventions, and skimpiness in complying with laws and regulations, self-assigned indulgences in the matter of exploitation, connivance with governmental officials—all touched on criminal categories.

The growth of corporate mischief that skirts on practices that would be deemed criminal if discovered in individuals is chiefly a product of the twentieth century. The possibility that monopoly capitalism might conceivably run athwart the criminal law arose when the Sherman Antitrust Act (1890) was brought to bear on large corporation mergers as implying restraint of trade. In several cases tested before the United States Supreme Court, that body ruled for the corporation on the theory that "business practices and callings are above the law." [3] The notion that a corporation could be immoral seemed to be an idea foreign to American thinking. As Commager, the historian, has stated:

The American mind and the American law were equipped to recognize and deal with old familiar personal sins—theft, embezzlement, assault, murder: confronted by new, impersonal social sin they were confused. . . . [4]

The corporation by its very nature could not be accused of unethical principles and conduct: the corporation was, as Ross put it, more than half a century ago, "an entity that transmits the greed of investors, but not their conscience." [5]

The language of the Sherman Antitrust Act did make monopoly a crime,

Every person who shall monopolize or combine or conspire with any other person or persons . . . to monopolize any part of the trade or commerce of the several states . . . shall be deemed guilty of a misdemeanor. . . . [6]

but the nation was not ready for this extension of criminal liability. As corporation control of industry spread, it became evident that the notion of public morality required implementation. Woodrow Wilson, in 1913, wrote indignantly of these matters:

Our government has been for the past few years under the control of heads of great allied corporations with special interests . . . it has submitted itself to their control. . . . What I am interested in is having the government of the United States more concerned about human rights than about property rights. Property is an instrument of humanity; humanity is not an instrument of property. [7]

Although a corporation, a nonhuman entity, cannot itself entertain criminal intent to defraud, it can be adjudged guilty of crime and be fined although not corporally punished, as by imprisonment. It is only when a corporation rigs its reports (through its directors or officers), enters into a conspiracy to fix prices, circulates false prospectuses, or misuses the names of men prominent in the financial world that the concept of criminal intent enters the arena.

The connotation of "criminal" action in cases where corporation heads were found guilty of price-fixing has been more keenly recognized during the last few years. In the case of the McDonough Company (1959), the Court, in fixing sentence for the corporation heads found guilty of price manipulation (under Section 14 of the Clayton Antitrust Act), said in part:

I do not think that the Congress would have put a jail sentence in the Statute if they did not intend for a court to use it if it thought it was proper.[8]

But the most widely known antitrust prosecution for price-fixing and bid-rigging, for which prison sentences were meted out after conviction, was the so-called "electrical equipment" or "Philadelphia price-fixing" cases. In 1960, some twenty-nine separate companies and a number of officers and employees were indicted; the corporations included such prominent names as General Electric Company, Allis-Chalmers Manufacturing Company, Ingersoll-Rand Company, Westinghouse Electric Corporation. The cases tried in the United States District Court in Philadelphia [9] attracted universal attention because of the imposition of fines *and* prison sentences upon corporation heads who were otherwise men of probity and good personal ethics. Nevertheless, the intricate system of manipulation that was brought to light, which involved secret meetings of heads of corporations, conspiratorial arrangements to reduce competition from companies not in the cartel, boosting prices on "competitive" public bids that had actually been prearranged among the corporation heads concerned, was clearly contrary to the American free-enterprise system. Judge Ganey, of the U.S. District Court in Philadelphia, before whom the cases were tried, summed up the ethical problems involved in these price-fixing activities:

At stake here is the survival of the kind of economy under which America has grown to greatness: the free enterprise system. These men and these corporations have flagrantly mocked the image of the economic system. . . .[10]

The price-fixing in the "G.E. case" was so extensive as to affect the operations of the Tennessee Valley Authority and municipal and governmental subdivisions purchasing electricity, as well as countless individual users of electrical current. The conspiracy to establish a high price for circuit breakers, essential in the transmission of electricity, affected the whole nation. This was indeed a flagrant mockery of the American economic system. The action of these great corporations had, said the late Senator Estes Kefauver, "gnawed at the vitals of the nation."

STOCK MARKET SPECULATION AND CRIME

A vantage point from which to view business crimes in their larger financial framework is in the stock market. The path of progression from high-powered salesmanship to unscrupulous promotion of mis-represented stocks has been traced by many economists. In this book our interest is in the development of the attitude that these activities may be criminal and in the psychology of those involved in crimes of this nature. For this purpose, a brief survey of attempts made to control white-collar crimes has been adapted from Ogg and Ray's [11] survey of stock-market defalcations. Following this, a psychiatric study of a man of "probity and ethics" whose business manipulations were marked as criminal will be presented.

The abuse of security sales through fraudulent practices, which had its climax before the financial debacle of 1929, had been observed for years. In 1910–11, Rhode Island and Kansas led off in legal efforts by states to make life uncomfortable for sellers whose promotional schemes reached "the bright blue sky above"; all traffic in stocks and bonds within these states was placed under public regulation. Other states followed suit until by 1933 every one of the then forty-eight states (except Nevada) had enacted so-called "blue-sky" laws to control dubious business practices. But such state regulations, although effective to a degree, required aid from the federal government since many businesses operated across state lines. The regulations imposed by the stock exchanges on their members were rather loose. Practices countenanced by the code of the local stock exchanges were "from the vantage point of today's financial market . . . scandalous—even criminal." [12] If action was brought against a stock promoter it was usually "too ambiguous to permit prosecution." [13] The whole complex of stock-market gambling, with the spectacular and tragic break of 1929, came to bear a significance beyond the limits of Wall Street in New York or Montgomery Street in San Francisco. Declaring stock-market trans-actions to be matters that affect the "national public interest," Congress enacted two carefully drawn statutes: on May 27, 1933, the Federal Securities Act, which focused on the issuance of new securities; on June 6, 1934, the Securities Exchange Act, which applied to the buying and selling of securities generally.[14]

The Act of 1933 required that all issues of stocks, bonds, or other securites (with, however, certain exceptions), if offered in interstate commerce or by mail, be registered with the Federal Trade Commission. Each such registration was required to be accompanied by a registration statement containing full financial facts and other corporate information, and by true copies of the prospectus prepared for use in soliciting stock or bond purchases by the public. The federal agency's only function up to this point was to see that complete information concerning a security offered for sale was made available to the investing public, that this information was accurate, and that no fraud was practiced in connection with sales. The emphasis placed on a full airing of the facts and figures behind stock offerings implied a growing awareness of the criminal aspects of fraudulent manipulation of financial matters. The Securities and Exchange Commission, created by the 1934 Act, made it crystal clear, in regulating stock issues offered for public sales, that securities registered with them

have not been approved or disapproved by the Securities and Exchange Commission nor has the Commission passed on the accuracy of this prospectus. . . .

The principle of *caveat emptor*, although not vitiated by these strict provisions, was at least modified to such an extent that the buyer was forewarned as to the veracity of the statements and promises made, or implied, in the prospectus. In one way, the ethics of the seller were also protected inasmuch as another significant point had become evident: although manipulation of stocks is not in itself unethical, it *is* illegal, as well as unethical, to send to prospective security purchasers printed information, or a prospectus that is not entirely truthful, and which is calculated to help sell a stock issue.

Before a close scrutiny of business crimes is undertaken, a brief statement contrasting manipulation and speculation should be made. There is a broad behavioral zone uniting speculation, manipulation, and gambling in the stock market that makes exact differentiation difficult, but which nevertheless contains vital distinctions for an understanding of business crimes. *Speculation* has been defined as buying against the probability of profit; *manipulation* covers hidden techniques calculated to improve the probability of increasing the value of a given security; *gambling* depends on the chance increase in the value of a stock. In the case of speculation, the securities to be purchased have some immediate value, but a greater growth value is anticipated; in manipulation of securities, a minimal value also exists. In gambling, however, the current value of the securities is mainly potential. A prominent stockbroker has stated this bluntly:

Gambling is risking your money on blind fortune, pure chance, the turn of the wheel. Speculation is taking a calculated risk with your money because you have studied it and decided that it is a promising risk whereby you may profit.[15]

Other authorities feel that the essence of stock-market gambling resides in the lack of intention of ever actually acquiring the stock. If a person contracts to buy stocks on margin with the intention to sell them in the future and not take possession, it is legal only if the material purchased can be produced on demand.[16] In the so-called "bucket shop," where no delivery of the stock was ever intended, selling on margin was considered illegal. In these instances, many convictions were obtained in the period preceding and following the market crash of 1929.[17]

Most commentators agree that manipulation involves indirect force or outside pressure exerted on the sale of a security. It is historically interesting that the basis for public airing of the facts surrounding manipulation derives from the Sherman Antitrust Act, although it was much later that manipulation acquired the criminal connotation under which it now labors.[18]

The significance of these distinctions is that public scrutiny has widened ethical applications to business to the degree that activities in that field that are potentially criminal have only recently been popularly so considered. As a result, there has been a gradual evolution in our century of a series of business crimes to which the studies of sociologists (Sutherland and others) and the exigencies of a complex commercial life have forced attention.

Earlier, as has been seen, the Securities and Exchange Commission took a long step toward placing responsibility for public ethicality on the corporation itself, as "clothed with human rights." The Sherman Antitrust Act spelled out both fines and prison sentences for violators, although the imposition of a prison term was discretionary with the courts. A review of criminal prosecutions under the Sherman Act has shown that in only twenty-five instances were criminal sanctions imposed during the sixty-year period 1890–1950, whereas an equal number were imposed during the following decade (1950–1960).[19]

From a psychological point of view, the criminal prosecution of a corporation member or of a financier confers an advantage in that the psychology of such an individual can be studied, whereas the corporation is intangible. This type of offender has been described in an earlier section on embezzlement (Chapter VIII), where his psychological motivational features were discussed. It was there pointed out that the embezzler absorbs the image of the corporation into his psyche, identifying with its power and immensity: he takes its image into his personality as he does its assets into his safe-deposit box. Similarly, the stock market larcenist absorbs the aura of wealth and power by fraudulently using the names of highly respected financiers in his prospectuses and selling activities. But the men who direct corporations that become embroiled in the law are men of a different stripe. They are larcenists once removed; the corporation is the offender and they are swept up in its train. The difference between the embezzler and the corporation director-offender lies in the psychologic reality that whereas the embezzler identifies with the corporation, the director-offender *is* the corporation.

Rarely a case is brought before the courts where the offender himself is a wealthy man of financial influence and power, one whose actual attainments match those fantasied by less affluent embezzlers. Here, in place of fantasied omnipotence, is omnipotence in fact. If fantasied participation in unlimited wealth represents a remnant of the infant's original egocentric conception of his universe ("I am alone in the world and everything belongs to me"), then the offender to be described—Richard Whitney—fulfilled that fantasy.

LARCENY AND THE FANTASY OF PLENTY

Why, then, did this financially powerful man become involved in fraud? Was it the "system," the social process, the credit structure that gave advantages to men of position? Was it an unconscious extension of autocratic power?

From the facts inherent in the case of Richard Whitney, convicted of grand larceny in the first degree,[20] it may be concluded that the fantasy of omnipotence far outweighs the reality of power as a durable piece of psychologic motivation. In 1933, Richard Whitney, president of the New York Stock Exchange and a stable figure in the financial market, became interested in a venture called Distilled Liquors Corporation. He and some associates issued stock amounting to about two million dollars that sold on the Curb Exchange and to individual subscribers. At the time of the stock issue, Whitney and his associates owned only about 8 per cent of the shares. The plan was to manufacture applejack, a spiritous product (cider brandy) that had a bright future (according to the originators of the issue) since Prohibition had recently been repealed and the consumption of alcoholic beverages had been restored to its legal and respected position. Distilled Liquors Corporation stock started off well at $15 a share, the price set on the original issue of 130,000 shares; it moved to $45 in a short time. Within a year, as the feasibility of applejack supplanting such time-honored spirits as Scotch whisky and bourbon faded, the stock slid in value. The public showed no interest in applejack; wholesalers who bought the year's output couldn't unload; Distilled Liquors Corporation went unpaid. "We'd bet he [Whitney] doesn't drink applejack," editorialized the New York *Daily News* after the debacle came to light. "Few city or suburban people have." The first year's production had been sold on contracts, chiefly on the name of the backers. Many of Whitney's friends as well as the general public was involved when, to maintain the market price, the corporation bought up 40,000 of the 120,000 shares outstanding. Nevertheless, the situation still looked stable, especially with Whitney's name to buoy it up.

Another year passed and applejack appealed even less to prospective purchasers. The company's stock dropped lower in value and, because it "was one of the duties of people whose names are connected with stocks," Whitney bought up more of his Distilled Liquors Corporation issue. He was already involved to the extent of nearly $70,000, but $600,000 more was needed. Some of this was raised from bank loans, some came from the reserve funds of the New York Yacht Club, of which Whitney was a trustee. More shares were purchased and the price pegged for a while, but trouble soon returned and another quarter of a million dollars was needed. Now Whitney dipped into his customers' securities, the Stock Exchange Gratuity Fund, and a retirement fund for the benefit of New York Stock Exchange employees. His involvement now approached the two-million-dollar mark. The situation was becoming desperate. Whitney now sought counsel of his banking friends, particularly that of his brother George, a member of the J. P. Morgan Company.

A seasoned banker, George Whitney advised Richard to liquidate his business immediately. Aghast at his brother's use of customers' securities, George offered to lend him one and a half million dollars to rescue him from ruin. Whitney accepted the loan, the Gratuity Fund of the Stock Exchange was replenished, and $650,000 restored to customers' funds. But applejack still did not sell; Distilled Liquors stock continued to decline. Whitney bought more stock, up to 95 per cent of the issue, borrowing from Peter to pay Paul in short-term bank loans ranging from $100,000 to $600,000. Meanwhile, other ventures—such as a large tract of land on a Florida beach and a plant to manufacture humus on a large scale—required large interest payments on floated loans. As the solvency of his own firm began to totter because he had secretly sequestered monies from the firm in a "Richard Whitney Control Account," Whitney began to pyramid loans from private sources. This reached such a point that when he finally declared himself insolvent (March, 1938), his obligations totalled close to five million dollars. The bankruptcy of Richard Whitney was important enough for the then president of the Stock Exchange to hurry to Washington "to confer with members of the Securities and Exchange Commission over the failure of Richard Whitney and Company and the revelations regarding it." [21]

When the news broke to an incredulous financial community and an indictment was brought against Whitney, the case attracted national notice. A New York newspaper editorialized:

> . . . it is an astounding case, the more so since Whitney has been looked on as one of the inside insiders ("Morgan broker") . . . of ancient and honorable ancestry. . . . We regret this crash of one of our financial genii . . . but some extension of Wall Street supervision by some (governmental) agency seems urgently indicated. . . .[22]

Generalized attacks by the press and public were refuted by the Attorney General who, together with New York County's Special Prosecutor, Thomas E. Dewey, had prosecuted the charges of grand larceny against Whitney. "The Whitney case," said New York State Securities Bureau Chief Ambrose McCall,

> is the result of regulation that is stopping a practice apparently widespread, in pledging customer's securities . . . pleas of Grand Larceny had been obtained from firms in no sense swindlers but legitimate securities firms whose customers were Blue Book people.[23]

Attorney McCall went on to cite several cases where customers' securities had been lost, up to values of one million dollars, by "reputable" concerns. "In some cases," he said, "no criminal indictments were brought because the securities were recovered and returned to the customers."

Nevertheless, the New York State legislature was asked by Senator Thomas F. Burchill to conduct an inquiry into the

> corrupt methods and practices of certain prominent members of the New York Stock Exchange which has shocked our state and nation. . . . It is the duty of the State of New York to protect its citizens from such unwholesome conditions . . . and prevent startling acts of fraud. . . .[24]

The preliminary investigation completed and the two indictments for grand larceny outlined in detail, Richard Whitney pleaded guilty on both charges, later explaining all his financial maneuvers openly. Those who came in contact with the offender described him as a "frank and willing witness," clearly accepting responsibility for his acts, involving none of his partners in his defalcations. Some agreed that his management of his firm was "autocratic," others commented on the fact that he had kept his partners in the dark concerning his juggling of accounts. His pleas of guilty to both counts of grand larceny were accepted and he was sentenced to from five to ten years in a state prison. Before imposition of sentence, a psychiatric examination of the offender was undertaken at the request of the Probation Department and Judge Owen Bohan.

The lay public and the press were intensely interested in Richard Whitney. Affected by a species of awe at the possibility of scrutinizing in detail the inner workings of a generally inaccessible tycoon, they expected a psychologic revelation. What kind of man was larcenist Whitney? Did he conform to the movie stereotype of the Wall Street banker? What were the Morgans of the world really like? Did the pattern of his life reveal elements that might be interpretable as explanations for his criminal behavior?

The psychological examination, which comprised a test of the mental functions—memory, retention, grasp of abstract material, general information, and ability—found Whitney to possess very superior intelligence. On the Army Alpha test he achieved a score of 174, in the 99-percentile group. In the tests for memory, general information, and language facility he showed particular excellence. In mathematical calculations, he was less effective, but in this the fatigue factor may have been operative. His cooperation was good.

There was no evidence in the clinic study of such judgment defects as are encountered in the presence of mental disease. He was completely oriented as to time, place, and person; there was no evidence of hallucinations or delusions. His stream of thought was normal, neither underproductive nor overproductive. There was a history of a head injury with skull fracture, following his fall from a horse at the age of eleven, but his recovery had been complete. During the examination, Whitney was self-assured and contained; his emotional reactions were appropriate and adequate. His surface attitude was characteristic of him—dignified, sober, slightly tense and guarded, he reacted to the interview in an urbane and sportsmanlike manner.

Every aspect of the offender's life was openly discussed and analyzed throughout prolonged interviews: his interest in sports and travel, literature, movies and plays, gambling, eating, clothes, his sexual habits and appetites, economic and personal philosophy, religious attitudes, and his total outlook on life—all were detailed with frankness and acumen. Perhaps his philosophy of economics and business was reflected in his credo, which emerged thus: "I am an Anglophile. The French are hard to deal with; they don't talk our language. Germans are too superior; I don't like them. An Englishman, when he gives you his friendship, gives you something secure. I believe in the English government, English ways, far beyond what I do in the American. I am a Republican, but more of a 'mugwump,' although often my feelings

are Democratic." Whitney's personal life followed a stable tradition.
Married, he had two daughters, maintained a family town house and a
495-acre estate in a suburban area; he and his wife led an active social
life.

The picture emerging from a personality-study of Whitney was sharp
and definitive, with no smudges of neurotic inferiority, depressive reactions, or other defenses against inner conflicts. A man of patrician
mold, Whitney had absorbed into his personality the accepted traditions, standards, and conventions of the wealthy class. During most of
his adult life he had been permissibly aggressive, believed in and practiced good sportsmanship, worked hard, and had long since suppressed
whatever adolescent, idealistic yearnings once pressed toward the surface. Essentially a realist, a man whose fantasy-life had been sublimated
along socially acceptable channels (or so he and others thought),
Whitney's interest in world movements, or the semiphilosophic concerns that swarm about humanity daily, was nil. His comments on
people were in terms of their business ability, and although he had
met and knew some of the world's great personalities, he saw them
through the myopia of business. More than once he made such remarks
as "You can't do business with a Frenchman and you can with an
Englishman." His social instincts well developed, he steered through the
bays and inlets of social intercourse with little effort.

All in all, Richard Whitney impressed the examiners as a realistic,
though relatively uncompromising individual, independent rather than
stubborn, yet unaware of his rather strong tendency toward reckless-
ness. On a deeper level, one could sense in him a certain rigidity of
character, expressed openly in stubbornness, independence, and lack of
compromise. Egocentricity and an unconscious feeling of omnipotence
shone through Whitney's character structure. This was borne out by
his stating that at no time during his five or six years of financial difficulty did he imagine that he could run afoul of the law—this in the face
of his long experience as an administrator of the New York Stock Exchange. This feeling of omnipotence, it might be noted, has frequently
been observed in larcenists, no matter how small were their operations.
Such psychologic mechanisms have also been commonly observed
among confidence men.

The personality type uncovered in Whitney's case holds true, with
individual variations, for other business-crime offenders. Many cases of
stock swindling, larceny by misrepresentation, conspiracy to defraud,
misappropriation of funds, and the like pass through the courts, which
on examination present a personality image startlingly like that of
Whitney.[25] In these offenders, there is more often than not a history of
success in industry or commerce, a seeming stability of make-up, a
ready sublimation of early yearnings through work, and a deep preoc-

cupation with business. The ego-ideal of the offender (the ideal by which his ego measures its performance) is almost synonymous with the superego (the conscience that "keeps guard" over the ego-ideal).[26] Little guilt is evident in these cases because there is little play between the superego and the ego-ideal. Business-crime offenders automatically assume the role of the conscience: *they* form the national business ego-ideal, or, in today's language, the national business "image." The image and conscience being one and the same, little room remains in their tightly packed egos for the presence of guilt.

To put it in less metaphoric language, the business-crime offenders (white-collar offenders) examined by this author and his associates in the New York courts display little guilt; their consciences have become identified with the common business ideal of success at any price. Beguiled by the need for success, their fantasies of omnipotence and wealth, indistinguishable from the reality of their financial world, outrun their judgment. On the base of a narcissistic character structure, a dichotomy develops insidiously between practical judgment and daydreams of conquest. Self-advancement through fraud easily enters the hiatus thus created; the transition from successful manipulation to larceny occurs unobtrusively.

THE BUSINESS OF CRIME

A startling similarity can be observed between the personality patterns of the business-crime offender and one who is engaged in the business of crime. Gangsters and racketeers studied by the author and his associates, in the same court clinic in which Whitney appeared, displayed the same history of, or striving toward, success (in crime), a seeming stability of make-up, preoccupation with making money or gaining power that will permit them to make money, sublimation of tender feelings or altruistic tendencies, and an identity of conscience with *their* ego-ideals.

As in the world of commerce, gangs and the underworld have their own codes, ethos, systems of checks and balances, rewards and penalties. They represent, as has often been said, a government within a government. In these cases the ego-ideal of the individual member matches the ego-ideal of the gang. One searches in vain among racketeers for distinguishing characteristics that can be called "neurotic," or that are otherwise indicative of an internal conflict. Included here are extortionists, percentage men, hustlers, gunmen, strong-arm protectionists, racketeers—in short, all those whose methods of earning a living are subject to criminal prosecution.

Although mental states or neurotic conditions, as clinical entities, are not commonly found among those engaged in the business of crime, many investigators agree that the racketeer or gangster may be diagnosed as an aggressive psychopath. Their ethical standards are blunted, their attitudes egocentric, their sentiments dulled; their physical organisms are pointed toward violent action and their emotional organizations tend toward instability. The picture presented by those in the business of crime, viewed from the vantage point of a law-abiding society, represents the antithesis of conformity; it is antisocial by definition, hence psychopathic by diagnosis.

A series of individuals involved in the operations of a notorious mob will be discussed below to illustrate these points. As a preliminary composite picture of this group, one may say that an attempt to analyze the internal emotional life of the gangster, or aggressive psychopath, meets with little success. Their attitudes are fixed; the law, they realize, will exact its toll from them as they have exacted theirs from society. Any discussion aimed at an understanding of the psychological processes in such an individual when under indictment is regarded as naïve in the face of the state's punishment—death or long imprisonment. Psychological analysis is met as an intrusion upon a closed circuit existing between the law and lawbreakers and accepted by both. One meets the accepted attitude in professional killers that the supreme crime among men is answerable by death. Paid killers waive their guilt feelings before the offense is completed. Their attitude toward the law and their crime is fixed in a balance between accepted guilt and a job to be done.

Discussion of the aggressive psychopath leads to a consideration of such individuals as professional thieves, gangsters, and labor-union racketeers, whose aggressive acts are not perpetrated through personal use of physical violence but by organized bands under their control. Racketeering is a form of extortion and its special character arises from the similarity between the organization and methods of rackets and the form and method of governmental control of commerce and industry. In providing "protection," in regulating the flow of trade, in organizing services in various industries, racketeers encroach upon the function of government, which alone has the right to regulate and tax industrial enterprises.

The organization of a racketeering gang parallels in form that of a government agency. At the head of the group is a leader chosen for his resourcefulness, political connections, and organizing ability. Each member of the group is delegated to a specific task, while strategy and planning are left to the leader. Territories are delimited, authority is imposed, threats made, payments collected regularly, and disbursements made in cash. Apart from the practical value of a division of labor within the organization, the structure of the racket thus guarantees a certain amount of secrecy for its members. This is the point at which the similarity between government and rackets ceases—anonymity of the members, lack of permanent records, and the use of aggression, arbitrarily imposed.

The racketeer is well aware of the similarity between approved methods of conducting business and his own organizational structure. Indeed, the existence and success of the group depends on both inner and outer controls. The external controls of a racket depend upon "purchased immunity for its protection," [27] and efficiency within the gang lies upon its own regulations, or inner controls, which one writer, investigating the history and activities of the Mafia, has called the "iron morality." [28] The racketeer assumes the power of government to inflict punishment and death when indicated. The rackets' usurpation of the governmental taxing function is upheld by its own code of punishment for noncompliance, both within and without its structure. Unwarranted penalties, unwarranted aggression, and violent "business" techniques—murder, mayhem, destruction of property, robbery, extortion—are accepted as valid techniques of "law enforcement." The racketeer explains these happenings as inevitable concomitants of methods designed to control the members. Of the cases examined that fell into the racket group, no one of them, in this examiner's memory, expressed regret or concern over the use of violent methods of control.

LABOR UNION RACKETEERS

The labor union racketeer presents a more obvious criminal identification. He demonstrates a sanctimonious attitude toward his union members, from whom he derives his power to lead. If the union czar is of the rank and file, his strength derives partly from the projected need of his followers for a father-figure. If he came to the union via the criminal route, his professed devotion to ideals of betterment for workers obscures a thinly disguised contempt for his constituency.

In the 1930's the garment industry in New York, which serves practically the entire nation, found itself in the grip of systematized extortion. One Lepke Buchalter had seized control of the crucial Teamsters' Union, and hence control of the immense trade centering around the fur and garment industries. Buchalter was no labor leader; he was a self-appointed collector of revenue for services rendered, the services consisting of protecting employers and workers simultaneously. The technique that Lepke introduced was simple and effective: He supplied strikebreakers for the employers at a reasonable price while at the same time he extracted payments from the union members for protection against the strikebreakers. Infiltration into the enemy lines by henchmen was a new technique in union warfare. It was to Lepke's discredit that he brought guerilla tactics into the union arena. Entering into unionism (though one could hardly dignify Lepke's activities as such) from criminality, he placed the business of levying tribute on a cash basis. During Lepke's trial,[29] it was estimated that the offender and his associates collected as high as half a million dollars in cash in a given year. Lepke's methods were crude, his organization primitive, his success short-lived. While serving a sentence in the federal penitentiary for drug selling, Lepke was convicted of the crime of extortion. While imprisoned on that charge he was convicted of a murder that had occurred earlier, and sentenced to death by electrocution.

Racketeering has been one of the many American contributions to life in the twentieth century. Now a commonplace word, the term "racket" came into popular use in the 1920's when organized crime emerged as a powerful force in American life. A racket has many connotations, but, from the standpoint of criminal actions, it can be neatly defined in the words of Special Prosecutor Thomas E. Dewey, spoken at the height of his effectiveness as a criminal prosecutor:

Racketeering is a much abused . . . word. It should be limited to the systematic extortion of money through intimidation by an organization conducted for that purpose.[30]

The situation in the 1930's had advanced to the point where extortion had become an art. Big money was the keystone, force and intimidation the psychologic elements, protection from arrest or prosecution through political aid and bribery the cement that held the racket organizations together. Narcotic rings, gambling groups, policy-number gaming, bookmaking, prostitution rings, union extortion, and industrial protection gangs flourished. There was nothing new about the existence of rackets, but there was a newness and efficiency to the cooperative efforts of a group said to be the *Unione Siciliano*, or Mafia (later set up as Cosa Nostra, "our gadget" or "thing"). "As late as 1935," wrote two veteran reporters, "with Mayor LaGuardia screaming death to gangsters in radio broadcasts, there were shakedowns of thousands a week in industrial rackets." [31] The prostitution ring headed by "Lucky" Luciano was the target at which Prosecutor Dewey aimed his legal weapons. In the prewar period the criminal syndicate had so evolved that Dewey commented:

A new type of criminal exists who leaves to his hirelings and front men the actual offenses and rarely commits an overt act himself.[32]

PROFILE OF A PROFESSIONAL

Luciano is generally held responsible for organizing the "industry" and upgrading the racketeer. His syndicate patterned its organization after the corporate image: the "boss" standing apart from his artisans and co-workers, "surveying, manipulating, directing. . . ."[33] It is reported that when Betillo and Fredericks, Luciano's first lieutenant and business manager, respectively, proposed that the brothels be operated by gang members directly, Luciano disposed: "It's best we run like a syndicate, like the A & P stores."

The Luciano case,[34] an instance of proven gang operation, held national attention. Because of its efficient organization and international ramifications, searched-out and uncovered by the brilliant and assiduous work of Prosecutor Dewey and his staff, this case serves to illuminate the social and psychological structure of criminal conspiracy. Although the charge of compulsory prostitution made against Luciano and his codefendants was covered in a few sentences by the prosecution, the interrogation of prostitutes, procurers, and disorderly-house operators, and the presentation of proof occupied months. When it had been proven that the "boss" controlled and extracted tribute, not only from prostitution but from narcotics, bookmaking, and hijacking to the extent of a quarter of a million dollars a year, Judge Phillip McCook summed up, with legal brevity, society's view of the convicted Luciano:

. . . You have been found guilty of leading a conspiracy or combination to commit these crimes. . . . I am not here to reprove you but there appears to be no excuse for your conduct nor hope for your rehabilitation. Sentenced to 30 to 50 years in State's Prison.

The record of Salvatore Lucania, alias Charles or "Lucky" Luciano, indicated a dedication to antisocial conduct. Starting at the age of eighteen with a sentence to the penitentiary for selling heroin, he traversed the gamut of criminal charges—robbery, assault, narcotic selling, hijacking, larceny, concealed weapons (New York), operating a gambling game (Florida), and "investigation" (Illinois and Ohio)— with only one conviction. He was as fastidious in avoiding punishment as he was in his dress. His lieutenant, David Betillo, similarly had a long record unmarred by prison sentences until his present conviction, but his personality structure differed from that of "the Chief." It was compounded of protective tenseness and inner aggressivity, matching his active role in the organization.

As befitted the position of tactician, Luciano was a quiet man, well dressed, his clothes obviously expensive. During the psychiatric examinations,[35] Lucky, pleasant and polite, was careful not to make errors; his perceptions were without defects, his intelligence within average range. The press reported the published results of the examinations in shrill terms:

Not one of the overlords of vice sentenced today (June 18, 1936) to spend long terms in Sing Sing Prison had a single brain cell more than was absolutely necessary . . . they had the mental capacity of punch-drunk boxers known to the trade as "stumble-bums." . . .[36]

The findings of the psychologist, however, stated:

In performance tests involving reasoning, Luciano does fairly well. He is a little over-cautious and is careful not to answer at all unless it can be a good answer. He has an attitude of reservation throughout the examination. In memory tests his responses are good. He makes a few errors in repeating six digits backwards but this is within the limits of normal. His cultural pursuits, as measured by his interest in the motion pictures, are a little restricted.

More significant were the attitudes from which one could interpret Lucky's personality structure. Affable and cooperative in all matters except those involving the offense (he stated flatly that he had only a passing acquaintance with any of the codefendants), Luciano agreed that his concern was only for himself and the gratification of his own wishes. Poised and admitting his love of luxury, the offender's whole manner reflected the characteristics of shrewdness and egocentricity. Nevertheless, his basic aggressiveness could not be obscured. As the psychiatric report to the court stated:

When he is not called upon to display this aggressiveness, he makes the impression of being smooth and pliant. In a difficult situation this surface attitude could easily give way before an onrush of aggressive feeling.

All observers agreed that the assets which made Luciano a leader were those that would lead to success in business: calmness in times of stress, faith in the favorable outcome of chance, reserve, and strength. To this was added that inner conviction that he could escape involvement with the law and a peasantlike directness that fitted the primitive, instinctive behavior patterns of the gangster world. Moreover, Lucky was successful in shunting attention away from himself, while directing every aspect of the syndicate's business. For this skill he was accorded an extra degree of underworld respect. Luciano's personality represented an incorporation of the ethos of modern business life. His premises accepted, his syndicate activities were attuned to the primary requirements of life—self-preservation, protection from competitors, control of income, expansion of trade opportunities, enjoyment of luxury, and so on. To this he added the free use of force, a shrewd use of underlings, and a complete absence of ethics in his ruthless handling of pawns in the game of profit-making.

Luciano's assistants and codefendants, on the other hand, were a different breed of men. Betillo, the strong-arm lieutenant—the "enforcer," in terms of the syndicate—was openly aggressive during the psychiatric examinations, but unable to hide instability, immaturity, and tensions that were patently responses to feelings of deep insecurity. In contrast to this suave chief, Betillo, on striding into the examination room, announced that he would permit the physician to examine his "heart and liver but don't give me any psychological tests." He was adamant about not having his "mind probed." In contrast to his codefendants, Betillo was unable to accept the examination situation or appraise it critically. On the other hand, Liguori, another lieutenant, whose fifteen years in school had permitted him to reach the sixth grade, agreeably answered all questions, relating volubly a long history that left his large income and criminal associations completely unexplained. His cooperation resulted in so superficial an account of his life as to make the truth appear simply by reversing his denials. Both of Lucky's lieutenants were dependable men in their management of the prostitutes under their "protection."

From the lesser members of the organization came a free-flowing story of the structure of the operation. Peter Balitzer, a "booker" under orders from the group, explained in detail the structure of the syndicate—the killers, the treasurer, the bail bondsman who rescued arrested prostitutes, the "mouth-piece," or attorney, for the enterprise, and the operators of the "complaint" department. The tremendous amount of evidence adduced by Prosecutor Dewey from witnesses on the stand was nicely summed up by Balitzer:

The bookies are men who send the girls to houses of prostitution. They get the girls from pimps who pick them up in small towns or the girls come in themselves. For this he gets ten per cent from each girl. The bookie then paid the "protection" $100 a week to see that he was not "bothered." . . . In case of arrest, the bookie would protect the girl by arranging her bail bond. After a while the muscle men wanted to take over the bail-bonding activity, for which they received $10 per girl from the madam. This was done at the point of a gun. Some of the independent operators (men with a few girls whom they booked) were absorbed by the syndicate. These men were put on a straight salary by the group. The girls themselves gave fifty per cent of their income to the madam, paid her board and room, paid the bookies for protection and bail bonds, were shunted around to different towns, beaten and burned with cigarettes if they refused to comply. The lower echelons never saw Luciano: they "heard" he was the boss.

An interesting sidelight on the psychological attitude of the "lower echelons" was provided by Balitzer himself in that the criminal charge using the terms "compulsory prostitution" and "extortion" evoked from him little reaction. He, for example, had a history of fifteen years of crime before he was caught in the dragnet. Basically of average intelligence, this thug (he had been arrested twice on suspicion of homicide) was shrewd in his activities, but without the planning capacity or egocentricity of his codefendant, Luciano. Absorbed by the same ideology that invested Luciano's world, Balitzer spoke freely of the "ethics" of his universe. Neither the abstract concepts of social morality that Prosecutor Dewey wove into his summation nor the antisociality that the press stressed in their voluminous accounts of the trial, impressed him. He had been part of an industry and he had filled his part fairly. Judge McCook at one point in his sentencing statement called attention to "every foul and cruel deed," in the history of the racket; the defendants never doubted their right to impose their will; their ethical system was firmly based on the right of conquest and domination. Their personalities bent and fitted with ease into the mosaic of organized extortion etched out by Luciano.

THE PROFESSION OF CRIME

The personality profiles of a band of extortionists, and a description of their respective roles in an organized conspiracy to extort, does not exhaust all aspects of the "business of crime." There is no doubt that larceny in its various forms and under various disguises can be a career, interrupted by the penality of imprisonment but conferring a comfortable living with a minimum of effort. The shoplifters, professional burglars, confidence men, extortionists, and loan sharks have been described; the petty thieves, gamblers, card sharps, check forgers, "hustlers," and jewel thieves who take their toll of property and money in this country need also to be noted. There are bands of men and women who merge, separate, rejoin, or realign in executing these crimes, some pursuing the same technique for a lifetime, some changing their type of operation. Together they constitute the profession of crime. A few of these crime groups have ascended to the level of artistry; the pickpocket, for example, claims an ancient and respected lineage and a skill that transcends the rough work of mere sneak thieves. In a sense, the law protects the pickpocket: his offense is accounted a misdemeanor (petty larceny) unless the victim is aware of the impending robbery, in which case it becomes a felony (grand larceny or larceny of the person).

The pickpocket usually plies his trade consistently throughout his entire life. The liabilities of possible incarceration, usually averaging three to six months in the penitentiary or workhouse, are regarded as a reasonable occupational hazard of this professional's life. The pickpocket's associates are limited to those whose proficiency matches his own; his friends are few but his knowledge of the criminal world is wide. Communication between pickpockets is quick, subterranean, and effective. Moreover, this type of thief is aware of social currents in the world about him. An example of the reciprocal relation between the thief and the world of affairs is seen in the account by a pickpocket who, while awaiting sentence in the city jail, was informed of the theft of a wallet belonging to Rabbi Stephen S. Wise, the eminent and internationally esteemed religious leader. Word went out that the pickpocket should return *that* particular wallet within twenty-four hours. Through the mediation of our prisoner,[37] the Rabbi's wallet was returned by an anonymous donor. Thus, there appears to be a sensitive relation between those who are legitimately "marks," that is, proper victims, and those who are not—a kind of indirect concern on the part of the offender for social propriety.

The pickpocket's exclusiveness in the underworld of crime rests, as does that of his female counterpart, the shoplifter, on the passive-aggressive nature of his crime. His criminal act is essentially furtive, although technically skilled. Because of the passive character of his theft, with its absence of affront or personal injury to the victim, the pickpocket claims immunity from punishment. Like the shoplifter, the pickpocket always denies his offense on interrogation with a blandness of attitude that betrays a *voluntary* ostracism from society. For the pickpocket believes he is *of* society not in it, even though he may live and earn his living on its rim. He behaves toward society as does the parasitic pilot fish toward the shark upon whose back it rides, and in whose forthright aggression it participates vicariously.

This peripheral psychologic identification can be seen obliquely in the complaint of a thirty-eight-year-old widow who supported several children on the proceeds of her shoplifting "work," which averaged as high as $200 per week. During the interview following one of her arrests, she set forth her views:

The store detective is a sadist. He gloats on making people miserable. . . . Let those who are going to be house drudges do it. I must make a living.[38]

To the pickpocket, the advantage of an affluent society is measured in the proceeds he can "pick up"; to the shoplifter, it is measured in the merchandise she can "boost." These offenders represent the type of thieves who feel themselves indigenous to the industrial empire: facets of the world of business—the beggar who earns his keep, the parasite who has "rights."

The crime groups alluded to in this chapter comprise a portion of the more spectacular offenses falling under the heading The Business of Crime. The reason for uniting crimes arising from the world of business itself and those committed in the business of crime resides in the subtle, meaningful relation between good and evil behavior in our society; for "good" actions one may read "law-abiding" and for "evil," those contrary to law. The constant presence of crime in our society permits the visualization of a homeostatic balance of good and evil that the professional criminal (thief, extortionist, confidence man) vaguely, or clearly, perceives. The philosophy of professional criminals is predicated on the integration within our society of elements antithetical to ideals of the common good. Those who have had contacts with professional wrongdoers would agree that the Lucianos of our time understand the import of Thurman W. Arnold's summation of practical moral problems in today's world. Arnold wrote:

A conflict often arises between an ideal and a social need not accepted as legitimate or moral. This creates a situation in which an immoral and undercover organization will arise. The ideal will be represented by a moral organization which proves that the social need is not a real need at all, but a form of sin. The need will be represented by an immoral organization, which will be accepted and tolerated as a necessary evil, in the same way that the Church accepted the existence of the Devil.[39]

Scrutiny of the mind-set and intuition of professional criminals provides evidence for believing that they are aware of this uneasy ethical balance. The professional weighs both sides of the scales—the police and law courts on one and crime on the other; his intuition tells him a final balance may never be achieved. The situation is one with which society has struggled for a very long time.

REFERENCES

1. SUTHERLAND, E. H., and CRESSEY, DONALD R., *Principles of Criminology* (J. B. Lippincott Co., Philadelphia, Pa., 6th ed., 1960), p. 56.
2. SUTHERLAND, E. H., *White-Collar Crime* (Holt, Rinehart & Winston, New York, 1961), rev. ed. (Donald R. Cressey), p. 9.
3. BARNES, HARRY ELMER, *The History of Western Civilization*, Vol. 2 (Harcourt, Brace & Co., New York, 1953), p. 846.
4. COMMAGER, HENRY S., *The American Mind* (Yale University Press, New Haven, Conn., 1959), p. 332.
5. Ross, E. A., *Sin and Society*, quoted in Commager, *ibid.*, p. 333.
6. *Sherman Antitrust Act, United States Statutes at Large*, Vol. 26 (1890), (U.S. Government Printing Office, Washington, D.C.), Sec. 2, p. 209.
7. WILSON, WOODROW, *Property Rights and Human Rights*, in *Man and the State*, W. Ebenstein, ed. (Rinehart & Co., New York, 1948), p. 508.
8. *U.S.* vs. *McDonough Co.*, U.S. District Court, Ohio, 1959, cited in

Trade Regulation Reports (Commerce Clearing House, New York), Cases 69, 482, p. 14280, annotation 63.

9. *Electrical Equipment Cases*, U.S. District Court (Eastern) Penn., 1960, summarized in *Trade Regulation Reports, ibid.*, Case 69, 699.

10. FULLER, JOHN G., *The Gentlemen Conspirators* (Grove Press, New York, 1962), p. 16.

11. OGG, FREDERICK, and RAY, P. ORMON, *Essentials of American Government* (Appleton-Century-Crofts, New York, 7th ed., 1952).

12. MAYER, MARTIN, *Wall Street: Men and Money* (Crowell-Collier Publishing Co., New York, rev. ed., 1962), p. 216.

13. *Ibid.*, p. 219.

14. *Securities and Exchange Act, U.S. Statutes at Large* (U.S. Government Printing Office, Washington, D.C.), Vol. 48 pp. 74, 771 (1933).

15. SCOTT, EDGAR, quoted in Mayer, *op. cit.*, p. 78.

16. CONYNGTON, THOMAS, and BEIGH, LOUIS O., *Business Law* (Ronald Press Co., New York, 1949), p. 53.

17. New York County, Court of General Sessions, files of Probation Department, 1928 to 1930; courtesy of Irving W. Halpern, Chief Probation Officer.

18. *Sherman Antitrust Act, Amended*, 15, United States Code, Sec. 1–7, (1958).

19. *Department of Justice and State Enforcement Procedure*, in *Trade Regulation Reports* (Commerce Clearing House, New York, 1961), Sec. 50, 170, 8801.

20. *People* vs. *Whitney*, State of New York, County of New York, Court of General Sessions, March, 1938, Ind. #216516 and 216517.

21. *The New York Times*, news story, March 31, 1938.

22. New York *Daily News*, editorial, April 12, 1938.

23. *The New York Times*, news story, March 17, 1938.

24. New York *Herald Tribune*, news story, March 15, 1938.

25. New York County, Supreme Court, Criminal Division, Psychiatric Clinic and Probation Dept. (1935–1963).

26. FREUD, SIGMUND, *On Narcissism*, in *Collected Papers*, Vol. 4, trans. by J. Riviere (Hogarth Press, London, 1950), p. 22.

27. JOHNSON, EARL, JR., "Organized Crime: Challenge to the American Legal System," *Journal of Criminal Law and Criminology*, LIII (1962), 399.

28. LEWIS, NORMAN, "The Honored Society," in "Profiles," *The New Yorker*, February 8, 1964, p. 42.

29. *People* vs. *Buchalter*, State of New York, County of New York, Court of General Sessions, 1937, Ind. #3222174.

30. WALKER, STANLEY, *Dewey: An American of This Century* (McGraw-Hill Book Co., New York, 1944), p. 61.

31. FEDER, SID, and JOESTEN, JOACHIM, *The Luciano Story* (Popular Library, Inc., New York, 1960), p. 73.

32. WALKER, *op. cit.*, p. 53.

33. FEDER and JOESTEN, *op. cit.*, p. 236.

34. *People* vs. *Luciano and Codefendants*, State of New York, County of New York, Extraordinary & Trial Term, Sup. Court, 1936, Vio. Sec. 2460.

35. New York County, Reports of the Probation Department, Court of General Sessions (June, 1936) Irving W. Halpern, Chief Probation Officer and Psychiatric Clinic: Dr. Walter Bromberg, Dr. Charles B. Thompson, and Dr. J. David Impastato, psychiatrists; Dr. Solomon Machover, psychologist.

36. KELLER, ALLAN, staff writer, *New York World-Telegram,* June 18, 1936.

37. Personal communication, 1936.

38. New York County, Files of the Probation Department, *op. cit.,* 1936.

39. ARNOLD, THURMAN W., *The Folklore of Capitalism* (Yale University Press, New Haven, Conn., 1938), p. 364.

CHAPTER XIII

The Path Widens:
Therapy and Its Future

CONTROL OF CRIME—TREATMENT
POSSIBILITIES / TREATMENT OF DELINQUENCY—
RESIDENTIAL THERAPY / PSYCHOTHERAPY OF
OFFENDERS ON PROBATION / TREATMENT
OF THE CRIMINAL IN PRISON / THE LEDGER
OF PUNISHMENT / THE DEBITS AND CREDITS OF
PSYCHOTHERAPY / A CRIME PREVENTION
PROPOSAL / REFERENCES

If an essence can be distilled from this analysis of crime and criminals, it is the accent on *crime viewed as behavior.* This investigation of the psychological motivations and social stresses that underlie crime has proved that those behavior patterns involved in criminal acts are not far removed from those of normal behavior. True, cases of obvious mental disease were also met with in this study. But the neuroses, character disturbances, psychopathies, and those subtle personality constellations that cannot be easily classified and that differ only slightly, if at all, from those found in noncriminal persons have also been encountered.

Our findings indicate that criminal behavior, as is true of all behavior, is responsive to inner and outer stresses. The external realities of mental life—social pressures, cultural emphases, physical needs, subcultural patterns of life—precipitate criminal action. The inner realities of behavior—neurotic reactions, impulses, unconscious motivations, preconscious striving, eruption of infantile aggressions—represent a precondition to criminal acts. This statement may unduly simplify the problem, but it will serve to show that criminal behavior is not as enigmatic as has been supposed. Crime is part of the human condition; the forces that make for crime are difficult to lay hold of or to control, but though they are widespread, elusive, and seemingly outside the scope of social coexistence, they are not beyond our conception.

The basic stuff of criminal behavior derives from three behavioral areas: the aggressive tendency, both destructive and acquisitive;

passive, or subverted, aggression; and psychophysiological needs. In some crime groups, the intricate mechanisms of industry and commerce —for example, the stock market—have been utilized to hide criminal intent; in others, naked aggression (homicide) and crude psychophysiological impulses (forceful rape) have been bluntly expressed. No matter how these forces are evidenced, we deal in the last analysis with aggressiveness or its analogues, trickery and deceit.

Society's attempts to control aggression, have been through legal punishment, but history bears testimony to the fact that criminal aggression cannot be so controlled. It may be suppressed, possibly even repressed, but it cannot be removed. Punishment does not quell aggression, and has not for over five thousand years. What other means, then, are available to control the mainsprings of criminality?

The one measure that responsible members of society have suggested for control of aggressiveness, one that has been used for generations, is that of education; education of the will and the emotions. The urging of this recommendation coincided with the elevation of the ideal of the "good life" and the development of "good will" in men. This ideal has been enshrined in the basic teachings of church, parents, and educators; it is implicit in those noble sentiments that are publicly and privately applauded. It is implicit in the lives of the sainted few to whom we listen in quiet moments, only to have their calm voices swallowed up in the turmoil that invariably follows.

CONTROL OF CRIME—TREATMENT POSSIBILITIES

This gargantuan task of curing the world does not properly face the criminologist. His job lies in a narrower range (and it is wide enough) than that of the statesman, social educator, or social philosopher-turned-reformer. The work of the psychiatrist or criminologist, then, is constricted into an area within which he can redirect or rechannel the inner aggression of offenders already in custody or under control. This is the area in which psychotherapy, working with groups or with individuals, can proceed on the knowledge it has accumulated.

The treatment of antisocial behavior touches on techniques dissimilar from those of clinical medicine. It does not depend on a brilliant discovery, as that of penicillin, nor on a series of imaginative and technically efficient improvisations as in heart surgery. The treatment of aggression involves slow, plodding work with the accent on softening resistances within the public and within the offenders themselves. Application of sound pedogogical principles, of well-tested psychological ideas, and an atmosphere that fosters acceptance of these ideas are required. How society has to be influenced indirectly and the offenders directly is best seen in the therapy of juveniles.

The beginnings of therapy for misbehavior among juveniles have been traced in Chapter III. Whereas truancy, incorrigibility, sex play, and destructive behavior among children were once handled by punishment, exhortation, and reprimand, gradually they were thought of as susceptible to treatment. When misbehavior spilled over into crime, juvenile courts sent their charges to public institutions and private corrective installations. At the present time, social and psychiatric treatment for delinquents has developed to the point where child and adolescent offenders are automatically considered to be in need of treatment. Cases of this type have been detailed in Chapter VII.

The basic therapeutic postulate states that the child's ego has not yet congealed, and hence will respond to warmth, interest, and example; this is accepted today without cavil. However, the same notion with regard to adult offenders has not yet gained credence although areas of growing confidence are evident; treatment may yet supplant punishment as a method of dealing with criminal behavior. The theory of probation and, to a degree, the theory of parole are based on the same reasoning that influenced the establishment of rehabilitation programs for children in state schools, schools of industry, private residential treatment centers, clinics for the treatment of adolescent offenders, school clinics, counselling centers, and private clinics. The credo born of this reasoning is, in brief, that the unstable and poorly integrated ego may be helped by skillful, compassionate, and realistic handling to reverse its identifications, realign its ideals, dissolve neurotic defenses, and reduce instability to the point where an ego more responsive to reality may be fashioned. This, in a word, is the meaning of rehabilitation through treatment: to permit an individual to resume the social and economic level to which his assets and training entitle him. Just how is this done? What does it mean to "treat" a sullen, rebellious youth, a sensitive, disinterested adolescent, a raw, brutal, egocentric youth, or a confirmed antisocial offender?

TREATMENT OF DELINQUENCY—RESIDENTIAL THERAPY

The outline to be presented here covers residential therapy and rehabilitation of juvenile delinquents. With necessary modifications, it might encompass programs in those progressive penal or correctional institutions for adult offenders where the indeterminate sentence is used. The model to be followed in this discussion is a composite of that used in institutions in which the author has served as consultant; it bears the closest resemblance to the California Youth Authority and the Medical Facility, Department of Correction, in the State Hospital System in California. It needs to be stated initially that the movement for treatment of delinquency has advanced to a point where the educa•

tion expert Benjamin Fine could write, in a work entitled *1,000,000 Delinquents*,[1] "Training schools must serve as a substitute for home, school and the community of the child." The detailed procedure in such a training situation may be summarized as follows.

The first step is the Reception Center processing, where an estimation is made of the juvenile offender's basic capacities, intellectual, physical, and social. The physical examination and psychological tests that are given here include projective tests to estimate emotional conflicts, phobias, deficits of perception and conceptualization, unconscious trends, and so on; these establish the available ego resources of the child. Then follows a social service review of the familial and cultural influences that impinge on the delinquent. This analysis covers the strengths or weaknesses of the parents and siblings; the meaning to the offender of the cultural plan of his, or her, community; the total ethos of his group, its accents and ideals, the presence or absence of religious influences; the economic position and aspirations of the family constellation, the values stressed or underplayed, and so forth. Often a clergyman adds his estimate of the spirituality of the child's environment, or its absence. The final evaluation is made by the psychiatrist, who relies on the information gathered by the staff psychologists and social workers and on his own perception and evaluation of the personality structure of the offender. A treatment program for the inmate is outlined by the responsible head (Superintendent or Review Board) of the Reception Center, referring him to a private counsellor or therapist, or recommending placement in another institution particularly suited for treating the offender.

If the delinquent is sent to a training school, diverse psychological elements of his personality structure require study, the first of which is the attitude of the new inmate. He may rapidly join a gang or clique in the institution, becoming either hostile to the therapist, teacher, or counsellor, or indicate a mock acceptance of his mentors. If his clique is hostile he makes fun of his therapist or counsellor, boasting of his toughness, snickering at the authorities, acting impishly with the benign expression common to schoolboys who, while enjoying their dependent status, simultaneously express contempt for adults. If he or she joins the group that subtly tries to outwit teachers or counsellors by a mock acceptance—acting as "nice" boys or girls, giving respectful attention, raising their hands, acting in an approved classroom style—they subvert their rebelliousness. If the child is an isolate, withdrawing from the group, he or she becomes inattentive, politely distant, or displays mannerisms that keep them occupied and out of the mainstream of necessary interreaction.

The reactions described above or, more accurately stated, the interreactions achieved between therapist, counsellor, cottage mother or father and the delinquent, become the vehicle through which defenses are minimized, ideas are absorbed, and emotional reliving goes on. The cottage mother or father is an important link in the therapeutic scheme: he, or she, is permissive yet firm, amused yet serious, and (if competent) ever alert to the emotional movements in each of his charges. The therapeutic process goes on in the group, in the classroom and in the lavatory, on the ball-field and in the cottage or dormitory. It goes on during occupation periods, in leisure time, at the table, during the recreation period. Ideally, each delinquent, in his or her own time, adopts a better behavioral pattern, depending on his rigidity, his needs, and the degree of emotion the therapist or cottage parent can give him or her. Stranahan and associates in their experiences in a residential treatment center, where the material outlined above is paralleled, describe three stages in the therapeutic process:

In the first stage, they began as a collection of individuals, little interested in one another, polite, eager to please, and restrained. They referred to the therapists as "teacher". . . . Early in this first stage, the "quiet period" was transformed into one of regressive behavior—re-enactment of customary and insatiable demands, rivalries, and aggression. Their relationships resembled those of two-year-olds playing side by side and making contact mainly through striking out at one another. . . .

In the second stage of group development the boys referred to the therapists as "teach." There was positive transferrence to the therapists as mother figures. Sometimes the boys called the therapists "ma" as a slip or intentionally. . . .

The last stage more closely resembles individual therapy grappling with the individual problems of the child.[2]

The extensive literature on residential treatment is replete with reports of therapeutic techniques for handling delinquents; only a bare outline is given here. The technique is fairly universal, encompassing the aims noted above. For examples: McCorkle and Bixby[3] work with a "guided group interaction"; Howland Shaw[4] comments on his experience with the intimate group, stressing the disregard of institutional features, the homelike atmosphere, the close personal relationship between all persons in the program that is permitted by the small size of the group; Hardman and Hardman[5] emphasize this fact: "The unique role of the institution is to replace a defective interpersonal relationship with a corrective one." Still another worker, Kasoff,[6] stresses the role of the cotherapist. Whatever the variation in technique employed, the essential feature is the skill of the worker and the psychological milieu, the atmosphere which binds the delinquent to the therapist within a matrix of firmness and warmth and insight into the nature of boys and girls.

PSYCHOTHERAPY OF OFFENDERS ON PROBATION

An increasingly important area of treatment of criminal offenders is that inspired by and carried out under the institution of probation. Here the probation officer, empowered by the court as a result of the suspension of sentence, works with the offender in his home environment. The probation officer, technically functioning as a supervising officer for the court, has recently extended his purview to active treatment. Probation officers now receive training in generic and psychiatric social work; the aim is to establish a "positive client-worker relationship." Since with the offender at home the circumstances of his situation differ from those of the delinquent in a residential institution, the management must be different. The probationer, whether young or old, is concerned with jobs, not cottage parents, with society's irritation and rejection, not with peer behavior—in a word, with the whole complex of a disinterested, if not hostile, world.

The probation movement has had many outstanding proponents, E. J. Cooley, I. W. Halpern, Charles Chute, and many others.[7] Its position is assured since, as Barnes and Teeters put it, "it is the only completely promising reformative technique." [8] Its evolution as a treatment technique is most promising. When supervision of the probationer moves on to treatment, certain specific aims can be delineated. Elmer Reeves, Chief Probation Officer, Supreme Court of New York County, summarizes these areas of treatment aims by showing that the probation officer (1) deals with the actual needs of the probationer, (2) uses crises in the probationer's life to enhance the development of a trust-relationship with him, (3) uses the client's "significant others"—family and friends—to continue this relationship.[9] The "needs" may be carfare, occupational counselling, encouragement; the "crises" may be marital tensions, the frustration of no job, tantrums, children's illness; the relationship-figures could be the probationer's wife, pal, fellow worker, girl friend, sibling, parent. These approaches are woven into a therapeutic pattern that finds material for psychologic work within the probationer's own world. In sum, caring for the needs of the probationer, a basic technique in social work, has become a release point for the development of probationary treatment methods.

The criminal offender who is alarmed at the word "psychotherapy" will respond to those who simply care for his daily needs without anxiety or defensive anger. The notion of treatment of criminal offenders is so recent, so against the grain of offender and public alike in its anxiety-producing potential, that the postulates of psychotherapy require modification and realignment in working with probationers. As is evident, the connotation "psychiatric" is eschewed as much as possible with offenders on probation.

In the early thirties, when psychiatric criminology was a-borning, psychiatrists were used primarily for their diagnostic help in determining the probationary potential of offenders. From this screening activity to sporadic attempts to treat criminals on probation was a natural step. Surprisingly, opposition to this development came from the offenders themselves, not only from the public. The author, in his early efforts with clinic treatment found, following Schilder's suggestion,[10] that in working with criminals large emotional blocks had to be tunnelled through before psychotherapy could be initiated. To quote from the writer's account of his experiences with probationers in the 1930's:

The patient who comes to a private physician for treatment expects no moral judgment of his symptoms by the physician. . . . On the other hand, the [criminological] psychiatrist cannot help but be . . . the representative of the public's attitude towards punishment. . . . The offender reads two notions in the public's mind: insistence on punishment as deterrence to further crime, and the proposition that antisocial conduct will inevitably repeat itself since crime arises out of the dictates of "bad" impulses.[11]

The atmosphere under which these pioneer efforts in psychotherapy with criminals placed on probation were attempted at the Psychiatric Clinic, Court of General Sessions, New York, was fraught with actual (situational) anxiety arising from the suspended sentence. For the convicted criminal to find himself outside a prison (that is, on probation) meant disbelief that the ordinarily hostile, vindictive world could have changed its attitude toward him. It was often observed in those days that the psychiatrist was viewed by the prisoner as representing a "refined type of psychological torture invented by a cunning district attorney, subtly calculated to increase the offender's punishment." [12] To be singled out for the *treatment* of crime, a condition everyone *knew* was unrelated to illness, could spring only from the sadistic interest of an "off-beat" psychiatrist—so felt the anxious, frightened probationer. Throughout the therapeutic contact, the wrappings of anxiety and fear and the defensive coverings of distrust and veiled anger introduced features of resistance that required special handling. Thus, the personal attitude of the offender—the operational field, so to speak—required therapeutic working-through before his individual problems could be reached. Indeed, early workers in this field frequently were informed by probationers that they "would rather do their time in prison and get out" than be held on probation, to endure the "meddling" direction given them by social workers and psychiatrists! The lay public, assuming that penal institutions give society its greatest protection from the criminal, objected to "coddling" the criminal through treatment, especially when given outside the institution.

By the 1950's, under the stimulation of experiences with behavioral problems of every kind during World War II and a broadened public interest in mental health, the idea of treating criminal offenders in or out of custody became more palatable. During the war-decade, therapy of military offenders had achieved some success in Army and Navy disciplinary barracks and prisons. In the East, Dr. Melitta Schmeideberg (at the Association for Psychiatric Treatment of Offenders in New York, limited to adolescents and young adults) and Dr. Ralph S. Banay (at the Brooklyn Association for the Rehabilitation of Offenders, known as BARO) expanded the Association's treatment of offenders on probation with the help of a staff of psychologists and psychiatric social workers. Indeed, it is only during the past five years (from 1959 on) that judges have "ordered" psychiatric treatment as part of the probationary regulations covering suspended sentences.[13] Even now most voluntary clinics shy away from treating offenders on probation [14]; few psychiatrists have the time or inclination to treat criminals privately; community agencies are not anxious to push therapy of criminals (except in the case of children); and the public is disinclined to favor contributing dollars for further treatment of criminals. Among probation workers and a small but slowly growing number of psychiatrists and ancillary workers in criminological fields, the view is solidifying that psychotherapy, although no panacea, is invaluable in rehabilitation efforts among both youthful and adult offenders.[15]

The use of psychotherapeutic techniques with paroled prisoners follows the methods described for probationers. In the former case, such follow-up work is even more essential since the ex-prisoner, now on parole, particularly needs the support and aid of a sympathetic, understanding person. Among parolees, attempts to probe into the psychologic background of crime is less important than the task of helping the ex-prisoner to adjust to his current world. Work with parolees has taken a new turn recently in the direction of the "halfway house." This idea draws its significance from the concept advanced by psychiatric social workers of sheltering foster homes for psychotic, alcoholic, and other disturbed individuals who require guidance during a period of adjustment to the outside world. Within the last five years the halfway house has achieved a marked growth, especially on the West and East Coasts (California and New York).[16] Here, much reliance is placed on manipulation of the living-environment, on group therapy, and individual counselling. In fact, the management of parolees is more akin to the Big Brother movement than it is to psychotherapy proper. In any event, the contact (with all its emotional connotations) that is maintained while the subject is on parole holds the essential meaning of parole treatment.

In this outline of therapeutic experimentation with offenders two tremendously important areas of concern have not yet been mentioned: (1) treatment of criminals confined in penal institutions; and (2) consideration of the potential, not yet known, offender. The first group involves problems not unlike those encountered among probationers; hence, treatment experiences within prisons and penitentiaries can be described objectively. The other group, which constitutes nothing less than *society itself*, introduces us to a skein of attitudes, unpredictable emotions, and workings of chance that almost makes a discussion of potential or unknown offenders a chimera. The convicted prisoner has clearly demonstrated by his acts the form that his inner conflicts have assumed in behavior, but the person who is *destined* to be a criminal offender, vaguely perceived or completely unknown to himself, whose crime is not yet contemplated, or even guessed at, constitutes the most impalpable material from which to fashion a program aimed at preventing crime. Nevertheless, ideas for such a preventive plan will be presented and discussed later in this chapter.

TREATMENT OF THE CRIMINAL IN PRISON

Therapeutic endeavors within the gray walls and steel fences of penal institutions vary so tremendously that only a composite picture can be given. In this area, the heavy hand of public prejudice and of official and traditional practice, holds back the few efforts being made to rehabilitate criminals. Yet the pressure of this hand is being insensibly lightened as the major states in the Union have, in varying degrees, embarked on pilot or organized programs for the treatment of prison inmates.

It would be difficult to cite all the institutions that have initiated psychotherapy among prisoners, and equally difficult to pinpoint the dates when such work was started. Religious leaders (the prison chaplains) have, from the early days, given spiritual and emotional help, insight, and psychological aid to inmates. The major religious denominations have provided chaplains in prisons for decades, their activities having recently been merged with that of the social worker and therapeutic staff.[17] Beginnings in the more specific field of prison psychotherapy are shrouded in dimness; perhaps the work of Thomas Mott Osborne, warden of Sing Sing Prison (1914–16), signalized the start of psychotherapy in prison. The much criticized Mutual Welfare League, which Osborne founded and organized, brought to the fore the notion that prisoners (then called "convicts") were predominantly individuals who needed humane handling, respect, and relief from the severe restriction of penal life. In fact, many forces converged to stimulate therapy in prisons; these included, in addition to Osborne's contributions, the "therapeutic community" of Maxwell Jones, group-therapy practices of various pioneers, educative programs, work programs, the individual efforts of enlightened wardens, and so on. From punishment through imprisonment to rehabilitation, from derogation to consideration of individual, human needs—the path toward a rational management of criminal offenders has indeed widened.

In general, therapy of prison inmates depends on many factors: the length of the prisoner's sentence, the institution's statutory function, the time, energy, and personality plasticity of the prison officials, the guards, medical and psychiatric staff, even the community in which the prison is located. In this situation, the offender's attitude toward the prison is as important as his own emotional structure. Whether it be a maximum-security prison with rigid rules or a minimum- security prison without fences, the prisoner has to wrestle with his own anger, resentment, and the acceptance of his own desperate reality. Further, prison treatment is mixed with many secondary factors: the sexual problem, the monotonous life, the routine, meaningless labor in the jute mill or carpenter shop, the exclusive company of males (or of females, in a woman's prison), the galling loss of liberty, and so forth.

To all this, one must add the many emotional problems that are intertwined with the process of treatment. These will be named without giving precedence to their importance: the conscious and unconscious hatred of guards for the inmates; the offender's own sibling rivalry; the reality of oppression and/or brutality in prison; occasional outbursts of anger, as in the condition called "stir bug," an involuntary emotional reaction to prolonged incarcerations; resentment toward society, related secondarily to the rise and repression of sexual feelings; the factor of absence of recreation; contact with the outside world, including reports received *sub rosa* of the behavior of wives, mistresses, partners, friends, family, and so on. The attitude of the psychiatrist and of the warden and guards is vital, as is the tradition of the local community where the institution is located. Is it a community whose economic welfare depends on the payroll of the prison? Does a hard core of "old-timers" run it? Is therapy spoken of in terms of contempt or fear, or of interest and respect? Does a prison hierarchy exist? Do gambling, business deals, and an active subterranean life go on? Is there gang control? [18]

A further significant factor is the readiness and motivation of the offender for treatment. This depends on whether he is aware that an emotional problem underlies his criminal behavior, or even suspects that something is wrong within his personality. Not unlike civilian patients, the offender has first to be convinced that his behavior arises from levels that he himself cannot perceive or touch before he can bring himself to request treatment. In this regard, the total atmosphere exerts a subtle influence, reflected in the terms used by the inmates of a penal institution. Whether the offenders talk in terms of "bum rap," "punks and stoolies," "politically mad district attorneys," "singing rats," "double cross" (as they did in old-line prisons), or whether in terms of "personality problems," "broken homes," "rejected childhood," and "tensions" (as one hears among patients in state hospitals), it may be assumed that the motivation and self-assigned explanations for criminal behavior will vary tremendously—as can be verified by a few minutes' conversation with inmates in institutions of many levels.

Assuming that the therapeutic atmosphere is predominant and that the offender is favorably disposed to treatment, the institution places its main reliance on group therapy. The aim of group therapy is to reduce hostilities, to develop insight into behavior, to assign the place of parents and early influences in the development of the prisoners' present personalities, and to ventilate emotional problems in inmates as they appear. The details of treatment are not as important as the atmosphere in which the treatment goes on. Of vital importance is the meaning to the offender of group sessions. He may attend sessions with a tongue-in-cheek attitude; he may scoff at therapy away from the session; he may be openly derisive; or he may completely capitulate to his new-found dependence on the leader or his peers. In any event, acceptance of therapy is a function of the individual offender, the total atmosphere of the institution, the positive ego forces in the offender, and the time allotted for therapy.

In the chapters preceding this, evidence has been given of occasional treatment of adolescent offenders, juveniles, homosexuals, some cases of assault, and cases of homicide, handled in varying degrees of therapeutic intensity. In effect, this sporadic therapeutic work carried on by many men throughout this country in state and federal institutions, constitutes an unofficial pilot-study of present-day institutional treatment of criminal offenders.

Now the question arises, Is this treatment effort, especially if it is to be extended, worthwhile? There can be no question that it is worthwhile in terms of human morale and relief of anxiety and anguish for the offender and his family (and, eventually, for the public), no matter how minute these efforts may be in the total sea of crime. To share the guilt and anxiety of a prisoner with him is itself a human achievement of no small proportion, but would expanded treatment of criminals justify the cost from the standpoint of society? This touchy question can be approached in two ways: one, by estimating the actual *cost of punishment* up to this point, wherein the therapeutic accent has been minimal; two, by estimating the *results of treatment* in terms of reducing recidivism and thus avoiding further costs, in either money or behavioral damage to society.

THE LEDGER OF PUNISHMENT

One does not commonly analyze the infliction of punishment for legal convictions in terms of financial cost, for deterrence, retribution, reprobation, and rehabilitation of criminals appear so vital to our ethical homeostasis that here, as in other crises of life, considerations of cost are overridden. Nevertheless, to be realistic, a recommendation of vastly increased rehabilitation of criminal offenders on a national scale requires a frank scrutiny of the cost in terms of tax dollars. We may well ask, therefore, What is the national bill for punishment? What is the cost of the "prison industry" or, more accurately, the "punishment industry" in this country?

In this regard, figures from federal sources [19] are more readily available than those from the various state governments. Department of Justice reports state that the total number of prisoners in federal institutions was 24,073 (1961), and that the cost of maintaining and caring for this group was $45,195,000 (1961). This figure does not take into account the projected cost of new buildings or of maintaining old structures—a sizable amount. For example, in 1961 a supplemental appropriation of $12,000,000 was granted in the Federal Prison budget, $10,000,000 of which was allocated for the construction of a new penal institution in Illinois. The total cost is high; James Bennett, Director of Federal Prisons, states: "During the 1961 fiscal year a total of $71,-000,000 was involved in the operation of the Federal Prison System." [20] Further, the total number of prisoners in both state and federal institutions in 1960 was 213,142,[21] and the fifty states spent a total of $480,600,000 for corrective activities in 1961. On a state level, the total annual expenditures for maintenance and care of felony-offenders shows a dramatic increase over the eighteen-year-period 1942 through 1960 [22] (see Table 9).

With allowance made for the war years, when the prison population was relatively small, and allowance made for the cost-of-living increase, as reflected in outlay for salaries, materials, food, and so on, there is a sharp rise in the cost of housing, feeding, treating, and managing felony-offenders throughout the states of the Union from 1942 to 1961. The total cited—almost half a billion dollars—as the cost of handling and maintaining prisoners in the various states of the Union does not include capitalization of existing buildings, the cost and value of the

TABLE 9

COMPARATIVE TOTAL EXPENDITURES FOR CORRECTION
BY STATE GOVERNMENTS FOR TEN YEARS IN 1942–60 PERIOD *

Years	Expenditures for Correction
1942	$ 80,000,000
1946	97,000,000
1950	198,000,000
1952	225,000,000
1954	252,000,000
1956	298,000,000
1957	333,000,000
1958	376,000,000
1959	420,000,000
1960	433,000,000

* For 1960, includes fifty states; for 1959, excludes Hawaii and Alaska. For 1958, and earlier, forty-eight states are included.

land, and so forth. In addition, the cost of trial and conviction or acquittal of prisoners in the more than 3,000 county and city jails throughout this country has not been included in the over-all figure. An example of this is seen in the report that for one *month* alone (October, 1961), 133 million dollars was expended for law-enforcement agents by the states of the Union,[23] the police function being a necessary adjunct of the penal function.

If every item of expense, hidden or budgeted, were listed, the bill presented to the taxpayer for apprehending, trying, and dealing with criminal offenders would stagger the imagination. In round figures, half a billion dollars would have been spent in 1963, and probably increasing amounts in succeeding years, on the business of legal punishment. In sum, the cost of punishment of criminal offenders is too high for the privilege of teaching the meaning of the categorical imperative: "Society has a moral obligation to punish!" Is it too high in view of the anticipated reduction of repeated crime?

The real test of the value of these expenditures, aside from the discharge of the public's moral requirement that punishment be administered, would be whether punishment has reduced the number of repeaters in crime. The deterrence effect of punishment on potential offenders in the population, measured by the incidence of first offenders and the constantly increasing number of such offenders (see Chapter IV), readily answers this in the negative. As to recidivism, it is generally recognized that the factors making for rehabilitation cannot be analyzed in a meaningful way unless one is able to make an intensive scrutiny of each criminal. In the face of the Bureau of Prisons report that 65 per cent of all federal offenders are repeaters,[24] we must draw the conclusion that the majority of offenders have *not* been benefitted by incarceration. Even more important is the fact that repetition of felony offenses occurs in the largest proportion among criminals within one to two years after release from a penal institution. Clearly, the total of half a billion dollars per year paid for punishment through incarceration is not yielding the results desired in the instances of either first offenders or recidivists.

THE DEBITS AND CREDITS OF PSYCHOTHERAPY

In what direction can society turn to realize a more profitable return on its investment in the penal system? It is true that both federal and state institutions produce manufactured articles of definite cash value, that they grow farm produce that cuts food costs, and so on. The essential purpose of a prison is neither industrial production nor economic gain, but hoped-for psychological gain through punishment, possible deterrence of others and rehabilitation of prisoners. But therapeutic handling of offenders presents an economic problem: it means a shift in allocation of vast sums already budgeted in penal institutions. The crucial question is: Assuming there is such reallocation of funds for therapy in any form in penal institutions of every grade, would society benefit from this activity? The experiences quoted in this work and those of other devoted workers in this field, lead to a reasoned answer in the affirmative.

Who can disprove that attempts at treatment have had beneficial effects, although these attempts, except in the case of children and adolescents, have been made in minute amounts? The psychologic and social therapist can only say with candor that if one offender, or a dozen or a hundred, have been benefitted in terms of personal morale, in reduction of emotional conflicts and compulsions, in neutralization of sexual or other neurotic conflicts that eventuate in criminal behavior, the effort is eminently worthwhile.

Yet the indisputable fact remains that the public, which through its legislators appropriates money for police, judicial, and penal functions, is not convinced, or often wholly aware, that the treatment of offenders is worth its salt. It is true that the subspecialty of psychiatric criminology has not developed to a point where it exerts a strong influence in professional psychiatric circles, and it certainly has little influence on the public. Whereas by sheer weight of interest aroused through the avenues of the entertainment world, books, education, and the news-gathering services (press, radio, television), psychoanalysis and psychiatry have enlisted the imagination of the public, the feeble voice of psychiatric criminology has received the scantiest of notice. Psychiatry may still suffer because of its caricatured public image, but psychiatric criminology suffers from simple neglect.

There are significant psychological reasons for this. Society is unconsciously involved in crime to a degree that passes expectation. The crime of murder, for example, is present *in potentia* in the overwhelming majority of people. How else explain the perennial fascination of crime stories or murder mysteries, from the days of Herodotus, the Greek who wrote mystery and horror stories, to Edgar Allan Poe, Conan Doyle, Erle Stanley Gardner—a continuing flow of popular writings about crime? Theodor Reik, the eminent psychoanalyst, in his book *The Unknown Murderer*, showed that the irrepressible cry "Who did it?" in a case of murder is a defense against the "citizen's own repressed impulses." [25] The criminal acts out those impulses and unrestricted fantasies that the law-abiding citizen abhors and represses. It is abundantly clear that *society loves its crimes but hates its criminals*.[26]

For these reasons, the public, under the protective device of decrying "coddling" of criminals, but actually motivated by justified anger at depredations and injury caused by the constant onslaught of homicides, assaults, robberies, thievery, and destruction, is unwilling to pay for therapeutic management of criminals to an appreciable degree. Professor Gerhard Mueller, of New York University, in an analysis of the psychopath, makes a pointed analogy between the psychopath's restricted emotional vista and that of the public in respect to long-term values:

Is the community willing to pay for such individualized treatment services? I fear that our community is rather psychopathic in this respect, as of yet, because of its inability to make proper long range decisions, i.e., to choose long term pleasure (relative freedom from crime) over short term pleasure (unwillingness to part with another tax dollar right now). Or perhaps our community is neurotic, by seeking self-punishment through a continued high crime rate. In any event, efforts to get the public to pay for the service necessary to prevent *repeated* crime have been singularly unsuccessful.[27]

Professor Mueller's interpretation stems from the reasonable position that the law's machinery is ready for extending treatment while the public is not. In this overview of the whole picture of therapy for offenders, the present author wishes to be understood as *not* advocating rehabilitation of those criminals who have selectively adopted crime as a means of livelihood. Without a wish to be helped on the part of the offender psychotherapy can be of no value. The person whose profession is crime is immune to, and scoffs at, such naïve notions of treatment, although it is known that a strongly negative attitude toward psychologic help often betrays an unconscious dependence on the very aid derided.

The total problem must be left on the doorstep of society. The essential question is whether the public, in its ultimate wisdom, will continue to authorize tremendous expenditures for punishing criminals without insisting that available methods be employed to attain those values in the offender that it prizes in society.

The advantages, hazards, and frustrations of offender-therapy have been outlined in this chapter as they apply to juvenile delinquent, probationer, parolee, and institutional inmate. Even while the dedicated worker stumbles along with his offender-patients, individually or in groups, he is aware that a larger body needs his therapeutic attention —society itself. For where is tomorrow's murderer, next month's larcenist or embezzler, the unrevealed rapist, the potential burglar, the pedophile-to-be, the assaulter-of-the-moment if not in the ranks of those who, until the moment of crime, are law-abiding persons? The worker struggling along with his offender-patient needs help—the help that an adequate preventive program in society would provide in resetting the total atmosphere conducive to effective treatment. This, to put it in simple words, is a big order.

A CRIME PREVENTION PROPOSAL

A preventive program should utilize the knowledge amassed concerning crime and criminals in conjunction with knowledge of criminal forces within the law-abiding public. The proposed program rests on two bases: one, that the behavior of all persons is eventually amenable to educational influences; two, that the same impulses that drive the criminal in his behavior are present in the law-abiding person. The background for this has been presented in Chapter I. A corollary basis for the proposed crime prevention program is that crime is a dramatic event and as such it must be approached in the same genre—namely, through drama itself. To attempt to educate against crime by words, sermons, or exhortations begs the question of the nature of criminal action, which is personal, dramatic, meaningful to the individual in terms of fantasies, needs, and desires. In the offender's inner world, threats and punishment belong to some familiar but external universe, foreign to that central core of being that knows only such modalities as *I want, I hate, I kill, I need, I can't tolerate.* The medium that can serve to open up the psychologic world of precrime in its dramatic, human, perceptual essence is drama—and its modern vehicle, television.

If television is used for education in academic subjects, why should it not be used in emotional education? Why should not a murder mystery that reaches to depths in the human personality that no words could plumb, a story of larceny, burglary, rape, or arson, be used to illustrate the plexus of inner emotions that lies beneath the crime portrayed? The present province of crime stories is to entertain, although it is never asked what inner responses of the viewer are being pandered to in the presentation of such stories. Why portray shootings, ambushes, double crosses, protection of honor, pummelings, larcenies, seductions without relating some of the psychologic background that moves the characters to act as they do? Is there a way to make sense out of this continuing psychopathy?

The technique to do this would involve a new way of writing and presenting crime stories. It would reverse the usual procedure in that the major portion of the presentation would be occupied in probing the psychological depths of the character portrayed, not in the crime itself. Rather than the play concentrating on the prelude to the crime, the act itself, the clues, investigation, chase, and apprehension and conviction, the presentation would accent the psychological background of the crime. What is suggested is that the *anatomy of the criminal* be laid bare, not the anatomy of society's legal position toward him or her. The details of the psychological explanation of the crime portrayed require dramatic treatment to the end that the criminal-to-be, and some who do not conceive of themselves as potentially criminal, may perceive the preconditions of crime and so be better equipped to control the aggressive impulses that lurk under our psychic surfaces. This experiment— a pre-set analysis, so to speak—involves a type of abreaction, or catharsis; it serves as an exposure of unexpressed hidden emotions where the individual is susceptible, before some real event triggers these into criminal action.

The idea encompasses the psychological equivalent of preventive medicine [28]; its efforts would be directed to exposing the public to an emotional reeducation concerning those impulses that form a prelude to crime.

Who are the potential offenders? They are any one of us, as implied in the overworked but valid saying "There but for the grace of God go I": the self-absorbed person who, wreathed in fantasies of destruction, drives a car carelessly and aggressively; the over-sensitive person who cannot control his humiliations; the social drinker whose larcenous impulses creep out under cover of the ego-dissolving effect of alcohol; the lover who is rejected, in fact or fancy; the neurotic who carries his inferiority on his sleeve, unable to tolerate his low self-esteem; the bank clerk dreaming of grandiose revenge on an impersonal and hated tyrant; the activity-drunk adolescent and the bruiser over-invested in his power-image; the woman whose thin libido carries the weight of her frustration and depression; the addict who cannot face life in the sunlight or in the shadows; the psychotic nurturing his distortions of reality; and many more whose psychopathies defy categorization—these may or may not become criminals.

In the preventive program here proposed these types and many combinations of life patterns would be compressed into dramatic presentations. The program, aimed at preventing crimes committed by persons unrecognized as potential criminals, would utilize the theory that a free, dramatized display of the psychological forces behind crime would *reduce*, not enhance, the eventuality of the acting-out of the driving impulses implied above.

There is little doubt that this scheme will be viewed as inciting behavior that might otherwise lie dormant or be suppressed. It may be pointed to as an absurd extension of a logical idea, an explication of authenticated psychotherapeutic techniques that may be applicable to individual patients, but not to an unseen, unselected audience such as is exposed to television. The project sketched out above calls for a virtual reorientation of the current presentations of crime as entertainment. Such a technique would add a new dimension to criminal reports; it would include the reactions of police, detectives, and society, as well as the actions and psychological status of the criminal. This type of crime recounting might at first prove less fascinating to the viewers than their present spectacles and reports of crime and criminals. Less of the color and excitement of crime—and so perhaps less of the aura of desirability—will be evident. The very stimulus to continued juvenile delinquency that, unknown to the youth, feeds upon the inner drive to experience the "creative," romantic aspect of a criminal act, will possibly be decreased by this maneuver. The clinical light thus shed upon crime would very probably bring about an evaporation of the "thrill" that attends crime. Eventually, there may be great gains in modifying antisocial attitudes that cannot be directly dealt with in individuals. Coincidentally, such a program might well provide clues in the search by researchers for a "cause" for crime, since the basic material for understanding the entire socio-psychological problem would be available for study.

Education has already deserted the time-honored methods of exhortation and lecturing; its eager and copious use of visual aids in the learning process gives validity to this species of education. With this historical precedent, the understanding of crime as a total human experience could develop with the widest possible dissemination of accumulated psychological data. Education can make this knowledge part of the public domain, and television is the prime medium for such a program of crime prevention.

A myriad of problems remain even after the premise of the outline is accepted—technical, political, and possibly ethical. One thing is certain, however: since the entirely praiseworthy work of moral education through church, school, and home and the excellence of police investigation has made only the faintest impression on the incidence of crime in these United States, it is possible that a capturing of the public imagination and understanding, through revised entertainment, might eventuate in the sober perception that crime—man's perpetual plague—is at least susceptible of prevention, if not of cure.

But will this grandiose plan of community education in the psychological and dynamic background for criminal action stop the flood of murder, mayhem, robbery, larceny, rape that is endemic and frequently epidemic in our land? Will the patient pedestrian treatment of individual offenders—for example, juveniles, while on probation, and in penal institutions—make an appreciable dent in further criminal activity? Do these plans lead to the condoning of crime? Does understanding really mean forgiveness? And how will the public, the victims of aggressive, acquisitive, and malevolent impulses and actions, be protected?

These very proper questions demand and deserve answers which lie in the change of values to be given these tendencies by the subtle processes of education. A century or two ago, education in literacy as a desirable aim for the masses was resisted by many. They didn't need to read or write, the educated classes could serve these functions for them! The literature of Dickens' day in England indicates that schooling was an activity that many juveniles fought, unless they identified with the ruling, the literate, classes. Sometimes force had to be used to teach boys the value of a literate education. The schoolmaster was indeed a "master," forcing learning on his captive charges. The switch and that later refinement, the ruler across the knuckles, were used as much for failure to learn as for misbehavior.

But today, the value of literacy has been so accepted—ingrained, in fact, as an organic component of our complex civilization—that opposition to more than elementary education has vanished and all that remains is a small pocket of resistance on the part of rebellious adolescents and some subcultural groups. Mass education in the Western world in an increasingly technological society has enhanced the value of literacy. Again, in the matter of racial equality and civil rights for racial groups, up to now tacitly living under the conditions of second-class citizenship, the Civil Rights Law of 1964 forced an alternate attitude, which had been held unenforceable by many. So also a program of education *against* criminal expression may change the values of aggression, acquisitiveness, and malevolent impulses. While outspoken aggression occurs, punishment is needed. When outspoken aggression in crime is modified or diminished, punishment, with its ethical presuppositions and traditions, will lose its value as a categorical imperative. Cultural changes inevitably find their way eventually into the interstices of each human soul. If human nature can't be changed, human values can. Idealistic as these aims may seem—the aims of altering attitudes which are at once individual and universal—they are also intensely practical.

REFERENCES

1. FINE, BENJAMIN, *1,000,000 Delinquents* (World Publishing Co., Cleveland, Ohio, 1955), p. 294.

2. STRANAHAN, MARION, and others, "Activity Group Therapy with Emotionally Disturbed and Delinquent Adolescents," *The International Journal of Group Psychotherapy*, VII, No. 4 (October, 1957).

3. McCORKLE, LLOYD W., and BIXBY, F. LOVELL, quoted in Ashley H. Weeks, *Youthful Offenders at Highfields, An Evaluation of the Effects of the Short-term Treatment of Delinquent Boys* (University of Michigan Press, Ann Arbor, Mich., 1958), p. 174.

4. SHAW, HOWLAND G., quoted in *ibid.*, p. 175.

5. HARDMAN, DALE G., and HARDMAN, MARGARET P., "Three Postulates in Institutional Care," *National Probation and Parole Association Journal*, IV, No. 1 (January, 1958), 22.

6. KASOFF, ARTHUR I., "Advantages of Multiple Therapists in a Group of Severely Acting-Out Adolescent Boys," *The International Journal of Group Psychotherapy*, VII, No. 1 (January, 1958).

7. BARNES, HARRY ELMER, and TEETERS, NEGLEY K., *New Horizons in Criminology* (Prentice-Hall, Englewood Cliffs, N.J., 3rd ed., 1959), chap. 34.

8. BARNES and TEETERS, *ibid.*, p. 565.

9. REEVES, ELMER, "A Fresh Look at Prediction and Supervision," *Crime and Delinquency* (National Council on Crime and Delinquency), VII, No. 1 (January, 1961), 37–41.

10. SCHILDER, PAUL, "The Cure of the Criminal and Prevention of Crime," *Journal of Criminal Psychopathology*, II (1940), 149.

11. BROMBERG, WALTER, "What Can a Psychiatrist Do for a Criminal Offender?" *Federal Probation*, V (July-September, 1941), 15.

12. BROMBERG, WALTER, "Psychotherapy in a Court Clinic," *American Journal of Orthopsychiatry*, XI (October, 1941), 770.

13. REEVES, ELMER, personal communication, 1964.

14. *Report*, Outpatient Psychiatric Clinic, National Institute of Mental

Health and National Association of Mental Health (U.S. Department of Health, Education, and Welfare, Bethesda, Md., 1962).

15. Articles in *Corrective Psychiatry* and *Journal of Social Therapy*, Ralph S. Banay, ed. (New York), January, 1954, *et seq.*

16. MANLEY, HARRY A., and SHERMAN, MELVIN B., in *Proceedings of the 93rd Annual Congress of Correction of the American Correctional Association*, Portland, Oregon, August, 1963.

SLOAT, NATHAN, Bureau of Social Work, Department of Mental Hygiene, State of California, Nathan Sloat, Director (State Printing Office, Sacramento, Calif., 1956).

17. BLOOM, H. I., "Religion as a Form of Institutional Treatment," in *Proceedings of the 93rd Annual Congress of Correction of the American Correctional Association, ibid.,* p. 17.

VUKCEVICH, SAMUEL U., "Teaching Social Adjustment Concepts to Incarcerated Offenders Utilizing Principles of Group Dynamics," *ibid.,* p. 115.

ERICKSON, MAYNARD L., "Research and Treatment at Pinehills: An Attempt at an Integrated Approach," *ibid.,* p. 253.

HARRISON, ROBERT M., "An Overview of Group Counseling in the California Department of Corrections," *ibid.,* p. 361.

18. SYKES, GRESHAM M., *The Society of Captives* (Princeton University Press, Princeton, N.J., 1958).

19. *Report, Federal Bureau of Prisons, U.S. Department of Justice* (U.S. Government Printing Office, Washington, D.C., 1961), p. 21.

20. *Ibid.,* p. 27.

21. *Statistical Abstract of the United States,* U.S. Dept. of Commerce, Bureau of Census, E. D. Goldfield, ed. (U.S. Government Printing Office, Washington, D.C., 83rd ed., 1962), p. 161.

22. *Book of the States,* Vol. 14 (Council of State Governments, Chicago, Ill., 1962; from U.S. Bureau of Census, Compendium of State Government Finances).

23. *Information Please Almanac,* Dan Golenpaul Associates (Simon & Schuster, New York, 1964), p. 593.

24. *Report, Federal Bureau of Prisons, op. cit.,* 1960, p. 33.

25. REIK, THEODOR, *The Unknown Murderer,* trans. by Katherine Jones (Prentice-Hall, Englewood Cliffs, N.J., 1945).

26. BROMBERG, WALTER, *The Mold of Murder* (Grune & Stratton, New York, 1961), p. 7.

27. MUELLER, GERHARD O. W., "The Failure of Concepts of Criminal Theory in Judging the Psychopathic Offender," *Archives of Criminal Psychodynamics, Special Issue on Psychopathic Personality* (1961), p. 578.

28. BROMBERG, WALTER, "*Crime*—Is There a Cause or Remedy?" *Archives of Criminal Psychodynamics,* I, No. 2 (1955), 326.

Index